OFFSHORE STRUCTURES ENGINEERING Volume 2

OFFSHORE STRUCTURES

Proceedings of the International Symposium
on Offshore Structures held at COPPE,
Federal University of Rio de Janeiro,
Brazil, October 1979

Sponsored by:
   RILEM *(The International Union of Testing and
       Research Laboratories for Materials and Structures)*
   FIP *(Fédération Internationale de la Précontrainte)*
   CEB *(Comité Euro-International du Béton)*

Edited by:
   F. L. L. B. Carneiro, A. J. Ferrante and S. H. Sphaier,
       Federal University of Rio de Janeiro
   C. A. Brebbia,
       University of California, Irvine

PENTECH PRESS
London : Plymouth

First published 1980
by Pentech Press Limited
Estover Road, Plymouth
Devon PL6 7PZ

British Library Cataloguing in Publication Data

International Symposium on Offshore Structures,
    2nd, Federal University of Rio de
    Janeiro, 1979
    Offshore structures.
    1. Offshore structures — Congresses
    I. Title II. Carneiro, FLLB
    620'.416'2   TC1505

    ISBN 0-7273-0151-9

PREFACE

In the last few years oil has become a very valuable natural resource, making economical the development of marine oil fields. Consequently, it is now necessary to design, build and operate equipment to look for and to extract oil from the sea. New engineering problems have been encountered, which in turn have stimulated many new research projects.

Latin America, having potentially important oil resources in its continental shelf, is one of the regions of the world most interested in the development of marine oil fields. In particular, an extensive exploration programme is underway in Brazil, which will make an important contribution in the near future to the development of oil fields situated in deep waters. In view of this the Federal University of Rio de Janeiro, through its Graduate Centre of Engineering, COPPE, has organized the International Symposium on Offshore Structures, to enable researchers and specialists to interchange ideas and to share experience collected in different parts of the world.

This Symposium was sponsored by RILEM (The International Union of Testing and Research Laboratories for Materials and Structures), FIP (Fédération Internationale de la Précontrainte) and CEB (Comité Euro-International du Béton), and had the support of Petrobras and CNPq (Brazilian Council for Scientific and Technological Development).

ORGANIZING COMMITTEE:

Prof. F. L. Carneiro, COPPE/UFRJ, Rio de Janeiro, RILEM Del., CEB Del., FIP M.

Prof. P. A. Gomes, COPPE/UFRJ, Dir., Rio de Janeiro, RILEM M.E.

Prof. A. J. Ferrante, COPPE/UFRJ, Rio de Janeiro, RILEM M.E.

Prof. L. M. Machado, INTI, Buenos Aires, RILEM Del.

Prof. C. A. Brebbia, University of California, Irvine, RILEM M.E.

Prof. T. Van Langendonck, University of Sao Paulo, CEB Del., FIP M.

Prof. F. A. Basilio, ABCP, Sao Paulo, RILEM M.E.

Prof. B. E. Diaz, UFRJ, Rio de Janeiro, FIP M.

CONTENTS

Preface

INTRODUCTION

INTRODUCTION   SCOPE OF THE BRAZILIAN EFFORT IN
               THE EXPLORATION AND PRODUCTION OF
                         HYDROCARBONS

SCOPE OF THE BRAZILIAN EFFORT IN THE EXPLORATION AND PRODUCTION
OF HYDROCARBONS

Jose Marques Neto and Nivaldo Ribeiro Costa

Petrobras, Brazil

1. Analysis of the International Effort for Hydrocarbon Exploration and Production

Hydrocarbons are of vital importance to the industrial and
transportation structure of the world, at present. According to
most of the available studies on the future demand and production of crude oil, supply difficulties may be experienced on the
international market in the eighties. In an article published in
the "World Oil" magazine of April 1976, a study of the Chase
Manhattan Bank is mentioned, according to which the investment
in global terms, with exception of the socialist block, totalled
US$ 121 billion for the 1965-1974 period, whereas the projected
investment needed to fund and develop new hydrocarbon reserves
required to meet the market's needs will be of the order of
US$ 500 billion for the next decade.

The investment for exploration of hydrocarbon reserves in the
world has been growing yearly, especially after 1973, when the
rate of growth increased markedly (Fig.1). The intensification
of the exploration and production effort has been determined by
the increasing hydrocarbon demand, by the need of reserves compatible with the present production level, by the international
market's price structure, and by the difficulties foreseen for
the supply of the future needs.

The level of the investment for exploration development and production of hydrocarbon reserves in the world, excepting the
socialist block, attained approximately US$ 32.5 billion in 1977
according to the Chase Manhattan Bank. Regarding the world-wide
investment in geology and geophysics, its value was US$ 3.4
billion in 1977, again with the exception of the socialist block.
This sizeable investments effort is also a consequence of the
energy-demand projections for the 1980-1990 decade, for which
most of the studies indicate crude oil and natural gas among the
main sources.

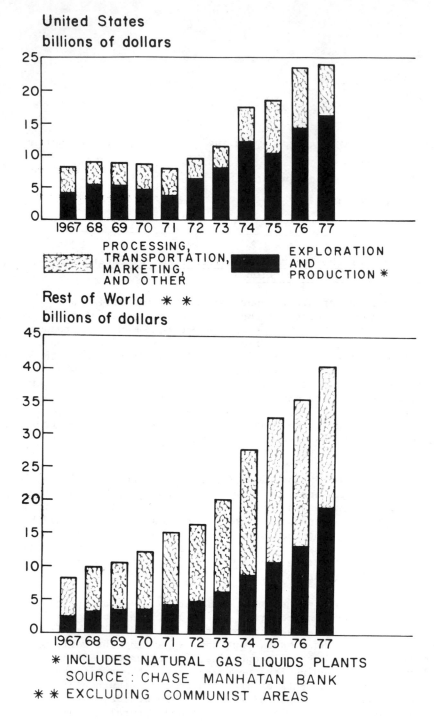

FIG.1 INVESTMENT IN THE PETROLEUM INDUSTRY

In view of the above, the oil industry is increasing its effort
for the discovery and production of new hydrocarbon reserves,
and also implementing the adequate technology for work in extremely hostile environments such as jungles, arctic regions, and in
deep offshore waters.

2. World Reserves of Hydrocarbons

The proven hydrocarbon reserves are related economically to their
market value and to the recovery factor, which depends also on
the techniques of secondary and/or tertiary recovery adopted in
each period and which may change with alterations of the above-
mentioned factors. According to data of the American Petroleum
Institute, the proven petroleum reserves evolved between 1969 and
1978 from 454 billion barrels to 645 billion barrels, whilst
those of natural gas reached 2,518 trillion ft^3 in 1978, that is,
about 71,332 billion m^3.

The evolution of the reserves, according to the above-cited
source, reveals in 1975 a maximum proven amount of some 712 billion barrels, showing that, starting with that year, the addition
of new reserves has been, as a rule, less than the annual production. Figure 2 shows the evolution of the yearly addition of
reserves and of the production, the socialist block excepted.

The ratio of yearly reserves/production attained in 1978 is 29.3,
for a yearly production of 22,022 million barrels of crude oil.
The conclusion is that in addition to the enhancement of the
effort for discovery and start of the production of new reserves,
a corresponding effort is required for conservation and rationalization of the use of petroleum derivatives, and the search
for new alternative sources to meet the future world demand of
energy. The effort is apparent for the development and improvement of secondary recovery techniques and for special methods of
recovery of oil and natural gas.

Research into technology adequate for the production of extra-
heavy oil, shale oil, etc. at acceptable cost is being done. The
importance of natural gas should be stressed, not only on the
energy scene, but also as a raw material for petrochemistry and
also, in the social sense, in domestic use. According to the
A.P.I., the world natural gas reserves in 1978 amounted to
2,519,909 billion ft^3, equivalent to 71,386 billion m^3. For a
production level servicing a market of 55 billion ft^3/year, that
is, about 1.56 billion m^3 yearly, the ratio reserves/production
is 46 (years).

In view of the above data and of the recoverable potential, natural gas will remain, in the near future, one of the main sources
of energy, on a world-wide scale.

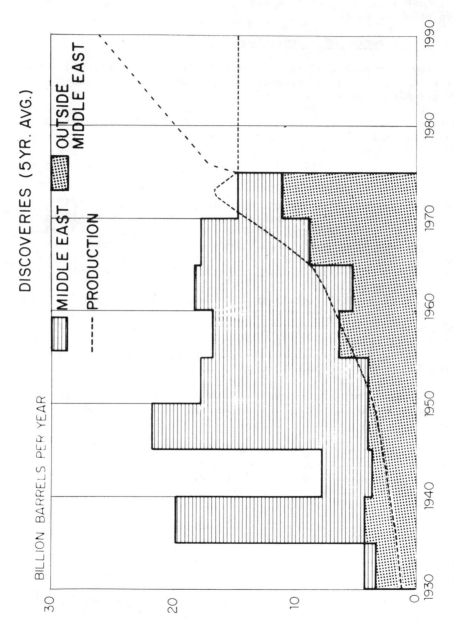

FIG.2   RATE OF DISCOVERY OF WORLD CRUDE OIL RESERVES (excluding Communist areas)
        Source: Wcrld Energy Outlook - Exxon Background Series

3. World Petroleum Potential

Although this is a controversial matter, the most consistent of the various estimates of the total recoverable volume of conventional crude is around 2,000 billion barrels. In the recent 10th World Petroleum Congress held in Bucarest, Halbouty and Moody estimated 2,100 billion barrels as the total recoverable volume in the world.

Table 1 lists the estimates of renowned scientists, in various periods of time, disclosed in the M.I.T. publication "Energy – Global Prospects 1985-2000" (WAES, McGraw Hill, 1977).

TABLE 1. ESTIMATES OF TOTAL WORLD ULTIMATELY RECOVERABLE RESERVES OF CRUDE OIL FOR CONVENTIONAL SOURCES

Year	Source	In Billion Barrels
1942	Pratt, Weeks & Stebinger	600
1946	Duce	400
1946	Pogue	555
1948	Weeks	610
1949	Levorsen	1500
1949	Weeks	1010
1953	MacNaughton	1000
1956	Hubbert	1250
1958	Weeks	1500
1959	Weeks	2000
1965	Hendricks (USGS)	2480
1967	Ryman (Esso)	2090
1968	Shell	1800
1968	Weeks	2200
1969	Hubbert	1350-2100
1970	Moody (Mobil)	1800
1971	Warman (BP)	1200-2000
1971	Weeks	2290
1975	Moody & Geiger	2000

According to an A.P.I. publication, the world petroleum reserves were 645.8 billion barrels in 1978, and for the cumulative production of 406 billion barrels at that date, we would have a recoverable remaining potential, that is, still to be discovered, of about 948.2 billion barrels. Many authors round out that value to 1,000 billion barrels, in view of the uncertainty in the estimates of the total recoverable volume.

The total recoverable volume of natural gas, according to Moody and Geiger, should be 8,150,000 billion ft^3, equivalent to some 1,400 billion barrels of crude oil. If we admit a cumulative production of natural gas of approximately 1,060,000 billion ft^3, for a present reserve of some 2,520,000 ft^2, we would have a remaining recoverable potential, that is, still to be discovered, of nearly 4,570,000 billion ft^3, that is, about 129,462 billion m^3.

4. Production versus World Demand

According to the "BP Statistical Review of the World Industry - 1978", the evolution of the world production and consumption of oil in the last ten years was as shown in Table 2 and Figure 3.

TABLE 2.

Year	Production (1000 bpd)	Consumption (1000 bpd)
1969	43,680	42,885
1970	47,970	46,490
1971	50,530	49,105
1972	53,215	52,590
1973	58,130	56,825
1974	58,340	56,045
1975	55,435	55,470
1976	59,830	59,135
1977	62,620	61,070
1978	62,965	63,120

As can be seen, in the last years the production and demand have been balanced, with a lower rate of growth of the latter, on account of the evolution of the market.

5. Present Fields of Activity

As we have already said, after 1973 the exploration and production on a world-wide scale have been intensified, due to the evolution of the international market. Between 1976 and 1978, the number of active drilling rigs in the world, with the exception of socialist-block countries, has grown from about 2,750 to approximately 3,750 units, as can be seen in Fig.4. The main areas of activity are: United States, Canada, Latin America, Middle East, and Africa.

6. Major Consumers

In addition to Russia, which is at present the largest petroleum producing country and which has large natural gas reserves, major consumers are the United States, Europe and Japan.

A recent Exxon study contains projections up to the year 1990,

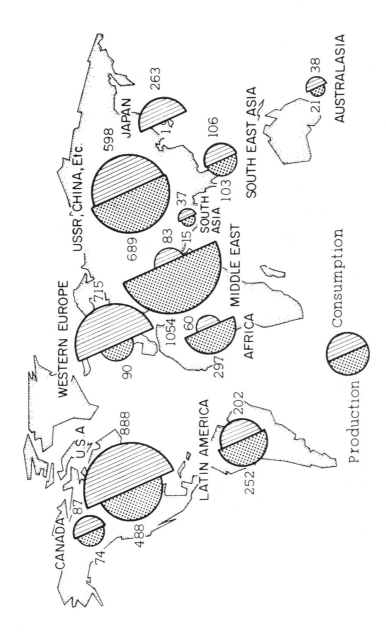

FIG.3 WORLD OIL PRODUCTION AND CONSUMPTION 1978 IN MILLIONS OF TONNES
Source: BP Statistical Review of the World Oil Industry – 1978

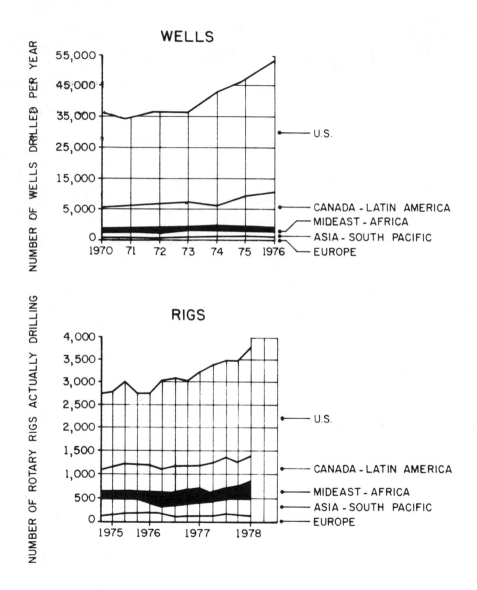

FIG.4   HOW NON-COMMUNIST DRILLING HAS SURGED
        Source: International Petroleum Encyclopedia – 1979

published by the "International Petroleum Encyclopedia - 1979",
forecasting for those countries in 1990 an energy consumption
supplied mainly by petroleum and natural gas, as can be seen in
Figs.5 and 6, obviously with the caution usually given to projections of this nature.

For the larger consumers, the energy consumption projection is
markedly below the projections of previous years, as a result
of the conservation endeavours, and also of the lower growth
rates of oil and natural gas, reducing their share in the total
energy consumed in the period. The other countries show increased
sharing in the world's energy total, changing from 23% in 1975
to 31% in 1990, because of a larger consumption growth rate,
taken as 5.5% in the 1980-1990 period, against a global average
rate of 3.5%, reflecting a higher demographic and economic
growth.

An aggressive exploration effort to discover and put in production new hydrocarbon reserves has been considered, together with
a great energy conservation effort, a growth of the gross national product of the industrialized countries below 4% yearly,
and the use of alternative energy sources.

7. Evolution of Reserves in the Middle East

The Middle East is a privileged area in terms of large hydrocarbon accumulations. According to A.P.I. data, that region has
reserves of some 370 billion barrels of crude oil, representing
57% of the world proven reserves. Not only because of the large
proven reserves, but due also to potential new discoveries, the
Middle East is increasingly important, being the main producing
region in the world.

According to the same source, the evolution of the petroleum reserves in that area is as shown in Table 3.

TABLE 3

Year		Billion barrels
1947	-	28.5
1950	-	41.5
1955	-	126.2
1960	-	183.1
1965	-	215.3
1970	-	344.5
1975	-	368.4
1978	-	370.0

DEMAND

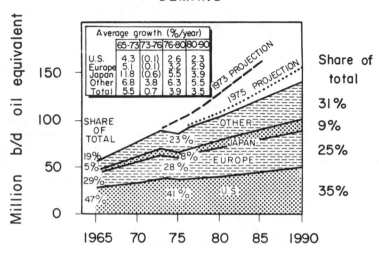

Average growth (%/year)				
	65-73	73-76	76-80	80-90
U.S.	4.3	(0.1)	2.6	2.3
Europe	5.1	(0.1)	3.2	2.9
Japan	11.8	(0.6)	5.5	3.9
Other	6.8	3.8	6.3	5.5
Total	5.5	0.7	3.9	3.5

SUPPLY

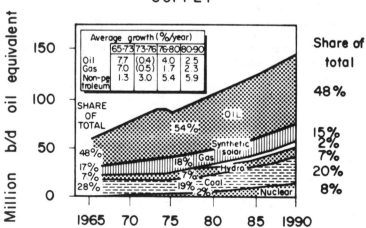

Average growth (%/year)				
	65-73	73-76	76-80	80-90
Oil	7.7	(0.4)	4.0	2.5
Gas	7.0	(0.5)	1.7	2.3
Non-petroleum	1.3	3.0	5.4	5.9

FIG.5 ENERGY SUPPLY/DEMAND

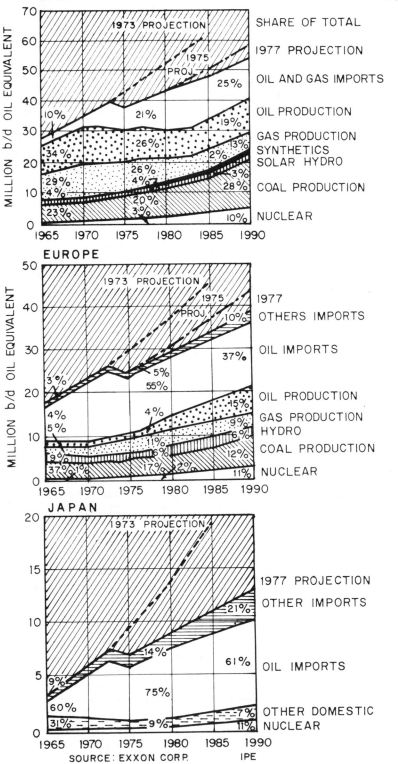

FIG.6 ENERGY SUPPLY/DEMAND (IN MAJOR INDUSTRIAL REGIONS)

It also has reserves of natural gas estimated at nearly 719,660 billion ft^3, equivalent to nearly 20,387 billion m^3.

As can be seen, the evolution of oil reserves grew markedly after the 2nd World War because of the interest in a very valuable raw material and for military reasons. Following a trend observed in various countries of the world, the main countries of the Middle East began to control their oil industry, nationalizing the oil companies and assuring their sovereignty over their greatest natural wealth.

8.   The International Petroleum Market

The marked growth of oil consumption in the last decades (Figs.7 and 8) led to a world production level of 22 billion barrels per year, very high in relation to the size of the proven reserves. This fact, together with the consumption growth, even if at lower rates, and the significant part of the reserves in the Middle East, which naturally sets the production at a level convenient to its interest, generates concern about the present situation, with difficulties foreseen in the supply situation in the near future.

Steps taken for the acceleration of exploration, conservation, and alternative sources should alleviate the problem. The discovery of substantial reserves such as those in Alaska, North Sea, and Mexico are attenuating the difficulties in meeting the needs of the market at present.

The price of crude oil on the international market stood until 1972 below US$ 2/bbl FOB, having increased markedly from 1973 on, and now exceeds US$ 20/bbl FOB for long-term contracts, attaining on the spot market values sometimes in excess of US$ 30/bbl. The behaviour of payments of the countries importing this raw material, vital to industry and transportation. The importing countries, especially the industrialized ones, are adopting a number of measures of a political and economic nature to overcome the present market situation and its projection in the future. In this way they are trying to slow down the rate of economic growth and adopt policies for the speeding up of oil exploration, search for alternative energy sources, steps for conservation, etc. However, in spite of all the above measures, the uncertainty of the supply is a serious threat to the stable economic development of the major importers.

In conclusion, it should be borne in mind that, faced with the future perspective, the oil industry should intensify its exploration and production efforts, expanding also its action area to little explored regions, and to hostile areas such as arctic, antarctic, deserts, wildernesses, and to the seas in deeper and deeper waters.

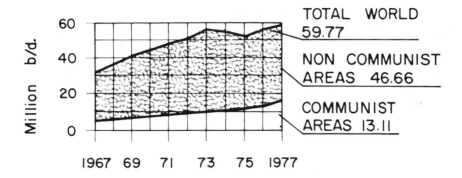

FIG.7   HOW GLOBAL OIL PRODUCTION IS CLIMBING
        Source: The Oil and Gas Journal

PHILLIPS PETROLEUM CO.

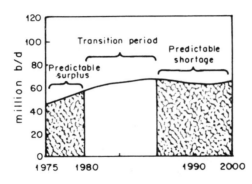

SHELL CANADA LTD.

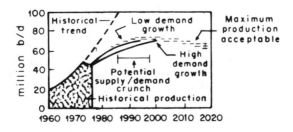

FIG.8   NON-COMMUNIST OIL SUPPLY/DEMAND CRUNCH

9. LATIN AMERICA - Reserves and Production

The Latin-American oil reserves have an important place among
the different world regions and, together with the discoveries
in Mexico in the last years, should be below only the Middle-
East and socialist-block reserves.

The proven reserves in Latin America, as of January 1979, according to the A.P.I., are approximately 41.2 billion barrels, and
should increase considerably with confirmation of the new Mexican
reserves. According to the same source, two countries hold most
of the reserves of that region: Venezuela, 18 billion, and
Mexico, 16 billion barrels of oil, in January of this year.

Because of the considerable value of the reserves, several countries are exporters of oil and/or derivatives, i.e. Venezuela,
Mexico, Ecuador, Trinidad, and, recently, Peru. The Latin American production is some 4,760,000 barrels per day, exceeding
consumption by approximately 25%. The main producers in the area
are Venezuela with 2,160,000 and Mexico with 1,500,000 barrels
per day.

According to the Informative Bulletin of ARPEL, dated August
1979, the Mexican proven reserves reached by the end of 1978 is
approximately 40 billion barrels of hydrocarbons (crude oil and
equivalent natural gas).

10. The Exploration and Production Effort in Latin America

The significance, in international terms, of the effort being
made in Mexico for the development of the great reserves of
hydrocarbons discovered in this decade, must be stressed. To
give an idea of the exploration and production effort, we list
the number of drilling rigs, according to the Petroleum Engineer
publication, June 1979, for the main activity areas as of March
1979:

Mexico	–	196
Brazil	–	59
Argentina	–	57
Venezuela	–	43

11. Activity Areas

The areas where the greatest efforts for the exploration and
production of hydrocarbons in Latin America are being exerted
are: Mexico, Brazil, Venezuela and Argentina.

12. Presence of State Control

In Latin America, a trend is observed similar to that of many
countries in the world. Most countries adopt State control of

their hydrocarbon resources. State control is imposed mainly because of the fundamental importance of this raw material in the industrial and transportation structure and because of its strategic value in the present world. Based on the Minutes of the 14th Ordinary Meeting of ARPEL, held this year in Rio de Janeiro, we give below some statistical data on the members of that association:

PEMEX (Mexico)

Total investment: US$ 15,600 million, 1977-1982
Exploration: 1,324 wells 1977-1982 (success rate:42% in 1978)
Production: 900,000 bpd (Dec.1976) - 1,500,000 bpd (Dec.1978)
Drilling rigs: 209
Production forecast: 2,250,000 bpd (by the end of 1980), export 1,100,000 bpd
Pipeline network: 50,000 km
Fleet of tankers: 30 ships, total capacity 700,000 ton
Sales: US$ 4,600 million in 1978
Assets: US$ 15.200 million in 1977
Total assets/total habilities = 2.2
Revenue in the 1977-1982 period: US$ 56,800 million (60% by export
Hydrocarbon reserves: 40,194 million bbls (Dec.78)
Ratio reserves/production: 60 years

ENAP (Chile)

Consumption: 100,000 bpd
Production: 25,000 bpd
Seismic: 12,064 km (1977); 3,252 (1978)
Drilling: 88 wells in 1978
Production: 928,000 m^3 in 1978
Risk contracts: 2 (ARCO-AMERADA-PHILLIPS)
Estimated share of the production in the consumption: 45% in 1982

GAS DEL ESTADO (Argentina)

Gas Pipeline: 15,000 km
Distribution network: 17,000 km (80% of the population)
Share: 25% of the consumed energy
Gas Pipeline Terra Fogo-Buenos Aires: capacity 11,300,000 m^3/day, 2,600 km
Gas Pipeline Bolivia-Buenos: capacity 9,800,000 m^3/day, 1,750 km
Gas Pipeline Neuquen-Buenos Aires: capacity 10,100,000 m^3/day, 1,200 km
Production: 9,000 million m^3 in 1978 (72% YPF, 20% Bolivia, 8% Chile)
Sales of gas US$ 540 million in 1978
Liquified gas sales: US$ 190 million in 1978
Natural gas reserves: 430,000 million m^3
Investments: US$ 150 million for 1979

Hydrocarbon production: 77% oil and 23% natural gas
Hydrocarbon reserves: 52% natural gas and 48% oil
Personnel: 10,000 employees

PDVSA (Venezuela)

Exploration:
Increase of reserves: 973 million bbls
Investment: US$ 181 million in 1978
Seismic: 17,000 km
Exploration wells: 61 in 1978
Drilling rigs: 13 in 1978
Seismic crews: 6 in 1978
Production: 791 million bbls in 1978
Utilization of natural gas: 94%
Reserves: 18,199 million bbls of oil
Reserves: 1,190 billion m^3 of natural gas
Development wells: 653 in 1978
Investment in Production: US$ 507 million in 1978
Development drilling rigs: 38 in 1978
Well-cleaning units: 34 in 1978
Exports: 1,963,000 bpd (63% oil and 37% products)
Net profit: US$ 1,447 million
Personnel: 29,822 employees
Training: 2,271 courses (14,172 employees)
Petrochemical training: 800 courses (11,460 employees)
Offshore drilling: 12 exploration wells (till May 79)
Investment foreseen for exploration: US$ 254 million for 1979
Investment foreseen for production: US$ 767 million for 1979
Investment foreseen for refining: US$ 577 million for 1979
Total investment foreseen for 1979: US$ 1,628 million

CEPE (Ecuador)

Reserves: 1,500 million bbls petroleum (Dec.78) proven and verifiable
Proven reserves: 1,170 million bbls petroleum (I.P.E.-1979)
Production: ≈ 237,000 bpd petroleum today
Transequatorian pipeline: 503 km
Consumption: 21.7 million barrels in 1978
Exports: 29.5 million barrels in 1978 (US$ 370 million)
Investments: US$ 486 million 1972-1978 (46% exploration and production, 24.4% transportation, 27.4% industrialization and 2.2% merchandising)
Internal training: 2,863 employees in 1978
External training: 438 employees in the 1973-1978 period

PETROBRAS

Capital: US$ 2.5 billion - Cr$ 56.6 billion in 1978
Investment: Cr$ 32.8 billion in 1978 (46.9% exploration and production, 18% refining, 14.4% terminals and pipelines, 7.5% maritime transport, 7% subsidiaries, 5.3% various, 0.9% shale)
(≈ US$ 2 billion)

Gross sales: Cr$ 207.8 billion in 1978
Foreign-exchange savings: US$ 2 billion
Drilling: 527,000 m (279,000 for exploration)
Reserves: 181.8 million m^3 (Dec.78)
Fleet: 48 tankers - 3.1 million dwt
Refining capacity: 190.000 m^3/day

PETROPERU

Personnel: 8,250 employees
Investment in exploration and production: US$ 1,314 million in
1970/1978 (19 companies)
Reserves: 700 million bbls petroleum
Potential reserves: 4 billion bbls
Investment in exploration and production (1978): US$ 183 million
(Petroperu) - US$ 27 x 10^6)
Seismic: 168 km in 1978 (contractors)
Exploratory drilling: 7 wells (contractors) and 13 wells (Petro-
peru)
Development drilling: 70 wells (Petroperu) and 67 wells (contrac-
tors)
Total drilling: ≈ 289,634 m
Drilling rigs: 16
Total yield: 18,102 m/drilling.year = 1,508 m/drilling.month =
49 m/drilling.day
Production: 151,000 bpd in 1978 (average)
Refining capacity: 185,000 bpd
Production in December 1978: 175,000 bpd (self-sufficiency)
Ratio reserves/production: 700/66 = 10.6 years
Forecasted exports: 50,000 bpd crude in 1979

YPF   (Argentina)

Sales: US$ 3,500 million
Profit on sales: US$ 450 million
Refining: 65% by YPF
Total number of wells: 22 thousand
Wells in production: 6,300 (4,000 by YPF)
Production: 460,000 bpd oil
Consumption: 500,000 bpd oil
Reserves: 2,200 million bbls oil
Ratio reserves/production: 12 years (oil)
Ratio reserves/production: 50 years (natural gas)
Natural gas consumption: 170,000 bpd oil equivalent
Readjustment of fuel prices: 2-3% beneath the monthly index
Fleet of tankers: 600,000 ton
Adopts risk contracts for exploration-production

YPFB   (Bolivia)

Sedimentary area: 16,461,667 hectares (about 30% explored)
Gas reserves: 6.4 trillion ft^3
Demand: 6.2 trillion ft^3 in 20 years (including projected exports'

to Brazil)
Investment to confirm gas reserves: US$ 25 million

13. BRAZIL - Situation of Hydrocarbon Reserves

As a result of the intensification of exploratory efforts, the
Brazilian hydrocarbon reserves have been showing marked increases,
as shown in Figs.9 and 10. The oil reserve increased from 136,280
million m^3 (857 million barrels) in December 1970 to 197,929
million m^3 (1,245 million barrels) in June 1979. It should be
noted that as a result of the exploratory effort on the continental shelf, its oil reserve exceeds that of the land. The natural gas reserve attained approximately 44,553,463 million m^3.

14. Expenditure with Crude Oil Importation

Brazil imports a significant volume of petroleum because of the
marked growth of the domestic market, motivated mainly by the
dimensions of the country and its economic and demographic
growth. Due to the marked growth of the prices in the international market after 1973 and to the increase of consumption, the
import figures have been reaching high values.

The evolution of the net foreign exchange expenditures with oil
and derivatives, at historical prices, was the following:

1971	-	US$	440 million
1973	-	US$	1,040 million
1975	-	US$	3,060 million
1977	-	US$	3,530 million
1978	-	US$	3,934 million

It is estimated that in 1979 the net foreign exchange expenditures with oil and derivatives may exceed US$ 6 billion, mainly
because of petroleum imports.

15. Intensification of the Exploration and Production Effort

PETROBRAS has been developing a large investment in the oil industry in Brazil, as shown by the table of investments per activity in the 1954-1980 period (Table 4). The evolution in real increasing values, especially in the exploration and production
activity, should be considered, not only in absolute values but
also as a share, which is expected to exceed the 50% mark of the
total investment.

The investments effort of PETROBRAS is further shown by a comparison for 1978 (when our investments exceeded US$ 2 billion)
with similar international corporations (Table 5).

Most of the investments in exploration and production budgeted
for 1979 are assigned to activity on the continental shelf, with
resources above US$ 1 billion. Nearly US$ 270 are budgeted in

Table 4.   PETROLEO BRASILEIRO S.A. – PETROBRAS INVESTMENTS 1954 – 1980

Cr$ million (prices of may 1979)

YEAR	Exploration and Production	%	Refinery	%	Transportation	%	Terminal and Pipeline	%	Schist (Shale) Oil	%
1954	155	15,9	701	71,9	1	0,1	–	–	25	2,6
1955	545	43,1	376	29,7	81	6,4	–	–	38	3,0
1956	949	54,0	273	15,5	66	3,8	–	–	31	1,8
1957	1.884	70,4	488	18,2	22	0,8	–	–	33	1,2
1958	2.764	62,0	1.446	32,5	10	0,2	–	–	35	0,8
1959	2.134	40,9	2.320	44,5	479	9,2	–	–	36	0,7
1960	2.195	27,0	2.647	32,6	1.571	19,3	1.116	13,7	55	0,7
1961	2.955	36,9	2.568	32,1	964	12,0	349	4,4	74	0,9
1962	3.530	42,8	2.667	32,3	626	7,6	597	7,2	84	1,0
1963	3.867	46,3	1.865	22,3	938	11,2	555	6,7	130	1,6
1964	4.008	45,7	1.978	22,6	721	8,2	1.081	12,3	108	1,2
1965	4.710	48,3	2.027	20,8	529	5,4	1.385	14,2	178	1,8
1966	4.711	47,1	1.679	16,8	1.004	10,0	972	9,7	173	1,7
1967	4.809	52,6	1.465	16,0	235	2,5	1.260	13,8	163	1,8
1968	4.725	50,6	1.280	13,7	129	1,4	1.576	16,9	156	1,7
1969	5.144	50,1	1.684	16,4	1.523	14,8	877	8,5	206	2,0
1970	6.100	39,5	4.286	27,8	803	5,2	1.865	12,1	335	2,2
1971	5.172	24,5	9.156	43,4	1.350	6,4	2.792	13,2	323	1,5
1972	6.212	29,9	6.040	29,1	3.209	15,5	1.304	6,3	171	0,8
1973	7.286	29,5	6.249	25,3	3.256	13,2	2.162	8,7	291	1,2
1974	9.395	26,9	13.426	38,4	1.677	4,8	5.246	15,0	271	0,8
1975	12.833	27,8	16.938	36,8	1.802	3,9	10.276	22,3	271	0,6
1976	15.970	36,3	13.586	31,0	2.805	6,4	6.639	15,1	315	0,7
1977	17.991	40,0	10.011	22,3	7.405	16,5	4.528	10,1	285	0,6
1978	21.378	46,9	8.189	18,0	3.401	7,5	6.569	14,4	408	0,9
1979*	29.359	53,8	7.391	13,5	5.463	10,0	3.232	5,9	594	1,1
1980**	35.104	59,8	7.520	12,8	5.736	9,8	2.312	3,9	1.280	2,2

*   Projection
**   "

Table 5.   INVESTMENT OF PETROBRAS IN RELATION TO OTHER INTER-
NATIONAL COMPANIES 1978

COMPANY	GLOBAL INVESTMENT US$ MILLION
TEXACO	1581
CHEVRON	1692
MOBIL	2042
GULF	3443
EXXON	5300
BRITISH PETROLEUM (BP)	2213
SHELL (ROYAL DUTCH)	4804
PETROBRAS	2072

Source: Annual Reports

1979 for exploration activities directly by PETROBRAS. With reference to indirect exploration activities, investments of US$
431 million are foreseen up to and including 1981, through the
26 risk contracts already signed.

We attach a map, Fig.11, showing the position of drilling equipment on the Brazilian continental shelf, concentrating the largest amount of equipment outside of the U.S.A.

In order to visualize the evolution of the drilling efforts in
Brazil, we include a diagram, Fig.12, showing the drilling foot-
age since 1965 and a table, Table 6, with the number of drilling
rigs of the most active countries, showing Brazil in sixth place
(not including the socialist-block countries).

Lastly, to allow an evaluation of the great exploratory effort
under way in Brazil, especially on the continental shelf, we
attach a map, Fig.13, giving the location of areas for risk contracts and Table 7 listing the wildcat wells drilled on the continental shelf in 1978, according to "Petroleum Engineer" of
June 1979, showing Brazil in second place, below only the United
States.

16.   Offshore Technology

To implement this aggressive program along the extensive Brazilian continental shelf, we have the most advanced technology,
including frontier technology, as is the case of early production
systems already installed in deep waters.

Exploratory drilling is under way along the Brazilian coast in
water depths over 300 m, with over 500 exploratory wells already

drilled. Platforms for the production of the fields discovered are being designed for depths up to 170 m, with a weight up to 40,000 tons, comparable therefore to many major projects in the North Sea.

For the execution of these programs, we count on our own resources, on specialized international industry, and on the Brazilian industry working sometimes in association with foreign companies, coordinated by us.

Table 6. NUMBER OF DRILLING RIGS
MARCH/79
(excluding countries of socialist block)

UNITED STATES	1936
CANADA	265
MEXICO	196
ALGERIA	101
INDONESIA	64
BRAZIL	59
ARGENTINA	57
VENEZUELA	43
INDIA	40
UNITED KINGDOM (North Sea)	33

Source: Hughes Tool Co.
Petroleum Engineer - (June 1979)

Table 7. NUMBER OF WILDCAT WELLS
DRILLED OFFSHORE IN 1978

UNITED STATES	295
BRAZIL	75
INDONESIA	58
PERU	40
UNITED KINGDOM	37
ITALY	23
HOLLAND	23
AUSTRALIA	22
NORWAY	19
CAMEROON	19
SPAIN	19
USSR	19

Source: Offshore (June 20, 1979)

17. Share of the Domestic Industry

PETROBRAS has been encouraging the participation of national industry, in some cases in association with foreign companies, in the engineering projects, as a form of transferring specialized technology in offshore projects.

In addition to some existing shipyards capable of building medium-
size structures, PETROBRAS sponsored the construction of a shipyard in Sao Roque, Bahia, and also provided the incentive for a
second shipyard in Parana, for the construction of large size
structures (Figs.14-17). It has also been encouraging the participation of national industry in exploration and production
work on the continental shelf, such as drilling and workover rigs.
The Sao Roque yard at Todos os Santos Bay was built for PETROBRAS
at a cost of over US$ 30 million, and three platforms for the
Campos Basin will be built there by the Montreal-Micoperi association. The yard under construction in Parana by the Tenenge-RDL
Consortium will have capacity up to 3 large size platforms.

18. Development of the Campos Basin

This is an area which yielded, up to now, the best results in the
exploration of the Brazilian continental shelf. Fields were discovered in deep waters, and we are concentrating the greatest
efforts therein. Besides the early production systems, several
projects have been approved for that basin, consisting of approximately six production platforms, so far.

Other projects may be approved, as a consequence of the exploratory work under way (Figs.18-20). Investments for the Campos
Basin (Table 8) are foreseen possibly up to an amount equivalent
to US$ 3 billion, including early production and land and marit-
ime pipelines systems.

Table 8. CAMPOS BASIN INVESTMENTS

Project	Cost - US$ (millions)
Garoupa	304
Namorado	414
Cherne	365
Badejo	188
Enchova	364
Pampo	182
Garoupa early production system	214
Enchova early production system	53
Offshore pipelines	356
On shore pipelines and gathering system	235

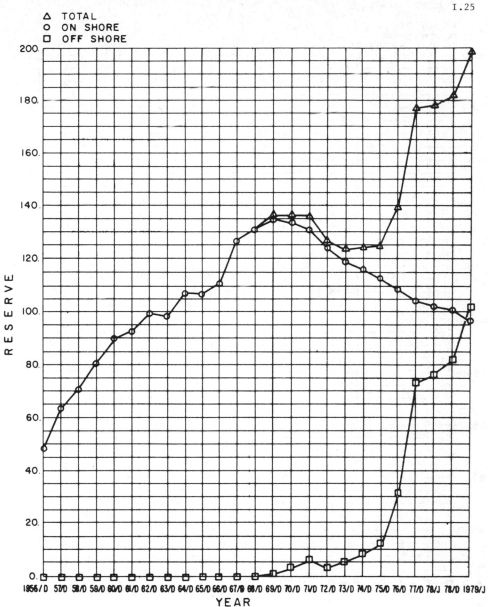

FIG.9 PETROBRAS - OIL RESERVE
MILLION CUBIC METER

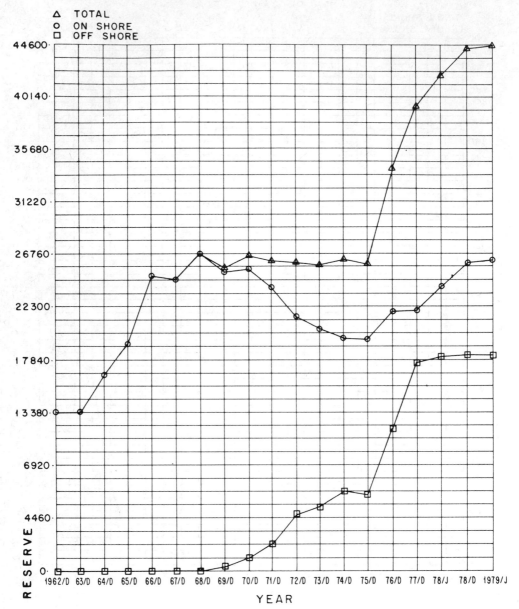

FIG.10   PETROBRAS - GAS RESERVE
MILLION CUBIC METER

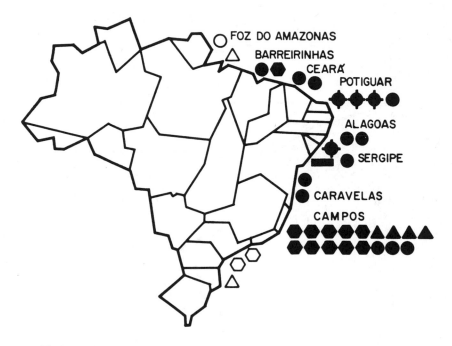

FOZ DO AMAZONAS
BARREIRINHAS
CEARÁ
POTIGUAR
ALAGOAS
SERGIPE
CARAVELAS
CAMPOS

⬢ — SEMI - SUBMERSIBLE

● — JACK - UP

▲ — DRILLING - SHIP

▬ — DRILLING TENDER

✦ — CONVENTIONAL RIG

⬡ △ ○ — RISK CONTRACT

FIG.11   EXPLORATION ACTIVITIES OFF SHORE-DRILLING UNITS

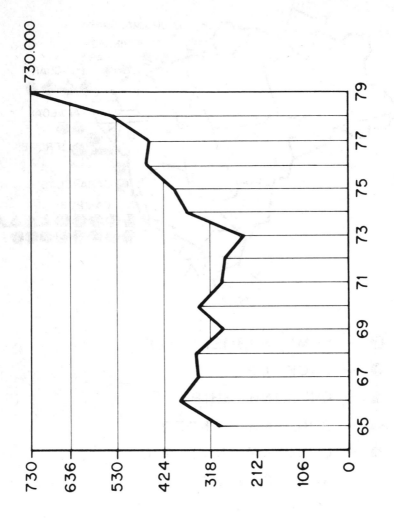

FIG.12 METERS DRILLED ON SHORE AND OFF-SHORE

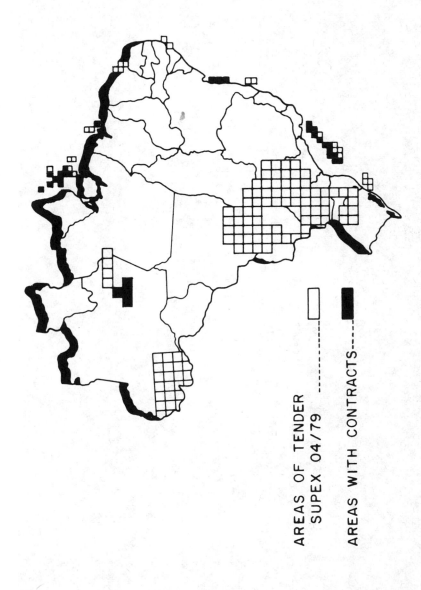

AREAS OF TENDER
SUPEX 04/79 ----------

AREAS WITH CONTRACTS-----

FIG.13 RISK CONTRACT AREAS

FIG.14   PETROBRAS - SAO ROQUE YARD - TODOS OS SANTOS BAY

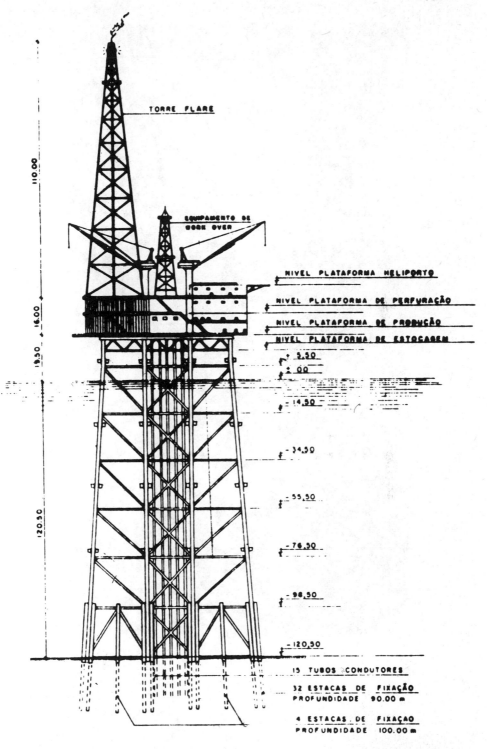

FIG.15   CENTRAL PLATFORM OF GAROUPA

FIG.16   CANTEIRO DE SAO ROQUE - BAHIA
PLATAFORMA PARA CAMPO GAROUPA
CONSTRUTORA - CONSORCIO MONTREAL-MICOPERI

FIG.17   JACK-UP PLATFORM - NORBE-1

COMPANY: NORBERTO ODERBRECHT - BRAZIL

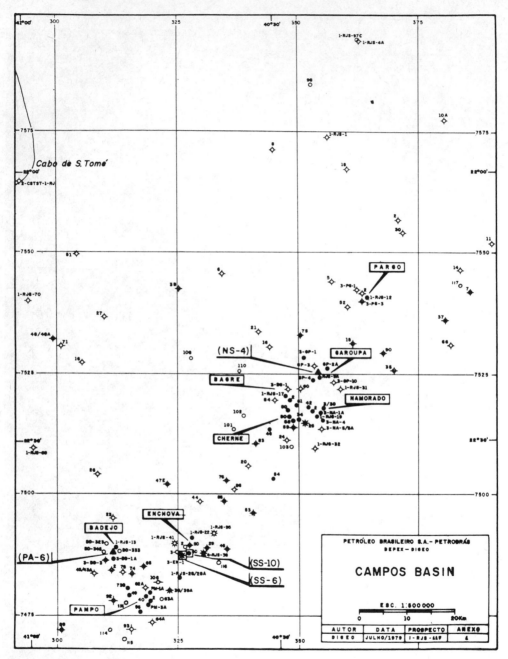

FIG.18

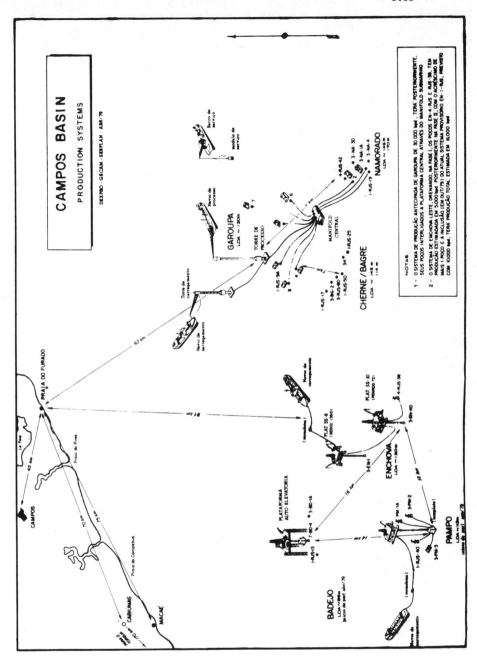

FIG.19

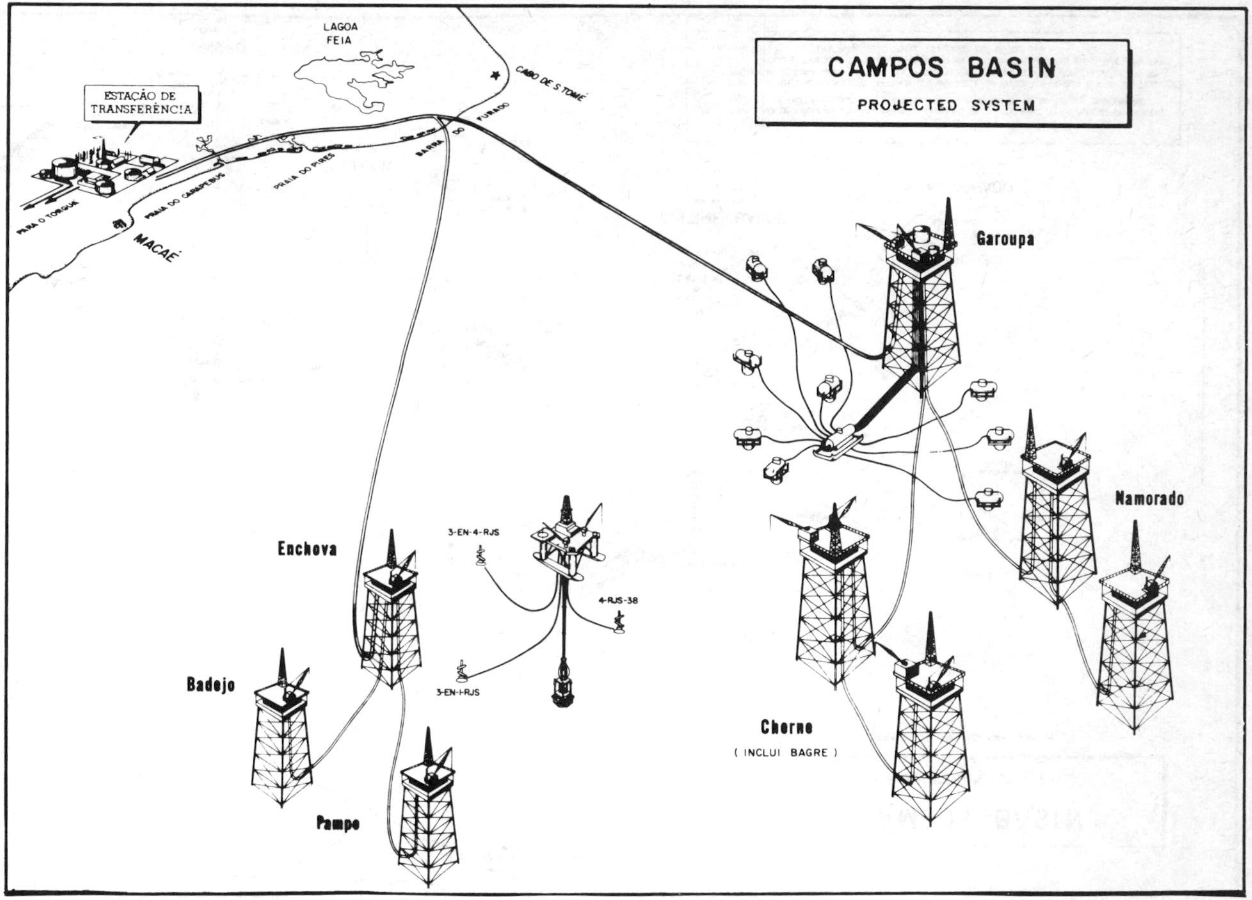
CAMPOS BASIN
PROJECTED SYSTEM
LAGOA FEIA
ESTAÇÃO DE TRANSFERÊNCIA
CABO DE S.TOMÉ
BARRA DO FURADO
PRAIA DO PIRES
PRAIA DO CARAPEBUS
MACAÉ
Garoupa
Namorado
Cherno
(INCLUI BAGRE)
Enchova
Badejo
Pampo
3-EN-4-RJS
4-RJS-38
3-EN-I-RJS

FIG.20

PART 1   BEHAVIOUR OF MATERIALS AND STRUCTURES,
OF STEEL OR CONCRETE, IN THE SEA

CYCLIC SHEAR CAPACITY OF OFFSHORE CONCRETE STRUCTURES

Ben C. Gerwick Jr.

University of California, Berkeley,U.S.A.

ABSTRACT

Extensive investigation has been carried out and
continues to be carried out in connection with the
endurance of reinforced and prestressed concrete
under cyclic flexure and, more recently, under fully-
reversing membrane axial forces. However, for certain
zones of typical concrete sea structures,the critical
failure modes occur under fully-reversing cyclic
shear.

Research on the behaviour under high-intensity
seismic excitation of the reinforced concrete shear
walls of buildings of cylindrical containment vessels
for nuclear reactors, has shown that extensive
diagonal cracking can occur, with relatively wide
cracks and severe degradation of stiffness. Were
cracking of this degree to take place under storm
wave loading, the serviceability of the structure
would be seriously impaired. Continued cycling could
soon lead to low-cycle fatigue failure.

Vertical prestressing, combined with adequate amounts
of horizontal steel is found to be a practicable,
economical, and effective means of resisting these
cyclic forces.

While this matter has current importance for fixed
(bottom-founded) concrete sea structures, it can be
of even greater importance for floating structures
such as large barge-shaped vessels, where the still
water shears and longitudinal wave shears are
augmented by torsional shear due to quartering waves.

The use of vertical prestressing is an effective

means to ensure the safe performance of such
structures, even after an extreme overload event has
exceeded the diagonal tension cracking capacity of
the concrete due to shear.

INTRODUCTION

The expanding use of reinforced and prestressed
concrete in sea structures, both fixed and floating,
for service in ever more hostile environments, has
generated intense interest in its fatigue endurance
capabilities, even though so far as is known, no
fatigue problems have yet arisen in actual sea
structures.

Several extensive test programs are underway,
developing data on concrete endurance under cyclic
membrane loadings in axial tension and compression.
These tests show a progressive loss of strength
under a high number of cycles at relatively large
stress ranges. Fortunately, and significantly, when
the Wohler curves for concrete, prestressing steel,
and conventional reinforcement are plotted against
the probable long-term stress range history of a
typical structure in the North Sea, it is found that
the cumulative usage is only a small fractile of the
allowable usage. This therefore explains the lack of
reported failures in service.

A recent paper (1) points out that the relevant
experience from research tests and from other uses
of prestressed concrete indicates that the low-cycle
end of the spectrum may actually be more critical
than the high cycle cumulative fatigue with which
steel structures are primarily concerned. With
prestressed concrete sea structures, cyclic loading
that extends into the cracking range on each cycle
can lead to water "pumping" in and out of the crack
as well as wedging action, eventually leading to
splitting of the concrete.(2)(3)

Prestressed concrete piles, which have been cracked
due to rebound tensile stress during pile driving,
often proceed to brittle failure under 50 to 100
cycles of fully reversing excursions into alternating
high tension and high compression. This indicates
that axial cyclic loadings of high intensity can
lead to low-cycle fatigue.

In a previous paper (1) the author shows that
adequate endurance under such low cycle high
intensity axial loading can be attained by the use

FIG. I – CRACK PATTERN TYPICAL OF HIGH –
INTENSITY CYCLIC SHEAR

of proper steel percentages, extended splice and anchorage developments lengths, and the proper use of confining stirrups in critical zones.

In a parallel development, extensive laboratory research has been directed to the behaviour of shear walls of buildings and the cylindrical shell walls of nuclear reactor containment vessel under very strong seismic excitation. In such tests, the shear elements are subjected to 5 to 10 cycles of fully reversing cyclic shear of high magnitude,simulating a major earthquake. (ref. 6,7)

In a typical test procedure, the specimen wall or cylindrical shell is first cycled through several cycles below the level of visible cracking (which develops some degradation of stiffness), then is subjected to a few cycles of high intensity which develop diagonal shear cracks in both directions. The resisting actions internal to the structure are friction on the cracked surfaces, dowel action in the steel, compression in the concrete "struts"along the diagonal, and tension in the reinforcing steel in both orthogonal directions. (fig. 1)

The usual pattern of conventional reinforcing steel is orthogonal. This is generally necessary because of the practicable problems of forming the concrete wales and of steel installation. Theoretical studies and test results both show that with such a grid pattern, the cracks are widened by a factor of 2 or more, while the reinforcing steel is very inefficiently utilized. The formulae developed are of the "$\cos^4$ plus $\sin^4$" form, indicating the cumulative inefficiency involved when the steel is at a significant angle (eg. 45º) to the principal tension.

Evaluation for Sea Structures

Fixed sea structures typically have several shafts supported on a base caisson. The base caisson may consist of interlocking cylinders or an "egg crate" of cubical segments. The vertical walls, parallel to the applied wave force, must transmit this force by in-plane shear to the base slab and foundation. (fig. 2,3)

With floating structures, such as barges, the vertical bulkheads, both internal bulkheads and sides, must transmit the longitudinal wave shear between the deck and hull bottom. Wave shear is additive to dead load shear (still water shear). In addition,the

Fig. 2 STATFJORD CONDEEP;   CELL WALLS

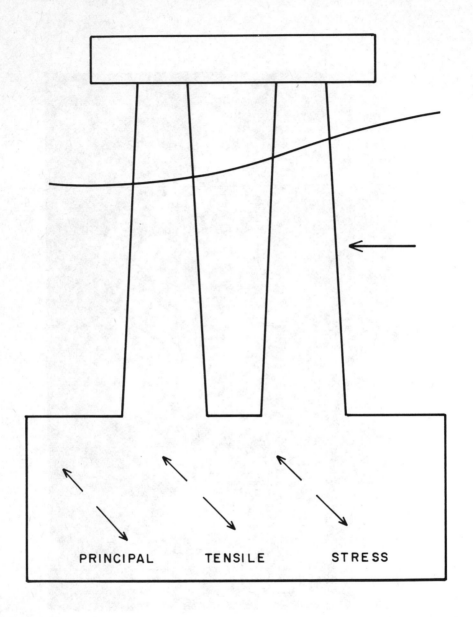

FIG. 3 – TYPICAL CONCRETE PLAT FORM

sides must transmit the torsional shear due to the quartering waves. This torsional shear also acts as principal tensile stresses with an approximate 45° inclination.

As far as is known, no tests have been made on such cyclic shear (into the cracking range) which is repeated for a great number of cycles, as would occur in a prolonged storm. Also,the author knows of no such tests being made underwater. However we can readily postulate by extrapolation from axial fatigue tests, both in air and under water, that (a) repeated cycling at levels which develops 50% to 70% of the tensile strength of the concrete will result in extensive diagonal cracking and (b) the effect of the water in the cracks will be to cause washing and erosion, wedging, and reduction of shear friction along the cracked surfaces.

These in-plane shear cracks will of course extend through the walls. With only conventional unstressed reinforcing steel, they will not close. Cracks will be twice or more as wide as our more usual flexural and axial tension cracks, which in further contrast, generally close upon removal of the load. Thus we have to be concerned not only with fatigue but also with corrosion. Particularly in the case of floating barges or ships, such cracks in the splash zone will be potential foci of corrosion.

The double-diagonal cracking causes a serious reduction in stiffness. This means that the natural frequency of the structure lengthens, which increases the dynamic amplification of wave-induced forces. It can thus be concluded that this cracking must be prevented or at least severely limited since the potential consequences are a reduction in durability, through cracks of relatively large width that do not close, a reduction in stiffness leading to higher dynamic amplifications of wave-induced forces, and the possibility of fatigue.

Reference (4) points out that for cyclic shear loadings   where the total shear exceeds 50% of the shear capacity,all shear should be taken by the steel acting alone. Under such cyclic ranges, the shear capacity (diagonal tension capacity) of the concrete degrades, so that reliance must be placed on the steel acting by itself. Since fatigue is of main interest in this paper, a few more points with respect to it will be examined.

Tensile fatigue will generally not occur if the

FIG.4A - CONCRETE FLOATING TERMINAL:BULKHEADS

FIG. 4B - ARCO ARDJUNA FLOATING TERMINAL

excursion into the tensile range is less than 50% of the splitting tensile strength. The same is true in the compression phase: if excursions are less than 50% of f'c, compressive fatigue is essentially prevented.

In the case of shear, we are primarily concerned with the principal tensile stress.

Once cracking does occur, repeated cycles cause small displacements along the diagonal crack, which leads to abrasion of the surfaces. Dowel action of the steel comes into play, with local bending of the steel bars and intensive bearing stress on the concrete adjacent to the crack. This bending is additive to the direct tensile stress. Thus fatigue of steel becomes of concern.

Practical Solutions

These problems of cyclic shear have been satisfactorily met for the concrete ships of World Wars I and II, by the use of high percentages of reinforcement in both directions. The design here was largely intuitive but was correct.

With concrete sea structures, which tend to get larger and larger, a recognition of the potential problem of cyclic shear has led to very careful finite element analyses, from which the proper amount of reinforcing steel has been determined. In some cases of recent offshore platforms, it has been necessary to use from 2.5% to 4% of reinforcement in each direction, in order to maintain crack widths below 0.25mm, a value believed safe under repeated loading. Allowable steel stresses in such cases range only up to about 130 MPa (18.000 psi)which is well below the endurance limit. (Bending stresses,largely indeterminate, are additive but are not appreciable, as long as crack width is kept small.)

With such high percentages of reinforcement, physical placement of the steel presents a problem of congestion, and of course makes the subsequent concreting very difficult.

Consideration has been given to the use of diagonal steel patterns to reduce the required amount of steel. Such a pattern presents obvious difficulties in field installation, particularly when slip forms are to be employed.

On the Ninian Central Platform, C.G. Doris employed vertical post-tensioning to counter these shear forces. (fig. 5,6) This suggests the wider application on this technique.

Vertical Post-Tensioning, and Efficient Solution

While the tests and studies previously referenced show clearly that one cannot adequately reinforce the walls by assigning the steel on the basis of vertical and horizontal components of the principal stress (as some codes now permit), the same is not true of prestressed concrete.

In a typical case where 4% of vertical unstressed steel, working at 130 MPa is required to keep crack width below 0.25mm, calculations show that about 0.5% of prestressing steel will fully resist the vertical component of the principal stress.

Assuming that prestressing steel in place costs 4 times as much per unit weight as ordinary reinforcing steel, the total cost is still only half as much. However, this is not all. The effect of the vertical prestress is to change the direction of the principal tensile stress so that it now acts horizontally. Now the horizontal reinforcing steel is able to function at 100% efficiency (about 40% more efficient that when at an angle). Thus there appears to be a major economic benefit to the use of vertical prestressing.

Such a scheme is inherently practicable as well, because the vertical ducts can be placed in the center of the walls, where they are clear from interference with the other bars. They do not impede the concrete placement as much as horizontal ducts would.

Congestion of steel is minimized, placement is expedited, and the slipformed concrete may progress more rapidly. However, more important by far than the economic and practical considerations, are the improved long term serviceability and freedom from cracking of the prestressed concrete.

As emphasized in reference(1),there still must be adequate steel area to ensure that under extreme or accidental overload conditions, inadvertent cracking does not lead to yeld and permanent cracking. Hence in the example cited, in addition to 0.5% prestressing steel, an additional amount of unstressed vertical steel (at least 0.5%) should be added in a conventional pattern, distributed on both faces.

The above discussion relates to one mode only of

1.14

FIG.5A - NINIAN CENTRAL PLATFORM: SHEAR WALLS

FIG.5B - NINIAN CENTRAL PLATFORM:SHEAR WALLS

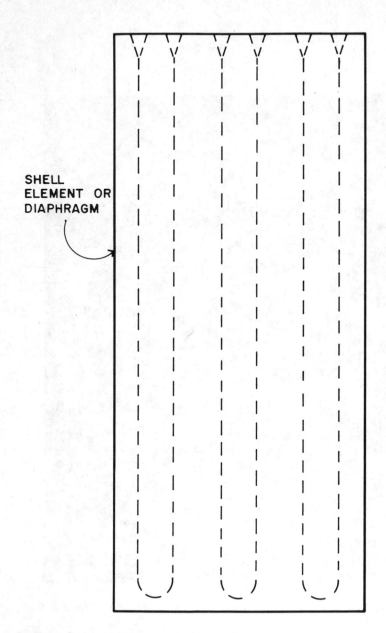

SHELL
ELEMENT OR
DIAPHRAGM

FIG. 6 – SCHEMATIC LAYOUT OF PRESTRESSING
TENDONS FOR VERTICAL POST –
TENSIONING.

shear failure, that of diagonal tension. However, another mode also needs to be examined, that of shear compression or web crushing. This occurs only when the total shear stress is relatively high (above $0.6\sqrt{f'c}$, in S1 units, or $7\sqrt{f'c}$ (English units). The use of prestressing can help extend the safe range, as can an imposed vertical load. In both cases, the additional compression acting on horizontal planes tends to increase the area on which the compression struts act and hence reduce the concentrated local compression which could lead to a shear compression failure. It has been shown (ref.6) that this pre-compression also increases the ductility, ie the ultimate capacity. Shear stresses up to at least $0.9\sqrt{f'c}$ (S1 units) or $10\sqrt{f'c}$ (English units) can generally be safely accommodated.

Ref.(1) emphasizes the importance of details and these need to be briefly re-stated here. Lap splices and anchorages need to develop the ultimate strength. Bond stresses under repeated loads are only about half those under static loads. Critical compression zones need to be confined by stirrups. Construction joints must be made with great care to prevent a plane of weakness on which sliding may occur.

This paper has been concerned with shear due to storm waves. It is believed that it is also relevant to ice loads, which are similarly imposed externally. Earthquake shears are due to inertial forces imposed by sudden ground displacements. For these latter, special consideration may have be given to ensuring ductility under overload and means such as confinement of vertical and horizontal bands in the wall may be indicated.

Summary
Concrete Sea Structures, both fixed and floating, have critical zones, such as cell walls and bulkheads, for which fully-reversing shear under cyclic wave loads may be the controlling design parameter. Should diagonal cracks form under high shear, the stiffness of the structure degrades. The cracks are wider than those associated with similar tensile stresses in flexure or axial load. Continued cycling may lead to low cycle fatigue, with failure in concrete compression and/or reinforcing steel in combined tension and bending.

The use of vertical post-tensioning is shown to be a practicable, economical, and effective means of providing long-term serviceability and ultimate

1.18

capacity for these critical zones of concrete sea structures.

References
Bertero, V.V. and Popov,E.P. (1979) Design of Reinforced Concrete Shear Wall Structural Systems, American Concrete Institute Symposium.

Fiorato, A.E. (1979) Design Criteria for Earthquake Resistant Structural Walls, American Concrete Institute Symposium.

Gerwick, B.C.Jr. and Venuti, W.J. (1979) High and Low-Cycle fatigue Behaviour of Prestressed Concrete in Offshore Structures,OTC Paper 3381, Offshore Technology Conference, Houston/Dallas, Texas.

Hawkins, N.M. (1975) Fatigue Considerations for Concrete Ships and Offshore Structures. Proceedings, Conference on Concrete Ships and Floating Structures, University of California Extension Division, Berkeley, California.

Lacroix, R. (1975) Design of Concrete Sea Structures. Proceedings of Underwater Construction Technology Conference, University College, Cardiff, Wales.

Taylor, H. and Sharp,J. (1978) Fatigue in Offshore Concrete Structures. The Structural Engineer.

Waagaard,K. (1977) Fatigue Offshore Concrete Structures - Design and Experimental Investigations OTC 3009, Offshore Technology Conference, Houston/ Dallas, Texas.

BEHAVIOUR OF FIBRE-REINFORCED CONCRETE STRUCTURES IN SEA ENVIRONMENTS

E. Backx
J.P. Rammant

Catholic University of Louvain

ABSTRACT

The strength behaviour of fibre reinforced concrete, especially in bending is completely different from that of unreinforced concrete. There exists a need for computation methods which take into account the specific properties of the fibre reinforced concrete.

The paper gives a design methodology for the computation of a floating pontoon in a coastal area. The analysis is simplified by the assumption that the sea behaves as a long-crested sea, so that the spatial distribution is excluded, leaving only the temporal wave height spectra as an input. The loads exerted by the waves on the structure are applied stochastically. The resulting response of the pontoon is then used to compute the midsection bending moment spectrum. From this spectrum, applying statistical analysis, it is possible to predict the long term behaviour of the structure, including fatigue behaviour.

1. INTRODUCTION

The use of conventional reinforced concrete for marine applications has a long history: since the beginning of this era concrete ships are being built among which several are still in service. Concrete pontoons are in use at Normandy since 30 years (Gerwich,1976). The growing demands of the offshore industry are nowadays responded by the construction of concrete gravity platforms, storage tanks etc.

Fibre reinforced concrete is a much younger material.

Experimental full scale tests on the use of steel fibre reinforced concrete in a marine environment are
only recently being performed in different parts of
the world. (Rilem,1975). For instance floating pontoons in fibre reinforced concrete are presently investigated to replace the conventional wooden pontoons. (Precast Concrete,1974). Other marine applications may soon be expected: cover of offshore pipelines, wave breaking units, constructional concrete (especially for thin sections) etc.

Fibre reinforced concrete has some distinguished
properties for marine applications: the ductility of
the concrete, the impact resistancy, the abrasion
resistivity are all increased by enormous amounts
for a few added volume percentages of fibres. The
crack propagation is restrained by fibres that bridge the cracks and that are pulled out subsequently.
While more experimental data are urged especially
for long term cyclic conditions, a need exists for
better design methods that take into account the
specific conditions under which the material is be-
having. In this paper a design methodology is outlined: a simple example of a floating pontoon is
considered under wave loading.

In figure 1 a typical pontoon element is presented:
a steel fibre reinforced concrete slab is resting
on two polyurethane foam beams. To simplify the presentation we only consider here the bending action
in the plane of the figure. The real plate behavior,
including torsion, is a further extension of the
method. However the beam behavior idealisation is
justified by the adoption of "swell" sea states as
explained further. This usual approximation of real
seas through long-crested seas (with parallel wave
crests) allows the use of unique temporal wave height
spectra, thus excluding the spatial distribution.
We start by computing the responses of the floating
pontoon for heave and pitch motions following a stochastic sea loading. Short and long term statistics
are applied.

2.PONTOON MOTIONS IN A RANDOM SEA

2.1 Strip theory for a pontoon
In appendix I the mathematical description of the
strip theory is briefly resumed with emphasis on the
hydrodynamical aspects of the considered pontoon.
The basic assumption of the strip theory is that the
time-dependent water flow adjacent to the wet surfaces of thin vertical slices of the floating body is
two-dimensional. (McCormick,1973).

Of the six degrees of freedom: surge, sway, heave, roll, pitch and yaw only two degrees are retained here, namely heave and pitch. The differential system that describes the deterministic body motions is then:

$$\left[M\right]\{\ddot{x}\} + \left[B\right]\{\dot{x}\} + \left[C\right]\{x\} = \{F\} \tag{1}$$

wherein $\left[M\right]$ virtual mass matrix (proper mass + added mass) with dimension (2x2)

$\left[B\right]$ hydrodynamic damping matrix (2x2)

$\left[C\right]$ restoring matrix (2x2)

$\{F\}$ column matrix of exterior wave forces (2x1)

$\{\ddot{x}\}$, $\{\dot{x}\}$, $\{x\}$ column matrices of acceleration, velocity and displacements of the two motions.

The elements of the matrices $\left[M\right]$, $\left[B\right]$, $\left[C\right]$ are calculated from the geometrical and hydrodynamical characteristics of the pontoon (appendix I).

Essentially it has been assumed that the pontoon responds as a rigid body; indeed, unlike fixed offshore structures, the own dynamic motions are negligible compared with the rigid body motions.

2.2 Wave height spectrum

It is generally accepted that irregular ocean waves are best represented by wave frequency spectra. The usual approximation consists in adopting a normal Gaussian probability distribution for the sea surface elevation with respect to time and space. Also the homogenity and the stationarity of the wave process is believed to be valid, resulting in tractable probabilistic formulations. Comparisons of these assumptions with experimental data have confirmed the validity (Roberts,1969).

Long-crested seas (for a unidirectional wave field) are completely characterized by the wave height-spectral density $S_{\eta\eta}(\omega)$ which may be seen as a measure of the energy content of the wave components of an irregular sea. Through Fourier analysis the spectrum is found out of measured wave heights. The Pierson-Moskowitz semi-empirical formulation for a fully developped sea state relates the spectrum to metereological site data

$$S_{\eta\eta} = \frac{\alpha \cdot g^2}{\omega^5} \exp\left[-\beta\left(\frac{g}{W\omega}\right)^4\right] \tag{2}$$

wherein W wind speed 20m above the sea surface

$$H_s = 2\frac{W^2}{g}\sqrt{\frac{\alpha}{\beta}} \quad \text{significant wave height}$$

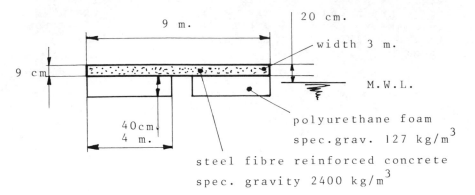

FIG.1   PONTOON

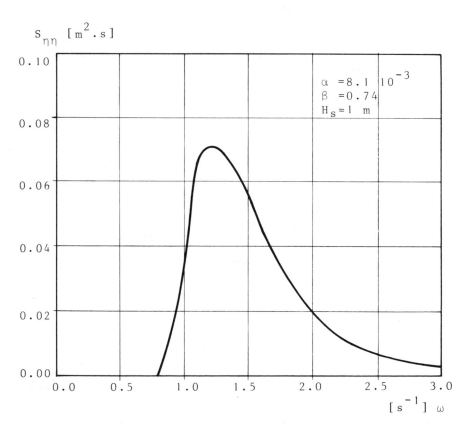

FIG.2   SEA SPECTRUM

$$T_m = 2\pi\frac{W}{g}(\frac{1}{\beta\pi})^{1/4} \quad \text{mean wave period}$$

For the North Sea, $\alpha = 8.110^{-3}$
$\beta = 0.74$ (Brebbia, 1975, Scott 1965)

$S_{\eta\eta}$ for $H_s = 1m$ is drawn in figure 2. These conditions have to be imposed on the pontoon: it concerns a harbour situation. The value of H_s will be a function of time. This time dependency will be included later. First we will assume a constant H_s. Suppose $H_s = 1m$. It follows then from the formulas given above: $W = 6,85$ m/sec; $T_m = 3,55$ sec.

Let us look at some short term statistical properties of the considered random process $\eta(t)$, i.e. the wave elevation above mean water. Given the wave spectrum, some useful wave properties can be derived by computing the so called spectral moments (Roberts, 1969; Van Marcke, 1972; Lin, 1967):

$$\lambda_n = \int_0^\infty \omega^n \cdot S_{\eta\eta}(\omega) \ d\omega \tag{3}$$

Figure 3 represents a typical time history proces of $\eta(t)$: one is interested in estimating the number of times that $\eta(t)$ crosses some amplitude level a in the time interval t_1 to t_2.

The treshold crossing probability is known for a zero mean stationary normal process, as considered here, (Lin, 1967): it follows from considerations on the joint distribution of $\eta(t)$ and $d\eta(t)/dt$. The average number of upcrossings of level a per unit time is given by:

$$\nu_a = \frac{1}{2\pi}\sqrt{\frac{\lambda_2}{\lambda_0}} \quad \exp \ (-\frac{a^2}{2\lambda_0}) \tag{4}$$

The average number of peaks in $\eta(t)$ which occur above level a per unit time is given by

$$M_a = \frac{1}{2\pi}\sqrt{\frac{\lambda_4}{\lambda_2}} \tag{5}$$

the probability density function for peak amplitudes follows from:

$$p(\zeta) = \frac{1}{\sqrt{2\pi}} \left[\varepsilon \, \exp\left(-\frac{\zeta^2}{2\varepsilon^2}\right) + \sqrt{1-\varepsilon^2}\,\zeta \, \exp\left(-\frac{\zeta^2}{2}\right) \int_{-\infty}^{\zeta\frac{\sqrt{1-\varepsilon^2}}{\varepsilon}} \exp\left(\frac{-x^2}{2}\right) dx \right] \tag{6}$$

wherein $\quad \varepsilon^2 = \dfrac{\lambda_0 \lambda_4 - \lambda_2^2}{\lambda_0 \lambda_4}$

$$\zeta = \frac{a}{\sqrt{\lambda_o}}$$

The parameter ε is a measure of the width of the spectrum of the process. For ε small (narrow-band process) the probability density function approaches the Rayleigh distribution: this is valid for quasi-sinusoidal processes since the probability of a peak occurring at negative amplitude levels is zero. For ε large ($\varepsilon \approx 1$, wide-band process) the probability density function is Gaussian.(Benjamin,1970).

We may apply these statistics to the considered wave height spectrum. The computed moments are:

$$\lambda_o = 0.0617 \text{ m}^2; \quad \lambda_2 = 0.171 \text{ m}^2\text{s}^{-2}; \quad \lambda_4 = 0.749 \text{ m}^2\text{s}^{-4}$$

We may check the mean wave period T_m by evaluating
a) the average time lapse between successive upcrossing of the zero axis; with (4) and a=0 one gets

$$\tilde{T}_u = \left(\frac{1}{\nu_a}\right)_{a=0} = 2\pi\sqrt{\frac{\lambda_o}{\lambda_2}} = 3.77 \text{ sec}$$

b) the average time lapse between successive peaks; out of (5) one gets

$$\tilde{T}_p = \frac{1}{m_a} = 2\pi\sqrt{\frac{\lambda_2}{\lambda_4}} = 3.0 \text{ sec}$$

while the given mean period equals 3.55 sec. Out of (6) one finds $\varepsilon \approx 0.60$ which means that the process is neither narrow-banded neither wide-banded. Typical actual wave records relate values of ε between 0.57 and 0.67 as reported by Cartwright and Longuet-Higgins, (Roberts, 1969). Following formula (6) the probability density function can be computed. Despite the large value of ε the simple Rayleigh distribution turns out to be a good fit to the amplitude distribution of most sea waves. (Chakrabarti,1977).

For the wave heigts H (fig.3) the probability density function is then

$$p(H) = \frac{H}{4\lambda_o} \exp (-\frac{H^2}{8\lambda_o})$$ (7)

The mean wave height is then $2.5\sqrt{\lambda_o}$ (=0.62m) and the
significant wave height (average of 1/3 highest wa-
ves) is $4.0\sqrt{\lambda_o}$ (=1m), confirming the initial data.

For estimating the fatigue damage accumulated in a
structure, long term sea state predictions are necessary. The probabilistic parameters, characterizing
the sea state conditions, are normally H_s, the significant wave height and T_m, the mean period. To
match the statistical properties a Weibull distribution function is frequently adopted (Roren 1976,
Houmb 1977), as shown later.

2.3 Stochastic response analysis
The spectral response functions are related to
the wave height spectrum by the following relations:

$$\begin{bmatrix} S_{zz}(\omega) & S_{z\theta}(\omega) \\ S_{\theta z}(\omega) & S_{\theta\theta}(\omega) \end{bmatrix} = \begin{Bmatrix} H_{z\eta}^* \\ H_{\theta\eta}^* \end{Bmatrix} \cdot S_{\eta\eta}(\omega) \cdot \{ H_{z\eta} \quad H_{\theta\eta} \}$$ (8)

wherein S_{zz} the heave motion power spectrum

$S_{\theta\theta}$ the pitch motion power spectrum

$S_{z\theta}$ the heave-pitch cross spectral function

$S_{\theta z}$ the complex conjugate of $S_{z\theta}$

$H_{z\eta}$ the frequency transfer function for
heave motions

$H_{\theta\eta}$ the frequency transfer function for
pitch motions

(*   indicates the complex conjugate)

The transfer functions are found by solving the e-
quilibrium equations for random forces, following
standard dynamical procedures, (Clough,1975).
We first compute the force resultant spectra out of
the wave height spectra. One takes simple harmonic
waves described by the linear wave theory (Wiegel,
1963)

$\eta = a \cos(k\xi - \omega t)$ (wave elevation) (9)

$\phi = \frac{ag}{\omega} \frac{\cosh(kz+kh)}{\cosh(kh)} \sin(k\xi - \omega t)$ (velocity potential)

1.26

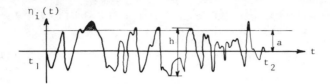

FIG.3   RANDOM VARIATON OF WAVE HEIGHT

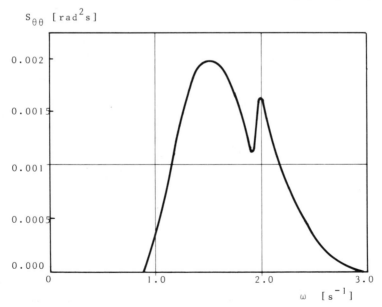

FIG.4 RESPONSE SPECTRAL DENSITIES FOR HEAVE AND PITCH MOTION.

wherein $\omega = \sqrt{gk \ \tanh(kh)}$ cyclic harmonic frequency

$k = \dfrac{2\pi}{\lambda_w}$ wave number (λ_w wavelength)

$h = $ waterdepth

In deep water, $h/\lambda_w > 0.5$ the equations can be simplified:

$\tanh(kh) \simeq 1 ; \quad \dfrac{\cosh(kz+kh)}{\cosh(kh)} \simeq e^{kz}$

The Froude-Krylov hypothesis is assumed to hold i.e.
the presence of the floating body does not alter the
pressure field in the wave from that existing when
no body is present.
The right hand side of the equilibrium equations (1)
is deduced in appendix 1:

$$\left\{ F \right\} = \left\{ \begin{array}{c} F \\ M \end{array} \right\} = e^{-kc} \left[\gamma_w b - i C_D \omega - (C_M + \rho b c) \omega^2 \right] \left\{ \begin{array}{c} \int \eta \, d\xi \\ \int \xi \eta \, d\xi \end{array} \right\} \qquad (10)$$

$$= (A+iB) \left\{ \begin{array}{c} \int \eta \, d\xi \\ \int \xi \eta \, d\xi \end{array} \right\}$$

Taking the Fourier transform and the Conjugate, applying the power spectrum definition, one gets:

$$\left\{ \begin{array}{c} S_{FF} \\ S_{MM} \end{array} \right\} = S_{\eta\eta}(\omega) \cdot (A+iB)(A-iB) \cdot \left\{ \begin{array}{c} \left(\int \eta \, d\xi \right)^2 \\ \left(\int \eta \xi \, d\xi \right)^2 \end{array} \right\} \qquad (11)$$

The frequency domain solution of the uncoupled e-
quations of motion of the pontoon are easily found.
Each equation of (1) can be written as

$m\ddot{\psi} + c\dot{\psi} + k\psi = f$

for which the transfer function is

$$H_\psi(i\omega) = \dfrac{1}{k \left[1 + 2i\beta \dfrac{\omega}{\omega} - \left(\dfrac{\omega}{\omega} \right)^2 \right]}$$

The response spectral densities are then

$S_{\psi\psi}(\omega) = |H_\psi|^2 \cdot S_{ff}(\omega)$ \qquad (12)

Table 2 assembles the main transfer characteristics for the heave and pitch motions

	Heave	Pitch
natural frequency $\bar{\omega} = \sqrt{\dfrac{k}{m}}$	1.936 s^{-1}	1.99 s^{-1}
damping ratio $\beta = \dfrac{c}{2m\bar{\omega}}$	0.015	0.016
natural period $T = \dfrac{2\pi}{\bar{\omega}}$	3.24 s	3.16 s

Table 2: Characteristics of the considered pontoon

Equations (8), (11) and (12) allow to compute the response spectral densities. Fig.4a and Fig.4b represent the heave and pitch spectral density functions for the pontoon. The heave and pitch motions are jointly normal distributed and are correlated to each other. However considering each of the motions separetely, the probabilistic properties are found out of the spectral characteristics, assembled in table 3.

	Heave	Pitch
λ_0	0.033	0.0021
λ_2	0.062	0.0063
λ_4	0.142	0.024
ε	0.43	0.43

Table 3: Spectral moments for the considered pontoon

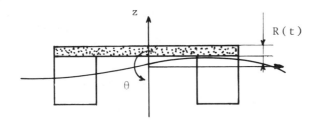

FIG.5   THE FLOATING PONTOON

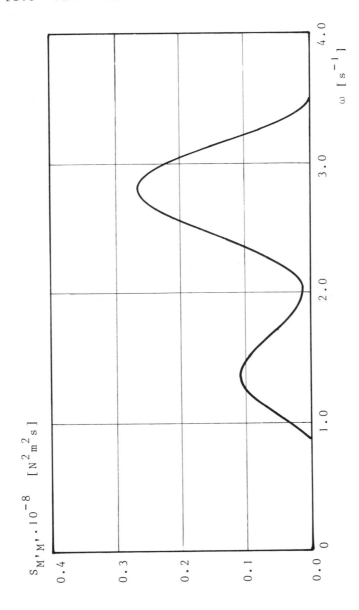

FIG.6   MIDSECTION BENDING MOMENT SPECTRAL DENSITY DISTRIBUTION.

Out of this follows that for the given sea the mean
heave amplitude equals 0.45m (=2.5$\sqrt{\lambda_{0}}$) and the mean
pitch angle amplitude equals 0.11 rad(=6,6°), following the short term statictics explained airlier.
Other treshold and peak value probability distributions can be found. An interesting question is to
know how the pontoon will response in rough sea conditions. One may consider the distance R(t) between
the pontoon floor and the water elevation, (Fig.5).
The distance is directly related to the waves and
the pontoon response (z(t) and θ(t)); its spectral
density function and dependant probabilistic characteristics are readily obtainable. For negative R(t)
the pontoon receives water.

3. MECHANICAL BEHAVIOR

3.1 Internal forces
The resultant upwards distributed loading on the
pontoon is the difference between the inertia forces
and the sum of the external forces. The external forces are composed of a static part, i.e. own weight
and service loading, and a dynamic part, i.e. the
wave excitation forces and the hydrodynamic forces.

The static stress distribution is readily obtained
since the pontoon is a simple beam structure supported on two foam bearings. The static bending moment
at midsection for a downward distributed pressure q
equals $q.b(d-a)^2/8$ wherein the notation of the dimensions refers to appendix I.

The dynamic loading and the wave excitation are mainly concentrated at the pontoon supports. We are then
able to compute the internal forces, i.e. bending
moment and shear force, at any section by expressing
the equilibrium of the considered pontoon-part. The
forces were discussed in appendix I and in 2.3, only
the integration limits are changed. For the bending
moment at midsection one gets for harmonic excitation:

$$M' = (M_o - M_1 - M_2 - M_3 - M_4 - M_w)_{x=0} \qquad (13)$$

each of these force contributions can be expressed
in terms of the wave height at midsection $\eta(0,t)$
since the forces are function of the pontoon motions.
For harmonic waves:

$$\eta(\xi,t) = e^{i(k\xi-\omega t)} = \eta(0,t).e^{ik\xi} \qquad (14)$$

And eq.(13) reduces to:

$$M'(t) = A(i\omega).\eta(0,t) \qquad (15)$$

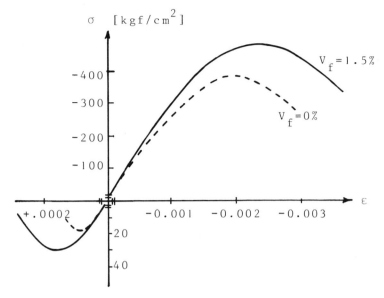

FIG.7 UNIAXIAL STRESS-STRAIN CURVES.

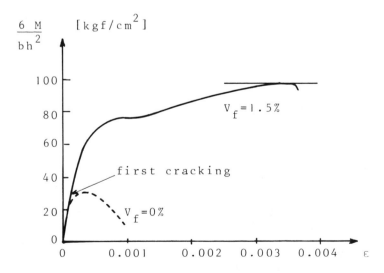

FIG.8   EXPERIMENTAL BENDING STRESS-STRAIN CURVES.

wherein $A(i\omega)$ expresses the dependance of all harmonic behavior on the midsection wave height.

The spectral density function for the bending moment is then:

$$S_{M'M'}(\omega) = A^{*}(i\omega).A(i\omega)\ S_{\eta\eta} \tag{16}$$

The result is drawn in figure 6. Similarly the internal force (or moment) at any section can be treated stochastically.

3.2 Fibre reinforced concrete properties

The mechanical characteristics of fibre reinforced concrete are reported in (Rilem,1975; ACT,1973; Swamy,1975); one has mainly been concerned with the static ultimate strength behavior of simple tests. For the usual small percentage of added fibres (1-2 Vol.%) the main effects are the improvement of the ultimate bending and impact strength over the corresponding strength of unreinforced concrete. The effects of sea water on fibre reinforcement is investigated in (Rider,1978). Especially the use of stainless steel fibres is very promissing.

The uniaxial tensile and compressive stress-strain curves are shown in figure 7. The addition of 1.5 Vol % fibres (fibre length 4 cm, diameter 0.035 cm, hooked ends (Bekaert,1975)) has only minor effects. Indeed, the ultimate tensile load is proportional to the total amount of reinforcement, which is small for the considered steel fibre percentages.

A simple beam bending test (beams of length 28 cm, heigth h= width b= 7 cm) reveals the major characteristics: in figure 8 the elastic bending stress is drawn as a function of the recorded strains at the tensile side at midsection of a test-specimen. The strength improvement by adding the fibres is drastic: the ultimate bearing capacity is increased by 3 times. The capability of absorbing energy is represented by the area under the curves: as one observes the fibres improve the impact resistance and the ductility by major amounts. The cracking resistance which leads to the improvements is linearly related to the large specific surface of the fibre reinforcement.

The effect of fibre addition for other structures is discussed in (Rammant,1976,1977) where a general theory for predicting the twodimensional static strength behavior of steel fibre reinforced concrete is discussed.
On the cyclic strength behavior of fibre reinforced concrete no experimental data are known.

The same effects of the fibre reinforcement are however valid: the fibres resist the crack propagation
considerably. The crack openings are smaller resulting in less loss of strength in cyclic conditions:
upon stress reversal the cracks are closed much earlier which leads to less stiffness degrading effects.
The pull-out behavior of the fibres and the bond deterioration are however not easily predictable so
that experimental cyclic tests are needed. In the
absence of better data one generally extrapolates
the static strength characteristics (Bazant,1977).

3.3 Probabilistic behavior of fibre reinforced
concrete

To illustrate the nonlinear response behavior under random loading we first extrapolate out
of the midspan-bending moment spectral density a typical random time history. One might decompose the
spectrum in an infinite number of harmonic contributions; it results

$$M'(t) = \sum_{i=1}^{N} A_i . sin(\omega_i t + \phi_i) \qquad (17)$$

wherein $N \to \infty$

A_i the Fourier amplitude $= \sqrt{2S_{M'M'} . \Delta\omega}$ (if the spectrum is considered discrete with axis increments $\Delta\omega$).

ϕ_i mutually independent random variables having each a uniform probability densi-ty between 0 and 2π

A particular result for M'(t) is shown in figure 9.
The internal stress distribution is not simply related to the bending moment as was explained for a
static bending test (fig.8). Due to the cracking the
position of the neutral axes of the section varies
considerably and the stress distribution is very irregular.
Some inelastic deformations are building up: significant results may be obtained by considering another process, namely the envelope Q(t) of the process
M'(t) (fig.9).

One considers the intersections of the envelope Q(t)
and a fixed two-sided treshold $|M'| = a$.

Two types of failure have to be considered: failure
occurs when the process first crosses a barrier or
failure occurs when the accumulated damage exceedes
the fatigue strength.

For the first failure type one incorporates the uncertainty of the fibre reinforced concrete strength

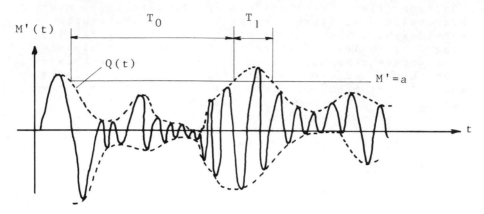

FIG.9   RANDOM TIME HISTORY OF M'

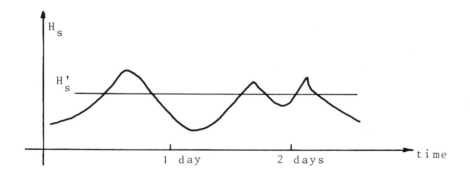

FIG.10 H_s AS A FUNCTION OF TIME SHOWING THREE STORMS

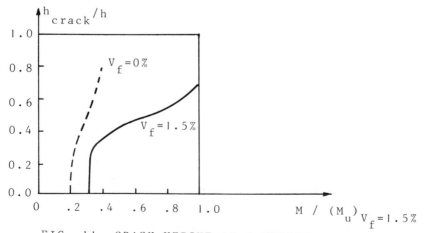

FIG. 11   CRACK HEIGHT AS A FUNCTION OF LOADING (following
          photoelastic tests and finite element analysis)

characteristics: the ultimate strength barrier $M'=a$ has a probability distribution $p(a)$, usually approximated by a Gaussian distribution. The bending moment $M'(t)$ for a sea state H_s' has a Rayleigh distribution for its maximum values (proces $Q(t)$):

$$p(Q) = \frac{Q}{\mu_o} \exp(-\frac{Q^2}{2\mu_o}) \qquad Q>0 \qquad\qquad (18)$$

$$\mu_o = \int_0^\infty S_{M'M'} d\omega$$

The failure probability, assuming a stationary sea state H_s', is found:

$$P_{failure}|H_s' = P[Q>a] = 1 - P[Q<a]$$

$$= 1 - \int_0^\infty p(Q) \cdot [\int_Q^\infty p(a)\,da]\,dQ \qquad\qquad (19)$$

Suppose the structure is permanently being used; $P_{failure/H_s'}$ is the failure probability for each time the moment M' attains a peak value. The time between peaks is of the order of the mean wave period

$$T_e = 1/f_e = 2\pi \sqrt{\frac{\lambda_o}{\lambda_2}} \qquad\qquad (20)$$

The significant wave height varies continuously. The assumption of stationnary sea states with constant H_s is only valid in the limit if one replaces the continuous curve $H_s(t)$ by stepwise $H_s = $ Ct. short processes. In what follows, we will use periods of 3 hours during which H_s remains constant. The failure probability for the pontoon for such a period is then:

$$P_{failure/H_s'/1\ period} = 1-(1-P_{failure/H_s'})^{f_e \cdot N_s} \qquad\qquad (21)$$

where $N_s = 3 \times 60 \times 60 = 10800$ sec/period

It is evident that only relative large H_s' values have to be considered for possible failure. Having choosen such a level, we need information on the probability distribution of Sea states with $H_s > H_s'$. Generally, this is approximated by a weibull distribution.

For the Belgian coast (North Sea), measurements are available (Van Cauwenberghe,1975). However, since this pontoon is to be used in a harbour environment, the values that are published are quite high. We have adopted the following distribution:

$$p(H_s) = \frac{(H_s)^{\gamma-1}}{(H_c)^{\gamma}} \cdot \gamma \cdot \exp\left[-\left(\frac{H_s}{H_c}\right)^{\gamma}\right] \text{ with } \begin{array}{l} \gamma=1.4 \\ H_c=1 \end{array} \qquad (22)$$

To obtain some information regarding the long term behaviour of the pontoon, two methods are presented.

a) Equation (21) can be modified to include the probability $p(H_s)$. The probability to survive one period is then given by:

$$L = \left[\int_{H_s'}^{\infty} (1-P_{failure/H_s}) \cdot P(H_s) \cdot dH_s\right]^{f_e \cdot N_s} \qquad (23)$$

Subsequently, the total probability of survival for t years is then:

$$L_T(10 \text{ years}) = (L)^{\text{number op periods in 10 years}} \qquad (24)$$

The results for the considered pontoon are obtained using:

$$a= 75000 \text{ Nm } (\sigma_M= 1500 \text{ N/cm}^2)$$
$$\sigma_a = 7500 \text{ Nm}$$

One finds   L= 0.999997; and

$$L_T= 0.9236$$

b) The probability to survive a storm of level H_s is given by:

$$L_{H_s} = (1 - P_{failure/H_s})^{f_e \cdot N_s} \qquad (25)$$

During a year, various storms of level H_s may happen, normally, fewer storms of level $H_s'(H_s'>H_s)$ are incoming. If $\nu(H_s)$ gives the expected number of storms of level H_s that occur in 1 year, their arrival rate can be approximated by a Poisson distribution:

$$P(n) = \frac{(\nu(H_s) \cdot t)^n}{n!} \exp[-\nu(H_s) \cdot t] \qquad (26)$$

The expected frequency $\nu(H_s)$ may be estimated from $P(H_s)$:

$$\nu(H_s) = P(H_s) . \text{number of periods in a year.} \qquad (27)$$

The survival probability for a period of T years for storms of level H_s is:

$$L_{T/H_s}(10 \text{ years}) = \sum_{n=0}^{\infty} P(n/H_s).(L_{H_s})^n \qquad (28)$$

The failure probability is then:

$$P_{failure/H_s/T} = 1 - L_{T/H_s} \qquad (29)$$

The survival probability for storms of all levels is then:

$$L_T(10 \text{ years}) = 1 - \sum_{H_s=H_s'}^{H_s=H_{max}} P_{failure/H_s/T} \qquad (30)$$

where the sum is made from H_s' to H_{max}. H_s' is such that $P_{failure/H_s/T}=0$ and H_{max} is such that $\nu(H_{max})=0$.

The results for the considered pontoon are:

$$L_T(10 \text{ years}) = 0.9012$$

Both methods give comparable results. The difference may be partially explained by the fact that in Equation 23, f_e is not completely determined since f_e is a function of H_s. The value of H_s, selected in Equation 23 to determine f_e was somehow arbitrarily selected.
If the same structure was made out of plain unreinforced concrete, Equation 23 gives:

$$L = 1.7 \times 10^{-30}$$

which shows the infeasability.

It is also not possible to make the same pontoon in conventional reinforced concrete since then the concrete plate should be thicker to cover sufficiently the top and bottom reinforcing bars. A heavier structure induces larger stresses.

The second type of failure is the fatigue failure. Let us consider again a typical time history for the midsection bending moment, (fig.9). Vanmarcke,1970 estimated the fraction of the peaks of $(M'(t))$ in the interval 0 to T which have a height between a and a+da, i.e. $g_T'(a)$;

for Gaussian narrow-banded processes the expected value was found:

$$E[g_T'(a)] = \frac{a}{\mu_o} \exp \frac{-a^2}{2\mu_o} \tag{31}$$

$f_e.T.g_T'(a).da$ equals the total number of peaks whose height lies between the treshold levels a and a+da.

The fatigue resistance of the material is known through the N(a) fatigue curve, wherein N(a) is the number of cycles to failure in a constant-amplitude fatigue test with bending moment (or stress) amplitude a.

Experiments confirm the engineers validity of the linear Palmgren-Miner damage law,(Tepfers,1977, Osgood,1970); henceforth for a stationary process of duration T the estimated accumulated damage equals:

$$D(t) = f_e.T.\int_\theta^\infty \frac{g_T'(a)}{N(a)}da \tag{32}$$

This damage can easily be computed for a stationary sea state of intensity H_s' and duration T.

For a period of 10 years:

$$D(10 \text{ years}) = \int_0^{H_{max}} D.P(H_s).dH_s \times \text{number of periods in 10 years} \tag{33}$$

Following another reasoning, one can incorporate the arrival rate of storms to obtain

$$D'(10 \text{ years}) = \int_{H_s'}^{H_{max}} [\sum_{n=0}^\infty P(n,H_s') \times D(H_s) \times n]dH_s \tag{34}$$

In absence of sufficient experimental data on the fatigue resistance of fibre reinforced concrete, the following fatigue curve was used

$$N(a) = (\frac{a_u}{a})^\alpha \qquad \text{where } a_u \text{ is the one cycle ulti-}$$
mate strength;
$\alpha = 30°$

These law is (Jacobson,1976,Award 1974)   found to be valid for plain concrete. Preleminary tests (ACI,1973) reported that the fatigue behaviour of steel fibre reinforced concrete does not differ substantially from that of plain concrete. Formula (33) and (34) with N(a) relate the following results:

D(10 years) = 0.0031

D'(10 years)= 0.0030

Other probabilistic results can be found in a similar way; we may focus on the crack development in the fibre reinforced concrete. Fig.8 shows clearly the early stage at which cracks first develop in a static bending test: let the first cracking level be determined by $M' = b$, b being characterized by a normal distribution. For a stationary sea state H'_s the probability of excuding the first cracking moment:

$$P_{crack}/H'_s = P[Q>b] = \int_0^\infty f_Q(x) \cdot p_b(x)\,dx \qquad (36)$$

wherein f_Q the cumulative distribution function for the enveloppe of M'

p_b the probability density for the first cracking resistance.

Fig.11 shows the crack height development in a static bending test of a beam (Rammant,1976). It is obvious that, under the assumption that the cyclic response behaviour is well approximated by the statics one finds the crack height probability out of the bending moment probability.

4. GENERALIZATION OF PROBABILISTIC RESPONSE ANALYSIS

A general strict statistical calculation, that accounts for the structural response at all stress levels, is quite involved.
To model the structure a finite element approach is to be followed incorporating all possible mechanical and hydrodynamical nonlinearities (elastoplasticity, cracking, damping,...). The general equations of motion must be solved in the time domain through a stepwise solution strategy.

The considered random sea is approximated with a discrete number (say 15) of harmonic waves each having a different wavelength. For each wave the steady state dynamic nonlinear response of the structure must be computed. At each point of the structure (e.g.a numerical integration point) the stress transfer function is found and spectra can be established. For long term predictions one has to repeat these analysis for a discrete number of sea states.

(say 6 sea states). Also the angle of incidence of the waves should be varied for each wavelength (say 5 angles). To account for the probabilistic material properties, an extension of a proposed Markov chain model can be followed (Kamil,1976): transition probability matrices are considered at each integration point of the finite elements. Various states may be considered: elastic, plastic, cracked, fibres pulled-out. The transition matrices at each load (or time) step are then determined from a known probability distribution model for the material strength characteristics (e.g. cracking level, ultimate strength level). It can be assumed that loads and strengths are statistically independent.

The equations of dynamic equilibrium are then solved using a "most probable" updated stiffness matrix which is found out of the Markov-chain model at each load step. Having found the spectra for the internal forces the probabilistic failure behavior can be established as was shown in 3.

Another approach consists in simulating the random sea response (for known H_s) by computing the transient response of the structure to artificial wave histories, built from the sea spectrum. A large number of time histories must be imposed for each state to have a sufficient large statistical sample. The same Markov-chain approach, as discussed above, may be followed to set up the probabilistic response at various points in the structure.

Neither of the two mentionned methods are appropriate for practical use due to the necessary large number of degrees of freedom and the many load cases. Studies are reported to overcome these drawnbacks by approximations: or one tries to replace the multi-degree of freedom structure by a simple one dimensional nonlinear model that incorporates the major nonlinear characteristics for the considered loading (Pique,1976), or one follows a static incremental failure sequence to formulate the complete structural reliability for a given loading system (Moses, 1978).

5. CONCLUSIONS

The strength of the considered pontoon for stochastic dynamic loading is greatly improved by adding steel fibres. The exposed analysis technique gives a measure of the estimated increase in reliability due to the better material. A further investigation could concern the effect of using steel fibre concrete only in critical sections of offshore structures as suggested by Prof.B.C. Gerwick (1976).

More work leaves to be done in evaluating the long term strength of fibre reinforced concrete and in the formulation of the sea behavior. Especially the modelling of storms in a harbour-environment is a difficult problem.

References

ACI Journal (Nov.1973) State-of-the-Art Report on Fibre Reinforced Concrete.

Award M.E., Hilsdorf H.K.(1974) Strength and Deformation Characteristics of Plain Concrete subjected to High Repeated and Sustained Loads. ACI publ.SP-41.

Bazant Z.P., Bhat P.O. (1977) Prediction of Hysteresis of Reinforced Concrete Members. ASCE-Journal of Structural Division, Vol.103,N°.ST1.

Bekaert NV (1975) Dramix, a new Concrete Reinforcement (advertisement).

Benjamin J.R., Cornell C.A. (1970) Probability, Statistics and Decision for Civil Engineers. McGraw Hill

Brebbia C.A. (1975) Vibrations of Engineering Structures. Comp.Mech.Ltd, Southampton.

Chakrabarti S.K., Cooley R.P. (1977) Ocean Wave Statistics for 1961 North Atlantic Storm. Proc.ASCE, Vol.103, N°.WW2.

Clough R.W., Penzien J. (1975) Dynamics of Structures. McGraw Hill.

McCormick M.E. (1973) Ocean Engineering Wave Mechanics. John Wiley & Sons.

Gerwick B.C., (1976) The future of offschore concrete structures, Proceedings BOSS'76, Norwegian Institute of Technology.

Hogben N. (1976) Wave Loads on Structures, Boss'76, proc.vol.I.

Houmb O.G., Vik I (1977) On the duration of Sea State, report Division of port and Ocean Engineering, University of Trondheim.

Jacobson A.B., Widmark (1976) Fatigue Properties of Reinforced Concrete Structures, Boss'76,proc.vol.II.

Kamil H. (1976) A Computer Oriented Deterministic-cum-Probabilistic Approach for the Extreme Load Design of Complex Structures. Int.J.of Comp.and Struct, Vol.6.

Lewis E.V. (1967) The motion of ships in waves. Principles of Naval Architecture, Ed.Comstock J.P.,Soc. of Naval Architects and Marine Engineers, N.Y.

Lin Y.K. (1967) Probabilistic Theory of Structural Dynamics. McGraw Hill.

Moses F, Stahl B (1978) Reliability Analysis format for offshore Structures, OTC 3046 Offshore technology conference, Houston.

Osgood C.C. (1970) Fatigue Design. Wiley Interscience, John Willey & Sons.

Pique D (1976) On the use of simple Models in nonlinear dynamic Analysis. M.Sc. Thesis M.I.T.

Precast Concrete (1974) Journal Practical Applications of fibres. pp.31-32.

Rammant J.P. (1976) Rupture Calculations of Fibre-Reinforced Concrete Continua with the F.E.M.,Ph.D. Thesis, Leuven.

Rammant J.P., Van Laethem M., (1976) Calcul de Résistance de Structures Planes en béton armé de fibres. Materials and Structures, Rilem bulletin,Vol.9 n°.51.

Rammant J.P., Van Laethem M., Backx E.(1977) Steel fibre Concrete, a safer material for Reactor Construction - A general Theory for rupture prediction. 4th Int.Conf. on Struct. Mech. in Reactor Techn., San Francisco.

Rider R.G., Heidersbach R.H. (1978) The effects of Seawater on the structural properties of metal-fibre reinforced concrete, OTC 3193, Offshore Technology Conference, Houston.

Rilem Symposium (1975) Fibre Reinforced Cement and Concrete. London, The Construction Press Ltd.

Roberts J.B. (1969) The probabilistic Theory of ship motion in ocean waves, M.I.T. Lect.notes.

Roren EMQ, Furnes O. (1976) State of the Art: Behaviour of Structures and structural Design, Boss'76, proc.vol.I.

Schenck H. (1975) Introduction to Ocean Engineering McGraw Hill.

Scott J.R. (1965) A sea spectrum for model tests and long-term Ship prediction. Journ.of Ship Research, Vol.9, n°.3.

Swamy R.N. (1975) Fibre reinforcement of Cement and Concrete Evaluation of Fibre Reinforced cement based composites.Materials and Structures,Vol.8,N°.45.

Tepfers R., Friden C., Georgsson L. (1977) A Study of the Applicability to the Fatigue of Concrete of Palmgren-Miner partial damage hypothesis. Magazine of Concrete Research, Vol.29, N°.100.

Vanmarcke E.H.(1970) First passage and other failure criteria in narrow band random vibration: a discrete state approach. Ph.D.Thesis, M.I.T.

Van Cauwenberghe C. (1975)Golfwaarnemingen vanaf 1958 tot 1971 aan boord van de Belgische Lichtschepen. Tijdschrift der Openbare Werken van België.

Wiegel R.L. (1963) Oceanographical Engineering. Prentice Hall.

Zienkiewicz O.C., Lewis R.W., Stagg K.G. (Editors, 1978) Numerical Methods in Offshore Engineering, John Wiley.

Appendix 1

Strip theory for a floating pontoon

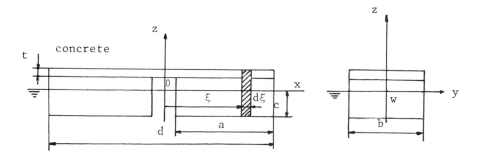

FIG. A-1

Table I	Dimensions in meter
d=9.	OG= .1088
a=4.	OB= .1469
b=3.	BM= 2.553
c=0.2938	BM'=25.81
f=0.4	
t=0.09	

O = Still water position
G = Gravity center
B = Boyancy center
M = Metacenter for rolling
M'= Metacenter for pitching
w = displacement of G
θ = rotation around y
η = position of watersurface $\eta = f(\xi, t)$

Equilibrium equations
A freely floating body is subjected to the following forces (Brebbia,1975, Hogben,1976, Lewis,1967 Schenck,1975).
- The forces caused by the waves acting on a fixed body
- The forces caused by the movement of the body in still water.

For each strip we obtain the following forces:

1. The weight of the body: F_W

2. The hydrostatic restoring force: F_1

$$F_1 + F_W = -\gamma_\omega bd\xi(w + \xi\theta - \eta e^{-kc})$$

3. The Froude-Krylov Force: F_2

$$F_2 = -\rho bcd\xi(\ddot{\eta}e^{-kc})$$

4. Inertia forces: F_3

$$F_3 = -c_M d\xi(\ddot{w} + \xi\ddot{\theta} - \ddot{\eta}e^{-kc})$$

5. Drag forces: F_4

$$F_4 = -C_D d\xi(\dot{w} + \xi\dot{\theta} - \dot{\eta}e^{-kc})$$

When we integrate ξ from $-d/2$ to $d/2$, the following equation for heaving is obtained:

$$M\ddot{w} = F_W + F_1 + F_2 + F_3 + F_4$$

$$(M + C_M \cdot 2a)\ddot{w} + CD\cdot 2a\dot{w} + 2a\cdot b\gamma w = e^{-kc}(\gamma_\omega b - iC_D\omega - (C_M + \rho bc)\cdot$$

$$\cdot \omega^2)\int_{-d/2}^{d/2} \eta d\xi$$

This is obtained with $\eta = a_\omega e^{i(k\xi-\omega t)} = a_\omega e^{ik\xi}e^{-i\omega t} =$

$$= A(i\xi)\eta_o(t)$$

It should be noted that although the forces are function of θ, the equilibrium equation is not.

The equilibrium equation for pitching is obtained similarly by writing the moments M_W to M_4. It results:

$$(I_y + I_{ya})\ddot{\theta} + C_\theta \dot{\theta} + \frac{\gamma_w}{12}b[d^3 - (d-2a)^3]\theta =$$

$$e^{-kc}(\gamma_\omega b - iC_D\omega - (C_M + \rho bc)\omega^2)\int_{-d/2}^{d/2}\xi\eta d\xi$$

where: $I_{ya} = C_M \cdot [d^3 - (d-2a)^3]/12$

$C_\theta = C_D \cdot [d^3 - (d-2a)^3]/12$

The determination of C_M and C_D

No attempt has been made to find the theoretical values of C_M and C_D.
The values used have been taken from Brebbia,1975.

$$C_M = c_m \frac{\rho \pi D^2}{4} \qquad \text{with D=b (see Fig.A-1)}$$
$$\text{and } c_m = 1$$

$$C_D = \frac{1}{2} c_d \rho D \sqrt{\frac{8}{\pi}} \sigma_{\dot{\eta}} \qquad \text{with } D=b$$
$$c_d = 1$$
$$\sigma_{\dot{\eta}} = 0.2$$

CORROSION OF REINFORCEMENT AND CRACK WIDTHS

A. W. Beeby

Deputy Head, Design Research Department,
The Cement and Concrete Association
Wexham Springs, Slough, England.

INTRODUCTION

The design and construction of large concrete gravity platforms
for oil extraction in the North Sea has led to an upsurge of
interest in the study of corrosion of reinforcing bars in
concrete.   This is due to the extreme severity of the
environment in the Northern North Sea and the difficulties of
maintenance and repair of these structures in service.   The
marine environment is accepted as being severe from the point
of view of corrosion and the rules and recommendations which
have been developed for the design of these structures are
very stringent compared with those governing the design of
structures in other situations.   Typically recommendations to
ensure durability consist of the specification of a minimum
cement content of around 400 Kg/m^3 together with a maximum
water/cement ratio of 0.4 to 0.45, minimum covers, which for the
splash zone may be as high as 75mm, and provisions for
controlling crack widths.

At the time when construction was starting on gravity platforms
in Britain, there was concern over the adequacy of knowledge on
the performance of concrete in the offshore environment.   To
try to fill these gaps in our knowledge a research programme,
jointly financed by Government and Industry was set up.   This
programme was called the Concrete in the Oceans Programme.
One area where considerable doubts existed was the specification
of appropriate crack width limits for the North Sea environment
and one of the first projects sponsored by the Concrete in the
Oceans programme was an evaluation of the currently available
information relating to crack control and corrosion.   This
study, though completed in 1976, has only recently been openly
published (Beeby (1978)).   Since the completion of this study,
a considerable number of additional papers from many sources
have appeared on the same general subject.   This paper surveys
the available literature on exposure tests of reinforced

concrete members and from this will attempt to draw conclusions
as to the value of crack control as a corrosion protection
measure.   This survey will largely be based on the Concrete in
the Oceans report by Beeby (1978) but account will also be taken
of more recent work.

It seems to have been generally assumed, more or less without
question, that some direct relationship will exist between crack
width and corrosion.   There are various reasons why this has
come about.   Firstly, it is quite often found that cracks are
associated with corrosion.   As will be discussed later, cracks
will often act as corrosion initiators.   However, a potentially
misleading circumstance must not be ignored: due to its expansive nature, corrosion can cause cracks and where the corrosion
is producing the crack, the width of the crack will be related
to the amount of rusting.   From inspection of damaged structures,
it is impossible to tell whether the corrosion was caused by the
presence of cracks or whether the cracking was caused by the
development of corrosion.   The second reason may be described
as 'common sense'.   A crack will permit corrosive substances
to penetrate to the reinforcement; obviously a wider crack will
permit the penetration of more corrosive substances than a
narrow one and therefore wider cracks will lead to more
corrosion than narrow cracks.   Thus, it has been considered as
axiomatic that crack widths need to be limited to control
corrosion damage.   The problems which faced researchers were,
firstly, how to predict crack widths in reinforced concrete
members and, secondly, the definition of suitable crack width
limits.   The first of these problems has received a great deal
of attention from researchers over the past 40 years or so while
the second has received very little.   This imbalance is not
surprising in view of the nature of the two problems.   The
first, the prediction of crack widths, is a classical engineering
research problem; it requires the testing of numbers of members,
the measurement of well defined quantities and the development
of a theory or empirical formulae to relate the measured
variables.   Any theoretical work will be within fields
familiar to engineers; mathematics and statics.   The second
problem, the definition of criteria, is far more difficult.
Firstly, meaningful tests will require a long time to carry out.
If structures are assumed to have an economic design life of
50 years or so, what is required is an estimate of the likely
damage which will occur over this period of time.   Clearly
50 year exposure tests are impractical but it is doubtful if
exposures of less than ten years can really be considered to be
useful.   Secondly, the actual measurement of corrosion damage
is difficult and thirdly, the definition of the limit to
acceptable corrosion damage is arbitary and a matter for decision
by the drafters of Codes and Regulations, not one which can be
defined by measurement.

The nature of corrosion damage A major difficulty in the
measurement of corrosion damage arises from a lack of any clear
idea of what should be measured. The variety of parameters
which have been used by various workers in the field illustrate
this. Some have measured depth of corrosion or reduction in
cross-sectional area of steel; some have measured the length
of bar corroded on either side of a crack; some have measured
the percentage of the bar surface area which is rusted; some
have made a qualitative visual assessment of the corrosion of
the bar, classifying the corrosion as insignificant, slight,
serious etc; some have measured the development of surface
cracking of the concrete and some the development of rust
staining. This obviously makes any quantitative comparison
of one series of tests with another almost impossible.

Before looking into the results of exposure tests in detail it
may be worth considering what corrosion damage is and how various
possible measurements might relate to this. What follows is
strictly related to reinforced concrete and is not necessarily
applicable to prestressed construction. It has commonly been
assumed that the basic problem of corrosion of reinforcement
was a reduction in safety due to loss of section. It is
argued by Beeby (1978) that this is not really so and that a
loss of safety is a secondary issue. This idea is not new, it
is what most practising engineers are well aware of. Rust
in most cases occupies a substantially larger volume than the
metal from which it is formed. This increase can be by a
factor of 2 to 3. Concrete is weak in tension and it can
easily be shown that rusting will cause splitting of the concrete
surrounding the bar well before any loss of section is significant from a safety point of view. Once cracking along the
length of the bar has initiated, more bar is exposed and the rate
of corrosion will increase. This will lead to a fairly rapid
increase in the size of the cracks and eventually to extensive
disruption and spalling of the surrounding concrete. The
protection which the concrete affords to the steel is thus
destroyed and corrosion will rapidly accelerate. It is at
this stage that loss of section of the exposed bars can become
structurally significant. It seems reasonable to accept that
the principal objective of design against corrosion will be to
ensure that the concrete is not disrupted. The definition of
excessive corrosion is thus that amount of corrosion which will
just cause the concrete cover to be disrupted. At this stage
the problem is one of maintenance: areas of spalling need to be
cleaned and protected. Only if this maintenance is neglected
for a considerable period will the corrosion become a safety
problem.

If this is accepted then, clearly, the aspects of corrosion which
require measurement are those which will influence the disruption
of the concrete. This would appear to include both the depth of
corrosion and the corroded length. Neither of these parameters

is sufficient to define the likelihood of disruption of concrete
by itself.   An alternative would appear to be to ignore the
reinforcement totally and simply study signs of disruption on the
concrete surface.

Having introduced these general ideas, the results obtained from
various series of exposure tests can now be studied.

EXPOSURE TESTS

General

Nine programmes of tests will be briefly considered.   Clearly,
in a paper of this type, only a very few significant points can
be extracted from each study.   Furthermore, due to the different
experimental techniques used and different exposure conditions,
comparison between test series is difficult, if not impossible.
The data presented in the various papers can, however, be used
to get a reasonably clear qualitative picture of the influence
on corrosion of various factors; in particular, the influence
of cracking.   Each test project will first be introduced
briefly; this will be followed by a general discussion.

Brief details of exposure test programmes

Tests by Tremper (1947)   Tremper tested 64 small specimens each
reinforced with three centrally placed bars or wires.   A
single flexural crack of specified width was induced in each
specimen.   The specimens were exposed for 10 years: 2 on
the shores of Puget Sound and 8 in the laboratory yard.
Tremper states that he does not believe that the proximity of
salt water contributed significantly to the corrosivity of the
environment.   The variables considered were: type of reinforcement, aggregate grading, mix proportions and crack width.
At the end of the exposure period the specimens were broken
open and the depth of corrosion and corroded length measured at
each crack.   In Table 1 below the results for all mix types
and reinforcement types have been averaged to indicate the
influence of crack width.

Table 1. Summary of Tremper's results

	crack width (mm)			
	0.13	0.25	0.51	1.27
Average depth of corrosion	0.16	0.16	0.18	0.21
Average corroded length	9.2	12.9	12.8	15.0

It can be seen that both parameters increase somewhat with increase in crack width though the depth of corrosion appears to increase less than the corroded lengths. What the table does not indicate is the considerable variability of the results. Tremper, himself, concluded that there was no definite trend with respect to crack width.

Tests by Duffaut, Duhoux and Heuze (1973)   108 specimens were exposed for a period of 12 years at various levels between low and high tide level in the estuary of the Rance in France. A large number of variable were considered of which three will be mentioned here; concrete quality, cover and cracking. At the end of the exposure period, the reinforcement was broken out and the amount of corrosion assessed visually in terms of a scale from 0 (no corrosion) to 4 (very severe corrosion).

Table 2 shows averaged values of their corrosion assessment for the three variables considered here.

Table 2.   Summary of results from Duffaut,
Duhoux and Heuze (1973)

COVER (mm)	AVERAGE DEGREE OF CORROSION		
	$f_{cu} = 8$ N/mm^2	$f_{cu} = 30$ N/mm^2	$f_{cu} = 30$ N/mm^2
	UNCRACKED		CRACKED
30	2.5	0.5	3.4
50	3.0	1.0	3.4
70	1.0	0.5	0.7
90	1.0	1.0	3.3

It will be seen that the presence of cracks has a considerable influence. Unfortunately, the widths of the cracks were not recorded and are merely stated as being between 0.5 and 1mm wide. The low strength concrete will be seen to have had a considerably worse performance than the higher strength concrete for low covers but no effect for covers of 70mm and above.

Tests by Carpentier and Soretz (1966)   Carpentier and Soretz tested 12 nominally identical beams under three different loading regimes:

(i)   loaded on alternate days to a load giving crack widths of 0.2 to 0.3mm.
(ii) loaded continuously to a level giving crack widths of 0.2 to 0.3mm.
(iii) loaded initially to the same load as for (i) and (ii) and then maintained unloaded.

The specimens were kept in the laboratory and were sprayed with water for a four hour period twice a week. At the end of two years the specimens were broken open and the length of corrosion at each crack position measured. These lengths were than related to the appropriate crack width. They concluded that the corroded length increased with increasing crack width though statistical analysis of their results suggests that any such relationship is barely significant.

Tests by the Technical University, Munich   These extensive tests, reported at various stages by various authors (Rehm and Moll (1964), Martin and Schiessl (1969) and Schiessl (1975)), are probably among the most carefully carried out. Pairs of identical beams were loaded back-to-back to a level which induced cracks in the range 0.15 to 0.4mm and then exposed in various environments for up to 10 years. Specimens were broken open after exposures of 1, 2, 4 and 10 years and evaluations made of the progress of the corrosion. The state of corrosion was evaluated by measuring the average depth of corrosion which had occurred at the location of each crack. These data were then related to the initial widths of the cracks.

After 1 and 2 years exposure it was observed that, with few exceptions, the reinforcement was corroded only at the cracks. The frequency, amount and local extension of the corrosion increased with increasing surface crack width. At this time, cracks less than 0.1mm wide rarely had corrosion associated with them while cracks larger than 0.25mm always did.

After 10 years exposure, Schiessl (1975), from a detailed statistical treatment of the data, concluded that there was no significant relationship between crack width and corrosion. Considering the detailed nature of the treatment of the results, there can be little doubt that this conclusion was justified. Schiessl also gave considerable attention to the theoretical aspects of corrosion and its likely relation to crack width and concluded that the result obtained from the exposure tests was what would be expected theoretically. This will be considered further later in the paper.

Tests by Houston, Atimtay and Ferguson (1972)   84 beam and slab units were exposed for a period of two years with daily spraying with 3% salt solution. The variables considered were: cover, stress level (and hence cracking), mix proportions, bar diameter and position of the steel in the mould during casting. During the test period, the specimens were observed and any deterioration recorded. At the end of the exposure period, the specimens were broken open and the percentage of the surface area covered by rust was recorded.

Observation during exposure showed that corrosion progressed very rapidly in cases where 25mm cover was given to 25mm bars: by the end of 19 months the concrete had heavily deteriorated with wide longitudinal cracks along the line of the bars and 100% of the bar surfaces were corroded. Less longitudinal cracking and less corrosion were found where there was 25mm cover to 20mm bars. 50mm cover behaved much better than 25mm; longitudinal cracking and corrosion decreased with decreasing bar diameter until with 20mm bars, almost no corrosion had occurred over the two year period.

The dominant variables found to influence the percentage corrosion were the water/cement ratio and the ratio of cover to bar diameter. Stress level and cracking were found to have only a minimal influence.

Tests by Raphael and Shalon These tests do not yet appear to have been fully reported. A large number of specimens were exposed in four different environments in Israel. It is intended to break open specimens at ages of 1, 2, 5 and 10 years but so far, information only appears to be available on 1, 2 and 5 years of exposure. In addition to environment, the variables considered are crack width and cover. When exposure is complete, measurements are made of the corroded length, corroded area and depth of pits. These are related to the appropriate crack widths. After two years of exposure, there would appear to be a fairly clear relation between crack width and corroded area but little relationship between crack width and depth of corrosion pits (Shalon and Raphael (1964)). After 5 years it is still possible to discern a relation between corroded area and crack width, though the correlation is low. There remains no discernable relation between crack width and depth of pitting (Raphael and Shalon (1971)).

Tests by Baker, Money and Sanborn (1977) These tests were basically carried out to investigate the effectiveness of various coatings for bars but data for ordinary reinforcement was obtained. The variables considered were steel type (6), cover, mix design and environment. Three environments were used:

    (a)   80ft from high tide
    (b)   5ft above high tide
    (c)   between high and low tide.

The specimens were uncracked. At the end of 11 years of exposure, the specimens were broken open and the percentage of the surface area of the bar covered by rust was measured. The Table below summarises the results obtained for normal reinforcing bars.

Table 3. Summary of results from Baker et al (1977).
(Average percentages of rust)

ENVIRONMENT	Water/Cement ratio	Cover (mm)	
		12mm	38mm
Atmospheric (a)	0.66	39	11
	0.71	83	15
Splash (b)	0.66	40	8
	0.71	68	45
Tidal (c)	0.66	2	10
	0.71	8	12

It will be seen that the tidal zone exposure is very much less severe than either the spash or atmospheric zones and that the effect of both cover and water/cement ratio is substantial.

Tests reported by Bertrandy (1978) Bertrandy gives results from 40 beams exposed for 14 years in marine conditions in Marseille. The variables considered were cement content, aggregate grading, cover and stress level. The condition of the specimens was assessed by calculating a 'cracking index' for each beam consisting of the sum of the length of each crack on the beam surface multiplied by its width. Table 4 below attempts to summarise the results obtained.

Table 4. Cracking indices from Bertrandy (1978)

Stress on least compressed face (N/mm^2) tension $-ve$	Cover to least compressed face (mm)	Continuously graded aggregate		Gap graded aggregate	
		Cement content		Cement content	
		300 Kg/m^3	400 Kg/m^3	300 Kg/m^3	400 Kg/m^3
0	41	20	0	75	20
+0.74	41	15	0	0	0
+2.03	41	25	0	10	10
+2.01	41	60	0	50	0
-0.77	16	170	0	160	80
-0.54	41	10	0	0	0
-2.44	16	170	0	125	30
-2.54	41	25	0	10	0
-5.40	16	175	40	80	110
-5.40	41	60	40	70	0

Though not specifically stated in the text, it seems probable
that the bottom four results in the table refer to beams which
would be cracked in flexure.   It will be seen that cement content
and cover are the factors which have had the dominant effect.
It may be inferred that flexural cracking has had some influence
but that this is relatively slight compared with the other factors.

DISCUSSION OF EXPOSURE TEST RESULTS

It is hard to find any aspect of the problem of corrosion of
reinforcement where there is complete agreement between the 9
research projects outlined in the previous section.   Nevertheless
it is possible to pick out some likely general trends.   The
principal objective of this paper was to study the possible
relationships between cracking and corrosion so this will be
looked at first.

Cracking and corrosion   None of the projects surveyed suggest
any significant relationship between initial crack width and
depth of corrosion.   Schiessl (1975) has investigated this
possibility in the greatest depth and there seems no reason for
not accepting his conclusion that such a relationship does not
exist.   There does, however, appear to be some evidence for a
relationship between corroded length or area and crack width,
though the correlation is not good.   Statistical study of the
data given by Carpentier and Soretz (1966) gives a correlation
coefficient between crack width and corroded length of 0.33.
Also, it should be noted that Houston, Atimtay and Ferguson (1972)
were unable to detect any significant effect of cracking on
corroded area from their tests.   Nevertheless, it seems clear
that cracks do act as corrosion initiators and that, after a few
years of exposure, there is likely to be some corrosion at the
points where bars intersect cracks.   Considering all the
evidence, it would appear that cracked members are probably at
more risk from corrosion than uncracked ones but that any influence
of crack width on the overall performance is slight.

Effect of cover   Cover is shown to have a major influence in
about all the projects where this was a variable.   The actual
influence indicated by the results depends upon what was measured.
Table 3 indicates about a 2.5 times increase in corrosion as
cover is decreased from 38 to 12mm while Table 4, which considers
the surface condition of the concrete rather than the condition
of the bar, indicates an increase in corrosion damage of roughly
5 times for a decrease in cover from 41 to 16mm.   Data on surface
condition of the concrete from Baker et al (not presented in this
paper) indicates an increase in corrosion damage by a factor of
12 for a decrease in cover from 38 to 12mm.   The indications are
thus that, while the amount of corrosion on the reinforcement is
strongly affected by cover, the disruption of the concrete caused
by the corrosion is even more strongly influenced by cover.
This seems reasonable since the resistance of the concrete cover
to the bursting forces produced by the corrosion is likely to be
proportioned to the cover, or, as suggested by Houston et al (1972)

to the ratio of cover to bar diameter.

<u>Effect of mix proportions</u>   The design of the mix can undoubtedly
have a very considerable effect as can be seen from Tables 2, 3
or 4.   It was also shown to be important by Houston, Atimtay and
Ferguson (1972).   Unfortunately, due to lack of information in
the papers, it is not possible to pin down the relative importance
of the various aspects of mix design.   High cement contents would
be expected to provide a reserve of alkalinity which could improve
corrosion resistance while high water/cement ratios could be
expected to produce a more permeable concrete which would be dis-
advantageous.   In almost all the papers, the variation in only
one of these quantities is mentioned while any adjustments made
to the other in order to maintain a reasonable mix is ignored.
However, while nothing very definite can be started, it does
appear that, as expected, increases in cement content and decreases
in water/cement ratio both lead to significant improvements in
performance.

<u>Summary</u>   Of the three variables considered above, cover and mix
design are by far the most important.   The effects of cracking
and in particular crack width are at best secondary and are
probably insignificant compared with the other two.

THEORETICAL CONSIDERATIONS

This paper has been concerned with presenting the findings from
exposure tests.   Theoretical work on the corrosion of reinforcement has been deliberately ignored and nothing more than the
briefest consideration of them will be given here to give a
perspective to the results from the exposure tests.

Fresh concrete is highly alkaline (pH 12-13).   In alkaline
environments, steel enters a passive state and will not corrode.
Fresh concrete thus provides very effective protection against
corrosion.   This protection can be broken down in either of two
ways: the alkalinity can be neutralised by the action of carbon
dioxide plus water (forming carbonic acid), a process referred
to as carbonation or the passive layer on the surface of the bars
can be broken down by the presence of chloride ions.   Where the
passivity of the steel is destroyed either by carbonation of the
concrete immediately in contact with the bar or by the penetration
of chlorides to the bar surface, the potential of that area of
bar becomes more negative and a potential difference develops
between the depassivated parts of the bar and those areas which
are still passive.   This potential difference drives a corrosion
cell with the passive areas as its cathode and the depassivated
area as its anode.   Oxygen is absorbed by the reaction at the
cathode and iron is removed at the anode to form rust through a
secondary reaction with more oxygen.   The rate at which the
reaction progresses depends upon two factors: the availability of
oxygen at the cathode and the resistance of the concrete between
the cathode and the anode.   Oxygen can only diffuse slowly

through saturated concrete and thus corrosion will tend to be stifled in this circumstance. As concrete becomes drier, its resistivity increases thus, again, reducing the likelihood of corrosion. It can be seen that ideal conditions for corrosion only occur in rather limited circumstances.

It will be seen that the corrosion process consists of two phases:

(i)   an initiation phase lasting from construction of the member until either chlorides or carbonation have reached the steel and

(ii)   an active phase during which corrosion is actually taking place.

What influence will the variables considered in the exposure tests have on the progress of these two phases?

Cracking   Cracks provide a means by which either carbon dioxide or chlorides can penetrate fairly rapidly to the reinforcement. This results in depassivated areas developing at points where bars intersect cracks. Cracks therefore act as corrosion initiators. Schiessl (1975) has shown that the rate at which carbonation will penetrate down a crack will depend upon its width. As a consequence, the length of the initiation phase will be influeneced by crack width. The exposure test results at early ages reported by Rehm and Moll (1964) and Shalon and Raphael (1964) confirm this. Once corrosion has started, however, the crack ceases to play any part in the process and the rate of corrosion would appear to be independent of crack width. This is discussed in detail by Schiessl (1975) and also, from a different point of view, by Beeby (1978). The result is that, provided the initiation phase is relatively short compared with the design life of the structure, crack width will have little influence on corrosion. A very detailed study of the influence of cracks on the corrosion process has been produced by Tuuti (1978).

Cover   The effect of cover is twofold. Firstly, increased cover increases the time taken for carbonation or chlorides to reach the steel. It thus increases the length of the initiation phase. Secondly, in the active phase, increased cover increases resistance to cracking and spalling due to the bursting forces generated by the corrosion. Schiessl (1975) concludes that cover does not influence the rate of corrosion.

Mix proportions   High cement contents are likely to produce denser, less permeable concrete in the cover and will therefore increase the length of the initiation phase in the absence of cracks. It may still have an effect in the presence of cracks due to an increased reserve of alkalinity.

Summary Corrosion of steel in concrete is a two phase process. Theoretical considerations lead to results which agree in general with those obtained from exposure tests.

CONCLUSIONS AND DESIGN AGAINST CORROSION

It appears that the control of crack widths is probably of little benefit as a corrosion control measure. The concentration on this in many recent Codes of Practice and similar regulations is probably counterproductive since it diverts attention from matters which are more significant. The best protection against corrosion appears to be obtained by ensuring an adequate amount of good quality, dense concrete in the cover.

The theoretical considerations given in the previous section suggest a logical approach to design against corrosion. This is developed in Beeby (1978). In this report it is suggested that design should be done so as to satisfy the relationship:

$$t_0 + t_1 \geqslant \text{Design life}$$

Where t_0 is the length of the initiation phase –
t_1 is the time from the initiation of corrosion
till the occurence of unacceptable corrosion
damage.

Unacceptable corrosion damage will normally be the disruption of the concrete surrounding the reinforcement rather than the unacceptable weakening of the bars.

REFERENCES

Baker, G.A., Money, K.L. and Sanborn, C.B. (1977). Marine Corrosion Behaviour of Bars and Metallic-Coated Steel Reinforcing Rods in Concrete. American Society for Testing and Materials. Special Technical Publication 629.

Beeby, A.W. (1978). Cracking and Corrosion. Concrete in the Oceans Technical Report No. 1. Cement and Concrete Association.

Bertrandy, R. (1978). Corrosion a la Mer de Structures en Béton Armé et Précontraint. Annales de l'Institut Technique du Batiment et des Travaux Publics No. 360, April 1978.

Carpentier, L and Soretz, S. (1966). Contribution a l'étude de la corrosion des armatures dans le béton armé. Annales de l'Institut Technique du Batiment et des Travaux Publics, July-August 1966.

Dauffaut, P., Duhoux, L. and Heuze, B. (1973). Corrosion des aciers dans le béton armé. Essais realises dans l'estuaire de la Rance de 1959 a 1971. Annales de l'Institut Technique de Batiment et Travaux Publics, May 1973.

Houston, Atimtay and Ferguson (1972). Corrosion of Reinforcing Steel Embedded in Structural Concrete. Research Report No. 102-1F. Centre for Highway Research, University of Texas at Austin, 1972.

Martin, H. and Schiessl, P. (1969). The influence of cracks on the corrosion of steel in concrete. Preliminary report of RILEM International Symposium on the durability of concrete. Vol. II. Prague. 1969.

Martin, H. and Schiessl, P. (1969). The influence of time and environmental conditions on the corrosion of deformed bars in cracked concrete. Preliminary report of RILEM international symposium on the durability of concrete. Vol. II. Prague. 1969.

Raphael, M. and Shalon, R. (1971). A study of the Influence of Climate on Corrosion of Reinforcement. Proceedings of the RILEM symposium on Concrete and Reinforced Concrete in Hot Countries, Building Research Station, Technion, Haifa. 1971.

Rehm, G. and Moll, H. (1964). Versuche zum Studium des Einflusses der Rissbreite auf die Rostbilding an der Bewehrung von Stahlbeton - Bauteilen. Deutscher Ausschuss fur Stahlbeton. Heft 169. Berlin. 1964.

Schiessl, P. (1975). Admissible crack width in reinforced concrete structures. Contribution II 3-17. Inter-Association Colloquium on the behaviour in service of concrete structures. Preliminary reports. Vol. II. Liege. 1975.

Shalon, R. and Raphael, M. (1964). Corrosion of Reinforcing Steel in Hot Countries. RILEM Bulletin No. 24. September 1964.

Tremper, B. (1947). The corrosion of reinforcing steel in cracked concrete. Journal of the American Concrete Institute. June 1947.

Tuuti, K. (1978). Cracks and Corrosion. Swedish Cement and Concrete Research Institute. Stockholm. 1978.

CHLORIDE CORROSION OF REINFORCING STEEL IN CRACKED CONCRETE

Kiyoshi Okada*, Wataru Koyanagi**, Toyoaki Miyagawa***

*Prof., Dept. of Civ. Eng., Kyoto Univ., **Prof., Dept. of
Civ. Eng., Gifu Univ., ***Assist., Dept. of Civ. Eng., Kyoto
Univ.

1. INTRODUCTION

When discussing the durability of reinforced concrete structures
in a saline environment, two problems must be dealt with, (1)
deterioration of concrete, (2) corrosion of reinforcing steel.
These two problems are related to each other.

When reinforcing steel rusts, the corrosion products generally
occupy considerably more volume than that of the original
steel. This expansion makes covering concrete cracked and
spalled. Then the rate of corrosion is increasingly accelerated.

In this paper, the corrosion of reinforcing steel is generally
discussed, and influence of cracks of covering concrete on
the corrosion rate of reinforcing steel was investigated using
model specimens.

2. CORROSION OF REINFORCING STEEL IN CONCRETE

(1) Corrosion reaction of reinforcing steel

Mechanism of metal corrosion depends on whether water takes
part in the corrosion reaction or not. The former case is
called wet corrosion and the latter dry corrosion. In the
marine environment, concrete is rarely situated in the perfect
dry condition. Thus, as to corrosion of reinforcing steel in
concrete, only wet corrosion is needed to be discussed here.
Wet corrosion of reinforcing steel in concrete is the electrochemical reaction accompanied by the anodic and cathodic
processes. In the anodic process, iron is transferred into
solution as hydrated ions with two electrons left in the
reinforcing steel. These two electrons are transferred to
the cathode to assimilate in the cathodic process.
The anodic process is represented in the following manner.

$Fe \rightleftharpoons Fe^{2+} + 2e^-$

At the cathode, oxygen depolarization takes place as follows

$O_2 + 2H_2O + 4e^- \rightleftharpoons 4OH^-$

1.62

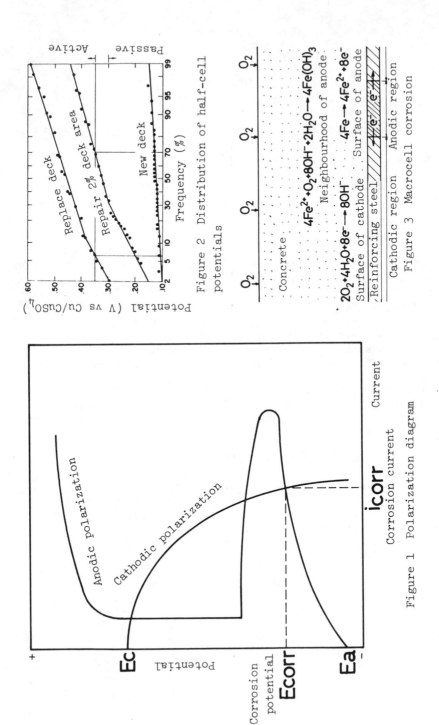

Figure 2 Distribution of half-cell potentials

Figure 3 Macrocell corrosion

Figure 1 Polarization diagram

This cathodic process is active in alkaline solution and rate
-determining step is diffusion of oxygen.
Equilibrium potentials of these reactions can be calculated
using Nernst equation. But in corroding, the anodic and
cathodic potentials change (polarization) respectively with
electric current. Usually the cathode and anode areas are
unequal, but the corrosion current is common to both the
anodic and cathodic processes.
Electrochemical corrosion cells are set up by heterogeneities
of media. Two types of corrosion cells may exist corresponding to the prevailing conditions. The first type, called
the microcell, is characterized by microscopic distance
separating the anode and cathode. When electrical resistance
of electrolyte is too small to neglect, potentials of anode
and cathode are equal due to both palarizations (Figure 1).
In microcell corrosion, natural potential means this one.
The second type is known as the macrocell, both the anodic
and cathodic processes frequently take place in different
places with a certain distance.
The potential difference between the anode and the cathode
of macrocell is larger than that of microcell. The corrosion
reaction in the former is more rapid than in the latter. In the
microcell, only the mixed potential at the anode and cathode
can be measured. But in the macrocell, each potential and
macrocell corrosion current can also be measured using the
appropriate method.
Therefore, the potential itself should be measured from
equilibrium potential to study the polarization of corrosion
reaction. At the same time the potential difference, which
is considered as the electromotive force of macrocell corrosion, should be measured to investigate the corrosion rate.

(2) Mechanism of macrocell corrosion
In concrete, macrocell corrosion frequently proceeds firstly.
Since concrete is macro-heterogeneous material, differential
concentrations of oxygen and chloride are set up and corrosion, which may be sufficient to cause spalling, occurs in
macrocells, the poles of which can be up to several feet
apart.[2]
Figure 2 relates the half-cell potential measurements to the
observed condition of the corrosion damaged bridge by showing the cumulative frequency distribution on three bridges.
For the bridge deck that required replacement, about 94% of
all of the potential showed that the steel was active or
corroding. For the deck repaired, only 30% of the measurements showed to be active, and the new deck had no active
potentials.[7]
These reports show that macrocell corrosion of reinforcing
steel in concrete proceeds. Schematic representation of
macrocell corrosion mechanism is illustrated in Figure 3.[5]
Lewis and Copenhagen[3] demonstrated the effect of factors

on corrosion rate, such as quality of the concrete, concrete permeability and environment of the concrete structure, and discussed five models of corrosion cell. The most actual model giving much corrosion current is shown as follows.

Steel (anode)	Permeable concrete low pH high Cl⁻	Less permeable concrete high pH low Cl⁻	Steel (cathode)

Formations of anodic and cathodic areas are not necessarily permanent, especially as far as the latter is concerned. As this process continues, various kinds of deposits accumulate on either the anode or the cathode. These deposits can greatly affect the process. Furthermore many factors may combine to cause a change in the potential difference between steel areas, which in turn lead to a change in the macrocell corrosion activity.[6]

(3) Influence of cracks on corrosion reaction of reinforcing steel

Cracks, in the reinforced concrete structures, not only permit air, salt and other impurities to penetrate to reinforcing steel, but also make reinforced concrete so heterogeneous as to form macrocell. The region near the crack may become the anode as suggested by Lewis and Copenhagen.[3]
As a measure of corrosion protection, many codes of practice and design regulations have provided the checking of permissible crack widths, depending on the aggressivity of the environment. There is very general agreement between Codes over what these limits should be.
But, influence of cracks on corrosion reaction of steel in concrete has not yet been made sufficiently clear to determine these limits.

3. PURPOSE OF INVESTIGATION

As discussed above, macrocell corrosion proceeds continually on the reinforcing steel in cracked structures. Therefore, it is necessary to measure the rate of macrocell corrosion, and to compare it with the rate of microcell corrosion.
The purpose of this investigation is to point out that electrochemical measurements are useful as nondestructive methods for detecting corrosion, and how cracks have effects upon the mechanism and rate of corrosion.

4. TEST PROCEDURE AND RESULTS

The mechanism and rate of corrosion are accurately obtained by measuring electrochemically the potential and electric current. Then, in order to confirm the expected corrosion reaction experimentally, other methods such as visual inspection, measurement of weight loss etc. had to be employed. Test consists of the following three series.

Series(1) Influence of cracks on potential distribution

Test program While reinforced concrete beams were loaded to form flexural cracks, sodium chloride solution (NaCl 3.13% sol.) was injected through cracks, and the half-cell potential (vs Ag/AgCl electrode) of the reinforcing steel was measured. Then, cracked beams were immersed in the sodium chloride solution (25 °C const.) and their potentials were measured intermittently for 43 days.
In this test, corrosion levels of reinforcing steel are defined as follows.
    Level H: Red rust is mounted.
    Level L: Trace of rust.
    Level M: between H and L.

Specimens The variables in this test are given in Table 1. The clear cover of reinforcing steel is 15 mm. Mix proportion and strengths of used concrete are shown in Table 2 & 3.

Table 1. Variation of 10x15x100^{cm} concrete specimens

Specimen	Mixing water	Surface condition of reinforcing steel
M - 1 2	Tap water	With mill scale
SM - 1 2	Sodium chloride solution	With mill scale
P - 1 2	Tap water	Polished

Table 2. Mix proportion of concrete

Slump	Air content	Water cement ratio	Absolute fine aggregate ratio	Unit weight (kg/m³)			
(cm)	(%)	(%)	(%)	Water	Cement	Sand	Gravel
10 ± 2	2	65	40	195	300	718	1097

1.66

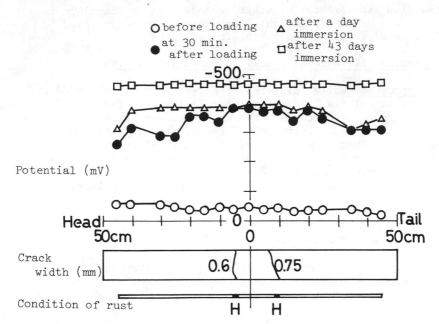

Figure 4   Relation between potential and cracks (M-1)

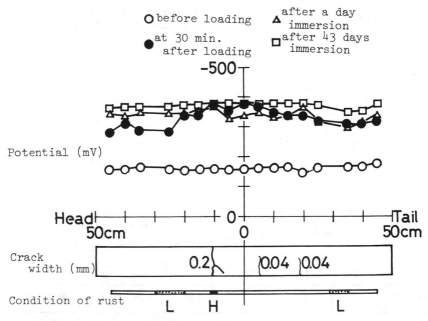

Figure 5   Relation between potential and cracks (SM-1)

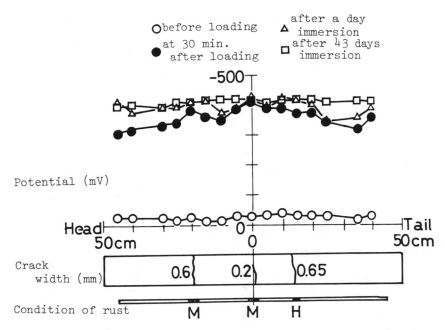

Figure 6   Relation between potential and cracks (P-1)

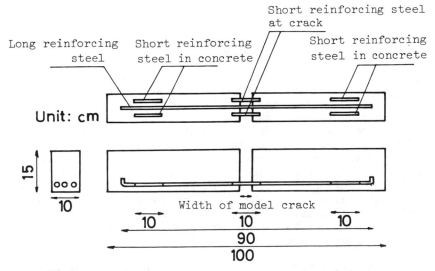

Figure 7   Specimen -Test series (2)-

Table 3.   Strengths of concrete

Mixing water	Compressive strength (kg/cm²)	Tensile strength (kg/cm²)	Flexural strength (kg/cm²)
Tap water	314	28.3	44.2
Sodium chloride sol.	292	27.8	47.3

Results During the injection of sodium chloride solution, the potential changed little in case of crack width of less than 0.1 mm. A typical relationship between the potential distributions and the conditions of rust is shown in Figure 4 - 6.

The tendency that the potential becomes less noble at the location of cracks could be recognized remarkably at 30 min. after loaded. After imersion in the sodium chloride solution, the potential became less noble and the potential difference became small. And at the location of cracks, the reinforcing steel is corroded. This phenomenon shows that the macrocell corrosion reaction proceed, in which the anode is near the crack and the cathode in the concrete.
Decrease of potential difference is mainly due to corrosion deposits formed at the anode and to consumption of oxygen at the cathode. Thus influence of macrocell becomes small whereas that of microcell becomes larger.
All the potentials of reinforcing steel after 43 days immersion were active, for specimens with large water cement ratio and small cover to the reinforcing steel.

Series(2) Relation between potential difference and macrocell current

Test program Potential and its difference are considered as the ability of corrosion and the electromotive force of macrocell corrosion, respectively.
As the anode and cathode exist apart in macrocell, separation of the anode and cathode can be made experimentally.
On the cracked model specimens as shown in Figure 7, which are immersed in the sodium chloride solution (25 °C const.), the distribution of potential on the long reinforcing steel was measured, and then the difference between the maximum and the minimum potentials was calculated. Macrocell current flowing from the short reinforcing steel embedded in concrete to that exposed at the crack was also measured.

Specimens Test variables are shown in Table 4. The clear cover of reinforcing steel is 15 mm. The details of specimen is shown in Figure 7. Mix proportion and strength of concrete are the same as in the test Series (1).

Table 4. Variation of specimens

Specimen	Width of model crack (mm)	Mixing water	Surface condition of reinforcing steel
M - 0	0	Tap water	With mill scale
M - 5	5	Tap water	With mill scale
M - 10	10	Tap water	With mill scale
M - 25	25	Tap water	With mill scale
SM - 0	0	Sodium chloride solution	With mill scale
SM - 25	25	Sodium chloride solution	With mill scale
P - 25	25	Tap water	Polished

*
Every type of specimen consists of two specimens.

Results The maximum potentials could be measured near the model crack and the minimum ones apart from the crack. Figure 8 shows the relation between the potential difference and the period of immersion. The potential difference decreased with elapsed time. When using the sodium chloride solution as mixing water, potential difference was smaller at first and later became larger than when using tap water. The effect of mill scale on the potential difference was not clear.

Figure 9 shows the typical relation between the current density (as the macrocell corrosion rate) and the period of immersion. The current density decreased with elapsed time. The sodium chloride solution as the mixing water, made current density larger than the tap water. Mill scale of reinforcing steel made the current density smaller at first, but later had no effects.

The time dependence of the potential difference and the current are shown in Figure 10-14. As the potential difference decreased, the macrocell current became smaller. Therefore, it becomes clear that the potential difference is the electromotive force giving rise to the macrocell corrosion. When the model crack is not fabricated, the current is very small because the anodic process is inhibited.

The current was not in proportion to the potential difference. This phenomenon is caused by physical and chemical factors, such as no model crack and the nonlinear relation between

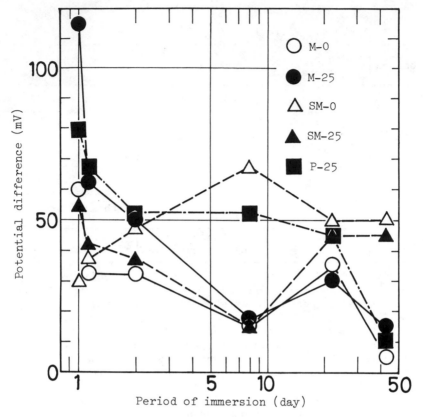

Figure 8 Relation between potential difference
and period of immersion

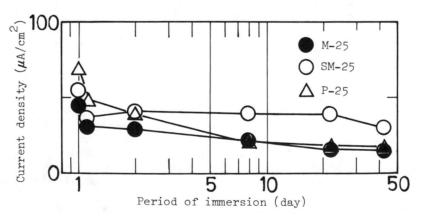

Figure 9 Relation between current density
and period of immersion

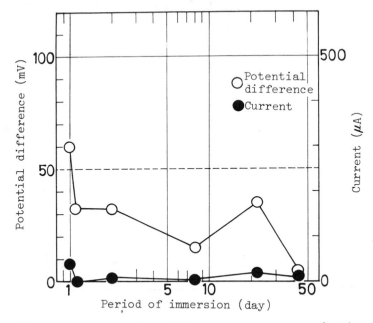

Figure 10   Potential difference and current (M-0)

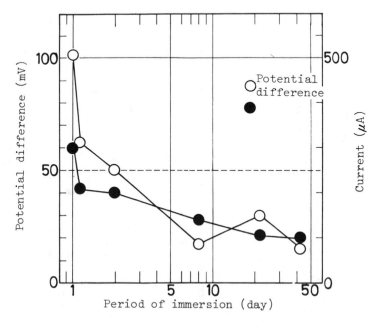

Figure 11   Potential difference and current (M-25)

1.72

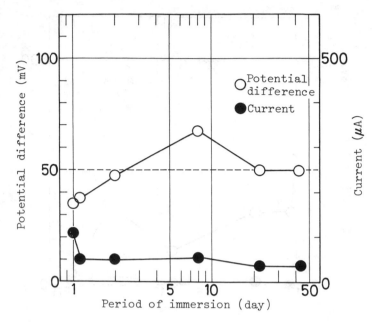

Figure 12   Potential difference and current (SM-0)

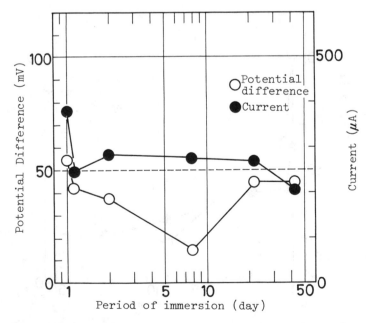

Figure 13   Potential difference and current (SM-25)

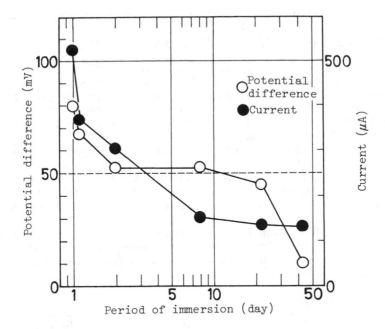

Figure 14   Potential difference and current (P-25)

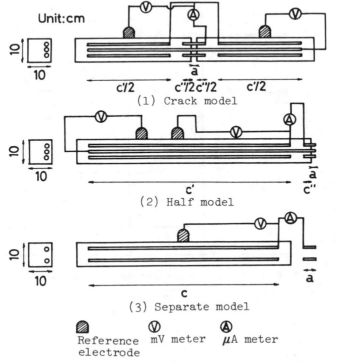

(1) Crack model

(2) Half model

(3) Separate model

Reference   mV meter   μA meter
electrode

Figure 15   Specimens -Test series (3)-

the potential and the current of the corrosion reaction.

Series(3) Influence of cracks on macrocell current

Test program It is considered that macrocell corrosion rate is controlled by both the availability of oxygen at the cathode and the electrochemical resistance of the concrete between the anode and the cathode.[1)] Thus the macrocell corrosion rate depends on the ratio of the cathodic area (Ac) to the anodic one (Aa).
To intensify the macrocell, the crack model specimens were subjected to the cycles of wetting (immersed in the sodium chloride solution) and drying (in the air). The potentials of reinforcing steel were measured. The macrocell current and the depth of damage due to corrosion were also measured.

Specimens Test conditions are shown in Table 5, and the details of test models are shown in Figure 15. The mix proportion and strength of concrete are as shown in Table 6 & 7. The clear cover of reinforcing steel is 20 mm.

Table 5. Variations of specimens

Specimen	Type of model	Length of anode a**(cm)	Length of cathode c**(cm)	Ratio of Ac/Aa
C - 30	Crack model	3	90	30
C - 19		3	56	19
H - 30	Half model	1.5	45	30
H - 19		1.5	28	19
S - 300	Separate model	1	300	300
S - 100		1	100	100
S - 30		1	30	30
S - 10		1	10	10
S - 0		1	0	0

* Every type of specimens consist of two specimens.
** See Figure 15.

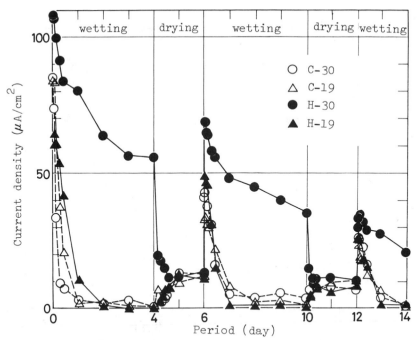

Figure 16   Relation between current density and period
(Crack and half models)

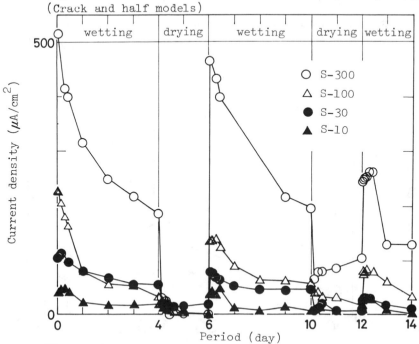

Figure 17   Relation between current density and period
(Separate model)

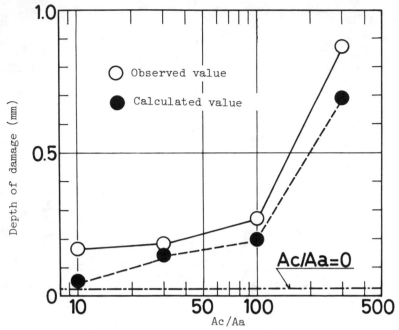

Figure 18   Calculated and observed depth of damage

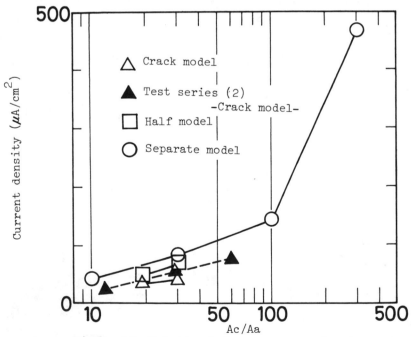

Figure 19   Relation between current density and
ratio of Ac/Aa

Table 6. Mix proportion of concrete

Slump (cm)	Air content (%)	Water cement ratio (%)	Absolute fine aggregate ratio (%)	Unit weight (kg/m³)			
				Water	Cement	Sand	Gravel
15±2	2	70	50	210	300	900	924

Table 7. Strengths of concrete

Compressive strength (kg/cm²)	Tensile strength (kg/cm²)	Flexural strength (kg/cm²)
285	29.7	43.9

Results The relation between the potential and the current density had the same tendency as in case of test Series(2). As shown in Figure 16 & 17, the current density decreased with the period of immersion, and increased after drying. This may be caused by the supply of oxygen. It is clear that the wetting and drying cycle makes the corrosion rate higher than the continuous immersion only.
The observed depth of damage are compared in Figure 18 with that calculated from the quantity of electricity. The close agreement between two was noticed. Thus, it is confirmed experimentally that measured current density means macrocell corrosion rate.
Figure 19 shows the relation between the current density (the maximum value during the 2nd wetting period) and the ratio of Ac/Aa. As the ratio of Ac/Aa increased, the macrocell current density and the corrosion rate became larger. In case of actual cracks, the ratio of Ac/Aa affects on macrocell corrosion rate when the crack width is large enough.

5. CONCLUSION

The results obtained from this study are summarized as follows.
(1) Cracks in the reinforced concrete structures will form macrocell corrosion of the reinforcing steel.
(2) The method of potential distribution measurements is applicable to actual reinforced concrete structures. And by using this method, the evaluations of the durability of reinforced concrete structures may be possible.

1.78

REFERENCES

1) Beeby, A. W. (1978), Corrosion of Reinforcing Steel in Concrete and its Relation to Cracking, The Structural Engineer, London, 56A, 77-81.
2) Browne, R. D. et al. (1975), The Long-Term Performance of Concrete in the Marine Environment, Off-Shore Structures, ICE, London, 49-59.
3) Lewis, D. A. et al. (1959), Corrosion of Reinforcing Steel in Concrete in Marine Atmosphere, Corrosion, Houston, 17, 382-388.
4) Okada, K. et al. (1977), Accelerated Corrosion Test of Reinforcing Steel in Concrete at Raised Temperature, Jour. of The Society of Materials Science, Kyoto, 26, 1110-1116.
5) Okada, K. et al. (1979), Chloride Corrosion of Reinforcing Steel in Cracked Concrete, Proceedings of JSCE, Tokyo, No. 283, 75-87.
6) Stewart, C. F. (1975), Considerations for Repairing Salt Damaged Bridge Decks, Jour. of ACI, Detroit, 72, 685-713.
7) Stratfull, R. F. (1973), Corrosion Autopsy of a Structurally Unsound Bridge Deck, HRR, Washington, D. C., No. 433, 1-11.

ETUDES EXPERIMENTALES DU COMPORTEMENT EN MILIEU MARIN DES STRUCTURES EN BETON

M. KAVYRCHINE   J.P. PEYRONNET   J. TRINH
   C.E.B.T.P.   C.N.E.X.O.   C.E.B.T.P.

L'exploitation des richesses des océans, a nécessité le développement de nouvelles structures dans lesquelles le béton peut trouver avantageusement sa place. Les plates-formes en béton des gisements de pétrole et de gaz en Mer du Nord, en sont de remarquables exemples. Les navires en béton en constituent un autre bien connu, plus ancien puisque datant du bâteau de LAMBOT (1848). L'emploi du béton en mer, n'est donc pas récent, toutefois jusqu'au début des années 1970 notre expérience se limitait surtout à des constructions littorales (quais, môles, phares, formes de radoub...). Ces réalisations ont dans l'ensemble montré un comportement satisfaisant, leur permettant de remplir pleinement leur fonction. Néanmoins dans le nouveau domaine d'utilisation en haute mer, la situation est quelque peu modifiée : les actions météo-océaniques , les conditions d'installation et d'exploitation sont différentes de celles du littoral.

Dans l'environnement marin, les causes principales qui pourraient empêcher une structure en béton d'avoir le comportement attendu pendant la période d'exploitation escomptée, sont de deux natures différentes :
- celles bien spécifiques du milieu ambiant, la corrosion des armatures, l'action répétée des vagues,
- celles relatives à la construction et à l'utilisation de l'ouvrage.

Les conséquences se manifestent à la fois sur le plan chimique, physico-chimique et mécanique. Etant donné les difficultés rencontrées pour procéder à des réparations, voire parfois l'impossibilité de les exécuter, il est important d'élargir nos connaissances sur ces phénomènes afin d'assurer à des structures installées en haute mer la durabilité et la sécurité normalement exigée.

En France, le Centre National pour l'Exploitation des Océans (C.N.E.X.O.) et le Centre Expérimental de Recherches et d'Etudes du Bâtiment et des Travaux Publics (C.E.B.T.P.), ont entrepris, depuis 1974, des études à caractère expérimen-

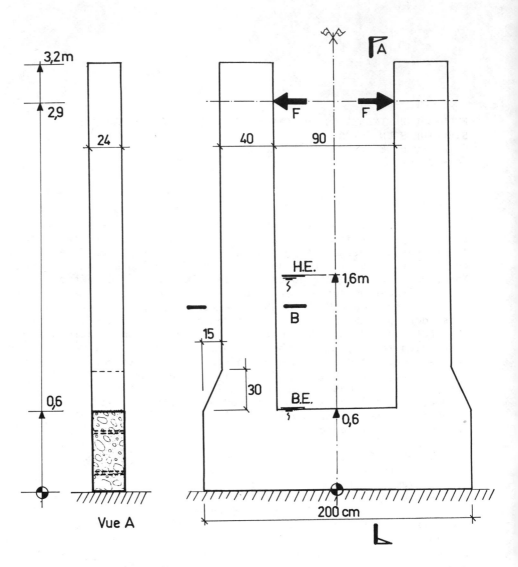

Figure 1 - Corps d'épreuve

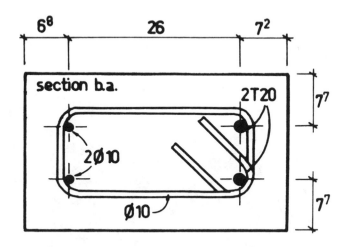

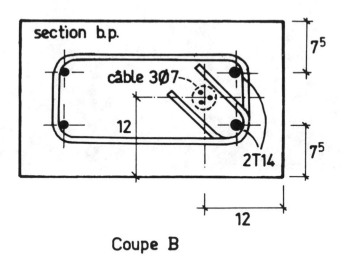

Coupe B

Figure 1 – (contd.)

Figure 2 - Vue du dispositif expérimental au C O B

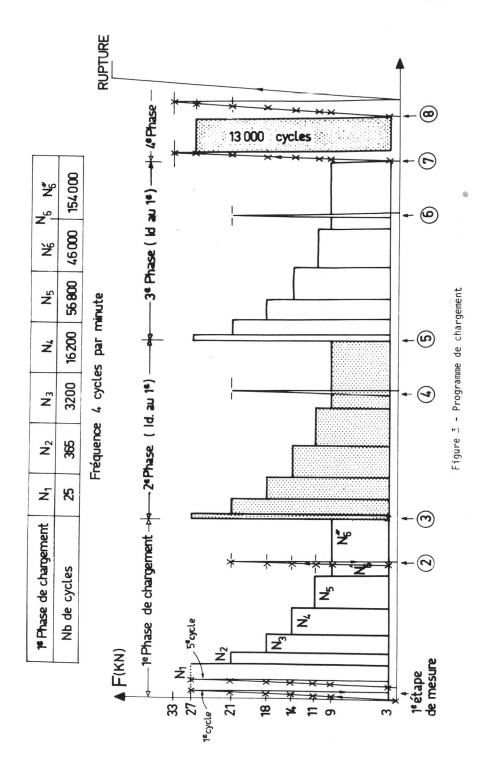

1ᵉ Phase de chargement	N_1	N_2	N_3	N_4	N_5	N_6'	N_6''
Nb de cycles	25	365	3200	16200	56800	46000	154000

Fréquence 4 cycles par minute

Figure 3 - Programme de chargement

tal sur le comportement du béton en milieu marin. Parmi les
actions entreprises [Peyronnet, Seguin (1978)] on se propose
de présenter ci-après celles concernant la tenue des éléments
structurels.
Les sujets traités ont porté sur :
- le comportement de structures en béton sous des actions
  dynamiques typiques de l'environnement marin ;
- la durabilité et la résistance de poutrelles en béton armé
  fissurées, en zone de marnage ;
- la résistance en fatigue de poutrelles en béton armé en
  zone de marnage ;
- le flambement de coques en micro-béton sous la pression
  hydrostatique.

ESSAIS DE POUTRELLES

Sur ce thème, ont été entreprises les trois premières recherches précitées. C'est le comportement de poutrelles en flexion,
et dans les conditions ambiantes de la zone de marnage, qui
est étudié.

Comportement de structures en béton sous des actions dynamiques typiques de l'environnement marin [Trinh, Peyronnet (1978)]

Cette première recherche s'attache surtout à examiner le
comportement en flexion de structures en béton armé ou précontraint, sous des charges d'environnement susceptibles de se
produire en haute mer pendant une durée de vie fixée. Quels
seront aussi les changements éventuels par rapport au comportement - que l'on connaît mieux - des structures terrestres
dans les mêmes conditions de chargement ?

Programme d'essai Quatre corps d'épreuve en forme de U (Fig.1)
sont soumis à l'essai de chargement dynamique. Tous sont identiques en formes et dimensions, et leur ferraillage semblable
deux à deux : deux pièces en béton armé, les autres en béton
précontraint.
     Un couple de U est conservé en ambiance terrestre au
Centre d'Essai de Saint-Rémy-lès-Chevreuse du C.E.B.T.P.
(C.E.S.), près de Paris. L'autre est au Centre Océanologique
de Bretagne du C.N.E.X.O. (C.O.B.) près de Brest, placé dans
un bassin à marée alimenté en eau de mer naturelle (Fig.2),
pour être périodiquement immergé (condition ambiante de la
zone de marnage). Le même chargement dynamique (Fig.3), est
appliqué dans les deux cas.
     On a cherché en premier lieu à reproduire un chargement
simulant au mieux celui des actions observées en haute mer, en
particulier la houle, dans les conditions de service. En sup-
posant une loi log-linéaire pour la distribution à long terme
des hauteurs classées de vagues individuelles [CNEXO-CTICM,
(1976)] , et l'hypothèse de proportionalité entre la hauteur
de vagues et la charge F, les phases 1 à 3 représentent les

plus fortes vagues susceptibles de survenir en dix ans. Les
charges caractéristiques F_o et F_1 répondent à peu près aux dé-
finitions des règlements en vigueur [FIP, DnV (1977)] pour les
conditions d'environnement extrêmes et ordinaires. La répétition des charges, au rythme de 4 cycles par minute, a permis
en six mois de simuler toutes les vagues de hauteur supérieure
au quart de la valeur maximum H_o dans la durée fixée. C'étaient
donc surtout les effets mécaniques et leurs conséquences les
plus immédiates qui étaient observées.

Tableau 1

Pièce	Recherche JJ 4 corps d'épreuve identiques en forme de U			
	1	2	3	4
Structure en	b.a.	b.p.	b.a.	b.p.
Conditions de conservation	à Saint-Rémy (C.E.S.) en plein air		à Brest (C.O.B.) dans la cuve à marée	
Chargement	dynamique identique aux 4 pièces (cf. programme de chargement)			

Toutes les structures parurent encore intactes après ce
premier chargement suivi du chargement à F_o , aussi l'essai se
poursuivait par des charges répétées jusqu'au niveau F_1
(13 000 cycles). Il s'agissait alors de vérifier la sécurité
qu'elles pouvaient encore fournir, et d'accélérer, dans les
essais du C.O.B., pour mieux les observer, certains phénomènes
de dégradation du béton dus à la présence de l'eau dans les
fissures.

Ces corps d'épreuve, avec les niveaux de chargement retenus ne vérifient pas les prescriptions relatives à la fissuration des textes précités. Il est peu probable que la fatigue
soit déterminante à l'air, car on reste bien inférieur au critère de MINER. Mais en sera-t-il encore ainsi dans l'eau de
mer ?

Exécution des essais et principaux résultats   1) La composition du béton employé et l'évolution de sa résistance en
compression dans diverses ambiances de conservation sont indi-
quées sur la figure 4. Le chargement commença à 21 jours d'âge
du béton, au moyen de vérin hydraulique tendant à écarter les
deux montants du U, et à les soumettre à une flexion (consoles
encastrées).

2) Tous les montants se fissurèrent au premier chargement, vers 18 KN pour le béton armé, et 27 KN pour le béton
précontraint. C'étaient des fissures de flexion s'ouvrant surtout dans les zones les plus fléchies. Elles continuaient à

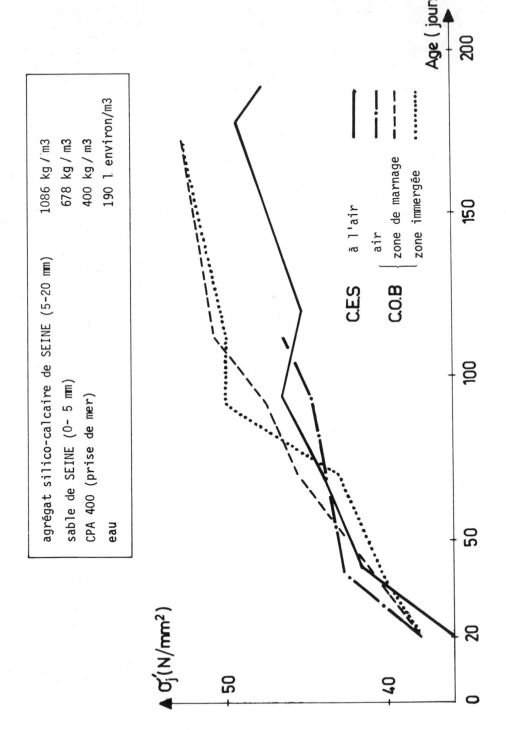

agrégat silico-calcaire de SEINE (5-20 mm)   1086 kg / m3

sable de SEINE (0- 5 mm)   678 kg / m3

CPA 400 (prise de mer)   400 kg / m3

eau   190 l. environ/m3

C.E.S   à l'air

C.O.B { air
        zone de marnage
        zone immergée

Age (jours)

σ'j (N/mm²)

Figure 4 - Résistance du béton en compression

1.87

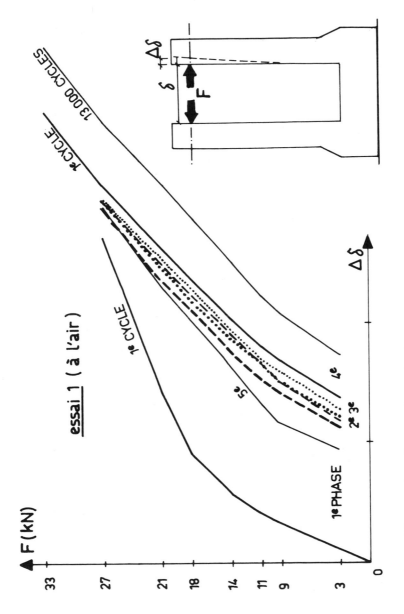

Figure 5 - Comparaison de déformations des corps d'épreuve en béton armé

1.88

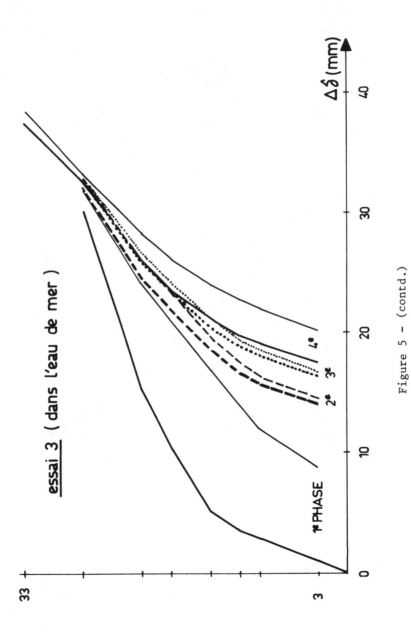

Figure 5 - (contd.)

se développer ensuite avec le chargement dynamique : prolonge-
ment horizontal de plus en plus vers le côté comprimé, et ouverture de nouvelles dans le haut des montants. Quelques fissures de rupture d'adhérence le long des armatures apparais-
saient dans la fin du premier chargement dynamique. Cependant
à l'achèvement de celui-ci (chargement représentatif de la
période de service de 10 ans), les parements de béton avaient
conservé une apparence saine. Le chargement qui suivait ensuite (13 000 cycles jusqu'au niveau F_1), n'avait accentué que
légèrement les traits soulignés, sans rien entraîner de vrai-
ment anormal ou d'inadmissible. Dans l'eau de mer, il se for-
mait sur les fissures une efflorescence de sels blancs
(aragonite Ca CO_3, Mg(OH)$_2$), cela dans les jours qui suivaient
l'ouverture. On a constaté ensuite avec le temps un effritement
progressif du bord des fissures et aussi un colmatage de celles
ci (actions physico-chimiques au contact de l'eau de mer).

3) Au chargement statique final, pour obtenir la
résistance et permettre l'examen de visu de l'état interne des
matériaux, les quatre U périrent sous des efforts sensiblement
identiques : de 55 à 56 KN en montrant de grandes déformations
ultimes. Les ruptures furent effectivement provoquées par la
flexion, par épuisement de la résistance des armatures à l'en-
castrement des montants. La résistance observée dépassa légèrement celle calculée : Ce chargement dynamique appliqué et
l'eau de mer, n'ont donc aucunement - du moins sur six mois -
altéré la résistance globale de ces corps d'épreuve.L'examen
ultérieur des armatures ne révéla que des piqûres de corrosion
sur les cadres transversaux de la pièce en béton armé testée
en eau de mer. Ceci corrobore les résultats de mesure du potentiel électrique des armatures.

4) Les mesures de déformation ont fait apparaître les
conséquences de la fissuration en présence d'eau de mer. Les
phénomènes physico-chimiques, qui se développent à son contact,
modifient le relief des fissures : effritement du béton et
dépôts de produits. Ainsi lors du déchargement, les fissures ne
peuvent plus se refermer librement comme dans l'air, ce qui se
traduit par d'appréciables déformations résiduelles (Fig.5).
L'autocolmatage des fissures pourrait être un facteur favorable
vis-à-vis de la pénétration d'eau vers l'armature.

Ces premiers résultats sur le comportement en service
de structures en béton en mer, demandent à être confirmés par
des essais de plus longue durée pour la corrosion, et sous des
charges de fatigue pour examiner les effets combinés (corrosion
-fatigue). Deux recherches ont été entreprises dans cette voie,
celles-ci ne sont pas encore achevées, aussi on se limitera à
la présentation des programmes prévus, et des premiers points
acquis sous réserve de confirmation par des résultats plus
complets.

Durabilité et résistance de poutrelles en béton armé fissurées, en zone de marnage

En milieu marin, un phénomène fondamental à éviter pour les constructions en béton, est la corrosion des armatures. L'attaque des aciers, en réduisant la section résistante, abaisse certes la capacité portante dans le temps, mais la perte d'adhérence consécutive au développement de la corrosion, à la surface des armatures,contribue autant à diminuer la sécurité en supprimant le mécanisme de fonctionnement du béton armé. Compte tenu des imperfections de fabrication et la taille des ouvrages offshore en béton armé, il serait raisonnable de négliger la période avant l'initiation de la corrosion : temps d'imprégnation du béton, puis de dépassivation des aciers [Beeby (1978)] . Ce qui importe donc, c'est la vitesse d'évolution des phénomènes par la suite, et de pouvoir compter de manière à peu près sûre sur quelques décennies pour définir la durée de vie des ouvrages.

Dans le but d'examiner la perte de résistance en flexion de poutrelles en béton armé, un programme d'essai sur cinq ans a démarré au C.O.B. en Avril 1977 (recherche JV).

Programme d'essai et corps d'épreuve Le comportement en flexion et la résistance de quinze poutrelles, sont examinés dans des essais de chargement après des périodes de conservation plus ou moins longues dans la zone de marnage (bassin à marée du C.O.B.). Les corps d'épreuve, tous identiques en formes et ferraillage (Fig.6), sont répartis en cinq séries de trois chacune : séries indexées de 1 à 5. La première JV1 fut soumise à l'essai de chargement jusqu'à rupture au commencement de l'étude, à deux mois et demi d'âge du béton, afin de servir de références aux essais ultérieurs. Ces derniers sont programmés respectivement après 6 mois, 1 an, 3 ans et 5 ans d'exposition pour les séries JV2 à JV5. Dans un même groupe, les trois poutrelles se différencient par le chargement permanent appliqué :
- soit sous le poids propre : poutrelles désignées A ;
- soit sous une flexion composée fournie par une précontrainte excentrée, deux niveaux d'effort normal sont retenus : respectivement P_1 = 175 KN, et P_2 = 225 KN pour les poutrelles B et C.
Deux pièces supplémentaires A6 et C6, étaient utilisées pour des tentatives de corrosion accélérée dans des chambres climatiques durant un an, cycles d'une semaine : brouillard d'eau de mer naturelle à 35°C (2 jours) et séchage à l'atmosphère ambiante (voir Tableau 2).

Sur tous les corps d'épreuve, on a pris certaines mesures et réalisé des traitements préliminaires destinés à assurer au mieux l'initiation de la corrosion des armatures dès le début de l'étude.
- Chargement jusqu'à la valeur caractéristique F_0 = 52 KN pour les fissurer, puis des charges répétées, entre 10 KN et la charge caractéristique F_1 = 42 KN, à 4 cycles par minute et sous arrosage d'eau de mer. Toutes les poutrelles auront à

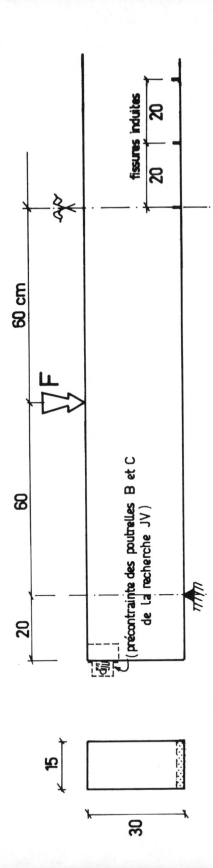

Figure 6 – Poutrelles d'essais.

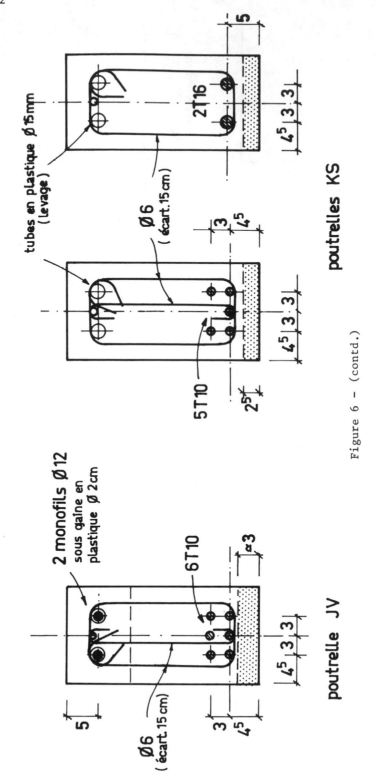

Figure 6 – (contd.)

Tableau 2 - Recherche JV

15 poutrelles[3] en béton armé de section rectangulaire
exposées à une ambiance marine (zone de marnage)

SERIE	1	2	3	4	5
Durée d'exposition	pièces de référence	6 mois	1 an	3 ans	5 ans
°Préliminaire[1] pris à chaque étape	90 cycles	45	30	22	18
°Permanent : ▪ poids propre	A1	A2	A3	A4	A5
▪Précontrainte[2] (P_1)	B1	B2	B3	B4	B5
excentrée (P_2)	C1	C2	C3	C4	C5

CHARGEMENTS

(1) Chargement à F_0 = 52 KN, puis des cycles entre 10 KN et F_1 = 42 KN .

(2) P_1 = 175 KN, et P_2 = 225 KN environ .

(3) 2 poutrelles supplémentaires A6 et C6,

sont exposées à des cycles de brouillard salin (eau de mer) .

subir 90 cycles (deux fois le nombre probable de vagues de hauteur égale à 0,8 H_o pour une période de 30 ans), répartis dans le temps de conservation avant rupture. La fissuration a été "induite" dans trois sections droites choisies, par de minces lamelles de cuivre (0,2 mm d'épaisseur) disposées avant le bétonnage. En ces endroits, les barres d'armature principale furent brossées légèrement pour enlever la rouille initiale. Ces lames étaient ôtées avant le chargement, laissant ainsi une découpe : "fissure" ouverte en permanence.

- Mise en précontrainte des poutrelles B et C au moyen de mono-fils Ø 12, placés dans des gaines en plastique remplies d'huile.
- Imprégnation du béton d'eau de mer sous pression, 3 cycles jusqu'à $2N/mm^2$ (200 m de hauteur d'eau) dans le caisson de 50 bars du C.O.B.

Exécution des essais - mesures effectuées Le béton a la même composition que celui utilisé pour les essais précédents (Fig.4).

Les poutrelles sont toujours posées à leurs extrémités en laissant une portée de 2,40 m. Le chargement est effectué à l'aide de deux vérins hydrauliques disposés symétriquement, distants de 1,2 m.

Les principales mesures relevées sont :
- le potentiel électrochimique des armatures, avec des électrodes en surface au calomel saturé (ECS) ;
- les déformations des matériaux à l'essai de chargement ;
- les ouvertures de fissures en surface au moyen de déformètre mécanique sur des bases à cheval sur la fissure et situées à 2,5 cm environ au-dessus de la face inférieure.Les ouvertures W lues initialement, dans les conditions d'exposition se répartissaient ainsi :

	POUTRELLES JV		
$W(10^{-2}mm)$	A	B	C
[0 - 5[	52 %	50 %	46 %
[5 - 10[	48 %	50 %	54 %

Ces mesures sont complétées par des observations régulières de l'état des parements du béton, et des armatures après rupture des poutrelles.

Premiers résultats (après 2 ans d'essai) 1) La préfissuration et l'imprégnation sous pression, ont conduit aux observations suivantes : à la sortie du caisson, toutes les fissures se couvrirent de sels blancs, sur certaines induites apparaissèrent des taches de rouille. Les potentiels des armatures s'abaissèrent brusquement jusqu'à des valeurs de forte probabilité de corrosion (arrivée d'eau de mer).

2) Les essais de poutrelles de la série 1 donnèrent une résistance P_u = 91 KN légèrement supérieure au calcul :

A5

B5

C5

Figure 7 - Vues des poutrelles JV de la série 5 après fissuration initiale.

1.96

Figure 8 – Vues de la rupture de poutrelle C3 de la recherche JV.

87 KN. Les grandes déformations ultimes et les grandes ouvertures des fissures verticales, confirmèrent la forme de la rupture en flexion par insuffisance des armatures avant la destruction du béton comprimé. L'examen subséquent des aciers, vérifia bien l'apparition de la corrosion sur les barres du lit inférieur du ferraillage. L'attaque, bien que limitée, à l'aplomb des fissures induites atteignait le mm en profondeur.

3) La dépassivation observée à l'imprégnation était suivie sur les autres poutrelles d'une remontée du potentiel, qui se poursuit encore légèrement après deux ans. Mais si les taches de rouille sur les fissures induites évoluaient légèrement dans les premiers temps, elles semblaient stabilisées jusqu'à maintenant. Les sels blancs ont colmaté les fissures dues au chargement, mais ont disparu par endroits dans les fissures induites à cause de la rouille formée.

La repassivation se révèlait très rapide dans les poutrelles A6 et C6. Dans ces cas, les résultats étaient négatifs. Il n'y avait apparemment aucune évolution, si ce n'était que la formation en surface d'une pellicule blanchâtre semblable aux sels des fissures. Ce que confirmèrent les essais de rupture au bout d'un an.

4) Les essais des séries 2 et 3, ne montraient pas encore de changement dans la résistance des poutrelles (mode de rupture et charge ultime).

Tableau 3 - Fu charge de rupture (KN)
des poutrelles JV

SERIE Essais	1 de référence	2 après 6 mois	3 1 an	6 1 an en brouillard salin
Poutre A	83*	77*	89	91
B	94,5	90	93	-
C	96	91,5	93	93

*résultats peu fiables

La poutrelle C3 sembla toutefois offrir moins de ductilité ultime. La pièce rompue dévoila une cassure de l'armature centrale du lit inférieur sur une partie corrodée (section de fissure induite), rupture avec cependant striction de la partie non corrodée (Fig.8)

La corrosion des aciers n'avait guère changé entre 6 mois et 1 an, mais paraissait plus prononcée par rapport aux observations faites au départ dans la série 1. Elle restait encore localisée dans les sections de fissure induite.

5) La mesure du potentiel électrique (mesure extérieure et ponctuelle) nécessite encore une interprétation plus fine

ou des mesures complémentaires pour permettre de contrôler la
corrosion des aciers dans le béton [Lemoine, Taché(1979)] .

Résistance en fatigue de poutrelles en béton armé, en zone de marnage (recherche KS)

En mer, le caractère fluctuant et répétitif du vent et des vagues, peut être déterminant dans le dimensionnement et le calcul
des constructions offshore. Les variations de contraintes qui
en résultent dans les matériaux, risquent de les soumettre à des
effets de fatigue. A cet égard, la situation des armatures
semble la plus critique comme le témoignent les projets faits
pour les récentes plates-formes en béton. Le danger apparaît
d'autant plus réel que l'on est dans un milieu corrosif :
fatigue-corrosion.

En outre, la répétition des charges dans l'eau peut
avoir de graves conséquences sur le béton fissuré à la longue
[Fauchart, Kavyrchine, Trinh (1975)] : érosion dans les fissures due à la circulation (pompages et refoulements successifs),
surpression localisée notamment à l'interface acier-béton.
L'ouverture initiale des fissures, la fréquence du chargement
et la pression d'eau extérieure, tiennent certainement un
grand rôle dans ce phénomène. Par ailleurs, l'autocolmatage des
fissures dans l'eau de mer serait plutôt favorable.

Ces quelques considérations nouvelles, ont fait sentir
le besoin d'informations sur la tenue et la résistance du
béton armé en mer sous des charges répétées. Ici également dans
une phase d'orientation, c'est le comportement de poutrelles
sous des flexions répétées en zone de marnage qui est étudié,
et en particulier la résistance en fatigue des aciers.

Programme d'essai et corps d'épreuve

Le programme expérimental comporte six essais de poutrelles de
formes identiques à celles de la recherche précédente (Fig.6).
Le béton utilisé a aussi la même composition (Fig.4). Les six
poutrelles sont partagées en deux groupes par l'armature principale, composée soit de 5T10 (poutrelle A), soit de 2T16
(poutrelle B). Leur résistance statique calculée, la même sensiblement pour les deux cas, est limitée par celle fournie par
les aciers, du moins dans l'air, Fu = 75 KN.

Ces poutrelles sont soumises, par couple à des charges
répétées d'intensité plus ou moins élevée, dans des conditions
ambiantes de la zone des marées. Trois niveaux de "durée de
vie" en fatigue (nombre maximal de cycles supportés) différents
ont été retenus.

Toutefois, compte tenu de l'évolution de la corrosion,
et de l'influence favorable des périodes de calme, le chargement est aménagé de façon à tester toutes les poutrelles pendant deux ans.

Tableau 4 - Recherche KS

Poutrelle	A1	B1	A2	B2	A3	B3
Charges répétées (KN)						
F_m			0,1 Fu = 7,5			
F_M	0,37 Fu = 27,5		0,55 Fu = 41,5		0,68 Fu = 51	
Contraintes calculées (N/mm^2)						
$\sigma_m(\sigma_m/\sigma_e)$	53(0,11)	52(0,12)	53(0,11)	52(0,12)	53(0,12)	52(0,12)
$\sigma_M(\sigma_M/\sigma_e)$	196(0,42)	192(0,44)	295(0,64)	289(0,66)	363(0,79)	355(0,81)
$\Delta\sigma(\Delta\sigma/\sigma_e)$	142(0,31)	139(0,32)	242(0,52)	237(0,54)	310(0,67)	303(0,69)
Chargement	par phases de 160 000 cycles réparties régulièrement sur deux ans, alternées aux périodes de repos		par phases de 80 000 cycles			
Nb total de cycles prévus	2.10^6 cycles		1,5.10^6 cycles		3.10^5 cycles	

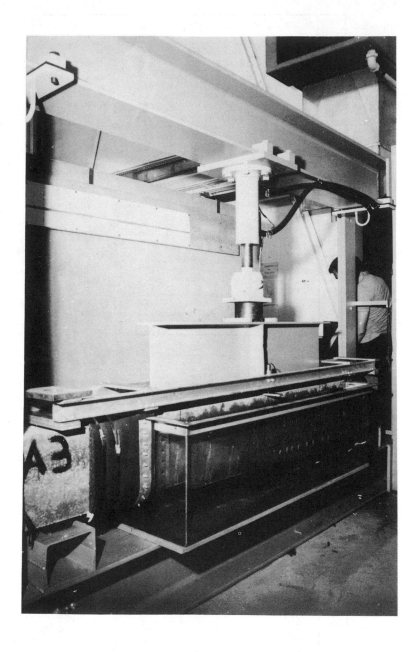

Figure 9 - Dispositif de chargement des essais en fatigue (recherche KS)

Exécution des essais de fatigue Les poutrelles, fabriquées au CES, étaient après 1 mois d'âge du béton placées dans le bassin à marée du C.O.B. Le schéma mécanique d'appui et de chargement, est analogue à celui des poutrelles JV. Les essais de chargement, sont effectués sur deux bancs munis de cuve à marée (2 marées/jour) alimentée en eau de mer naturelle laissée à la température ambiante (Fig.9).

Les fissures induites au bétonnage ont été utilisées en vue de favoriser l'initiation de la corrosion des armatures. On avait effectivement détecté avant l'essai de chargement, qui se situa vers 4 mois et demi d'âge du béton, des traces de rouille sur certaines poutrelles dans les fissures induites. Les mesures du potentiel des armatures en apportaient la confirmation, chute à des valeurs basses du domaine de dépassivation des aciers.

Un premier chargement statique fut opéré pour provoquer la fissuration des poutrelles, jusqu'à F = 45 KN pour les séries 1 et 2, et à F_M = 51 KN pour la dernière série. La figure 10, présente, à titre indicatif, des vues des poutrelles 3 fissurées. Les charges répétées sont appliquées, au moyen de vérins hydrauliques, à la fréquence de 6 cycles/minute (0,1 Hz) variant sinusoïdalement entre les valeurs extrêmes F_m et F_M. Le programme de chargement de fatigue, est réalisé par phases séparées, des "blocs" de 160 000 cycles consécutifs (durée = 1 mois) et de 80 000 cycles (environ 2 semaines) sont retenus respectivement pour les deux premières séries et la troisième. Ceux-ci se répartissent régulièrement sur la durée retenue, s'alternant avec des périodes de repos durant lesquelles les corps d'épreuve sont conservés dans le bassin à marée du C.O.B. On devrait atteindre ainsi en deux ans, les nombres de cycles prévus, évaluation très sommaire extrapolée des quelques essais connus [Bannister (1978)] .

Les essais débutèrent en Juillet 1978.

Premières constatations (8 mois d'essai) Les fissures ouvertes au chargement sont colmatées par les sels blancs formés, surtout sur les poutrelles les moins sollicitées (série 1). Le colmatage ne se présente que partiellement dans les autres séries plus fléchies. En surface ces sels apparaissent aux apex des fissures anciennes (dites primaires) et sur les fissures secondaires ouvertes sous la répétition des charges (Fig. 11).

La rouille dans les fissures induites était visible sur les poutrelles des séries 1 et 2, après les premières phases de chargement. Elles l'étaient déjà dans la série 3 avant le chargement. De façon générale, ces taches ont évolué ensuite. Le potentiel des armatures relevé, avec une électrode de référence extérieure, a ici aussi remonté graduellement après une chute rapide dans les premiers temps.

Les effets de la répétition des charges sur ces poutrelles fissurées dans l'eau, semblent dépendre du degré de fissu-

Figure 10 - Vues des poutrelles de la série B de la recherche KS.

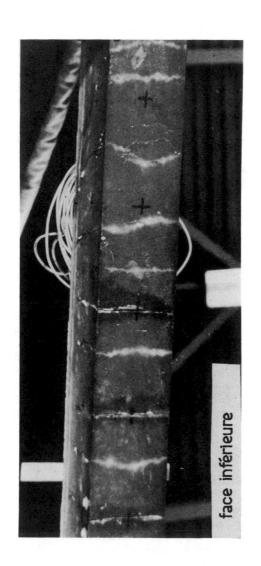

Figure 11 - Vue de la poutre KS B2 après 80 000 cycles.

ration (hauteur et largeur des fissures), et par conséquent du
niveau de sollicitation. Les essais des poutrelles de la série
3, ont montré l'ampleur des effets de pompage, on a vu l'eau
ressortir sous la charge maximale sur toute la hauteur de la
fissure alors que la surface d'eau affleure à peine la face inférieure. A marée montante, la fissuration se détache ainsi nettement du béton sec par l'humidité qu'elle libère. L'effet est
bien moins sensible avec la série 1.

La circulation alternée de l'eau dans les fissures, a
dégradé après un temps plus ou moins long suivant le niveau de
chargement, les bords des fissures : gonflement et écaillement
du béton. Le phénomène survenait relativement vite sur les poutrelles de la série 3, avant 80 000 cycles. Le béton autour des
fissures se distinguait par une coloration blanchâtre.

Des fissures de rupture d'adhérence ont apparu, sur les
faces inférieures et latérales dans les portées d'effort tranchant, avant 300000 cycles pour la série 2, et 80 000 cycles
pour la troisième série.

Comparativement aux fissures de flexion, celles incli-
nées d'effort tranchant semblaient être plus effritées.

ESSAIS DE FLAMBEMENT DE COQUES EN MICROBETON SOUS PRESSION
HYDROSTATIQUE

On aborde ici le problème de stabilité de structures-caissons
immergées. Cette question s'est posée récemment pour les réservoirs de plates-formes, lors de l'immersion soit pour la mise
en place du pont supérieur, soit lors du ballastage sur le site.
Les difficultés rencontrées d'une part dans le calcul de ces
structures, et d'autre part dans le respect des dimensions à la
construction, obligent parfois à la prudence et à adopter des
marges de sécurité plus élevées vis-à-vis du phénomène de l'implosion. Cette condition souvent est déterminante pour les dimensions de ces ouvrages. Certes, le problème a reçu des solutions par des modèles théoriques plus ou moins complexes, il
reste néanmoins à vérifier leur représentativité de la réalité.
La mise au point d'une technique expérimentale d'étude sur modèle, constitue donc en soi un outil complémentaire indispensable et souhaitable.

C'est dans cette perspective que se situe cette recherche, qui dans cette première phase (recherche KR), s'attache
surtout à démontrer la faisabilité et la validité de l'expérimentation, en particulier sur les points suivants :
- fabrication de modèles en micro-béton ;
- choix des moyens d'acquisition et des informations significatives pour la compréhension du phénomène ;
- conduite des essais en pression dans le caisson de 1000 bars
  du C.O.B.

Coques cylindriques en micro-béton Trois essais d'implosion de
coques sous pression hydrostatique, étaient prévus pour cette

partie d'étude. Le corps d'épreuve est composé en fait d'une coque cylindrique en micro-béton, fermée aux extrémités par des tapes métalliques relativement plus rigides. Ces dernières comportent une rainure circulaire dans laquelle vient s'encastrer le cylindre rendu solidaire par un collage à la résine. Les dimensions théoriques du corps cylindrique, sont (Fig.12) :
- diamètre extérieur : 50 cm ;
- hauteur : 1,43 m (environ le triple du diamètre) ;
- épaisseur de la paroi : 2 cm, c'est à la limite des possibilités de bétonnage compte tenu des autres dimensions. C'est sensiblement un modèle au 40e des cellules de réservoirs des plates-formes de la mer du Nord. Le rapport épaisseur/diamètre = 0,04 serait légèrement en-dessous du seuil entre la rupture par instabilité et celle par compression sous la pression hydrostatique [Albertsen (1973)] .
La composition du micro-béton utilisé, est :

	Sable (D en mm)			Filler calcite 75 D	Ciment CPALC 325	eau
	0à0,5	0,5à1,6	1,6à2,5			
Poids(kg/m^3)	340	300	885	60	500	≈240

La résistance en compression effectivement obtenue au jour de l'essai (vers 5 à 6 mois d'âge), s'élevait à 65 N/mm^2 en moyenne par l'essai de compression simple de cylindres $\emptyset$ = 11 cm, h = 22 cm.
Les deux premières coques cylindriques (KR1 et KR2), étaient armées d'une nappe d'armature à mi-épaisseur : treillis de fils de 1 mm, à maille 1 cm (hauteur) X 25 cm (pourtour). Le dernier KR3 comportait deux nappes, de même armature, disposées près de chacun des parements.

Procédure expérimentale 1) Un relevé des profils internes et externes du cylindre, était effectué afin de juger de sa forme réelle, de la position et de l'importance des défauts géométriques éventuels : variation de l'épaisseur, de concentricité... Ceux-ci, selon leur degré, interviennent sur la résistance et la zone d'initiation de la rupture.
Au cours de l'essai en pression, deux types de mesure sont effectués :
- mesure de déformations du béton au moyen de jauges électriques collées sur les faces interne et externe, notamment aux points jugés critiques d'après l'examen précédent ;
- mesure de déplacements à l'aide de capteurs (palpeur inductif), et de proximité (émetteur-récepteur à ultra-son), montés sur un dispositif tournant fixé sur les couvercles métalliques.
Sont aussi relevées en permanence, sur des enregistreurs, les pressions intérieure et extérieure au corps d'épreuve.
2) Le cylindre en micro-béton, une fois équipé des jauges, rendu étanche par plusieurs couches de résine, assemblé à ses

supports métalliques haut et bas muni du dispositif tournant,
est placé dans le caisson 1000 bars du C.O.B. (Fig.13). L'intérieur est rempli d'huile pour l'isolation électrique, un circuit
hydraulique avec vannes (Fig.14) permet :
- soit d'isoler le volume interne, la pression interne p_i croît
alors avec la déformation de la coque sous la pression extérieure p_e ;
- soit d'y laisser s'établir la pression atmosphère en l'ouvrant.
     L'extérieur du corps d'épreuve (intérieur du caisson de
pression), est rempli d'eau douce. Les variations de sa pression sont commandées manuellement à l'aide de vannes à débit
réglable en mettant en communication :
- soit un caisson secondaire servant de "tampon" pour les
montées de pression ;
- soit à l'atmosphère pour les descentes en pression.
     Cet ensemble de commandes permet d'intervenir, de maniè-
re souple et fine, sur le chargement par pression hydrostatique
de la coque. Le but cherché est de faciliter autant que se peut
le contrôle des déformations du corps d'épreuve à la phase ultime (chargement par déformations imposées). Cela est nécessaire
à cause du caractère fragile du flambement, et de l'influence
notable du fluage. La figure 15 résume le déroulement de l'essai KR2.

Premiers résultats 1) La figure 16 présente une vue du cylindre KR2 après implosion.
     Les pressions ultimes obtenues dans ces essais sont :

KR	1	2	3
$p_e - p_i$ (N/mm^2)	4,8	4,6	5,5

     La figure 17 montre les déformations successives de la
section droite du cylindre KR2 dans la zone critique.
     2) Ces premiers essais ont permis d'élaborer et de tes-
ter, un dispositif expérimental et une procédure d'essai de
flambement de coques en micro-béton sous la pression hydrostatique. Les résultats acquis sont assez prometteurs pour que
l'on puisse envisager des études poussées sur le phénomène
considéré et sur des modèles plus représentatifs de problèmes
concrets.

CONCLUSION

Nous avons cherché au-travers de cette brève présentation des
recherches expérimentales sur les éléments structurels et des
premiers résultats obtenus à montrer :
- l'intérêt que le C.E.B.T.P. et le C.N.E.X.O. portent à
l'utilisation du béton à la mer ;
- les efforts apportés pour une meilleure connaissance des
problèmes posés.

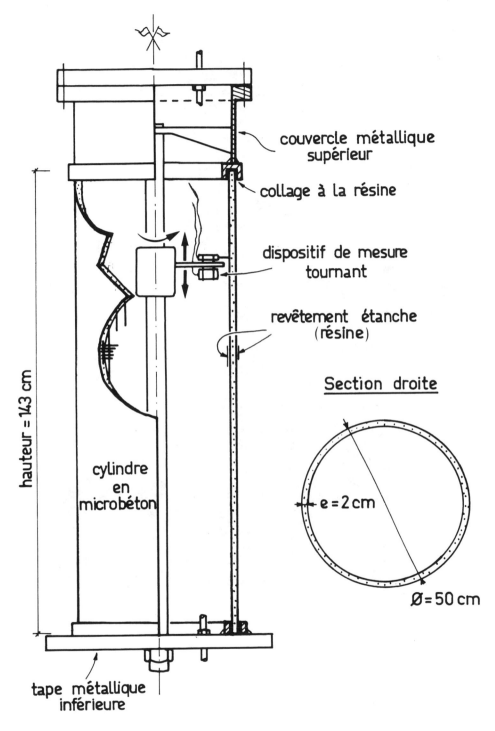

couvercle métallique
supérieur

collage à la résine

dispositif de mesure
tournant

revêtement étanche
(résine)

Section droite

hauteur = 143 cm

cylindre
en
microbéton

e = 2 cm

Ø = 50 cm

tape métallique
inférieure

Figure 12 - Corps d'épreuve en micro-béton des essais d'implosion.

Figure 13 - Dispositif expérimental de flambement de coque,
Vue du corps d'épreuve et du caisson de 1000 bars.

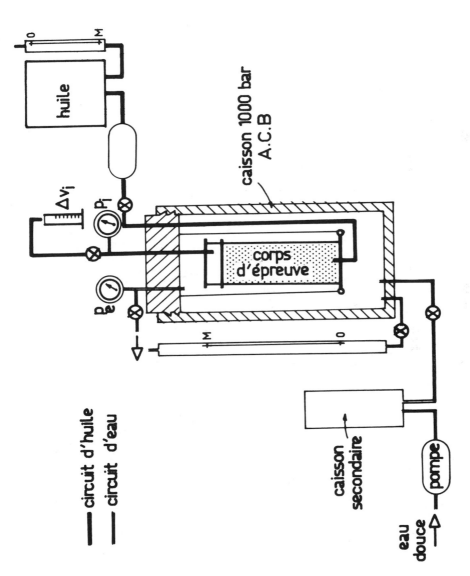

Figure 14 – Schéma du dispositif de mise en pression.

1.110

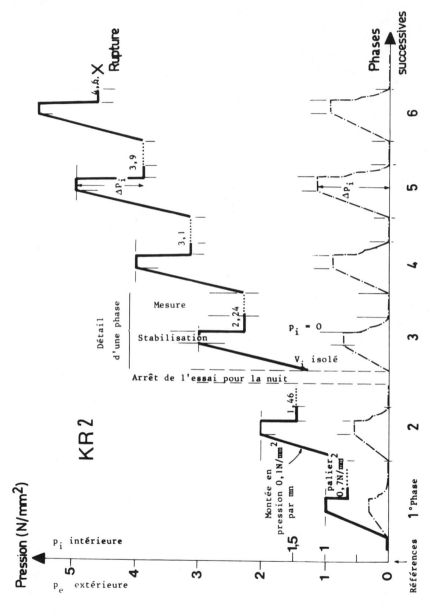

Figure 15 – Schéma de conduite de l'essai KR 2

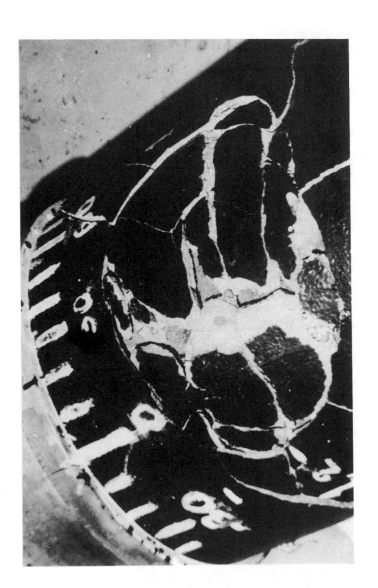

Figure 16 – Vue du cylindre KR2 après rupture.

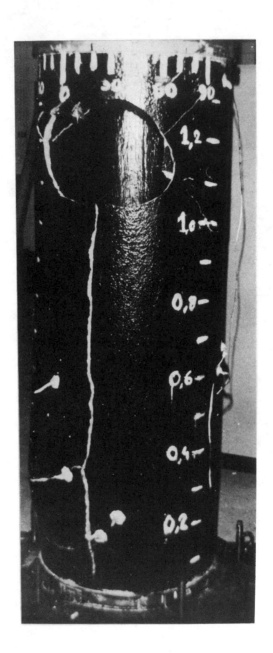

Figure 16 – (contd.)

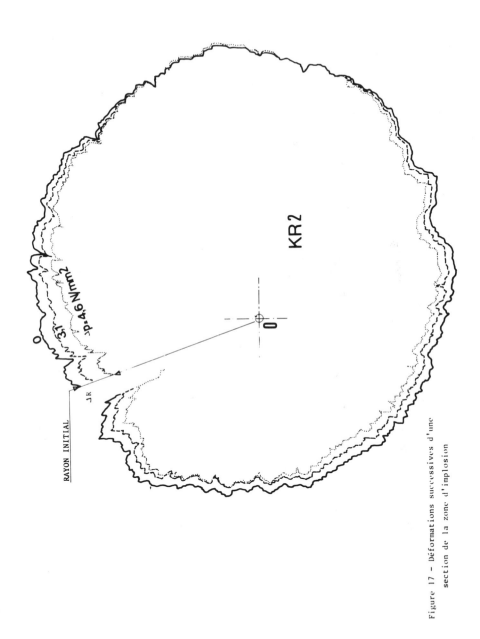

Figure 17 – Déformations successives d'une
section de la zone d'implosion

Par ailleurs, d'autres études sont menées en parallèle au niveau du matériau, de la corrosion, des méthodes de contrôle, etc...

REMERCIEMENTS

Nous tenons à exprimer ici nos remerciements à toutes les personnes du C.E.B.T.P. et du C.N.E.X.O. qui ont contribué à la réalisation de ces études et en particulier les techniciens d'essai pour la qualité de leurs travaux.

REFERENCES

- Albertsen, N.D. (1973) : Influence of compressive strength and wall thickness on behavior of concrete cylindrical hulls under hydrostatic loading. N.C.E.L., Technical Report R 790, Port Hueneme.
- Bannister, J.L. (1978) : Fatigue and corrosion fatigue of TorBar reinforcement. The Structural Engineer N° 3, Vol. 56A, Londres, 82-86.
- Beeby, A.W. (1978) : Corrosion of reinforcing steel in concrete and its relation to cracking. The Structural Engineer N° 3, Vol. 56A, Londres, 78-81.
- CNEXO-CTICM (1976) Structures en mer. Publication CNEXO, Paris.
- Det Norske Veritas (1977) : Rules for the design, construction and inspection of offshore structures. Oslo.
- Fauchart, J. ; Kavyrchine, M. ; Trinh, J. (1975) : Comportement sous charges répétées de poutrelles en béton armé précontraint. Communication au Colloque International, Liège, Tome II, 797-805.
- F.I.P. (1977) : Recommendations for the design and construction of concrete sea structure. 3ème édition, Wexham Springs.
- Lemoine, L. ; Taché, G. (1979) : Utilisation des méthodes électrochimiques pour l'étude et le contrôle de la corrosion des armatures dans le béton soumis à un environnement marin. Communication au Symposium International Corrosion et Protection offshore, Paris.
- Peyronnet, J.P. ; Seguin, M. (1978) : Travaux de recherches sur les ouvrages béton en haute mer. Revue Travaux N°525 Paris, 53-58.
- Trinh, J. ; Peyronnet, J.P. (1978) : Etude expérimentale du comportement d'éléments en béton en milieu marin. Annales ITBTP n° 360, Paris, 42-58.

EVALUATION OF THE DAMAGE CAUSED BY SEA WATER TO CONCRETE-LIKE MATERIALS

Guillermo D Di Pace, Roberto J Torrent & Hector J Bunge

Civil Engineers, National Institute of Industrial Technology
Buenos Aires, Argentina.

ABSTRACT

Using the fracture mechanics parameters the damage produced to
concrete-like materials subjected to an agressive environment,
such as sea water or high sulfate concentration, can be
quantified. For this purpose sets of beams were casted; one
set was subjected to an agressive environment and another was
maintained at 20°C in laboratory. Notches were practiced to
half of the beams, calculating the pseudo-fracture toughness
for each one. Applying this value to Irwin's expression, an
equivalent crack's lenght has been calculated.
This paper aims at checking the fact that every
environment's action which alters the original condition of
concrete components will be reflected in variations of the
pseudo-fracture toughness and that every environment's action
which is traduced in cracking will be reflected in a variation
of the equivalent crack's length.

INTRODUCTION

Concrete-like materials can be thought as fragile and compound in which, as it has been proved (Evans, 1946) there are cracks and microcraks even before being subjected to external loads. The behaviour of these materials is generally measured by compression and tension tests, the last ones usually indirect. Likewise, the action of an agressive environment on a material is usually measured by losses of weight, elasticity modulus or strength plotted against time.

An agressive environment's action basically reveals in two different ways:

a)Altering one or more of the concrete components.

b)Increasing the material's crack pattern.

The evaluation and discrimination of the effects of a given agressive environment, such as sea water's action, has the indubitable advantage of showing the material's response to the environment. This enables a better selection of those components which improve concrete durability. Bearing in mind that concrete-like materials are fragile and are cracked, the use of fracture mechanics to attack the problem is proposed. Concrete heterogeneity is overcomed considering the values of the obtained parameters as a combination of those corresponding to the cement paste and an arresting action of the aggregates (Loth and Kesler, 1965).

Applying fracture mechanics

Griffith has theoretically proved the condition for the quick propagation of an existing crack in an homogeneous material (Griffith, 1921). He considered the hypothetic case of a semi-infinite plate of an elastic and homogeneous material, with a line crack of length 2C, which is subjected to uniform tension ($+\sigma$).(Figure 1)

If a virtual propagation of the crack (dC) is imagined, there will be a virtual elastic energy release (dU). Based on theoretical studies of the stated case, elaborated by Inglis (Inglis, 1913), Griffith calculated the amount of liberated elastic energy for a unit increase in the crack's surface (dA). He obtained the following equation:

$$\frac{dU}{dA} = \frac{\pi \sigma^2 C}{E} \tag{1}$$

E: Elasticity modulus.

For the generation of a new free surface a certain amount of energy must have been consumed to anulate the material's cohesive strength. Calling γ the specific surface energy, that is to say, the necessary energy to create a unit of free surface, the necessary energy to produce a virtual increase of the crack in dC, will be:

$$dW = \gamma 2 dA$$

$$\frac{dW}{dA} = 2\gamma \tag{2}$$

We must remember that γ is a property of the material.

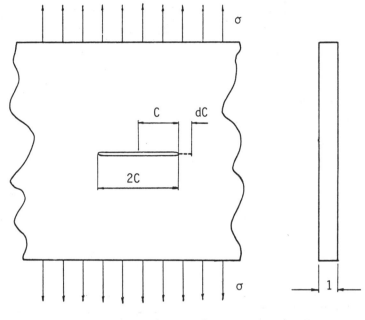

Figure   1

Griffith postulated that the crack will propagate quickly (without increasing the external loads) when the released elastic energy by the virtual increase dC is at least equal to the consumed energy during the increase.

$$\frac{dU}{dA} \geq \frac{dW}{dA} \qquad (3a)$$

$$\frac{\pi\sigma^2 C}{E} \geq 2\gamma \qquad (3b)$$

Therefore, the minimun tension that will produce the quick propagation of a crack of length 2C will be:

$$\sigma = \left(\frac{2E\gamma}{\pi C} \right)^{1/2} \qquad (4)$$

Irwin (Irwin, 1958 and 1962) made an important contribution to fracture mechanics when he introduced a somewhat different approach to this problem, starting from Westergaard's equations. Westergaard analized the stress field near the crack and determined that, for plane stress and for different systems, he had the same stress configuration (W'gaard, 1939):

$$\sigma_y = \frac{K}{(2r)^{1/2}} \cos \frac{\Theta}{2} \left(1 + sen \frac{\Theta}{2} sen \frac{3\Theta}{2} \right) \qquad (5a)$$

$$\sigma_x = \frac{K}{(2r)^{1/2}} \cos \frac{\Theta}{2} \left(1 - \text{sen} \frac{\Theta}{2} \text{sen} \frac{3\Theta}{2}\right) \tag{5b}$$

Stresses normal and parallel to the crack plane.

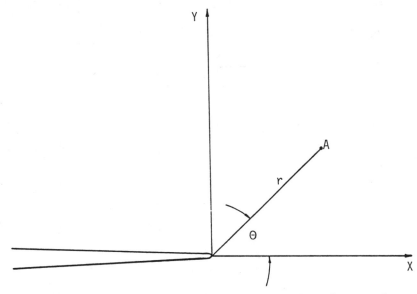

Figure 2. Coordinate system at leading edge of a crack.

K is the stress intensity factor and it depends of the specimen's geometry and of the loads acting over the system. K has the important property that if "different load systems Q_1, Q_2,...Qn act on a body, the total stress intensity factor, which governs the behavior of a crack in the body, is given by $K = \pm K_1 \pm K_2 \ldots \pm Kn$. in which K_1 is K-value associated with loading Q_1, and a minus sign indicates that the loading system tends to close the crack. The above equation also assumes the same crack extension mode for each loading system." (Moavenzadeh and Kuguel, 1969).
The value of K can be theoretically calculated. In Inglis' model employed by Griffith it comes out to be:

$$K = \sigma C^{1/2} \tag{6}$$

Irwin, starting from Equations 5, calculated the amount of elastic energy released by the crack's propagation and arrived to:

$$\frac{dU}{dC} = \frac{\pi K^2}{E} \tag{7a}$$

Being $dA = 1 \times dC$

$$\frac{dU}{dA} = \frac{\pi K^2}{E} \tag{7b}$$

When Equation 7b accomplishes Equation 3a, a catastrofic propagation of the crack will take place. From the theoretical point of view, in that moment (K becomes critical (Kc)) it would be:

$$\frac{\pi K_c^2}{E} = 2\gamma \tag{8}$$

Therefore Kc is also a property of the material and it is known as fracture toughness.
So as to consider the material's heterogeneity Loth and Kesler introduced the concept of pseudo-fracture toughness (K_c^1) which will be related to the fracture toughness of the cement paste (K_{pc}) and to the arresting action of the aggregates $(F(ARR))$.

$$K_c^1 = K_{pc} + F(ARR) \tag{9}$$

PROPOSED EXPERIMENTAL METHOD

a) Determination of the pseudo-fracture toughness (K_c^1)
The method that will be employed to determine K_c^1 is the one of four-point bending over a beam notched at the midspan.

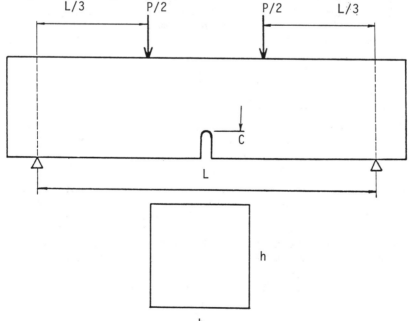

b
Figure 3

The Equation that allows the calculation of K for this case
(Figure 3) is similar to the one corresponding to Inglis'
ideal case, with the exception of a certain factor(F) which is
a function of the C/h relation (Kitagawa and Suyama, 1976).

$$K = F \sigma C^{1/2} \tag{10}$$

K: Stress intensity factor ($Nmm^{-3/2}$)
σ: Maximun stress on the tensile face ($MPa = 10^6\ Nmm^{-2}$).
C: Length of the notch (mm)
F: $1,93 - 3,07\ C/h + 14,53\ (C/h)^2 - 25,11\ (C/h)^3 + 25,8\ (C/h)^4$
   (ASTM E 399, 1970).

$$K_c^1 = F \sigma_{rup} C^{1/2} \tag{11}$$

$$\sigma_{rup} = \text{rupture nominal stress} = \frac{Mrup}{\frac{1}{6}bh^2} = \frac{Prup\ L}{bh^2}$$

Replacing in Equation 11

$$K_c^1 = F \frac{P_{rup}\ L}{bh^2} C^{1/2} \tag{12}$$

Prup = rupture's load

b) Determination of the equivalent crack's length (C_e)
We define the equivalent crack's length as the one that
causes the same effects as the great number of cracks and
microcracks actually existing in the material, from the
fracture mechanics point of view.

Actual fissuration   Equivalent crack

Figure 4

The procedure consists in calculating the equivalent crack's
length (Ce) which causes the beam's rupture with the same
nominal tension as the one actually fissurated tested without
a notch. To determine Ce one must know the value of K_c^1
measured as indicated in (a). The beam without notch is
tested and the rupture's nominal stress is determined.

$$\sigma_{rup} = \frac{6M_{rup}}{bh^2} \tag{13}$$

In Equation 11,C is obtained as

$$C_e = \frac{K_c^{1\,2}}{F^2 \sigma_{rup}^{\,2}} \tag{14}$$

Having found K_c^1 and applying σ_{rup} obtained testing the beam
without a notch in Equation 13, Ce is calculated.
As F depends of relation C/h the use of Equation 14 implies
an iteration.

HYPHOTESIS

This paper aims at checking the fact that every environment's
action which alters the original condition of concrete
components will be reflected in variations of K_c^1 and that
every environment's action which is traduced in cracking will
be reflected in a variation of Ce.
This theory has been proved succesfully with portland
cement's mortars exposed to high temperatures (Di Pace and
Torrent, 1978). Authors' intention is to check the suitability
of this theory when aggressive environment is sea water or
sulfate solutions. Regarding the latter, authors' aim was not
to create a quick sulfate test but to cause a quick damage in
the mortar specimens. After a review of the literature, two
methods were elected which seemed to be the most expeditive
ones (Biczoc, 1972): very high sulfate concentration combined
with normal and high temperatures.

EXPERIMENTAL DETAILS

Sets of mortar 40 x 40 x 160 mm beams were casted at INTI's
laboratory. Two kinds of portland cement were used,basically
of different tricalcium aluminate content. The sand used in
all mixes was the normal one. For half of the sets the
proportion of sand to cement was 5 by weight with a water-
cement ratio of 0,5 ,and for the others the proportion of
sand to cement was 6,5 by weight with a water-cement ratio of
0,65. The specimens after casting were stored 24 hs in their
moulds and then cured 28 days under water at 20°C. At the end
of the normal curing period the beams were separated in three
sets: one was kept in water at 20°C, the second was subjected
to a SO_4Na_2 solution (1,2M concentration) at 20°C and the last
one was subjected to the same solution, but at 35°C. This
second curing period lasted 56 days.
Mix proportions and environment's details are given in Table 1
The mortar beams subjected to sea water were casted at LEMIT's
laboratory and were similar to those casted at INTI. The
portland cement used was of low tricalcium aluminate content.
The proportion of sand to cement was 4 to 1 by weight.
The specimens after casting were stored 24 hs in their moulds
and then cured 28 days in water at 20°C. After that period

half of the specimens were suspended from a raft in
contact with sea water in Mar del Plata's port.
Harmful ions detected in the water were (Batic and
Sota, 1976):

$$SO_4^{-2} \ldots\ldots\ldots \quad 2.810 \ g/m^3$$

$$Mg^{+2} \ldots\ldots\ldots \quad 1.410 \ g/m^3$$

$$Ca^{+2} \ldots\ldots\ldots \quad 480 \ g/m^3$$

$$Cl^- \ldots\ldots\ldots \quad 20.000 \ g/m^3$$

$$Na^+ \ldots\ldots\ldots \quad 11.100 \ g/m^3$$

$$K^+ \ldots\ldots\ldots \quad 400 \ g/m^3$$

Mean-values of many determinations.

The specimens were maintained 5 years in those
conditions. Equivalent specimens were casted and
kept 5 years in water at 20°C.
Mix proportions are given in Table 1.

Testing procedure
All specimens were tested in four bending with a
span of 150 mm. An Instron universal machine was
used for testing the beams with a constant rate of
5×10^{-2} mm/min. Before being tested all specimens
were kept in water at 20°C during 3 days, and then
tested wet.
Half of the beams were carefully notched with a
diamond saw. The notch was 13 mm high and 4 mm wide.
When tested, Prup was recorded and then K_C^1 and Ce
were calculated as indicated in (a) and (b).
Mean-values of K_C^1 and Ce are given in Table 1.

Table 1 Mix proportions , environment's details and fracture mechanics parameters

Set Number	Bogue's AC_3 %	Proportions by weig. Cement	Sand	Water	K_c^1 (N.mm$^{-3/2}$) and C_e (mm) Water K_c^1	C_e	SO$_4$Na$_2$ 20°C K_c^1	C_e	35°C K_c^1	C_e	Sea water K_c^1	C_e
101/103	5.2	1	5	0.5	20.41	3.15	19.92	3.31	19.67	3.89	--	--
104/106	5.2	1	6.5	0.65	17.47	3.33	17.04	3.79	15.91	4.21	--	--
111/113	7.9	1	5	0.5	21.74	2.89	20.94	3.76	21.40	3.76	--	--
114/116	7.9	1	6.5	0.65	17.47	3.26	16.32	4.21	15.85	5.16	--	--
201/202	3.0	1	4	Flow T. 180 %	21.70	3.25	--	--	--	--	13.80	4.90

CONCLUSIONS

Since fracture mechanics parameters are probability
functions, a loading system which produces a wide
constant moment zone, such as four point bending,
seems to be the most adequate one.
Test results indicate that, after the sulfate
agression, Ce increases and K_C^l decreases slightly
with increasing water-cement relation and
temperature, and with AC_3 content. In the beams
subjected to sea water is more notable the
decrement in K_C^l. This indicates a higher alteration
of the cement paste while sulfate's action is
traduced principally in fissuration.
Bearing in mind that nowadays many accelerated
testing methods use destructive evaluation on
little beams, the proposed method can be used with
advantage.
Further investigation must be done, this time with
concrete, to analize the factors influencing K_C^l and
Ce, but anthors think that the exposed method, if
succesfull, will be one of the first applications
of fracture mechanics to concrete with an
evaluating purpose.

ACKNOWLEDGEMENTS

The anthors wish to express their gratitude to
Eng. Oscar Batic and Jorge Sota for permitting them
the use of information and specimens of the
investigations made at LEMIT, and to Lic. Mónica
Sureda de Peruilh for her help in the final version
of this paper.

REFERENCES

Batic, O and Sota, J (1976) Comportamiento de los cementos portland nacionales sumergidos en agua de mar. LEMIT, La Plata, Arg.

Biczoc, I (1972) Concrete corrosion, concrete protections. Akademiai Kiadó, Budapest.

Di Pace, G and Torrent, R (1977) Comportamiento de los hormigones sometidos a alta temperatura. Internal report. INTI, Buenos Aires.

Evans, R.H. (1946) Extensibility and modulus of rupture of concrete. Structural Engineer, Lond, Vol 24, pp 639-659.

Griffith, A.A. (1921) The phenomena of rupture and flow of solids. Philosophical Transactions, Royal Society of London, Vol A 221.

Inglis, C.E. (1913) Stresses in a plate due to the presence of cracks and sharp corners. Transactions, Institution of Naval Architects, Lond. Vol 55

Irwin, G.R.(1962) Crack extension force for a part-through cracks in a plate. Journal of Applied Mechanics Vol 84 E, N°4.

Irwin, G.R.(1958) Fracture. Handbuch der Physik Springer, Berlin Vol 6 pp 551.

Kitagawa, K and Suyama, M (1976) Fracture mechanics study on the size effect for the strength of cracked concrete materials. The Society of Materials Science. Proceedings of the 19° Japan Congress on Materials Research, Kyoto.

Lott, G.L. and Kesler, C.E. (1965) Crack Propagation in plain concrete. TAM Report. Department of Theoretical and Applied Mechanics, University of Illinois, Urbana.

Moavenzadeh, F and Kuguel, R (1969) Fracture of concrete. Journal of materials, JMLSA, Vol 4, N°3, pp 497-519.

Westergaard, H.M. (1939) Bearing pressures and cracks. Journal of Applied Mechanics. Vol 61 A, pp 49.

RESEARCH OF A RUPTURE ENVELOPE FOR CONCRETE STRENGTH TO BE
ADOPTED ON DEEP WATER CONCRETE STRUCTURES DESIGN

Wander Miranda de Camargo

Hidroservice, Engenharia de Projetos Ltda, Sao Paulo, Brasil

INTRODUCTION

With the advent of deepwater constructions in the practice of
engineering, a new milestone has been reached in the technology
of structural concrete. The evaluation of strength characteristics under multiple states of stress, the control of properties
of intrinsic behaviour, and the consideration of the interaction
between methods of calculation and those of construction are no
longer exceptional conditions and have become an integral part
of the routine of the design and of the execution of the works.

The knowledge of conditional factors of internal constitutive
structure of concretes themselves, which explain their different
standards of behaviour, has come to predominate over the mere
evaluation of conventional 'characteristic' parameters. In the
field of strength of the material, it is the prevalence of the
experimental envelope over the 'characteristic' strengths obtained in uniaxial tests. In deformation control, the predominance
of the integral evaluation of stress–strain diagrams instead of
the extensive use of 'deformation moduli'. In the consideration
of non linear time dependent properties, the predominance of the
knowledge of multiple interferences of properties of aggregates
and mortar, of their relative compositions, and of preformed
internal microcracking over the behaviour of concretes for various ages and loading conditions instead of the simplistic utilization of 'standard' behaviour parameters applied in 'universal'
theoretical formulas.

This paper takes its place among the efforts now being made to
systemize concepts of the internal structure of concrete with the
purpose of evaluating, in a uniform manner, its behaviour, guaranteeing their application to design for underwater works according to the rationality and generality required by their operational and conceptual conditions.

Within this major perspective, this paper is concerned with aspects related to the determination of the rupture envelope of the
concretes, in order to define the capacity for resistance of this
material when submitted to severe conditions of multiaxial stress
in which compression created by submersion predominates.

Although the behaviour of concretes submitted to triple states of
compression have been the object of conceptual investigation and
of experimentation in many technological centers throughout the
world, and although the first speculations along this line date
from the beginning of the century, the practical application now
aimed toward is obviously a contemporary of the first underwater
constructions, which were first undertaken in the last decade.

In at least one aspect, these applications restrict and complicate
the problem: in the presence of water, under pressure, within the
pores and discontinuities of the concrete. Even considering the
theoretical scheme of correct composition of the concretes, which
guarantees the incommunicability of the micropores of correctly
mixed structural concretes, it is fitting to ask up to what level
of confining hydrostatic pressure this condition is valid, up to
what point elevated compression would not put in balance the
fluids internal to the concrete mass and the water of immersion
of the structure, such as occurs, in emersed constructions, with
the hygrothermic equilibrium between the air, vapor, and water
content of the concrete and the environmental air with its own
temperature and humidity degrees. Something like a 'hyperbaric
retraction', and likewise, a 'hyperbaric creep', would be the
opposite of differential behaviour of deeply submerged concretes,
in conditions unforseeable in the light of knowledge relative to
the integral behaviour of this same material in surface works.

Already in the examination merely of the problem of mechanical
strength of the concrete, to which this contribution is limited,
it will be seen how hypotheses relative to deformability of the
internal structure of concrete by the action of elevated compression may be made, altering the perspective of resistant response of this material under the new ambient conditions considered herein. Detailed examinations of all other aspects of concrete behaviour should likewise be made, and are being considered
in conceptual and experimental research programs in various technological centers.

2 SUMMARY OF A UNIT BEHAVIOUR MODEL FOR CONCRETE

2.1 STRENGTH THEORY OF CONCRETE

Among the theories which try to explain concrete behaviour, uni-
fying its multiple answers to mechanical load, the evolution of
intrinsic properties with time, the theory that takes into account the 'elastic-brittle' behaviour of concrete under external
stress and establishes a link between this kind of behaviour and
the malformations undergone by concrete during early stages of

its hardening and curing, has received more and more acceptance
in the technical centers occupied presently with advanced concrete technology.

To summarize this strength theory of concrete, we depart here
from the simplification which considers concrete as a solid in-
alterable material in its quality and properties along time, not
susceptible to autogenic volume variations or intrinsic variations
in its form and state of stress. Naturally concrete is far from
meeting this description, but separate consideration of mechanical
and time dependent and intrinsic properties is legitimate if we
are prepared to superimpose, on each practical problem to be
treated, the result of the simplified analysis made by the method
described below and the complementary behaviour related to other
properties disregarded here.

Actual knowledge about mixing, hardening and use of concrete in
usual works enables the following ideas to be considered.

Hardened concrete can be treated as a macroscopic homogeneous
and anisotropic perfectly elastic material having in its mass a
set of little discontinuities irregularly distributed and oriented,
in the form of acute elipsoids which have no contact or interconnection in the initial state of no external stress, the entire
body remaining monolitic. The response of this kind of material
to external loads will be greatly influenced by the existence of
these discontinuities, in the contour of which will appear stress
concentration, interrupted fractures, limited progress of rupture
areas, formation of a set of rupture areas which come in contact
(through paths of least resistance) with the original discontinuities and, finally, the complete loss of material monoliticity
due to its disintegration along the surfaces interconnecting the
set of internal areas of rupture.

This idealization is very well described, especially in its experimental fundamentals, in the work of Desayi and Viswanatha
(1967), which is an accessible resume of the main results obtained from the world's principal researchers in this field such
as Prof. Rüsch, Prof. L'Hermitte, Dr.Jones and Dr.Hognestad. As
a result of their observation and knowledge, this theory reflects
well two known characteristics of concretes:
a)   the existence of internal cracks, independent of loads, distributed throughout the entire mass of concrete, due to intrinsic
inevitable deformations suffered by concrete mainly because of
shrinkage phenomena;
b)   the fact that under increased external forces, these cracks
progressively increase until crumbling occurs.

2.2   GENERAL RUPTURE THEORY OF ELASTIC-BRITTLE MATERIALS- GRIFFITH
THEORY APPLIED TO CONCRETE

The search for a general theory to explain the behaviour of materials such as concrete, leads different authors agreeing remark-

ably with respect to criteria, to be priented by the studies of
A.A. Griffith (1921), an English engineer working for an aeronautical entity at the beginning of this cantury.

His basic work 'The Phenomena of Rupture and flow in Solids', was
done trying to explain the influence of metallic pieces finishing
over its strength (little notches in the surface of metallic
pieces shortened its fatigue strength much more than its small
dimensions allowed for).

Considering an elliptical crack with a length c, in the interior
of an infinitely large plate subjected to external forces such
as, at a great distance from the crack, reign a uniform stress
field with a principal stress σ perpendicular to the plane of
the crack, Griffith deduced that the variation in deformation
energy liberated by the crack formation (U), related to the
crack surface (A) could be expressed by:

$$\frac{dU}{dA} = \frac{1}{4} \frac{d}{dc} \left(\frac{4\pi\sigma^2 c^2}{E} \right) = \frac{2\pi\sigma^2 c}{E} \tag{1}$$

He deduces that the variation in surface potential energy of the
crack (W) related to the crack surface (A) can be expressed in
terms of the material surface tension (T) as:

$$\frac{dW}{dA} = \frac{d}{dc} (4Tc) = 4T \tag{2}$$

As he theoretically expressed in his energy equilibrium theorems,
failure will occur when (1) and (2) are equal:

$$\frac{2\pi\sigma^2 c}{E} = 4T \tag{3}$$

$$\sigma = \sqrt{\frac{2ET}{\pi c}} \tag{4}$$

Griffith's experimental work was limited to glass fibres, material whose surface tension he obtained in high temperature tests,

extrapolating these results to ambient temperature conditions. Other authors find possible the determination of experimental parameters applied to concretes, Kaplan (1961) having one of the best summaries on this subject; more recent data were published by Welch and Haisman (1969). Recent publications of experimental and conceptual analysis may be found in technical literature, such as Kesler & Al. synopsis on fracture mechanics (1971) and Desayi speculations and experiments (1973, 1975, 1977).

The method found by the researchers to express materially the energy phenomena due to cracking progress, consists in testing, under bending, concrete prisms having peripheral artificial notches simulating a pre-formed crack.

Glucklinch (1963) synthesises and develops more the theoretical relation between the original studies of Griffith applied to concrete.

2.3 ANALYTIC STUDY OF THE PROGRESS OF A PRE-FORMED CRACK IN A GENERIC PLANE STRAIN FIELD

A next step in this theoretical approach is concerned with the rational evolution of a pre-formed crack in a generic plane strain field. Considering a discontinuity with a regular form (an ellipsoid of revolution) immersed in a thick plate in a plane strain state, subject to a triple state of stress with the principal stress values $\sigma_1 > \sigma_2 > \sigma_3$ being known (tension being considered as negative) let β be the angle of inclination of major discontinuity axis with the principal discretion of stress σ_1 , and let the major axis be in the plane σ_1, σ_3 or near it. These conditions allow for the equation at the following expressions for σ_y and τ_{xy} stresses referring to an adequate system of coordinates (see Figure 1):

$$2\sigma_y = (\sigma_1 + \sigma_3) - (\sigma_1 - \sigma_3)\cos 2\beta \qquad (5)$$

$$2\tau_{xy} = (\sigma_1 - \sigma_3)\sin 2\beta$$

$$(6)$$

It will be shown that σ_x and σ_2 will have a minor interference in the results.

Inglis (1913) demonstrated that tangentially to the contour of an elliptic hole in a plate such as shown in Figure 1, the principal local stress can be written as:

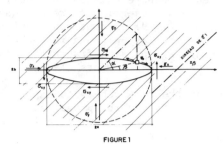

FIGURE 1

ESQUEMA ADOTADO NA ANÁLISE DO ORIFÍCIO ELÍPTICO NA PLACA EM ESTADO PLANO DE TENSÕES
ELIPTICAL HOLE IN A PLANE-STRAIN PROBLEM

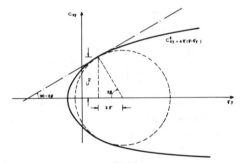

FIGURE 2

ENVOLTÓRIA DE MOHR DO INÍCIO DE PROGRESSO DA FISSURAÇÃO EM MATERIAIS ELASTO-FRÁGEIS
MOHR ENVELOPE FOR ELASTIC-BRITTLE MATERIALS START OF CRACKING PROGRESS

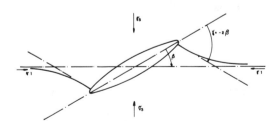

FIGURE 3

FORMA COMO PROGRIDEM AS FISSURAS EM MATERIAIS ELASTO FRÁGEIS
(EXPERIENCIAS DE WALSH, BRACE, PAULDING E SCHOLZ)
PATTERN OF CRACKING PROGRESS ALONG DISCONTINUOUS EDGES OF
PRE-FORMED CRACKS

$$\sigma_b =$$

$$\frac{\sigma_y \left[m(m+2)\cos^2\alpha - \sin^2\alpha\right] + \sigma_x \left[(1+2m)\sin^2\alpha - m^2\cos^2\alpha\right] - \tau_{xy}\left[2(1+m^2)\sin\alpha\cos\alpha\right]}{m^2\cos^2\alpha + \sin^2\alpha}$$

Where: $\quad m = \dfrac{b}{a}$ \hfill (8)

For very thin ellipses $\underline{m}$ is small and the maximum σ may occur for small values of α. Making $\alpha \to 0$ and $\underline{m}$ small in (7) it is possible to eliminate the quadratic parcels and make some trigonometric simplifications, with the result:

$$\sigma_b = \frac{2(m\sigma_y - \alpha\,\tau_{xy})}{m^2 + \alpha^2} \hfill (9)$$

Where the stress σ_x no longer appears thus eliminated for further derivation.

Maximum σ_b is now calculated by:

$$\frac{d\sigma_b}{d\alpha} = 0 \hfill (10)$$

$$\frac{4(m\sigma_y - \alpha\sigma_x) + 2\tau_{xy}(m^2+\alpha^2)}{(m^2 + \alpha^2)} = 0 \hfill (11)$$

Given that $\underline{m}$ and α could not simultaneously vanish, that expression $\overline{is}$ simplified to:

$$- 2\tau_{xy}(m^2 + \alpha^2) = 4\alpha(m\sigma_y - \alpha\tau_{xy}) \hfill (12)$$

and, combined again with (9)

$$\sigma_b = - \frac{\tau_{xy}}{\alpha} \hfill (13)$$

In another way, it is possible to deal with (12) dividing both sides of the equation by $(m^2\alpha^2)$ which makes explicit the 2nd degree trinomial in $(1/\alpha)$

$$\frac{1}{\alpha^2} + \frac{2\sigma_y}{m\tau_{xy}} \cdot \frac{1}{\alpha} - \frac{1}{m^2} = 0 \hfill (14)$$

which, solved, gives:

$$\frac{1}{\alpha} = \frac{1}{m\tau_{xy}} \cdot \left[\sigma_y \pm \sqrt{\sigma_y^2 + \tau_{xy}^2} \right] \tag{15}$$

Equation (13) with this explicit value of $(\frac{1}{\alpha})$ is, at least

$$m\sigma_b = \sigma_y \pm \sqrt{\sigma_y^2 + \tau_{xy}^2} \tag{16}$$

The application of (16) to the Glucklich problem of simple tension referred to in the last item is made with $\tau_{xy} = 0$ and $\sigma_y = \sigma$, resulting in:

$$m\sigma_b = 2\sigma \tag{17}$$

Joining (16) and (17) it is possible to establish a correlation between the generic plain strain state considered and the simple tension case, through the 2nd degree parabola:

$$\tau_{xy}^2 = 4\sigma(\sigma - \sigma_y) \tag{18}$$

Applying (17) to the critical situation near failure (i.e. putting σ as the tension strength of the material), equation (18) will correspond to a Mohr envelope covering the generic states of stress which indicates the beginning of peripheral failure around the elliptical cavity.

2.4   INTEGRAL MOHR ENVELOPE FORMULATION FOR CONCRETE

It is possible now to formulate an integral Mohr envelope for concretes based on the theoretical approach above.

Let us suppose a plain strain problem examined under the premises of the anterior paragraph. If $\beta > 0$ and σ_3 is negative (tension), after the alignment of cracking with direction   , the crack progresses until disaggregation of the material occurs once this alignment is obtained; it is possible to calculate stresses in (16) putting $\sigma_y = \sigma_3$ and $\tau_{xy} = 0$ resulting

$$m\sigma_b = 2\sigma_3 \tag{19}$$

which coincides with (17) which is a failure condition

$$\sigma_3 = \sigma \tag{20}$$

If both principal stresses are compressive, cracking tends to
be interrupted as far as after its alignment with direction σ_1.
In that case the increase in external forces, not considering
the possibility of opening of new cracks, will lead to concrete
disintegration through a slipping rupture along the crack faces
maintained in contact under compressive stresses. Real rupture
of concrete must consider multiple cracking effectively occurring with increase of external forces, and the phenomena will be
entirely described by a combination of cracking and slipping
along the path of interconnection of cracks.

The slipping along the crack faces can be described as a
"Coulomb" rupture by an expression such as

$$\tau_{xy} = \tau_o + \mu\sigma_y \tag{21}$$

τ_o is the intrinsic shear strength of the material and μ is
the internal friction coefficient.

Among all the inclination β of pre-formed cracks, there is a critic
critical value β_c which corresponds to the minimum σ_y, τ_{xy}.

$$\frac{d\sigma_y}{d\tau_{xy}} = - tg\ 2\beta_c = \frac{1}{\mu} \tag{22}$$

Based on those considerations it is possible to draw an envelope
(Figure 4) collecting the many modes of rupture inferred from
the equations already derived.

The parameter K^2, shown in Figure 4 as a relation between compression and tension strength of concrete, defines the brittle
side of the envelope. Lobo Carneiro (1968) associates a value
of $K^2 = 3$ to poor concretes, $K^2 = 4$ to medium ones and $K^2 = 5$
to good structural concretes. This judgement can coincide, to
some extent, which may be investigated experimentally, with
possible increase in intrinsic capability of concrete to resist
initial cracking propagation and to demonstrate greater resistance to this propagation, interconnection and failure. From
Figure 4 results too:

$$K^2 = \frac{\tau_o}{\sigma}\ tg(45^o - \frac{\phi}{2}) \tag{23}$$

and

$$\sigma' = 2K^2\sigma = 2\tau_o\ tg(45^o - \frac{\phi}{2}) \tag{24}$$

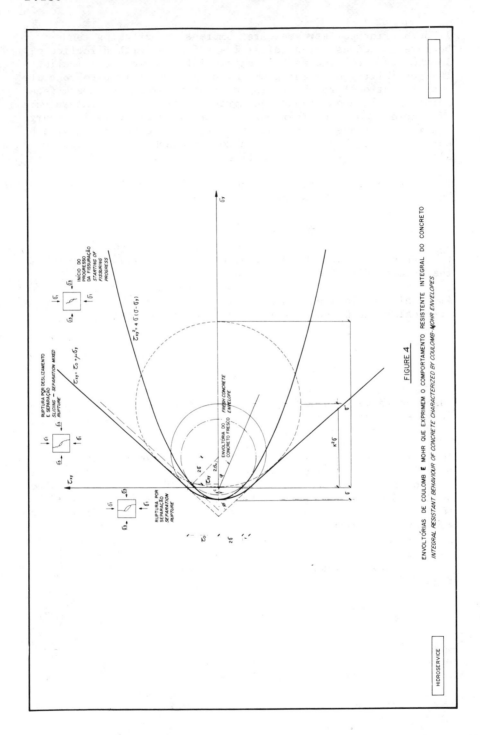

FIGURE 4

ENVOLTÓRIAS DE COULOMB **E** MOHR QUE EXPRIMEM O COMPORTAMENTO RESISTENTE INTEGRAL DO CONCRETO

INTEGRAL RESISTANT BEHAVIOUR OF CONCRETE CHARACTERIZED BY COULOMB-MOHR ENVELOPES

HIDROSERVICE

3   THE GRIFFITH - BIENIAWSKI RUPTURE MECHANISM

3.1   INTRODUCTION

The occurrence of a predominantly elastic-brittle behaviour of
rocks in the mechanical characterization tests induced specialists - concerned with the systematization of the resilience
conditions of these materials - to use the Griffith theory for
a more profound study of the way the rocks respond to mechanical
load.   This assimilation is linked to the characterization of
crystalline agglomerate which is generally presented by the
rocks found mostly in natural masses, in whose junctions or
contacts voids and microscopic or macroscopic gaps are found
that are the centre of stress concentrations and, subsequently,
become local, and after, generalized ruptures, to the extent in
which the portions of rock that make up these agglomerates are
loaded by increasing mechanical stresses.   This mechanism is
very similar to what Glucklinch (1963) and Kaplan (1961) described for the concrete and is being generally described and
improved for several particular applications by different
authors, having been the object of recent systematizations by
the author of this work for publication in Brazilian Technical
Circles - Camargo (1970, 1971).

The memoranda of the Bieniawski experiemtanl studies (1967) made
in South Africa, extended the range of application of this
theory to rocks submitted to high tri-axial compression.   The
generalized strength criteria for these load conditions established by Bieniawski for rocks can be extended to concretes
submitted to similar load conditions, as shown below in this
article.

The theoretical-experimental results available for rocks should
be compared with those gathered for concrete.   The purpose of
this comparison is the differential analysis of behaviour
between two types of materials formed of mineral agglomerates,
one artificially composed (concrete), and the other as obtained
from nature (the rocks).   Together they establish a more complete picture in respect to behaviour of the elastic-brittle
materials,opening a phenomenological view that multiplies the
potential of the practical applications of these behavioral
concepts to a great variety of similar construction materials.

Within this scope and after a summary review of Griffith's
general theory applied to the concretes, the following items of
this article summarize the scope given by Bieniawski to the problem examined from the viewpoint of the particular rocks to be
examined.

Following is a summary of similar existing knowledge as to the
concretes, which proposes the assimilation of these results to
the technological practice of this construction material when

applied under severe states of triaxial compression.

3.2 TYPICAL EVOLUTION OF ROCK SUBMITTED TO MULTIPLE STRESS STATES

3.2.1 Remarks from Bieniawski Analysis - Submitted to any loads that impose a state of multiple stresses on material mass, the rock demonstrates progressive fragmentation in relation to its original monolithicity, which is imposed starting from the previously existing internal cracks through the phenomenon of crack propagation up to rupture by disintegration. This evolution even occurs under strong states of triaxial compression, by sufficiently increasing the maximum compressions in terms of absolute values so that the phenomenon manifests itself and controls the behaviour of the test samples. Numerous test programs of this type can be found in specialized literature, such as Hundron Jr. (1968), whose technological memoranda are being published in several university abstracts and at the main technical congresses held recently.

The response of rock to increasing loads is very similar to that already described for concrete: tensile stresses concentrate around previously existing cracks, therefore causing a restricted rupture of material in the peripheral discontinuous points of maximum stress; later this restricted rupture progresses to the mass continuity rupture and disintegration of solid tested.

Two very characteristic differential phenomenon occur with the rock in relation to equivalent behaviour in concrete. First, experience shows that friction between the previously existing crack faces interferes with level of stress necessary to start the beginning of crack when placed in contact by compression, at least for those stress states in which great absolute compression values predominate. For concrete a theoretical envelope was deduced for the beginning of pre-formed internal crack propagation, which is the parabola.

$$\tau_{xy}^2 = 4\sigma(\sigma - \sigma_y) \tag{18}$$

As yet shown, this equation was deduced directly from the condition of overcoming of stress from simple tensile strength of material in the periphery of a very elongated elliptical gap, calssically treated by the elasticity theory. The tests performed by several experimenters, in the synthesis presented by Bieniawski, indicate that the envelope for beginning of the propagation of previously existing cracks has the form of a Coulomb straight line, whose defining parameter is the angle of friction between crack faces (in practice, the internal angle of rock friction). Thus for great compressions, the Mohr circles that tangency this envelope are secants to the parabola given by

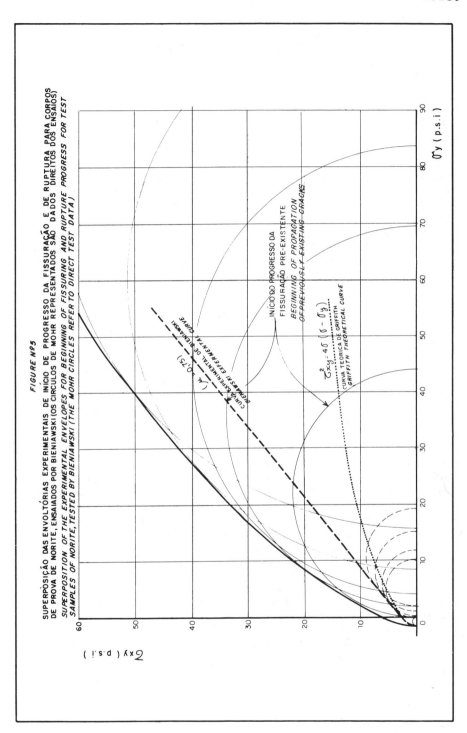

FIGURE Nº5

SUPERPÓSIÇÃO DAS ENVOLTÓRIAS EXPERIMENTAIS DE INÍCIO DE PROGRESSO DA FISSURAÇÃO E DE RUPTURA PARA CORPOS DE PROVA DE NORITE, ENSAIADOS POR BIENIAWSKI (OS CIRCULOS DE MOHR REPRESENTADOS SÃO DADOS DIREITOS DOS ENSAIOS)

SUPERPOSITION OF THE EXPERIMENTAL ENVELOPES FOR BEGINNING OF FISSURING AND RUPTURE PROGRESS FOR TEST SAMPLES OF NORITE, TESTED BY BIENIAWSKI (THE MOHR CIRCLES REFER TO DIRECT TEST DATA)

the equation:

$$\tau^2_{xy} = 4\sigma(\sigma-\sigma_y) \tag{18}$$

A typical Coulomb envelope for this phase of rock strength has the appearance shown in Figure 5, in which it superimposes the two conditions discussed herein.

It is possible that this improvement of behaviour to great compressions, whose consideration is indispensable to certain rock engineering problems, could also be introduced in unit analysis of behaviour of concrete material, with advantages in special applications for triaxially loaded structures. It is the case, for example, of the domes and other structures constructed on underwater platform to support great hydrostatic water pressures, which are presently in the experimental phase, but which in the near future could be commonplace in off-shore constructions.

In the tests with rocks, described by Bieniawski, crack propogation procedes in a manner very typical of aggravation of internal gaps: that of so-called 'forking', a phenomenon which is observed in many rocky materials tested.

Forking corresponds to the beginning of the ultimate stage of strength of the rock, characterized by the attaining of the highest stress value tolerated by the material, and by the occurence of a type of 'yield' (the increase in deformations occurs as a result of maintenance or reduction of loads), until the test body disagregates.

Forking should correspond, in a manner analogous to concrete, to swelling of the test body when near rupture, characterized by the same volumetric manifestation observed in the complete compression testing of concrete samples: in the immediate stage of rupture, the record of volumetric deformation, which in the elastic phase always indicates volume reduction, reverts and comes to indicate expansion, even to values greater than the original volume before the test.

Another characteristic in which the rocks may differ somewhat from the behaviour model studied for concretes, is in its initial behaviour, for the first loads applied in the test. The previously existing cracks which have an angle of incidence transversal to the direction of compressions which are progressively placed in the mass tend to close, and this closing is much more significant, in certain rocks, than in any type of concrete which may be studied , except in cases of testing of concrete at very young ages.

This closing may be evidenced, in a normal test, by an upward concave curring of the stress-deformation diagram; the additional

deformations 'without addition of load' during this phase, is a
pseudoplasticity which reflects the closing of these cracks and,
therefore, the greater compaction of the internal structure of
the rock up to a loading stage which begins to produce internal
crack propogation. Since rocks are more sensitive than concrete
to this closing of cracks, a mobilization hypothesis of additional friction at the contact between closed faces of cracks, allud-
ed to at the beginning of this paragraph, is even more plausible
for rocks. Along this line, the greater internal 'rigity' of the
concrete structure would render this mobilization more difficult,
making the envelope scheme originally established for this material more probable than its substitute currently established for
rocks, except when very high tri-axial compressions act up to the
values necessary to overpass that internal rigidity, which is the
hypothesis herein discussed.

3.2.2 Velocity of Propagation of Previously Existing Cracks -

As a systematic experimental result, Bieniawski points out the
possibility of controlling the stage of internal crack propagation of rocks submitted to growing stresses knowing the velocity
with which additional splits are propagated, beginning with the
previously existing basic cracking. Two intermediate stages are
established based on such determination: one stage of stable
crack propagation, followed by another in which the propagation
is considered unstable. In the first of these stages, cracking
already proceeds irreversibly (removing of the load does not re-
generate the integrity violated), but it is possible to control
this propagation suppressing the loading which motivates it. In
the second stage, this control is impossible; above a certain
level of loading, even if the acting stresses are suppressed, the
cracking continues, many times until the structure crumbles.

Bieniawski lists numerous triaxial tests carried out with test
samples from different rocks, with different relationships between major stresses

As the lesser stress σ_3 approaches the greater stress, the form
of internal crack propagation will be less directed. One may
effectively examine, in the overall presentation of Griffith's
theory made in paragraph 2, the tendency toward internal crack
propagation with the increase of a uniaxial load; the cracks
seek parallel positions which follow a flow perpendicular to the
direction of loading; if this loading is exerted by means of compression, it will come to compress, ideally, the fractured faces,
and the rupture of the material cannot be explained by additional
crack propagation from the moment in which they come to be placed
perpendicularly to the direction of stress. Thus, reducing the
ratio σ_3/σ_1 , the second stress becomes all the more prevalent,
until a stage is reached in which the fractures are interrupted
in the same manner as in the uniaxial case, when they are all
arranged perpendicularly to the direction of the two major

1.142

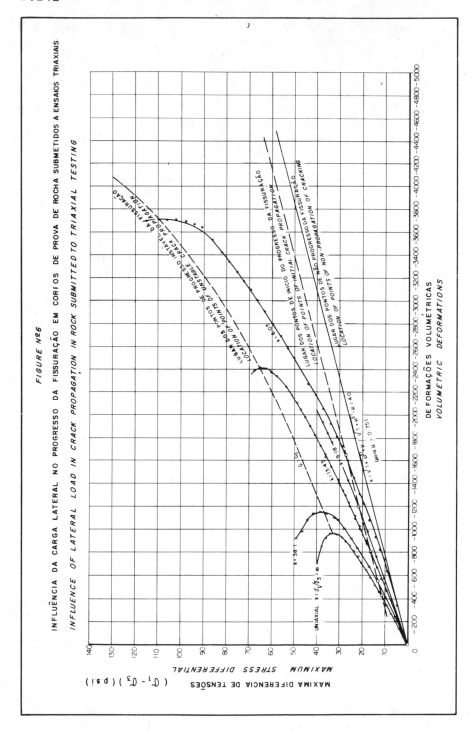

FIGURE Nº6

INFLUÊNCIA DA CARGA LATERAL NO PROGRESSO DA FISSURAÇÃO EM CORFOS DE PROVA DE ROCHA SUBMETIDOS A ENSAIOS TRIAXIAIS

INFLUENCE OF LATERAL LOAD IN CRACK PROPAGATION IN ROCK SUBMITTED TO TRIAXIAL TESTING

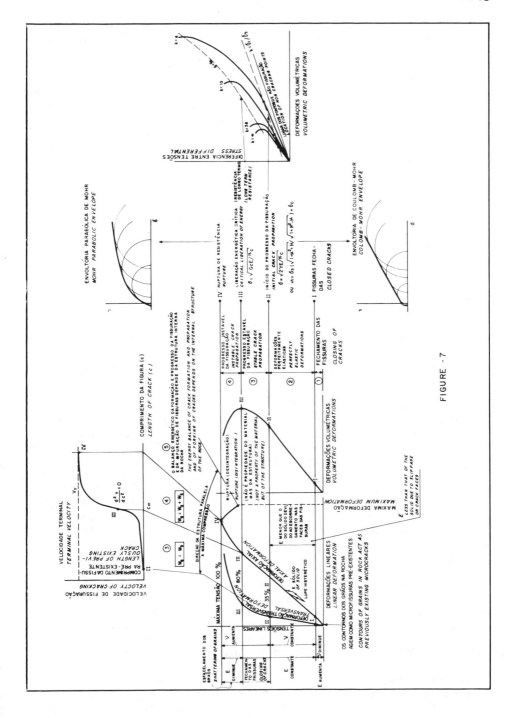

FIGURE - 7

Since for rocks it is admitted a considerable friction with resistance to loading by contracting surfaces of cracks (measured by the angle μ) may be deduced the 'locus' of points with the ratio σ_3/σ_1 in which there is no unstable cracks propagation, i.e., in which (according to the Griffith-Bieniawski theory) the rock would theoretically not split beyond the stage of stable internal crack propagation. From this level of loading, one comes to consider the intervention of other weak spots in the material, for instance, the resistance of the crystalline grains themselves, through which the rupture may be propagated and finally occur, even in this theoretical position of the non-destructive combination of triaxial compression stresses.

$$k = \frac{\sigma_3}{\sigma_1} = \frac{\sqrt{1+\mu^2} + \mu}{\sqrt{1+\mu^2} - \mu} \tag{25}$$

In Figure 6, the results summarizing the tests published by Bienawski take into account this tendency toward a process of rupture in the rock, constituting an adequate guideline for determining the theoretical limit established in equation (25), that is, for evaluating the internal friction coefficient μ for the contact crack faces. This is constant for any loading stage (Coulomb straight line). With respect to the final internal angle of friction of the material, this angle may be different, and it is important to note that Bienawski (as with Hoek and other experimenters) in this case (of final rupture of the rock) also interposes the broad perspective allowed for concretes: the envelope of final resistance is not a mixed Coulomb-Mohr envelope, but a parabolic Mohr envelope, that is the final internal angle of friction for rupture of the rock is not a constant, but is a function of load level at the moment of rupture. This final envelope (in a typical example) appears also in Figure 5 superimposed upon the already-discussed envelopes of initial crack propagation.

3.2.3 Summary Diagram - Figure 7 summarized graphically the presentation made in the foregoing paragraphs. In it, special emphasis is given to stress-deformation diagram for testing of triaxial rock test samples, and to the stages and levels of internal disintegration of the intercrystalline structure as a function of different load levels and their relative ratios.

The fact that numerous types of igneous, metamorphic, and sedimentary rocks have been tested by the various experimenters consulted, and that all of these tests have confirmed the same qualitative performane represented therein, is proof that a conceptual summary based on the Griffith-Bieniawski theory has a great

chance of being the most adequate to the complete study of the
deformation and rupture phenomenon in rocks, submitted to multiaxial mechanical loads.

4 RESEARCH OF TRUE RUPTURE ENVELOPES OF CONCRETE UNDER MULTI-
AXIAL STRESSES

4.1 BRIEF HISTORY

Putting together information relative to how much research has
been done in the search for the determination of general criteria
of concrete strength is a task outside the scope and intention of
this paper. As has already been pointed out, this concern is contemporary to the first scientific activities of analysis of behaviour of this important construction material; at the beginning
of the century, references to laboratory work were not uncommon,
already with results that could be considered to be of current
interest with respect to the new challenges to be met by concrete
construction. From symposia and conferences dedicated to the systemization of knowledge in this field and, in general, to the
investigation of the basic properties of concrete, there are records available for consultation: one could mention the activities
undertaken by the University of Illinois, inspired by Prof. Boris
Bresler (1969, 1971), and the two international conferences on
the mechanical behaviour of materials, held in Japan (1971) and
in the United States (1976), among many other collective and
individual works already published. More recently, the issue has
reappeared in congresses directed towards off-shore works, as
can be seen in the records of the Ninth Conference of Offshore
Technology in Houston, Texas, held in 1977, (Highberg, R., 1977;
Peyronnet, J, 1977; Gausel, E., 1977) or in the Conference on
Concrete Ships and Floating Structures, sponsored by the University of California, in 1975 (Hawkins, N.M., 1975).

The concern with the systemization of strength conditions in
double and triple states of stress may be examined in various
works of excellent quality. Escorel (1957), in a thesis submitted
to the Sao Paulo University, Brazil, may be considered to be one
of the pioneers, having made an excellent summary of previous
experience in a general work which revealed extremely interesting approaches to this generalization. In his footsteps, more
current studies of various foreign researchers may be examined;
this may be exemplified by the articles of Liu, Nilson and Slate
(1972), Kupfer, Hilsdorf and Rusch (1973), and Cedolin, Crutzen
and Dei Poli (1977).

Nevertheless, the correlation between the results published in
this extensive bibliography and the properties of the internal
structure of concrete formation, in the manner propounded in
previous items of this work, did not have the same development.
After the classic works of Kaplan (1961) and Gluklich (1963),
which have already been mentioned, and which are the basis for
any attempt along this line, the issue had its development

interrupted, perhaps in hopes that new challenges would come to make imperative a more in-depth examination of such as important correlation. The author of this article has systematically brought up the issue, proposing norms for research for elucidation of some of the major items of application to practical cases; the correlation with mixing (properties of mix composition, Camargo, 1977); the analysis of crack-resistant capacity of mass concretes (Camargo, 1978 a); the correlation between the properties of re-traction and creep (Camargo, 1978 b).

It is certain, as has already been pointed out in the introduction to this article, that the continued application of concrete in offshore projects, for structures subject to more and more sol-icitations, under great external pressures produced by submersion, will give new impetus to the studies and research which will better interconnect the extrinsic design criteria and the intrin-sic properties of concrete composition. This will immediately guarantee greater rationality of concrete application in these constructions, further providing economy and safety.

4.2 EXPERIMENTAL COULOMB - MOHR ENVELOPES

Following are some of the major results of available research in technical literature, relative to experimental programs involving the determination of Coulomb-Mohr envelopes in rupture testing of concrete test samples under biaxial and triaxial stresses (Fig-ures 8 to 17).

A complete discussion of the influence of intermediary stress in triple states (known to be disregarded in the Mohr criterion) is purposely left out of this summary. What is of interest is the opportunity this collection presents of examining a very vast group of results which, in one way or another, lead to the form-ulation of typical envelopes for different concretes, tested un-der various loading conditions and testing devices.

The tests of Duke and Davis (1944), summarized in Figure 11, are particularly important. The core of more general research invol-ving the delineation of retraction and creep behaviour of con-crete under multiaxial loads, they brought to light, possibly for the first time, the concern with the presence of interaction between water under pressure distributed throughout the contour of the compressed concrete and the water with hygrothermical equilibrium existing in the interior of the concrete mass. Even without furthering this research, this is undoubtedly the basic issue in determining the rupture envelope of concretes applied in submerged works, as well as the basic issue in other matters involving the basic properties of this material, such as retract-ion and creep.

From the group of experimental results put together in the Fig-ures inserted herein, some conclusions are derived, already known by the specialists, but without doubt important to the

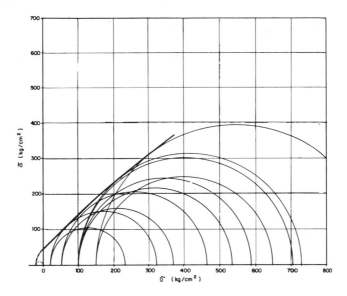

Figure 8 – Triaxial tests with test samples of mortar attributed to Mesnager and Considere according to Guerrin (1952), whose results should have been communicated to the Paris Academy of Sciences in 1909.

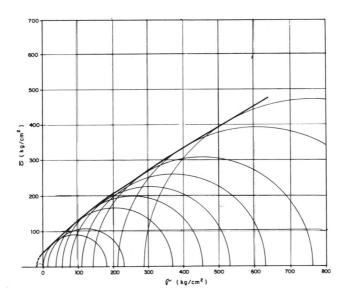

Figure 9 – Tests by Richart, Brandtzaeg, and Brown (1928), at the University of Illinois, held with test samples of concrete mix in bulk 1:2,1:2,5. (Three series of tests were carried out, the first under biaxial compression, the other two under triaxial compression, for various mixes and two basic forms of ratio of maximum to borderline stresses).

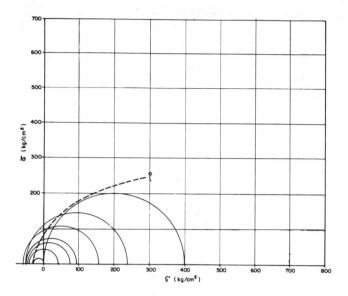

Figure 10 - Tests by L'Hermitte (1942), bringing up, perhaps for the first time, the extension of the
envelope to the traction zone, combining stresses of compression and torsion in the same
test sample. The aaparent incoherence in the superimposing of the Mohr circles should
be attributed to the difficulty of transposing the experimental results in terms of stresses
by the use of elasticity theory equations.

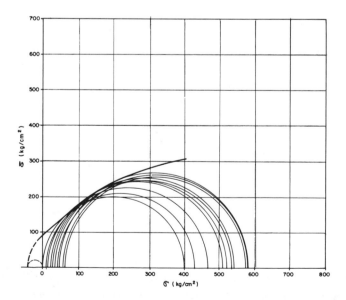

Figure 11 - Tests by Duke and Davis (1944), part of an extensive investigation program of the
University of California relative to concrete creep under combined stresses.

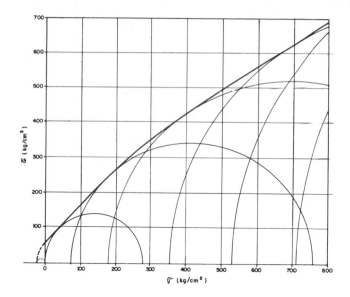

Figure 12 - Tests by Balmer (1949) held at the U.S. Bureau of Reclamation, with cylindrical concrete test bodies submitted to triaxial compression. Concrete 28 days of age.

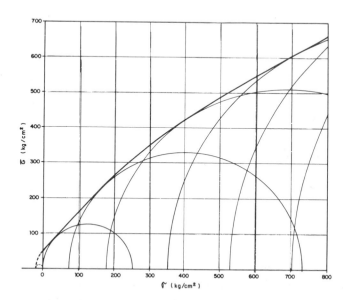

Figure 13 - Tests by Balmer (1949), same as above. Concrete 90 days of age.

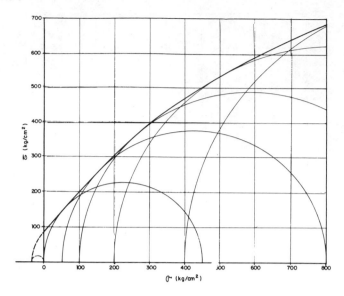

Figure 14 - Tests by Brice (1934), component of a first phase of research by this French experimenter, who afterwards would obtain much more in-depth results, summarized in the following figure and ju taposed for comparison.

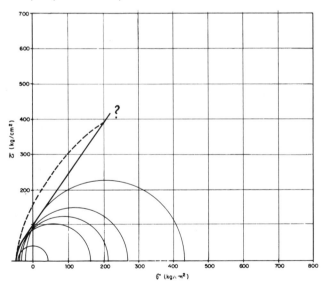

Figure 15 - Test of the second phase of research by Brice (1954), according to orientation by L'Hermitte (tests of simultaneous compression and torsion). The careful follow-up of evolution of each test allowed the experimenters to record the initial cracking which precedes rupture. The corresponding envelope of Mohr circles is typically a Coulomb straight line, similar to that propounded by the theory set forth in previous items of this paper (Griffith-Bieniawski theory), and should be secant to the Mohr rupture envelope for which, unfortunately, the source consulted did not supply experimental results.

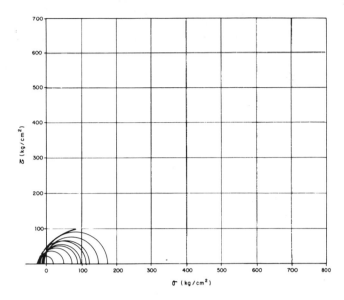

Figure 16 – Tests by Bressler and Pister (1955), which refers especifically to tension-compression area of the rupture diagram. They are incomplete for the purposes of this study, but elucidates about the envelope tendency, which could be extrapolated qualitatively.

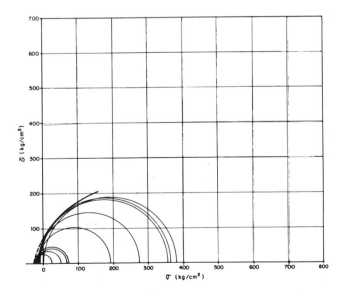

Figure 17 – Tests by McHenry and Karni (1958), done in continuation of Bressler and Pister program and extending the scale of the results by the use of three tipes of concretes, and high final resistence.

continuation of the work proposed in this article:

1 - None of the rupture envelopes for the tests recorded has the rectilinear form adopted in the design standards as a breaking point, for normal use in current concrete works. Naturally this result was to be expected, taking into account the fact that the classic Coulomb-Mohr envelope is an idealization limited by the Mohr circles representing simple axial compression and simple axial tension tests, and that in all tests represented herein, the experimental upper limit for classical construction is exceeded.

2 - The extension of the Mohr envelope for concretes submitted to bi- or triaxial tests, therefore, should not obey the classic Coulomb straight line, but be tangent to the set of experimental circles. This extension has the parabolic form anticipated in the theory expounded in previous items.

3 - The initial cracking envelope for concretes in triaxial states appears to approach a straight line in the manner predicted by the Griffith-Bienawski theory at least if the available data are held to be valid (Brice tests, 1954).

4.3 TECHNOLOGICAL GUIDELINES WHICH POINT TO FUTURE RESEARCH PROGRAMS

The set of technological programs made available in this collection is heterogeneous enough so that it can be said to cover a wide range of possible workable concretes used in the laboratory. Indeed, a table summarizing the characteristic parameters of envelopes thus obtained covering more than 50 years, and considering everything from mortars to concretes of various compositions, prepared partly in America, partly in Europe, (and therefore, with certain different workabilities and water contents, given the known tendency of the Europeans to adopt mixtures much dryer than those of the Americans) appears as a discloser of very interesting aspects.

The classic Coulomb-Mohr envelope indicates an emergence angle (pending from the Coulomb straight line) varying between 45 and 34 degrees for k^2 between 5 and 3, respectively. From the results available, all concretes tested showed slopes (at the intersection of the rupture envelopes with the axis of τ) with values greater than and very close to 43° (except the data from the tests of l'Hermitte which, as has been mentioned, may have been subject to an error of interpretation). The curves continue deviating from the Coulomb tangent, and the deviation may be measured using the conventional stress level of 300 kg/cm^2, chosen for convenience, in view of the group of charts dealt with in this study. This reduction of the envelope is, in general, somewhat less than the value of the parameter   (tangential stress at the origin of the diagram), being in both cases equal (Duke and Davis, 1944) and slightly greater (Richart,

Brandtzaeg and Brown, 1928). The high quality, evident in the
publication consulted, of the experimental services executed by
Duke and Davis seems to indicate that this result (equality)
should represent a more probable tendency; perhaps even its variation i proportional to the better structural quality of the
concretes tested (k^2) or to the better qualification of this
material in the tests.

TABLE 1

PARAMETERS OF COMPARISON OF VARIOUS MOHR ENVELOPES OBTAINED IN REFERENCE
TESTS (HEADING ACCORDING TO SCHEMATIC FIGURE Nº 18)

Program		Year	Material	φ_o	φ_{300}	$\Delta\tau_{(\varphi_o-\varphi_{300})}$ (kg/cm^2)	$\dfrac{\tau_o}{\sigma_c}$	$\dfrac{\Delta\tau}{\tau_o}$	Reference Figure
Mesnager and Considere		1909	Mortar	44°	38°	26	0,16	0,58	8
Richart, Brandtzaeg and Brown		1928	Concrete, bulk 1 = 2,1 = 2,5	44°	33°	50	0,22	1,25	9
L'Hermitte		1942	Concrete	56°	-	-	-	-	10
Duke and Davis		1944	Concrete	43°	18°	90	0,23	1,00	11
Balmer (28 days)		1949	Concrete	49°	37°	40	0,20	0,80	12
Balmer (90 days)		1949	Concrete	48°	38°	37	0,20	0,67	13
Brice		1934	Concrete	49°	39°	36	0,19	0,42	14
Bressler and Pister		1955	Concrete	46°	16°	190	0,26	3,80	16
McHenry and Karni		1958	Concrete 1:1,9 : 2,5	49°	24°	220	0,21	2,75	17
Data from Classic Coulomb-Mohr Envelope	$K^2 = 5$	-	Concrete	45°	-	-	0,20	-	-
	$K^2 = 4$	-	Concrete	39°	-	-	0,22	-	4
	$K^2 = 3$	-	Concrete	34°	-	-	0,24	-	-

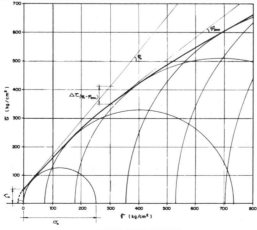

FIGURA (Esquematica) nº 18

1.154

5 REFERENCES

Balmer, G.G. (1949)   Shearing Strength of Concrete Under High
Triaxial Stress. Computation of Mohr's Envelope as a Curve. U.S.
Bureau of Reclamation Structural Research Lab, Report no. SP-23,
1949

Bascoul, A., Maso, J.C. (1974)   Influence de la Contrainte Inter-
mediare sur le Comportement Mecanique du Beton en Compression Bi-
axiale, Bull. Rilem, no. 42, 1974

Bieniawski, Z.T. (1967)   Mechanism of Brittle Fracture of Rock.
Rock Mechanics Division, National Mechanical Engineering Research
Institute, Pretoria, South Africa, Jan. 1967

Bressler, B., Pister, K.S. (1955)   Failure of Plain Concrete
Under Combined Stresses, Proc. ASCE, V 81, no. 674, April 1955

Brice, L.P. (1934)   Determination Experimentale et Trace de la
Curbe de Resistance Intrinseque du Beton, Rev. Science et Indus-
trie, 1/1934

Brice, L.P. (1954)   Etude des Conditions de Formation des Fissures
de Glissement et de Decohesion des Solides, Rev. Travaux, no. 6

Camargo, W.M.de (1970)   A Teoria Unitaria do Comportamento do
Concreto (A Unitary Theory of Plain Concrete Behaviour) in 'A
Abordagem Tecnologica no Projeto de Estruturas Especiais de Con-
creto' (Technological Approach for Structural Concrete Design).
Escola de Engenharia de Sao Carlos, Universidade de Sao Paulo,
Notas de Aula, Sept. 1970

Camargo, W.M.de (1971)   Fundamentos Para uma Teoria de Resistencia dos Macicos de Embutimento dos Tuneis de Pressao (Fundamentals of a Strength Theory for Rock Mass Embedment of Pressure
Tunnels), 3ª Semana Paulista de Geologia Aplicada, Sao Paulo

Camargo, W.M.de (1977)   Theoretical Approach to an Effective
'in situ' Concrete Quality Control. International Symposium on
Testing 'in situ' of Concrete Structures, RILEM, Budapest, Sept.
1977 (by correspondence)

Camargo, W.M.de (1978a)   Uma Hiptese para a Explicacao da Genese
da Microfissuracao do Concreto Visando o Estudo da Resistencia ao
Fissuramento do Concreto de Barragens (A Hypothesis to Explain
Microcracking Genesis in Plain Concrete to Permit the Study of
Fissuring Resistance of Concrete Dams). Xll Seminario Nacional de
Grandes Barragens, Sao Paulo, April 1978

Camargo, W.M.de (1978b)   Anotacoes a Respeito da Retracao e da
Fluencia do Concreto Tendo em Vista sua Heterogeneidade e Cont-
eudo de Vazios (Notes concerning Shrinkage-Creep Properties of
Concretes considering its Heterogeneity and Voids Content, Col-
oquio IBRACON, May 1978

Cedolin, L., Crutzen, Y.R.J. Dei Poli, S. (1977) Triaxial Stress-Strain Relationship for Concrete, Journal of the Engineering Mechanics Division, ASCE, EM-3, p.423-439, June 1977

Darwin, D., Pecknold, D.A. (1977) Nonlinear Biaxial Stress-Strain Law for Concrete, Journal of the Engineering Mechanics Division, ASCE, EM-2, p.229-241, April 1977

Duke, C.M., Davis, H.E. (1944) Some Properties of Concrete under Sustained Combined Stresses, ASTM, Proc., 44-p.888-896, June 1944

Desayi, P., Viswanatha, C.S. (1967) True Ultimate Strength of Plain Concrete, Bulletin Rilem, no.36, September 1967

Desayi, P. (1977) Fracture of Concrete in Compression, Materials and Structures (RILEM) p.139-144, May-June 1977

Escorel, F.J. (1957) Os Invariantes das Tensoes e a Ruptura do Concreto (Stress Invariants and Concrete Rupture), Tese apresentada a Faculdade de Arquitetura e Urbanismo da Universidade de Sao Paulo, 1957

Gausel, E. (1977) Concrete Offshore Structures - Behaviour of Full Scale Shells, Hydrostatically Loaded, 1977 Offshore Technology Conference, Proceedings, Vol.1V, p.323-328, Houston, Texas, 1977

Guerrin, A (1952) Traite de Beton Arme, Vol.1, Ed. Dunod, Paris,

Glucklich, J. (1963) Fracture of Plain Concrete, Proceedings, ASCE, Journal of Engineering Mechanics Division, Dec.1963

Griffith, A.A. (1921) The Phenomena of Rupture and Flow in Solids, Philosophy Transactions of the Royal Society, London, Part A, Feb,1921

Hendron Jr., A.J. (1968) Mechanical Properties of Rock, in 'Rock Mechanics in Engineering Practice', John Wiley and Sons, New York, 1968

Highberg, R.S., Haynes, H.H. (1977) Ocean Implosion Test of Concrete (Seacon) Cylindrical Structures, 1977 Offshore Technology Conference, Proceedings, Vol. 1V, p.363-370, Houston, Texas, 1977

Hoek, E. (1968) Brittle Failure of Rock, Capitulo 4 da Coletanea Intitulada 'Rock Mechanics in Engineering Practice', editada por Stagg e Zienkewicz (John Wiley & Sons, London,1968)

Hsu, J.Etal Microcracking of Plain Concrete and the Shape of the Stress-Strain Curve, Journal ACI, February 1963

Inglis, C.E. (1913)   Stress in a Plate Due to the Presence of Cracks and Sharp Corners, Trasn. Institution of Naval Architects, London, Vol.55, Part 1, 1913

Kaplan, K. (1961)   Crack Propagation and the Fracture of Concrete, Journal ACI, November 1961

Kupfer, H.B., Gerstle, K.H. (1973)   Behavior of Concrete under Biaxial Stresses, Journal of the Engineering Mechanics Division, ASCE, EM-4, p.853-866, August 1973

Kupfer, H.B., Hilsdorf, H.K., Rush, H. (1969)   Behaviour of Concrete under Biaxial Stresses, Journal American Concrete Institute, Proceedings, Vol.66, no.8, p.656, August 1969

L'Hermitte, R. (1942)   Recherches Nouvelles en Resistance des Materiaux, Circul. no.7, Serie 1, 25-7-1942. Institut Technique du Batiment et des Travaux Publics

Liu, T.C.Y., Nilson, A.H., Slate, F.O. (1972)   Biaxial Stress-Strain Relations for Concrete, Journal of the Structural Division, ASCE, ST-5, p.1025-1034, May 1972

Lobo B.Carneiro, F.L. (1968)   Aplicacoes da Teoria da Plasticidade aos Concretos (Applications of Plasticity Theory to Concrete), Publicacao no.1/68 da COPPE, Rio de Janeiro, 1968

McHenry,D., Kami, J. (1953)   Strength of Concrete under Combined Tensile and Compressive Stresses, Journal ACI, Vol.54, p.829-839, April, 1958

Peyronnet, J.P. (1977)   Experimental Study on the Behaviour of Concrete Structural Elements in Natural Sea Water, 1977 Offshore Technology Conference, Proceedings, Vol.1V, p.371-378, Houston, Texas, 1977

Richart, F.E., Brandtzaeg, A., Brown, R. (1928)   A Study of the Failure of the Concrete under Combined Compressive Stresses, University of Illinois Eng. Experimental Station Bulletin no.185

Romualdi, J.P. e Batson, G.B. (1963)   Mechanics of Crack Arrest in Concrete, Proceedings ASCE, Journal of the Engineering Mechanics Division, June 1963)

Welch & Haisman (1969)   The Applications of Fracture Mechanics and the Measurement of Structural Thoroughness, Bulletin RILEM, May-June, 1969

UNIAXIAL IMPACT TENSILE STRENGTH OF CONCRETE

H.W. Reinhardt

Stevin Laboratory, Delft University of Technology, Delft, the Netherlands

INTRODUCTION

The usual loading of civil engineering structures is static or cyclic. But besides these normal cases there are some extraordinary ones of very short duration such as pile driving, explosions, wave action ship collisions or airplane crashes. The duration of these loading cases varies between a few hundred µs and some ms. In offshore engineering, dynamic actions are of major importance.
Even if the tensile strength of concrete is neglected in normal design and analysis, it is the property which largely determines the cracking behaviour, i.e., crack width and crack spacing, the bond between steel and concrete and the shear capacity of structural elements without stirrups. This is true of static loading, but applies even more to failure due to impact loading where the absorbed energy is important with regard to behaviour.

REQUIREMENTS APPLICABLE TO THE TEST METHOD

The foregoing leads to three requirements which should be fulfilled by a test method, which is suitable for studying the impact tensile behaviour of concrete. The *first* is a rather high and adjustable stress rate, of the order of 2000 to 50000 N/mm^2s. The *second* is that not only the impact strength should be determined, but also the stress-strain diagram up to failure. The *third* is a general requirement that the stresses in the specimen are well defined and known during the test. The axial tensile test is most suitable for this purpose, but because of the high rate of loading some modifications have to be made.

THE TEST METHOD

The origin of the test method is the split Hopkinson bar which

is used in the compression testing of metals, natural stones
and concrete (Hopkinson 1913, Davies e.a. 1963, Hakaletho 1964,
Aronsson e.a. 1976). It consists of two coaxial elastic bars
between which the specimen is sandwiched (Fig. 1). A pulse
travelling from the left passes the interface A where a portion
α_1 is transmitted and a portion α_4 is reflected. The magnitude
of α_1 and α_4 depends on the mechanical impedances I of the
elastic bar and the specimen, respectively, as designated in
Fig. 1.

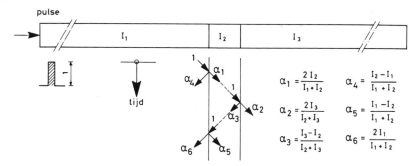

Figure 1. Principle of the split Hopkinson bar technique
(I = c.ρ with c = one-dimensional wave velocity,
ρ = specific gravity)

Mismatch of the two impedances leads to excessive reflection,
i.e. energy which is lost for the test. Therefore aluminium
bars are used ($I_1=I_3=13.6\times10^6$ kg/m^{2}s) for concrete testing
($I_2= 9\times10^6$ kg/m^{2}s for an average concrete).
The theory is valid for a rectangular unit pulse. If a linearly increasing pulse is to be treated, it must be approximated
by short pulses and the results must be superimposed.

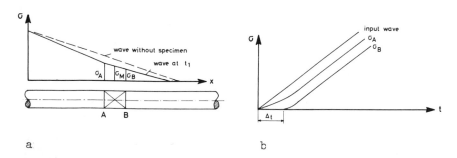

Figure 2. a) Stress at time t_1 along the bar
b) Stress-time relation for the input and the interfaces ($\Delta t=l/c$, l=specimen length, c=wave velocity)

In an experiment, the drop weight hits the anvil and a tensile
stress pulse starts to travel up the bar at a velocity of
about 5 km/s. The slope of the pulse is determined more particularly by the contact between drop weight and anvil. For
different slopes (i.e., stress rates) different layers of more
or less hard material are used such as rubber or cardboard.
The maximum stress is governed by the height of fall of the
drop weight.
The pulse is measured at points 1 and 2 by electrical strain
gauges. From the modulus of elasticity of the bars the acting
force can be calculated. The strain in the specimen is measured
also by electrical strain gauges (60 mm long) or by two
contactless LVDTs which are mounted along the specimen. Both
methods give reliable results. The measuring signals are
amplified and fed into a four-channel transient recorder which
has a maximum measuring frequency of 2 MHz and 4 k core.
Repeated loading (impact fatigue) is facilitated by a pneumatic device which lifts the drop weight and releases it at the
predetermined height. The number of blows up to failure is
recorded.
An example of a test record is given in Fig. 4 which shows
at the upper left a stress-time relation, at the lower left
a strain-time relation as measured by strain gauges on the
upper aluminium bar and by contactless LVDTs along the
specimen, respectively. The diagram on the right is generated
by the transient recorder synchronizing the two measurements
and eliminating the time in the two graphs.

The result of such a calculation is given in Fig. 2 from which
it can be seen that the stresses at A and B are not quite the
same.
The difference is smaller with shorter specimens and lower
stress rates (0,2 to 1,5% of the average value). Another, more
important feature is that, after a short period of time, the
stress rate in the specimen is the same as that of the input
wave. This behaviour is due to the multiple reflection within
the specimen.

THE TESTING EQUIPMENT

Fig. 3 shows the testing equipment schematically with the two
aluminium bars ϕ 74 mm and the specimen sandwiched together.

The lower bar ends in an anvil which is hit by the drop weight
sliding along the bar. The upper bar is fixed in a damper in
order to minimize the reflection of the pulse.
The specimen is a drilled core with plane-parallel ground
surfaces. It is glued with a filled polyester resin.

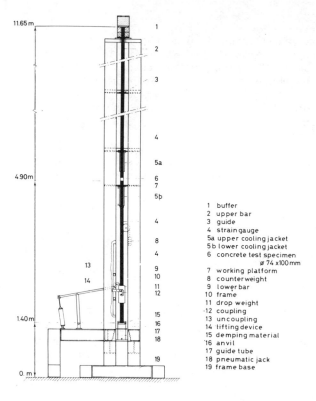

Figure 3. Testing equipment, schematically

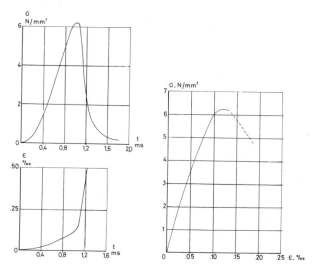

Figure 4. Stress-time, strain-time and stress-strain relation
as recorded in a test

TEST PROGRAM

In a preliminary program, the variables of Table 1 were investigated. The results can be summarized as follows:

Table 1. Variables of the preliminary program.

cement type	Portland, furnace slag
cement quality	A, B, C
cement content	325, 375 kg/m^3
water-cement ratio	0.40, 0.45
aggregates	rounded
maximum grain size	16, 24 mm
stress rate	3000, 30000 N/mm^{2}s

It turned out that the cement type and the cement quality did
not have a significant influence on the influence of the
stress rate. A maximum grain size of the aggregates of 24 mm
leads to much scatter in the results. The difference in the
water-cement ratios of 0.40 and 0.45 was too small for a
distinct determination of its influence.
After these preliminary experiences, the following test series
were carried out with the variables of Table 2.

Table 2. Variables of the test program.

cement type	Portland B
cement content	325, 375 kg/m^3
water-cement ratio	0.40, 0.50
aggregates	rounded, max. 16 mm
specimen humidity	dry, wet
stress rate	< 3000, 3000, 30000 N/mm^{2}s
loading cycles	1, 1000

All the tests were carried out at a temperature of 20°C at an
age of 28 days. In so far as the specimen humidity is concerned, "dry" means that the specimens were cured at 20°C and
100% rel. humidity for 14 days and additionally at 20°C and
50% rel. humidity for 14 days. "Wet" means curing at 20°C and
100% rel. humidity for 28 days and subsequently testing in
the wet condition.

The grading curve of the aggregates corresponds to the line A
according to the Netherlands Standard VB74. This Portland B
cement had an average compressive strength of 40.3 N/mm^2 at
28 days.
Besides the impact tests, the compression strength and tensile
splitting strength were each determined on six 150 mm cubes.
The average values and the standard deviations of these tests
are summarized in Table 3.

Table 3. Results of the standard tests of the concrete used.

cement content, kg/m^3		325	325	375	375
water-cement ratio		0.40	0.50	0.40	0.50
dry	f'_c	62.25	48.75	58.33	46.62
	s	0.76	3.01	3.71	1.57
	f_{spl}	3.51	3.01	3.34	3.12
	s	0.42	0.30	0.34	0.30
wet	f'_c	57.25	45.60	54.98	44.80
	s	6.34	2.51	4.00	0.91
	f_{spl}	3.46	3.07	3.57	3.07
	s	0.30	0.38	0.57	0.10
mean strength of the cement at 28 days: compression 40.3 N/mm^2 flexural strength 9.0 N/mm^2					

TEST RESULTS

Impact tensile strength under single loading

First, the presentation of the results calls for some comment:
there are always two interesting features, i.e., the absolute
value of the tensile strength and the increase in strength due
to the higher stress rate. The increase in strength can be
related to the statically determined tensile strength.
Because of some difficulties, the uniaxial tensile strength
has not always been determined whereas the tensile splitting
strength has been measured in every case.
If the strength only is treated - as in this paper - the impact tensile strength is always given in absolute values and
relative to the splitting strength.
Another point is the expected strength stress-rate relation.
A theoretical treatment modelling the concrete fracture as a
stochastic process (Mihashi e.a. 1977) suggests that there
exists a relation of the type

$$\frac{f_{imp}}{f_{static}} = \left(\frac{\dot{\sigma}}{\dot{\sigma}_o}\right)^{\frac{1}{1+\beta}} \qquad\qquad 1$$

with the stress rate $\dot{\sigma}$ during impact and $\dot{\sigma}_o$ during static
loading. β is a coefficient depending on the material properties only. For the following evaluation the equation 1 will
be used. The results will be given in graphical form with the
stress rate plotted to a logarithmic scale.

Absolute values Fig. 5 shows the absolute values of the impact tensile strength of various concretes

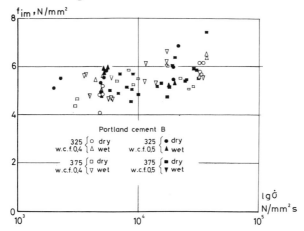

Figure 5. Impact tensile strength of various concrete.

as a function of the stress rate which ranges between 2000 and
40000 N/mm²s. In spite of different cement contents (325 and
375 kg/m³), different water-cement ratios (0.40 and 0.50) and
specimen humidity (dry and wet), the test results belong to
one population without significant differences. The average
value is about 5.5 N/mm².
The only result which is clear in spite of the scatter of the
measurements, is the increase in strength with increasing
stress rate. This somewhat meagre result can be much improved
by evaluating the ratio of impact to static strength.

Relative values The results of the impact tests are divided
by the accompanying tensile splitting strength giving the
ratio of impact to static strength. The following four graphs
show the results for the different concretes with the theoretically determined relation according to eq. (1) as dashed
lines.
The coefficient β is the mean value derived from the test
results belonging to one concrete type and one humidity condition.

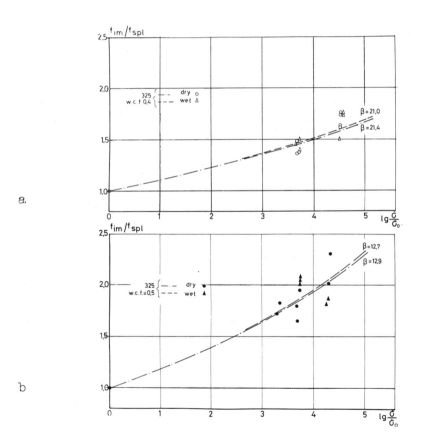

a.

b

Figure 6 a till d.   Ratio of impact to static strength for
various tests.

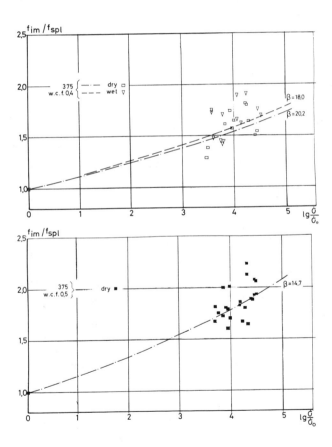

Fig. 6 (continued)

Using this type of presentation, the test results can be
clearly distinguished. The most suitable term for a proper
comparison is the coefficient β which is given in Table 4
for the various concretes and humidity conditions. A low
value of β means a strong influence of the stress rate on the
tensile strength, whereas a high value would mean that the
tensile strength is only slightly influenced by the stress
rate.

Table 4. Coefficient β for various tests and average strength
increase.

cement content, kg/m^3	325				375			
water-cement ratio	0.40		0.50		0.40		0.50	
specimen humidity	dry	wet	dry	wet	dry	wet	dry	wet
coefficient β	21.4	21.0	12.9	12.7	20.2	18.0	14.7	-
strength increase at $\dot{\sigma}=40000$ N/mm^{2}s	1.60	1.62	2.14	2.17	1.65	1.75	1.96	-

For instance, β = 14.3 gives an increase in strength by 100%
at a stress rate of 40000 N/mm^{2}s.

Table 4 calls for the following comment: an increasing
water-cement ratio results in a lower value for β and therefore in a higher influence of the stress rate. If the assumption is correct that mainly the inelastic behaviour (plasticity, micro-cracking) is influenced by the stress rate, it would
mean that a low water-cement ratio produces a rather elastic
and brittle material.
This conclusion is in fact in accordance with considerations
on results from static uniaxial and multiaxial tests (Reinhardt 1977).
The *specimen humidity* affects the results only slightly.
Nevertheless the results tend in the direction which can be
expected from creep results from which it is known that wet
concrete creeps more than dry concrete. Obviously, the marked
influence on creep is much diminished at very high rates of
loading.
Not much can be said about the influence of the *cement content*
because the results are contradictionary for the two water-
cement ratios. While the influence of the stress rate becomes
lower for a water-cement ratio of 0.50 when more cement is
used, it is just the opposite for a water-cement ratio of 0.40.
An answer could perhaps be found in the amount of bond
cracking and matrix cracking, so that different fracture
types could occur, depending upon the cement content and the
accompanying water-cement ratio. More test results are required
for arriving at a reliable conclusion.

Impact tensile strength under repeated loading (impact fatigue)
In order to get a constant stress rate in the single load
test the drop height is made relatively large, so that the
input pulse produces much higher stresses than would be
necessary. In repeated loading tests the upper stress is
given as a limit. This entails a low drop height , and the
stress rate is then no longer constant.
An example of a pulse is shown in Fig. 7, where the stress
rate is defined by the tangent on the left.
Another consequence of the low drop height is that the
attainable stress rate decreases with decreasing upper stress.
This is inherent in this testing equipment.

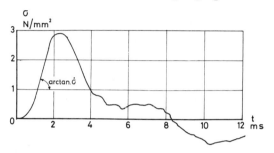

Figure 7. Stress pulse in repeated loading.

Absolute values In the following diagram the absolute values
of the upper stresses are plotted against the number of impact
cycles with stress rate between 2000 and 6000 N/mm^{2}s.

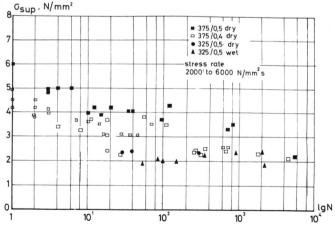

Figure 8. Tensile strength vs number of cycles.

It can be seen that even only 3 to 5 cycles cause the tensile
strength to decrease and that after about 20 cycles the reduction in strength is less. But here, too, the results can
be better interpreted in terms of relative strength.

Relative values The ratio impact tensile strength/static
splitting strength is plotted against the number of cycles
in Fig. 9. The same tendency as in the preceding diagram is
discernible, but the specific behaviour of the various
concretes can be better compared.

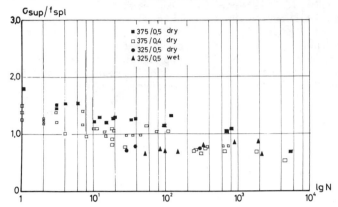

Figure 9. Relative strength vs number of cycles.

The top results belong to a concrete with 375 kg cement/m^3
and a water-cement ratio of 0.50. Due to the high water-cement
ratio the relative impact strength is high, it exceeds the
static value up to 700 cycles. The results for the water-
cement ratio of 0.40 show less strength gain due to impact;
also, the loss due to repeated loading is considerable, so
that the relative strength drops below 1.00 after only 4 cycles.
After about 1000 cycles the remaining strength is 70% of the
static value.
The influence of the water-cement ratio on this behaviour can
be explained and illustrated by fracture mechanics methods.
In these terms, fatigue means crack initiation, stable crack
growth and finally unstable crack growth. If a lower water-
cement ratio is assumed to result in a more brittle material,
every stress cycle must cause more extension of a crack than
at a higher water-cement ratio. Or, for the same crack growth
a different water-cement ratio, the stress level must be less
in the case of the lower water-cement ratio.

In regard to cement content, it can be inferred from the
test results that concrete with lower cement content is more
sensitive to repeated loading.
More tests will be carried out in order to explain this
behaviour.
In so far as the stress rate in cyclic loading is concerned,
the influence in these tests was negligible, probably because
of the small variation in stress rate.

SUMMARY AND CONCLUSIONS

The first part of this paper deals with the development and
design of a testing equipment based on the split Hopkinson
bar which is suitable for the uniaxial tensile testing of
concrete at stress rates between 2000 and 50000 N/mm^2s.
Stress and strain can be measured with a measuring frequency
of 2 MHz.
In the second part some results are discussed. It emerged
that in every case an increasing stress rate leads to a
higher strength. The impact strength varies between 1.5 and
2.5 times the static strength. The increase depends upon the
following influences:
- water-cement ratio. With higher water-cement ratios the
  impact strength becomes relatively higher.
- specimen humidity. Wet specimens show more increase of
  impact strength than dry specimens.
- cement content. More cement leads to higher impact strength
  at a water-cement ratio of 0.50, but to lower impact strength
  strength at o.40.
- cement type and cement quality. No specific influence on
  the strength increase due to impact could be detected.

The gain in strength due to high stress rates is lost by
repeated loading. With higher water-cement ratios the reduction is less than with lower water-cement ratios.

ACKNOWLEDGEMENT

This investigation has been carried out in close cooperation
with the Netherlands Concrete Research Foundation (CUR-VB),
committee C35. The author would like to thank all members for
their support and encouragement.

REFERENCES

Aronsson, R., G. Fagerlund, B. Larsson (1976) Betongs
slagseghet i Palar. Cement - och Betonginstitutet, Stockholm,
Report nr. 7676.

Davies, E.D.H., S.C. Hunter (1963) The dynamic compression
testing of solids by the method of the split Hopkinson pressure bar. J. Mech. Phys. Solids 11, 5: 155-179.

Hakaletho, K.O. (1969) The behaviour of rock under impulse
loads - A study using the Hopkinson Split Bar Method.
Acta Polytechnica Scandinavica, Helsinki, Ch81.

Hopkinson, B.A. (1913) Method of measuring the pressure produced in the detonation of high explosives or by the impact
of bullets. Phil. Trans. Roy. Soc. A 213 : 437-456.

Mihashi, H., M. Izumi (1977) A stochastic theory for concrete fracture. Cement and Concrete Research 7: 411-422.

Reinhardt, H.W. (1977) Ansprüche des Konstrukteurs an den Beton hinsichtlich Festigkeit und Verformung. beton 27, 5: 195-199.

CONCENTRATED LOADING ON A THICK WALLED CONCRETE CYLINDER

J. Brakel, H.W. Reinhardt, L.J. Oostlander

Delft University of Technology, Delft, The Netherlands

Hollandsche Beton Maatschappij, Rijswijk, The Netherlands

DESCRIPTION OF THE PROBLEM

Offshore-structures are exposed to the risk of being hit by
a ship. Especially as one of the support columns of such a
structure is severely damaged the results can be catastrophic.
The collision is represented in Fig. 1.
The deadweight of the superstructure can be taken into
account in the model by an external centric longitudinal
prestressing.
Sørensen (Ref. 1) for example proved that the dynamic impact
force can be replaced by a static load, if the duration of
the impact is several times higher than the natural period
of the stricken part of the structure. This happens here.
If the supporting structure is built up of steel pipes the
concentrated load develops a diamond shaped imprint, a
yield line pattern, that will be enlarged by an increasing
load (Ref. 2). See Photo 1.
The energy developed during the collision is absorbed by
the crushing of the ship and the impression of the cylindrical steel column.
However, what happens if the supporting structure consists
of thick walled reinforced concrete cylinders which are
prestressed or non-prestressed? To answer this question
research has been done at the Stevin Laboratory of the
Delft University of Technology, The Netherlands.

RESEARCH

The tests are made on 4 specimen, which represent in a
simplified shape and on a scale of about 1:10, the supporting
columns of the Dunlin platform A at a height of 120 m,
measured from the underside of the reservoir. Fig. 2 gives
the dimensions and other data of the specimen.

To avoid collapse of the cylinder by longitudinal bending, extra reinforcement is applied over 3/8 of the lower part of the circumference.
In the research is observed:
- the collapse form;
- the magnitude of the collapse load;
- the influence of the size of the loaded area;
- the influence of the velocity by which the load increases;
- the influence of longitudinal prestressing.

The first test on a specimen is the well-known three points bending test (Photo 2). Then the tests are continued on the non-damaged parts of the cylinder.
Now the cylinder is supported at the opposite side of the loaded area by means of a saddle (Photo 3).

TEST RESULTS

The collapse form
Already under a small load a crack develops at the inside of the cylinder shell just under the loaded area. This longitudinal crack, shown in Fig. 3 with the number 1, extends and opens rapidly with increasing load. Successively axial cracks on the outside of the cylinder develop.
These cracks are shown in Fig. 3 with the numbers 2, 3, 4,...
..., n. The crack marked n is the last axial crack which can develop and is situated at a distance of about three times the cylinder wall thickness from the edge of the loaded area.
By further increase of the loading, the applied load suddenly pushes a cone-shaped part out of the cylinder wall. In other words the load "punches" through the cylinder wall. Study of the shear planes show that these have a relatively steep shear angle in the transverse direction and a more flat shear angle in the longitudinal direction.
In Fig. 4 is shown the crack pattern which was visible after the end of the first test on specimen 4 (test 4.1).
It is supposed that the collapse happened as follows. After the development of the last axial crack n in Fig. 3 no more axial cracks can develop because the necessary rotation capacity of the cylinder wall in this area is no more available. By increasing the load, a shear crack with a shear angle ϕ develops in the area between the cracks 1 and n. The load has now to be carried by a plate shaped part of the cylindrical wall, that is fixed in longitudinal direction and free in transverse direction. The construction tries to find a new equilibrium in this situation.
This is not possible, so the load punches through the cylinder wall. The shear angle ψ is almost equal to the shear angle of punching tests on flat slabs.

It is supposed that the local bearing capacity is exhausted after development of the shear crack with the angle ϕ in transverse direction (fig. 3).

Ultimate limit load
An empirical formula has been developed, based on the observed collapse behaviour. In this formula the parameters are used of which it is supposed that they influence the value of the ultimate limit load. This formula is:

$$P_u = 2\alpha_1 . \alpha_2 . \alpha_3 . f_c . d \ (a_1 + d)$$

with:
$\alpha_1 \geqslant 1,0; \quad \alpha_2 \geqslant 1,0; \quad \alpha_3 \geqslant 1,0$

Explanation of the formula (see also fig. 5):
α_1 - According to the test results this coefficient has a mean value of 2,0 for the ratio $d/D_o = 0,10$

α_2 - This coefficient can be determined with the empirical formula:

$$\alpha_2 = 1,00 + 0,015 \ \sigma'_{cpl}$$

Here σ'_{cpl} is the concrete stress caused by the longitudinal prestressing force at the place where the decisive shear crack occurs. The longitudinal compression of the concrete at this point in the real structure consists of a contribution of the possible longitudinal prestressing and/or compression caused by longitudinal bending of the column.
The formula for α_2 is the equation of the straight line which corresponds approximately with the test results. See fig. 6.

α_3 - It is expected that transverse prestressing increases the ultimate limit load. It is not known how large this increment is. Because this influence is absent in the tests, here a value of $\alpha_3 = 1,0$ should be used.

Limitations: Because the formula is based on test results the following boundary conditions have to be used when applying it:

$$d/D_o \approx 0,10$$
$$0,5 \ d \leqslant a/l \leqslant 0,25 \ D_o$$
$$l \geqslant 5 \ D_o$$

Fig. 7 shows the ratio of the measured ultimate limit load P_{exp} and the ultimate limit load P_{form} calculated with the above mentioned formula; the squares represent on scale the loaded area.

The velocity of loading to failure

The time to increase the load from zero to failure has been reduced in a number of tests to about 1 second. It was not observed a perceptible difference with loads of longer duration. The testing equipment did not allow a more rapid increase.

Dimensions of the loaded area (fig. 7)

Only the dimension in the longitudinal direction of the cylinder seems to be important.
See also the section about the limitations of the formula.

Longitudinal prestressing

The presence of centric prestressing in the longitudinal direction and/or bending moment introduces compression stresses in the area where the decisive shear crack occurs, which increase the ultimate limit load. The empirical coefficient α_2 gives an indication of this increase (fig. 6).

CONCLUSION

If the thick walled concrete tower of an offshore drilling platform does not collapse by longitudinal bending, the concentrated load "punches" through the tower wall. This local failure does not mean that the structure as a whole has collapsed.
The energy which comes free during the collision will be almost completely absorbed by the crushing of the steel ship.

ACKNOWLEDGEMENT

This article is based on the results of Research nr. 7.1.76.67 of the Department Concrete Structures, Faculty of Civil Engineering, Delft University of Technology, The Netherlands. The research has been carried out as part of the final study for the grade of civil engineer, discipline construction (concrete).

REFERENCES

1. Sørensen K.A.: "Behaviour of reinforced and prestressed concrete tubes under static and impact loading". Proc. Behaviour of Offshore Structures, Stavanger 1976, pp. 798-813.

2. ANDOC: "Boat impact on steel columns" Internal report, Delft 1976.

Nomenclature

		dimension
α_1	coefficient depending of d/D_o	--
α_2	" " " σ'_{cpl}	--
α_3	" " " σ'_{cpt}	--
a_1	length of the loaded area in the longitudinal direction of the cylinder	mm
d	thickness of cylinder wall	mm
D_o	outside diameter of cylinder	mm
f_c	concrete tensile strength	N/mm^2
f'_c	concrete compressive strength	N/mm^2
σ'_{cpl}	concrete stress by prestressing in longitudinal direction	N/mm^2
σ'_{cpt}	concrete stress by prestressing in transverse direction	N/mm^2
l	length of cylinder	mm

Additional test data

- Concrete cover 5-7 mm

- Maximum seize of aggregate 8 mm

- To prevent collapse by longitudinal bending extra reinforcement
  has been applied over 3/8 of the circumference (lower part).
  cylinder 1 en 2: 7 ϕ10; FeB 400
      "   3 " 4: 7 ϕ16; FeB 400

- The centric longitudinal prestressing consists of 2 dywidag bars
  ϕ36 mm and is unbonded. This prestressing is only applied at the
  cylinders 2 and 4; it caused a longitudinal prestressing stress
  of 5,0 N/mm^2 in the cylinder wall.

- CONCRETE PROPERTIES

Cube compressive strength	mean	53,7 N/mm^2
	standard deviation	3,8 "
Cube tensile strength	mean	3,9 "
	standard deviation	0,4 "
Cylinder tensile strength	mean	4,8 N/mm^2
(from cut out cylinders)	standard deviation	0,6 "
Youngs modulus	mean	3,19.10^4 N/mm^2
	standard deviation	0,25.10^4 N/mm^2

- STEEL PROPERTIES

ϕ 4	yield stress	730 N/mm^2
	tensile strength	751 "
ϕ10	yield stress	445 N/mm^2
	tensile strength	672 "
ϕ16	yield stress	454 N/mm^2
	tensile strength	653 "

model

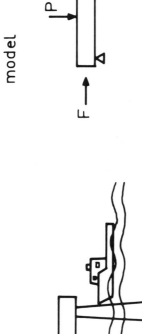

P = concentrated static load on a concrete cylinder.

F = unbonded centric prestressing force

Beam on two supports

prototype

Collision of a tug with the concrete column of an offshore platform.

Fig. 1   Schematization of a collision problem.

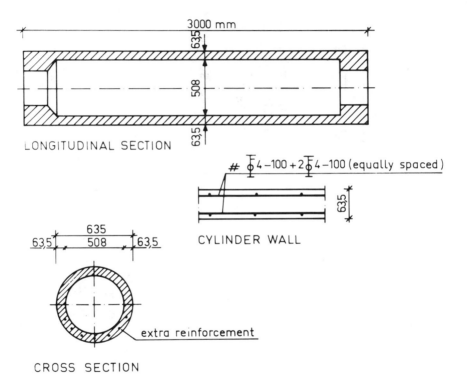

LONGITUDINAL SECTION

CYLINDER WALL

CROSS SECTION

Fig. 2   Dimensions and other data of specimen.

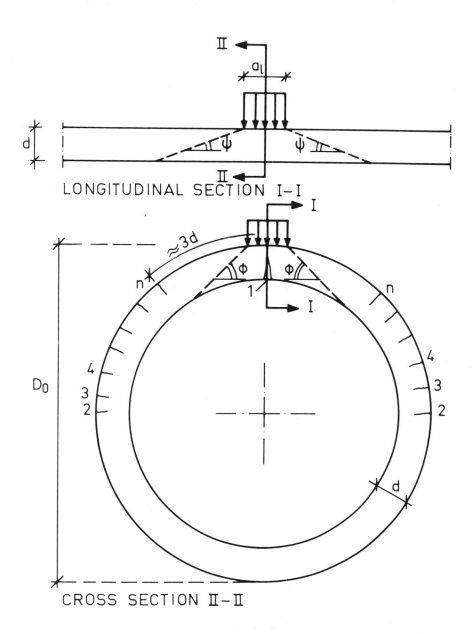

Fig. 3   Sequence of crack development.

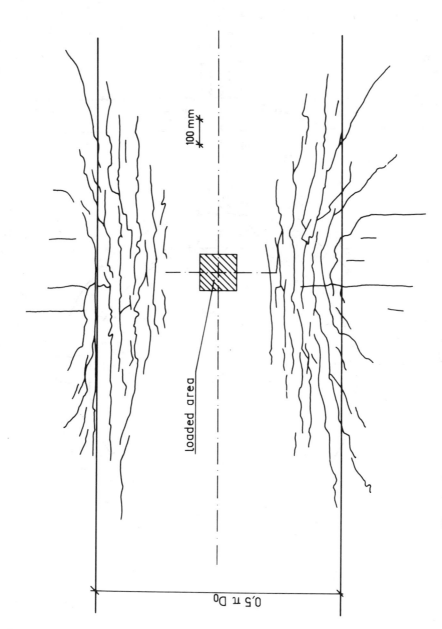

100 mm

loaded area

0,5 π D₀

Fig. 4 Crack pattern test 4.1.

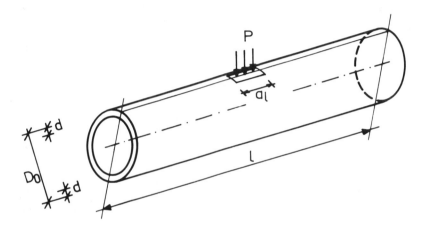

Fig. 5   Concrete cylinder with concentrated load.

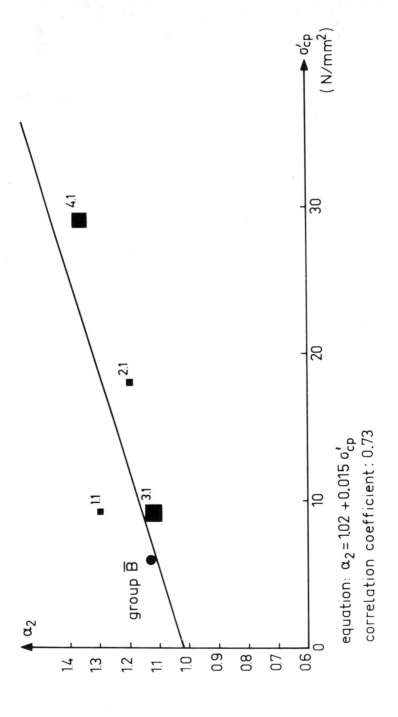

Fig. 6 Coefficient α_2 as a function of the longitudinal prestress σ'_{cp}

equation: $\alpha_2 = 1.02 + 0.015 \, \sigma'_{cp}$

correlation coefficient: 0.73

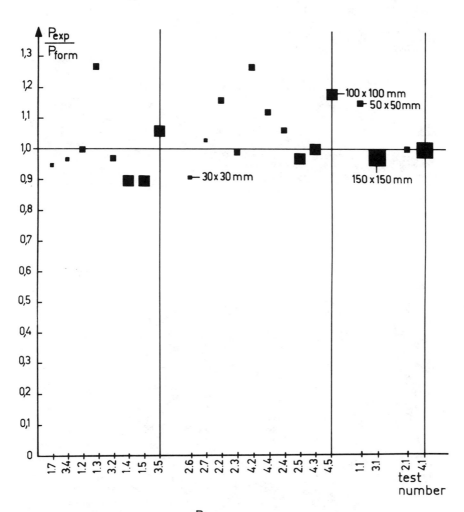

Fig. 7   For each test $\dfrac{P_{exp}}{P_{form}}$ is shown.

Photo 1. Deformation of a thinwalled steel cylinder by a
concentrated load.

Photo 2. Testing stand for the first test of a specimen.

Photo 3. Arrangement for further tests of a specimen.

Appendix

1. The experimental results have been compared with theoretical
   investigations by C.T. Morley (1) and experimental results
   cited there. The following diagram shows the theoretical
   and experimental results and it can be seen how curvature
   of a shell and width of the loading plate influence the results.
   As comparison, the loads are also given according to the
   CEB-FIP Model code (2).

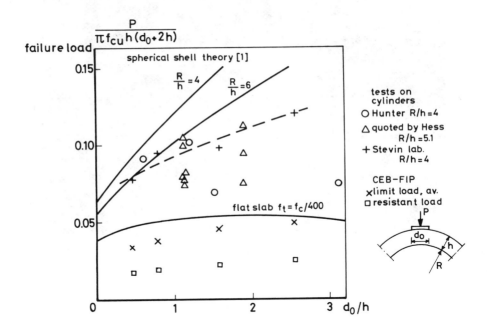

2. The experimental results of the Stevin Laboratory have also
   been compared with the empirical formula given by Colbjørnsen
   and Lenschow (3) which leads to an average of 1.05 with a
   standard deviation of 0.12.

References:

(1) Morley, T.C. Punching shear of hollow concrete spheres.
    IABSE-colloquium Plasticity in reinforced concrete.
    Kopenhagen 1979.

(2) CEB-FIP Model Code for concrete structures. 3rd ed. 1978.

(3) Colbjørnsen, A., R. Lenschow. Lokalbelastning på
    forspente sylinderskall, beregningsformel.
    FCB-rapport F 78021, Trondheim, 1978.

COMPUTER SIMULATION STUDY OF ... COLLISIONS AND

ANALYSIS OF SHIP-PLATFORM ...

Jørgen Amdahl

Det norske Veritas

oil activities ... l types of risks. Col-
... platform ... e of the main acci-
... ırred, but fortunately
... North Sea so far.

... by both the probabi-
... sequence. These
... llisions endangering
... must have low
... ing frequently must
... ften defined as the
product of the probabi... ·consequence. As far
... of collision ... ıe marine traffic
... .

... stallations.
... area.

... ıture of causes as
... fferent for the
... alysis methodology
... n the activity

... ility of ship/
... orted by N.M.I.
... lable information
... and environmental
... as proposals for
... structures have been studied by Carlin
et al (1977) and Larsen and Engseth (1978). At Det norske
Veritas a research project on this matter is in progress,

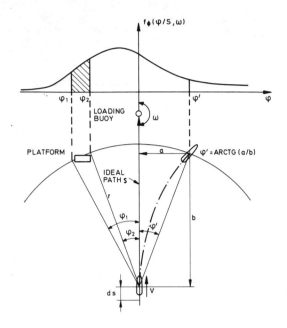

Fig. 1   Collision probability simulation model

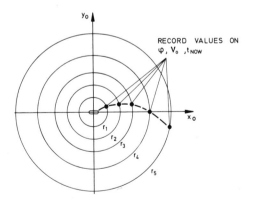

Fig. 2   Collection of simulation statistics

reported by Amdahl et al (1978). The objective is to
obtain knowledge of the probabilities and consequences of
collisions in order to develop rational design criteria
such as realistic impact forces, energy distribution and
related protective means for fixed offshore structures.

ANALYSIS OF THE COLLISION PROBABILITY

The fault tree method

Obviously a complex variety of causes of a ship/platform
encounter exists. Considerable insight may be gained by
applying the fault tree method. The fault tree is a
schematic representation of causes or combination of
events that may lead to a certain type of collision. If
the probabilities of the combination of events are known,
it is in principle possible to put up a probability calculation. However, it is readily realized that the data foundation of failure probabilities of even mechanical systems
are rather sparse. Besides it is generally extremely
difficult to assess the probability of human failures. In
view of this it is stated that it is a very comprehensive
task to evaluate the total collision probability. It is
therefore rational to perform studies of more simplified
situations initially thus investigating systematically the
elements needed to represent more complex collision events.

Outline of the probability model

The probability of collision connected with any critical
failure event in the fault tree may formally be written:

P (collision) = P (collision/failure) · P (failure)   (1)

Consider for instance a tanker approaching an offshore
loading terminal. The failure rate related to a particular
failure (e.g. loss of propulsion) is denoted λ . The tanker
is required to sail along the course line denoted by s, as
shown in Fig. 1. If the instantaneous speed of the ship is
V, the probability of failure by passing a line elements ds
reads

$$dP \text{ (failure)} = \frac{\lambda}{V}ds$$ (2)

The probability that the consquence of the failure will be
a collision between the vessel and the platform is obviously
affected by several factors such as ship speed and heading
angle, speed and direction of wind and current, direction
and height of waves, etc. described by x_1, x_2, ... x_n.
The values assumed by these variables at the instant of
failure are random. Thus there exists a joint probability
density function

$$f(x_1, x_2, \ldots x_n/s) \tag{3}$$

which in general depends on the intended course line s.

The path of the ship subsequent to failure may be given with reference to a polar coordinate system centered in the ship. The path intersection with a circle through the platform is given by the angle ϕ. This angle is not only a function of the random variables x_1, x_2, $\ldots$ x_n, but depends also on the position at the instant of failure, s:

$$\phi = g (x_1, x_2, \ldots x_n/s) \tag{4}$$

It is not possible to solve eq. (4) analytically. However, for each value of s and each possible combination of x_1, x_2, $\ldots$ x_n, as determined by eq. (3), the ship path may be solved numerically by simulation. Additional results of this calculation are the speed and direction at any point of the path. Evidently, if

$$\phi_1 < \phi > \phi_2 \tag{5}$$

the course of the ship results in a collision with the platform. Consequently the probability of collision given failure at position s is given by

$$F_\phi (\phi_2/s) - F_\phi (\phi_1/s) = \int_{\phi 1}^{\phi 2} f_\phi (\phi/s) \, d\phi \tag{6}$$

where $f_\phi (\phi/s)$ is the probability density distribution of ϕ. The problem is then to find the distribution function of ϕ.

$$F_\phi (\phi/s) = \int_{R_\phi} f (x_1, x_2, \ldots x_n/s) \, dx_1 \cdot dx_2 \cdot \ldots \cdot dx_n \tag{7}$$

where R_ϕ is that region where $g (x_1, x_2, \ldots x_n/s)$ is less or equal to ϕ. By repeated simulations it is possible to determine eq. (6) numerically. The collision probability during one approach along the line s is expressed by

$$P (\text{collision}) = \int_s \int_{\phi 1}^{\phi 2} f_\phi (\phi/s) \cdot \frac{\lambda}{V} \, d\phi \, ds \tag{8}$$

In practice the approach course will be chosen according to the pilot's judgement of the prevailing environmental conditions. The actual course, s, in a given weather situation may, for instance, be formally characterized by a single parameter, ω, denoting the directional angle of the course line. ω is a random variable described by the probability density function of $f_\Omega(\omega)$.

Eq. (8) may then finally be written

$$P(\text{collision}) = \int\limits_{o}^{2\pi} \int\limits_{s} \int\limits_{\phi_1}^{\phi_2} f_{\Phi}(\phi/s,\omega) \cdot f_{\Omega}(\omega) \cdot \frac{\lambda}{V} \, d\phi ds d\omega \qquad (9)$$

Computer simulation study

The method described above has been applied to analysis of the consequences of loss of propulsion in the approach of a loading buoy. It is also supposed that the rudder locks at the instantaneous position. At least twelve random variables enter the problem:

s, Ψ	= ship position and heading at failure
u, v, w, w_r	= ship velocity components and yaw rate
δ	= rudder angle at failure
v_c, γ	= current velocity and direction
h_s, α	= wave height and direction
V_A, Θ	= wind speed and direction

Evidently several of these variables are correlated. For instance the wave height and wave direction are not independent of the prevailing wind speed and wind direction. However, data concerning their joint distribution are scarce. As previously mentioned the course line depends also on the instant weather state, and the ship speed will be a function of the distance to the loading buoy.

Besides the problem of determining the distribution of all the relevant parameters, a considerable number of simulations are required to obtain confidence in the results. Hence, the problem is reduced by introducing several simplifying assumptions.

For example, the sea state is assumed characterized by the wind speed and wind direction only, corresponding to a steady-state situation and long fetch. The tanker is supposed to approach the buoy into the wind, following a realistic velocity profile.

In this manner it is possible to reduce the number of independent random variables to five:

s	= ship distance to the loading buoy
Θ	= wind direction
V_A	= wind speed
γ	= current direction
δ	= rudder angle at failure

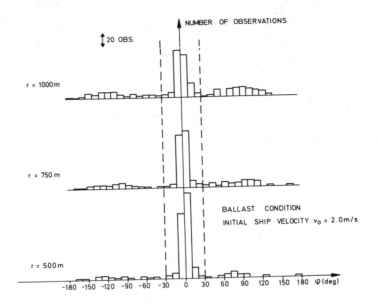

Fig. 3 Histogrammes for crossing angles

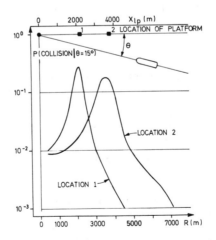

Fig. 4 Collision probability versus ship position

The probability density function of the ship path may now at first be predicted without regard to the position of the ship at failure and wind direction. For a given initial velocity at the instant of failure, the remaining independent variables are generated stochastically from their respective distributions by means of a random number generator. With these parameters determined, the ship path is simulated collecting statistics at selected distances of the start point, as illustrated in Fig. 2. The sample mean and standard deviation of crossing angle ϕ, absolute velocity, V_0, and sailed time t are estimated. The crossing angle and velocity distributions are in addition presented in the form of histograms.

Mathematical model

The equations of motion as described by Norrbin (1971), constitute the mathematical model for the simulations. In studying the basic steered motion of a surface vessel, the roll, pitch and heave motions are generally assumed negligible and motions in the horizontal plane are considered only.

The calculations account for hydrodynamic still water forces, wind forces and wave drift forces. Both wind and wave forces are assumed constant for a given weather situation. The wave forces considered are the mean component of the slowly varying second order wave drift forces. The numerical integration and statistics collection were carried out by applying the general simulation programme GASP IV, developed by Prietsker (1977).

Numerical studies

The principles of collecting data of crossing angles in histogrammes are illustrated for a particular simulation run in Fig. 3. The tendency of increased spreading of ship paths with increasing sailed distance is clearly demonstrated. The central parts of the histogrammes relate to ship sailing ahead while the external parts are broadly recordings of drifting ships.

Goodness of fit tests may be applied to determine whether values of the crossing angle follow a theoretical probability density distribution. Among the various standard tests available, the chi-square test was selected and the data were tested for goodness of fit to the normal distribution. Although the tests in some cases revelaed that the hypothesis of normality should be rejected, the normal distributions were employed in all the calculations.

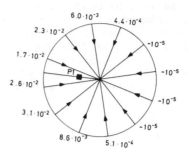

Fig. 5   Collision probability for various directions of
         approach

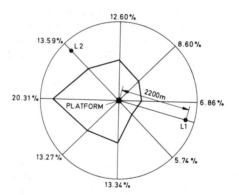

Fig. 6   Distribution of wind directions.
         Two different locations of the loading buoy:
         L 1 and L 2.

The main parameters governing the distribution of crossing
angle are the initial ship velocity, u, at failure and the
sailed distance, r. For intermediate values of u and r,
the distribution parameters were found by interpolations.
This was performed by approximating functions of second
degree and applying the method of least squares.

Estimation of the collision probability

The procedure of calculating the collision probability is
as follows: On the assumption that the propulsion failure
is time-invariant, the entire approach activity is divided
into equal time intervals. To each time interval the ship
is assigned a mean velocity and a mean distance of the loading buoy according to the chosen velocity profile. Within
a given field geometry the corresponding distance of the
platform is determined. Based on the particular values of
u and r, the parameters of the crossing angle distributions
are estimated as described previously. The collision
probability in the current position is given by eq. (6).

The calculation is carried through all time intervals and
the entire set of possible approach angles.

Twelve equally spaced approach directions and two different
locations of the platform relative to the loading buoy
were investigated.

In Fig. 4 the collision probability related to the course
closest to the platform is plotted in terms of the ship
position at failure. It appears that the collision probability has a peak when the ship passes the platform. The
peak is more pronounced for decreasing minimum distance.

The collision probability in terms of the approach angle,
obtained by integrating the probability density functions,
are presented in Fig. 5 for location 1 (see Fig. 4).

The total probability of collision given failure is computed
by introducing the long term distribution of wind direction.
The directional wind distribution as well as two alternative locations of the loading buoy (1) relative to the platform (equal distance) are shown in Fig. 6. The conditional
collision probability is presented in Table 1 for the most
favourable and the most unfavourable location of the loading
buoy. The probability may be approximately halved by placing
the loading buoy at the most favourable position on the lee-
ward side of the platform.

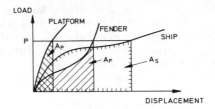

Fig. 7 Load-displacement relationships

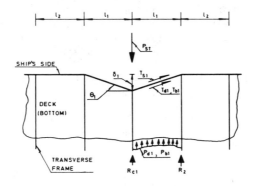

Fig. 8 Collapse model for ship side

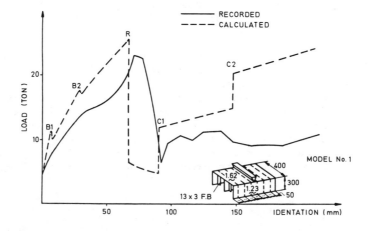

Fig. 9 Load-penetration diagram

Location	L 1	L 2
P (collision/failure) $\cdot 10^{-3}$	6.2	12.3

Table 1   Probability of collision given failure
            for two alternative positions of the
            loading buoy.

Finally, on the assumption that the failure intensity of
prolonged loss of propulsion is $5 \cdot 10^{-5}$/hr and that the
number of tankers loading a year is 70, the collision
probability pr. year for the best location is assessed
to

P (collision) = $3.2 \cdot 10^{-5}$

IMPACT MECHANICS

In a collision, parts of the kinetic energy must be
absorbed by elastic and plastic deformation of the ship,
any fender system and the platform itself. The amount of
energy that has to be absorbed is mainly a kinergetic problem as the energy is determined by the masses, velocities
and geometries of the impacting bodies.

With known load-deformation characteristics for the platform, fender and ship, it is possible to associate the
absorbed energy with a certain damage.   In general. the
load-deformation curves are non-linear as illustrated
in Fig. 7.

The area under each curve represents the absorbed energy
for a given load level. By equalling the absorbed energy
to the change in kinetic energy, it is possible to
associate an impact velocity with a damage level. For a
central impact, the energy audit reads:

$$\tfrac{1}{2} mV_0^2 = A_P + A_F + A_S \tag{10}$$

where m is the mass and added mass of the ship and A
denotes the area under the load curves.

It is rather complex to establish the curves principally
shown in Fig. 7. It is further impossible to find analytical formulaes for the force and the duration of impact
for general load curves.

In the following the impact capacities of ships and
platforms will be discussed and various simplified
procedures will be described.

PENETRATION OF SHIP HULLS

General

The mechanical properties of ship hulls in collision were
studied by Minorsky (1959) who derived an empirical correlation between resistance to penetration and energy absorbed in ship collisions. However, the formula does not
assess the force development during indentation and analysis
of low energy cases - corresponding to a supply vessel
collision showed a wide scatter. Generally more damage
was done than indicated from the striking speeds reported.

A comprehensive study of structural damage of tankers in
minor collisions is reported by M. Rosenblatt and Son, Inc.
(1975). The various phases of the structural behaviour
during a collision were studied using a plastic analysis
procedure.

Assumptions

In order to determine the relationships between the force
and indentation of the ship's side and the corresponding
energy absorbed by the hull during collision, a computer
programme was made.

- The striking load and the indentation of the
  hull can be determined according to a static
  load-deformation case (i.e. - dynamic effects
  are disregarded).
- The struck object is considered infinitely stiff.
- The indentation of the hull is constant over
  the entire length of the ship.
- The energy involved is completely absorbed as
  plastic deformation energy. Possible elastic
  flexural deflection of the ship hull girder is
  not considered.

Brief outline of the calculation model

At the initial time of collision, only the part of the hull
in-between the incursion line and the neighbouring transverse frames is considered to be affected by the distortion
of the hull.

The striking load which simplified has been assumed to act
along the incursion line only, is calculated for selected

deflections of the ship's side.

The striking load P_{ST} acting on the side is determined according to the membrane tension force of the ship's side, deck and bottom and the plastic buckling load of the deck, bottom and frames appearing during indentation:

$$P_{ST} = 2 (T_{S1} \sin\Theta_1 + (T_{d1} + T_{b1}) \cdot \sin\Theta_1 + (P_{d1} + P_{b1}) + R_{C1}) (11)$$

For notation, reference is made to Fig. 8.

The reaction force at the neighbouring transverse frames (at the end of the collapse model) is:

$$R_2 = (T_{S1} + T_{d1} + T_{b1}) \sin\Theta_1 \qquad (12)$$

If the reaction force, R_2, is less than the buckling load of the frame, R_{C2}, the calculations are repeated for an increased indentation of the side. Otherwise the collapse model is extended with two more frames and the deformation at the buckled frame and the corresponding striking load of the new collapse model are calculated. In a similar manner, the deflection at the frames and the striking load can be calculated for a collapse model involving a large number of buckled frames. Due to bending and stretching of the shell plating, rupture of the side will finally occur at a particular indentation. For indentations beyond this limit, the membrane tension forces of the ship's side are neglected.

Due to the great influence that the rupture of the shell will have on the load-deformation pattern and the energy absorption of the hull, it is rather important to deter-mine this failure condition with some degree of confidence. On the other hand, it is extremely difficult to accurately calculate the strain in every part of the hull. For the time being, the failure criteria is basen on the simple philosophy that rupture will occur when elongation of the side in-between any of the transverse frames exceeds the ultimate strain limit (approximately 30% for mild steel).

Load-penetration curves and energy absorption

Analyses based on the theoretical model have been compared to several model tests with a vertical infinitely stiff bow indenting the side of different ship models measuring the static relationship between load and deformation, as reported by SRA, Japan (1970) and SNAME, Japan (1965). The models represented a variety of hull strength. One

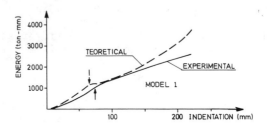

Fig. 10   Energy absorption versus indentation

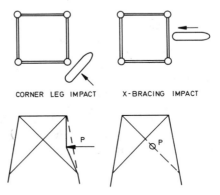

Fig. 11   Supply vessel impact against steel jacket

example of a recorded load-penetration curve from these
experiments together with the corresponding calculated
curve is shown in Fig. 9. The recorded graph does not
give any information about the longitudinal extension
of the plastic deformations or the increase of the extension with increasing indentations. This is, however,
indicated on the theoretical curve where the different
deformation processes developing during penetration have
been shown.

At the initial deformation of the model the theoretical
crushing load is determined according to the buckling
resistance of the deck, bottom and transverse frames in the
contact zone of the colliding objects. In the first stage
of penetration, or before rupture of the side will occur,
the striking load will increase almost monotonously with
indentations. The magnitude of the load will, in most
cases, primarily depend on the membrane stresses in the
side. During this process, a number of transverse frames
may start to form, indicated by B1, B2, etc. in the figures,
resulting in a longitudinal extension of plastic deformations
that may several times exceed the breadth of the physical
contact zone. This extension will depend on the ratio between the strength of the ship's side compared with the
strength of the transverse frames with deck and bottom
plating. At the point of rupture R, the striking load
will drop due to the disappearance of membrane stresses in
the side.

At still larger indentations, cracks will progress into the
deck and bottom resulting in an almost constant penetration
load, until the bow directly strikes the neighbouring transverse frames of the cracks, C1, C2, etc.

Comparison of the calculated and recorded load-penetration
curve reveals that the magnitude of the striking load
during penetration can be reasonably prediced in a theoretical way. However, discrepancies exist at several points.
These may be due to various reasons: the uncertainty with
regard to the ultimate strain limit of steel, crack propagation in deck and bottom etc.

The energy absorbed by the models during indentation,
based on integration of the theoretical and recorded load-
penetration curves, is shown in Fig. 10. The arrows in the
figures indicate where rupture of the side occurred.

Parametrical study

The predominant parameters of the theoretical model are
supposed to be the assumptions regarding:

-    the collapse load of transverse frames
-    the membrane tension stresses in the ship's side
-    rupture criterium

To investigate the influence of these parameters, a parametrical study was performed. Improvements of the theoretical
estimates were achieved by changing one or a combination of
the parameters listed above. However, to establish rational criteria for making adjustments, further model tests are
required.

IMPACT CAPACITIES OF STEEL JACKETS

Type of damage

It seems reasonable to consider two types of damage to the
structure based on the possible impacts shown in Fig. 11 -
either complete failure of a single bracing or x-bracing,
or deformation of a jacket corner leg. The steel structure
will absorb the energy in the following ways:

-    local deformation of the cross section of bracing/leg
-    global deformation of adjoining frame
-    overall deformation of the platform.

Local damage

Evidently the extent of local damage and energy absorption
of the platform members will depend on the nature of the
impact. A head-on collision will presumably give a more
concentrated impact force than a sideways collision,
entailing larger local damage for a given impact velocity.
Unfortunately, simple formulae of load-deformation relationships for large, plastic deformations of cylinders do
not exist. Solutions may be obtained by plastic limit
analysis or non-linear computer programmes. However, the
need of experimental verification is obvious. At present,
laboratory tests with impact loads on cylindrical shells
are planned to be carried out by DnV.

Global deformation of bracing/leg

To determine the limit load and energy absorption in global
deformation of bracing and leg, simple plastic analysis is
presumably sufficiently accurate. If the bracing supports
are rigid against inward displacements, large membrane
tension forces will arise in the bracing, improving the
ability of absorbing energy considerably. For a fully
clamped rectangular beam, the following theoretical expressions for the plastic load-carrying capacity yield:

$$\frac{P}{P_C} = 1 + \left(\frac{w}{D}\right)^2 \qquad \frac{w}{D} \leq 1 \qquad\qquad (13a)$$

$$\frac{P}{P_C} = 2\,\frac{w}{D} \qquad\qquad \frac{w}{D} \geq 1 \qquad\qquad (13b)$$

where w and D are the plastic deformation and the height of the beam respectively and

$$P_C = \frac{8\sigma_y \cdot W_P}{\ell} \qquad\qquad (14)$$

is the static collapse pressure of a beam of length ℓ, centrally loaded, with plastic section modulus W_P and yield stress σ_y. The formulae are also approximately correct for a cylindrical beam. An indispensible condition is that the strength of the tubular joint is not exceeded before the axial force becomes significant.

Eq. (13a) represents the transition stage with simultaneous large out-of-plane bending stresses and axial stresses. This is normally considered as an unfavourable loading condition, as reflected in current design rules; API (1977) and NPD (1977), based upon punching shear strength of tubular joints. However, these formulae are intended to ensure a low level of stresses in working condition and are not meant to be a criterion for ultimate stress. Recent research carried out by DnV seems to confirm that the capacity is almost independent of the combined stresses.

Considering the global deformation of the leg, the joints cannot be assumed fixed against inplane displacements and hence significant membrane tension forces will not develop. Instead the compressive axial stress caused by the functional load should be retained in the analysis. The local damage to the leg will affect the collapse load in the global failure mode. This failure mode interaction emphasizes the significance of determining the local deformation characteristics.

Global deformation of platform

The part of the energy that is absorbed by the adjoining frame may be studied by ordinary frame computer programmes. In most cases a linear elastic analysis will suffice.

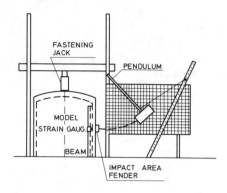

Fig. 12   Arrangement for impact tests

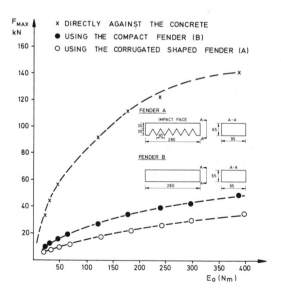

Fig. 13   Max. impact force versus impact energy

The amount of energy absorbed in global bending will in
most cases be small compared to local deformation provided
local damage will prevail. However, the global
contributions may be significant for deep-water flexible
jackets. The global deformation abalysis is conveniently
carried out using a truss or a space-frame model. Assuming
that the static deflection phase is close to the first eigen-
mode of vibration a first estimate may easily be obtained
from the corresponding natural frequency. The equivalent
stiffness becomes:

$$k^1 = \omega^2 M_{eq} \tag{15}$$

where M_{eq} denotes the equivalent mass (including deck,
jacket, added mass), and ω is the lowest eigenfrequency.
For a collision load at the height L_1 at sea level, the
stiffness is:

$$k \sim k^1 \left(\frac{L}{L_1}\right)^3 \tag{16}$$

where L is the height of the platform.

IMPACT CAPACITY OF CONCRETE STRUCTURES

Pilot tests

In order to obtain early information about relationships
between impact energy and impact loads for various degrees
of fendering, two concrete cylindrical shells were tested
with a local impact load acting radially. The models had
previously been exposed to external pressure up to an ultimate failure load in connection with another research project. Originally the models represented the upper part of a
storage cell in a typical offshore concrete structure.
Thus the models were only understood as "foundation" or
suitable impact receiving bodies for the impact tests.

The scale of the models was approximately 1:10. However,
reinforcement on the inside face of the cylinders was
lacking in the mid-portion, so that only poor resemblance
existed between the available models and, for instance,
a concrete tower of a gravity platform at sea level. This
invalidates any transfer of results to actual concrete shaft
structures.

Test aparatus

Fig. 12 shows the testing arrangements. Fixed supports
were provisioned by the frame and fastening jack. The

pendulum consisted of a hollow beam section and a head of
massive iron. The acceleration of the pendulum during the
impact was measured by means of an accelerometer fixed to
the mass. The radial deflection of the cylinder wall was
found by measuring the deflection of a simply supported
beam attached to the wall, being in contact with the wall
through a bolt at the center. The deflections of the beam
was measured by means of strain gauges. In this way all
the interesting relations could be determined regarding
impact force, radial deflection and energy absorption
during impact.

Two fender types were chosen as shown in Fig. 13. They
did not pretend to represent any typical design of present
offshore fender systems. However, the actual design was
capable of giving a relative comparison between a massive
and a corrugated shaped fender. The material properties
of the rubber were realistic. The tests were carried out
by increasing the drop height both with and without the
fenders. In addition, static load tests were performed.

Experimental results

Recorded maxima of impact forces versus impact energy is
shown in Fig. 13, and radial deflection is reproduced in
Fig. 14. The main purpose of the fender is to increase the
impact area on the cylinder thus reducing the maximum
force considerably compared to an unprotected cylinder.
The difference between the two fender types is relatively
small, although the largest force reduction was obtained
by the corrugated shaped fender. The radial deflection decreased also in the protected cases. The failure load for
both static and dynamic tests showed reasonably good
agreement.

Design against impact forces

As for the design of steel structures the energy absorbed
by the deformation the ship, the fenders and the structure
have to be considered. Offshore concrete shell structures
with a thickness of 0,5 m or more are stiff compared with
the ship's hull and this may lead to quite serious damage
to the ship before the forces have reached a critical
level with respect to the local strength of the concrete.
Local spalling and chipping at the point of contact can
hardly be avoided in an unfendered zone, but the punching
shear strength should be checked using design forces from
the above-mentioned energy absorption analysis.

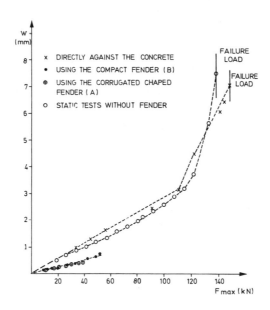

Fig. 14   Radial deflection versus max. impact force

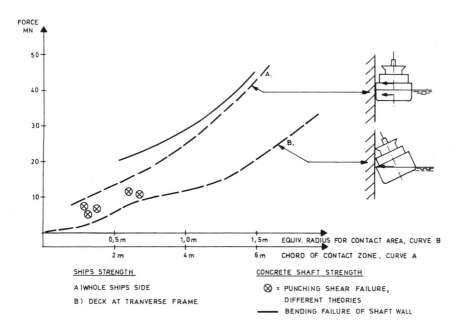

Fig. 15   Curves relating impact force and contact zone

The total shear resistance may be expressed as the sum of the following components:

$$V_r = V_{cr} + V_{pr} + V_{sr} \leq 0,25 \cdot f_{cr} \cdot b \cdot d \qquad (17)$$

where

V_{cr} is the shear resistance due to the concrete and the longitudinal reinforcement

V_{pr} is the shear resistance due to prestress or axial force

V_{sr} is the shear resistance provided by shear reinforcement

f_{cr} is the design compressive strength of the concrete

$b \cdot d$ is the width and thickness of the studied member.

More detailed design formulae may be found in DnV's Rules for the Design, Construction and Inspection of Offshore Structures or in relevant national codes.

The punching shear strength of a number of concrete shaft designs have been estimated by scaling experimental results or using the CEB-FIP Model Code for concrete structures. To make a comparison possible the results have been scaled to a typical column with an internal diameter of 12 m and a wall thickness of 0,6 m using (x) CEB-FIP: Model Code for concrete structures 1978, a load factor γ_f = 1,0 and material factors $\gamma_m$concrete = 1,5 and $\gamma_m$steel = 1,15.

The results have then been plotted together with force-contact zone curves for a typical supply-boat with 2500 tonnes displacement (Fig. 15). It is seen that in the early stages of a collision, for a given equivalent radius of contact zone, the strength of concrete in punching shear is apparently greater than the force which the supply boat can apply.

The capacity of the concrete column to absorb energy in a collision will, however, not be limited by an eventual punching shear failure in case of underestimation of the local stiffness of the boat or an inappropriate shear design. In a sideway collision especially, the structure of the ship will bridge across the hole and apply force to the undamaged part of the shaft.

If a punching shear failure can be prevented in the early
stages of a collision it seems unlikely that such a failure
will occur later beacuse of spreading of the contact zone
due to deformation of the ship and the rapid increase of
punching shear strength with the area of contact.

However, elastic theory calculations may predict the stress
in the reinforcement in the contact zone to reach yield or
the concrete to crush. It is then necessary to allow for
inelastic deformation of the concrete, in order to calculate
the energy absorption. In the absence of a non-linear computer programme capable of analysing a concrete cylinder
under radial load, estimates of the load required to cause
a local bending failure of the column have been made using
a form of yield-line or plastic theory. Where possible,
conservative assumptions have been incorporated in the
plastic theory, and the usual material factor γ_m = 1.5 has
been included. The corresponding failure loads and contact
chord lengths are plotted in Fig. (15). The concrete capacity is apparently much greater than the force which the
ship can apply on the same contact area (using the entire
ship's side).

Thus it seems that a typical supply boat is not strong
enough to cause a local failure of a typical concrete
column in a sideways collision, although it can cause local
yielding and cracking. However, this conclusion is based
on rather simplified calculations and needs experimental
confirmation. Bow-on collisions have not been investigated in full detail, and of course if the boat were heavier
or the column less substantial the conclusion would
require amendment.

If a local failure does not occur, an overall bending
failure of the platform leg will not occur either, in a
sideways collision with a typical leg. The force which the
ship can apply is limited in two ways: firstly the ship's
inertia can cause a plastic flexural hinge in the ship in
a heavy collision, limiting the sideways force on the
column, and secondly for heavy indentations the force from
the ship's side will drop when the plating reaches its
ultimate strain and begins to tear. Both these limits
appear to be below the force necessary to cause an overall
failure of the leg, unless it has been damaged fairly
extensively locally.

CONCLUSIONS

In order to account for the risks involved by the activity
of ships in the neighbourhood of offshore platforms, rational
design criteria for collision accidents should be developed.
This implies that probabilities as well as inherent consequences of various collisions have to be analysed and assessed. The risks associated with ship traffic of different
categories must be considered separately.

The paper outlines a method to evaluate the probability of
collisions between ships and fixed offshore installations
by making use of simulation techniques. The greater benefit
of the method is to compare various alternatives by assessing
the relative frequencies of collision. A total risk assessment is not feasible for the time being due to the scarcity
of data concerning collision events.

In order to account for the influence of both human failures
as well as actions taken to avoid collisions, the model is
being linked to an interactive simulation unit developed presently by DnV.

In order to determine the structural damage during ship
collisions the load-deformation relationships must be known
for the ship, the platform and any possible fender system.
Based on comparisons with small-scale model tests it is tentatively concluded that the load-penetration and energy absorbtion characteristics of ships in sideways collisions in many
a case may be predicted fairly accurately by elasto-plastic
methods of analysis. However, further analysis of actual
ship collisions are needed. Possible dynamic effects occurring in collisions involving stiff parts such as bow, stern,
transverse frame etc, should be investigated.

In the paper, energy absorption of steel platforms is briefly discussed. Such analysis will make extensive use of
plasticity methods. A better knowledge of local strength
and deformation mechanisms of steel cylinders is particularly
needed. To this end, DnV is considering to carry out relevant laboratory tests.

Dynamic tests with pendulum impacts on concrete cylinders
have provided useful information of the physical phenomena
occuring during impacts between impacting bodies and fixed,
shell-shaped structures. In particular, useful qualitative
information was obtained concerning relationship between
incoming impact energy and collision forces for various
degrees of fendering. However, further tests will be required with better modelling of the contact zones of actual
colliding units in order to produce sufficient information
for the purpose of adequate impact design.

References

National Maritime Institute (1977). The Risk of Ship/Platform
Encounters in UK Waters, Report on Project No. 402002.

Carlin B. et al (1977). Offshore Fender Systems
DnV Report No. 77-156

Larsen, C.M., Engseth, G.E. (1978). Ship Collision and
Fendering of Offshore Concrete Structures, European
Offshore Petroleum Conference & Exhibition, London.

Amdahl, J., Hysing, T., Furnes, O. (1977-79). Impact and
Collisions Offshore, DnV Project Reports, Progress Reports 1-6.

Norrbin, N.H. (1971). Theory and Observations on the Use of
a Mathematical Model for Ship Manoeuvring in Deep and Confined Waters, Swedish State Shipbuilding Experimental Tank
Publ. No. 68.

Faltinsen, O.M., Løken, A.E. (1978). Drift Forces and Slowly
Varying Forces on Ships and Offshore Structures in Waves,
Norwegian Maritime Research No. 1, Vol. 6.

Prietsker, A.A.B. (1977). The Gasp IV User's Manual,
Prietsker & Associates, Inc.

Minorsky, V.V. (1959). An Analysis of Ship Collisions with
Reference to Protection of Nuclear Power Plants, Journal of
Ship Research 3, 2.

M. Rosenblatt and Son, Inc., New York (1975). Tanker
Structural Analysis for Minor Collisions, Department of
Transportation, United States Coast Guard, Washington.

The Shipbuilding Research Association of Japan (1970).
Studies on Collision Protective Structure of Nuclear Powered
Ships, Rep. No. 71.

The Society of Naval Architects of Japan (1965). Journal
of Zosen Kioakai, Vol. 118.

API (1977). Recommended Practice for Planning, Designing
and Constructing Fixed Offshore Platforms.

NPD (1977). Regulations for the Structural Design of
Fixed Structures on the Norwegian Continental Shelf.

IMPACT OF FALLING LOADS ON SUBMERGED CONCRETE STRUCTURES

Jens Jacob Jensen
Dr. techn. FCB-Cement and Concrete Research Institute. SINTEF
The Norwegian Institute of Technology, Trondheim, Norway.

1. INTRODUCTION

On production platforms of the Condeep type, there will be a possibility that falling objects from the platform deck can strike the upper domes and cause damage.

This paper summarizes an examination of the impact problems of falling objects, related to the Condeep project, and it comprises of the following items (figure 1).

. Free fall in air from platform deck to water surface
. Impact with the water surface
. Free fall in water from water surface to the container domes
. Impact of the objects with the domes including local damage such as penetration into concrete and spalling of concrete.
. Dynamic elastic and non-elastic response of the structure

Theoretical models based on physical laws and on experience from experimental work of related problems have been developed and used in design proposals.

2. MOVEMENTS OF FALLING OBJECTS THROUGH AIR AND WATER

The falling objects usually have shape like a bar, sphere or cube, and probable examples of falling objects are "Drill Collar", "Casing", "Conductor Pipe Section", "Hydrill" and "Mud Pump". Geometrical and mass-data for some typical objects are given in fig. 4.1.

Free fall in air from platform deck to water surface.

A falling object which has been dropped from height h above the water surface, hits the water surface with the velocity v_1, neglecting the air resistance

$$v_1 = \sqrt{2gh}$$

(2.1)

where g = acceleration of gravity.

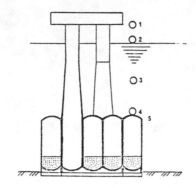

Figure 1.   Problems

Impact with the water surface

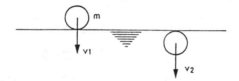

Figure 2.1.   Impact with the water surface.

The falling object with the mass m hits the water surface
with the velocity $\bar{v}_1$ and the impact force P_1.   Due to the impact, the falling object loses some of its kinetic energy and
proceeds with the velocity v_2 below the water surface.
By using the impulse law

$$m\, v_1 - \int_o^t P(t)\,dt = mv_2 \qquad\qquad (2.2)$$

the velocity v_2 can be deduced.   The second link, at the
left hand side of eq. 2.2 shows the impact energy loss.   The
main problem can be traced back to the determination of the
impact force and the impact time of the falling object.   The
impact of a sphere, and a cylinder with the water surface has
been treated in |1| and |2| whilst the impact of bodies with
plane surfaces has been investigated theoretically and experi-
mentally in |3|.

The impact of rotation symmetric bodies against a water sur-
face has been investigated theoretically in |1|.   The impact
force of a cone with the top angle of 2α and the base radius
r hitting the water surface can be expressed as:

$$P_1(t) = 3\mu_o m\, v_1^2\, \frac{r^2}{u(r)\,(1+\mu_o r^3)^3}. \qquad\qquad (2.3)$$

where
$$\mu_o = \frac{4}{3}\frac{\rho_2}{m} \quad \text{and} \quad \bar{u} = \frac{\pi}{4} \cot g\alpha$$

m ≐ mass of falling object

ρ_2 = density of water

The impact time can approximately be estimated as the time the body uses to cross the water surface with the velocity v_1. If the falling object has the dimension of d_1 the impact time can be estimated to

$$t_1 = \frac{d_1}{v_1} \tag{2.4}$$

Assuming a triangular impulse shape, the impulse of impact can then be found as

$$I_s = \int_o^t P(t)\,dt = \frac{1}{2}P_1 t_1$$

Hence, the velocity v_2 which is the starting velocity of the falling object in water can be found as:

$$v_2 = v_1 - \frac{P_1 t_1}{2m} \tag{2.5}$$

The corresponding impact force of a cylinder with the base diameter D, and the length L can be expressed as $|2|$.

$$P_1(t) = 0,5 \cdot \rho_2 D \cdot C_s v_1^2 \cdot L \tag{2.6}$$

where the usual value of C_s = 0,3 - 0,4.

The impact time and velocity might be analysed according to eq. (2.4) and (2.5)

A falling prism can hit the water surface in different ways. In the following two cases have been investigated as shown in figure 2.2.

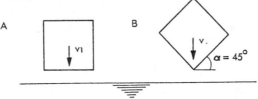

Figure 2.2. Impact of prism-shaped bodies.

In the first case, (A), an air pad can be built up just before impacting and soften the impact. This effect will take place only in the case of small angles α = 0-3°. Taking the effect of the air pad into account, the impact pressure p can be calculated to

$$p = 111,7 \cdot v_1^{1,1} \tag{2.7}$$

p is given in kN/m^2 when velocity v_1 in m/s. In general, the impact pressure depends on the shape and angle α. In the case of α = 45°, the following relationship exists:

$$p = 1,59 \cdot v_1^2 \tag{2.8}$$

The impact force can be deduced from eq. (2.7) and (2.8) and, by means of eq. (2.4) and (2.5), the velocity v_2 after splashing can be calculated.

A bar-shaped object falling with the translation and rotation velocity V_1 and $\overset{\bullet}{\alpha}$ will swerve in water and probably strike the platform legs, the container domes or even go outside the structure. The most unfavourable case will be when the bar hits the surface with its cross-end. The loss of energy in this case, compared with the total kinetic energy, will be moderate or negligible.

Free fall in water from water surface to the container domes

With the starting velocity V_2 at the water surface, the object is falling through the water approaching the structural elements below. The falling object will reach a constant velocity V_t, the termal velocity, which depends on the shape and the size of the falling object. The termal velocity can be determined according to:

$$V_t = \sqrt{\frac{2D}{C_d A \cdot \rho}} = \sqrt{\frac{2(W-O)}{C_d A \cdot \rho}} \qquad (2.9)$$

where the drag force D has been replaced by the gravity force W and buoyancy force O. ρ is the density of water, A = cross section area, and C_d the shape coefficient of the falling object depending on the Reynolds number

$$R_e = \frac{V_o d}{\nu} \qquad (2.10)$$

where V_o = velocity (in this case $V_o = V_t$), d= dimension of object and ν = viscosity of water (dependant on temperature).

The velocity of the falling object at the water surface is V_2. Depending on the termal velocity of the object, the body will increase or decrease its velocity approaching the structural elements below. Given that the velocity at which the falling object strikes the structural elements is V_3, the following energy relationship at the water surface and at the place of impact can be written

$$\frac{1}{2} mV_3^2 = \frac{1}{2} mV_2^2 + \int_o^h (W-O-C_d A\rho \frac{V^2(z)}{2}) dz \qquad (2.11)$$

where the last link at the right hand side expresses the work carried out by the water resistance of the falling object. From eq.(2.11) the velocity V_3 can be found. However, the last link depends on the velocity and therefore the integration has to be carried out in steps. If the velocity of the falling object in the depth z is called V_z and the velocity in the step before in the depth $z-\Delta z$ is called $V_{z-\Delta z}$, the velocity V_z can be found by modification of eq. 2.11 to:

$$V_z = \sqrt{V_{z-\Delta z}^2 + \frac{2\Delta z}{m}(W-O-C_d A \cdot \rho \frac{V_{z-\Delta z}^2}{2})} \qquad (2.12)$$

where Δz means the difference in depth between two steps. By solving V_z step-by-step starting with the velocity $V_{z-\Delta z} = V_2$ at the water surface, the impact velocity V_3 can be determined.

When the falling object is approaching the cylinder domes, the object may retard due to the water pad which may be built-up just before the impact. This problem has been discussed theoretically in |4|, in the case of a sphere and used in the following investigation. Due to the limitation of this paper, the deduction will not be carried out here, since the practical results of the numerical studies are of less importance.

3. IMPACT THEORY AND DYNAMIC RESPONSE ANALYSIS ON STRUCTURAL
   ELEMENTS

When a falling object hits the container domes, the magnitude of the impact load, the duration of the impact, the dynamic response and possible local damage of the structural elements have to be examined.

Type of impact.

When an object impacts with a structural element, different kinds of impact may occur. Usually, we distinguish between elastic impact and non-elastic or plastic impact. On elastic impact the body will rebound after the impact whilst on a fully non-elastic impact, permanent deformations may occur and the impact bodies will stay together after the impact. The real cases will be between the two mentioned limitations and the type of impact will be of importance when calculating the impact force and impact time.

The impulse I of a mass m with the velocity V can be written as

$$I = m \cdot V = CPt_d = \tfrac{1}{2} Pt_d \tag{3.1}$$

where P = impact load and t_d = duration of impact. In eq. (3.1), a triangle-shaped impulse has been assumed ($C = \tfrac{1}{2}$). The impact load can then be found to

$$P = 2 \cdot m \, V/t_d \tag{3.2}$$

Knowing the impact time, the impact load can be found.

The elastic impact problem has been dealt with in |5, 6, 7|, In the following, the elastic impact will be examined, according to the method given in |7| where a sphere has been examined. Then the impact time t_d can be found as

$$t_d = K_1 V_o^{-1/5} \tag{3.3}$$

where

V_o = velocity of hitting object
K_1 = constant defined in terms of elastic properties and geometry of the system.

$$K_1 = 2{,}94 \left(\frac{15}{16} \frac{m \cdot m_1}{m+m_1} \, g\right)^{2/5} \cdot R^{-1/5} \tag{3.4}$$

where

m = mass of the hitting object
m_1 = mass of the structure (part of it)
R = curvature of the surface of the hitting object

$g = (1-\nu^2)/E + (1-\nu^2)/E$, where E_1 and E are the Young modulus of the materials of the two colliding objects and where ν and ν_1 are Poissons ratio of the same materials.

From eq. (3.3) and 3.4), it is visible that the impact time increases with increasing mass of the hitting object and decreases with increasing velocity of the object.

A non-elastic impact causes permanent deformations which can be formed on the surface by crushing or penetrating the concrete. Knowing the penetrating depth D, the impact time t_d can be estimated on the basis of the impact velocity.

$$t_d = \frac{2D}{V_o} \tag{3.5}$$

Non-elastic impact problems have been discussed in |8| and |9|. According to |8|, the penetration can be found by the relationship

$$V_c \doteq \frac{1}{2} \frac{m\,V_o^{\,2}}{Y} \tag{3.6}$$

where

V_c = volume of penetration area
m = mass of hitting object
V_o = velocity of hitting object
Y = "yielding" strength of material

In figure 3.1, the penetration of a conical-ended, spherical and square-ended object is listed.

SHAPE	PENETRATION
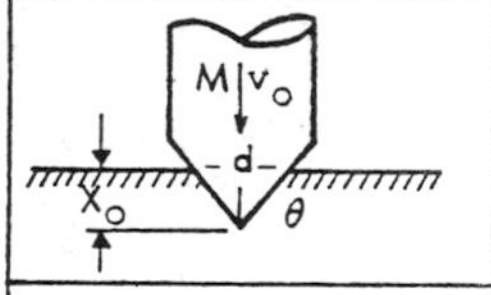 $M\|V_o$ $-d-$ X_o θ	$d_o = 2tg\theta\beta^{1/3}V_o^{\,2/3}$ $\beta = \frac{3}{2}\dfrac{M}{Y_\pi\,tg^2\theta}$ $X_o = d_o\,cotg\,\dfrac{\theta}{2}$
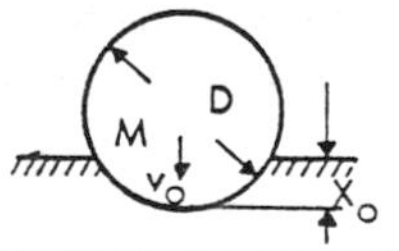 D M v_o X_o	$X_o = \left\|\dfrac{M}{Y}\pi D\right\|^{1/2} v_o$
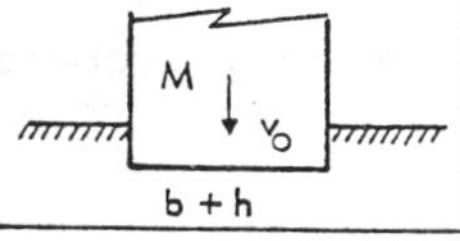 M v_o $b+h$	$X_o = \dfrac{1}{2}\dfrac{M}{Y}\dfrac{V_o^{\,2}}{bh}$

Figure 3.1. Penetration of hitting objects of different shape.

The penetration can also be estimated according to |9| as

$$D' = K_p \; A \cdot v' R \qquad\qquad (3.7)$$

where

    D' = penetration in ft.
    K_p = material properly constant
    A = sectional mass, i.e. weight of object per unit cross-
        sectional area (lb/ft^2)
    v' = velocity factor

$$v' = \log_{10}(1 + \frac{v^2}{215000})$$

    v = velocity of object. ft/sec.

The material constant K_p is, for concrete, K_p = 7,99, for reinforced concrete, K_p= 4,76 and for specially reinforced concrete, K_p = 2,82 |9|.

Local damage

The local damage caused by impact of falling objects can be local penetration or spalling of the concrete in the region of the impact. The penetration problem has been discussed in the previous chapter and the spalling problem will be out-lined.

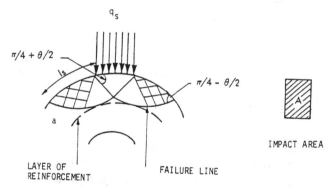

Figure 3.2. Spalling failure model.

In figure 3.2, a failure model is shown, where a failure line touching the reinforcement layer has been assumed. The failure load P_f can be found as

$$P_f = N_c \; (C + \sigma^1 tg\Phi) \cdot b \cdot h \qquad\qquad (3.8)$$

where

    N_c = nondimensional constant depending on the geometry
        of the object, usually N_c = 6,0-8,0.
    C_1 = cohesion of concrete
    σ^1 = effective normal stress at failure line
    Φ = angle of friction
    $b \cdot h$ = dimension of impact area

A possible example of the material properties C and Φ for a concrete with one-dimensional compression strength (cube) of 40 N/mm^2 and w/c-ratio 0,40 is Φ = 40, C = 9,11.

The failure load is dependant on the material properties, i.e. angle of friction and material cohesion. Subjected to repeated loading, the material cohesion will be broken down, and the load capacity depends, in this case, on the normal stress and friction angle Φ. The spalling length l_s can be estimated by assuming the failure line touching the reinforcement layer

$$l_s = \frac{2a}{tg(\pi/4 - \phi/2)} \qquad (3.9)$$

where a = distance between surface and reinforcement layer.

Dynamic response analysis

The response analysis of the container domes imposed to impact load has to take the non-elastic behaviour of the structural elements into account. In figure 3.3, an impact load acting on an elastic-plastic system is shown.

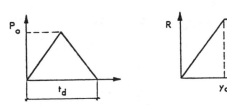

Figure 3.3.   Impact load on an elastic-plastic system.

The kinetic energy of the falling object can be expressed in terms of its impulse or the impact load and impact time in the following way

$$E_a = \frac{1}{2} mv^2 = \frac{I^2}{2m} = \frac{P_o^2 t_d^2}{8m} \qquad (3.10)$$

where   m = impact mass
        V = velocity of impact mass
        I = impulse (triangular shape assumed)

The energy work carried out by elastic and plastic behaviour is

$$E_i = R_m y_{el} \left(\frac{y_{max}}{y_{el}} - \frac{1}{2} \right) \qquad (3.11)$$

where the notation can be taken from figure 3.3.
Using (3.10) and (3.11) and taking the vibration period of the structural element T with the mass m_s into account

$$T = 2\pi \sqrt{\frac{m_s \cdot y_{el}}{R_m}} \qquad (3.12)$$

the impact load P_o can be expressed as

$$P_o = \frac{R_m}{\pi} \frac{T}{t_d} \sqrt{\frac{m}{m_s} \left(2 \frac{y_{max}}{y_{el}} - 1\right)} \qquad (3.13)$$

The relationship

$$\beta = \frac{y_{max}}{y_{el}} \qquad (3.14)$$

has been called the degree of plasticity and expresses the
relationship of the maximum deformation to the elastic deformation.

The equation (3.13) gives a more correct expression of the impact load taking the dynamic response of the system into
account. The analysis has, therefore, to be carried out as an
iteration procedure in the following way:

- Analysis of the period T of the system.
- Evaluation of impact time from theory of elastic impact,
  or non-elastic impact.
- Evaluation of impact force based on the impact law (eq.3.2).
- Calculation of elastic or non-elastic deformations. For
  single degree of systems, the theory outlined in |11| can
  be used, for multidegree of systems, a computer program
  for non-elastic dynamic response analysis has been deve-
  loped |12|.
- Calculation of inpact loads and impact time according to
  eq. 3.13.
- Repeating of analysis

The procedure ensures a rapid convergency.

Local flexural and shear capacity.

The local flexural and shear capacity of the spheric shells in
the case of impact loading have to be investigated.
The moment capacity can be calculated by means of a simple
yield line model where the acting normal stress in the shell
under hydrostatic loading can be taken into account, as well
as the rotation capacity of the cross-section has to be
checked. The bending moment capacity depends on the amount of
the reinforcement.

The shear capacity is however a little more complex. Important
parameters are the general stress situation, the loading time,
the loading area as well as the degree of reinforcement and
material quality. As basis for the design, the results of
J. Moe's tests |13| concerning punching of slabs have been
chosen. Compared to a lot of punching shear theories and test
results, which also contain recent tests, the Moe formula is
not too extreme. Further, the influence of size and shape as
well as reinforcement can be considered. The shear capacity
increases strongly by a two-dimensional stress situation |14|,
at the same time the shear capacity also increases under rapid
dynamic loading |15|. Based on verified experimental test
results, a rising of the shear capacity, caused by the two-dimensional compression stress-situation and the dynamic loading
has been proposed. The magnitude of this rise factor of the
shear capacity can be discussed, but the value will probably be
in the range of 1,5 - 2,5. Due to the brittle character of a
shear failure, restrictions to the degree of plasticity of
shear failures have to be set.

4.   NUMERICAL STUDIES AND SUMMARY OF RESULTS

In figure 1. a general view of the problem was shown. For the numerical study the following assumptions with respect to geometry, material properties, falling objects and load parameter were made:

. Free fall in air	h_1 = 30m
. Free fall in water	h_2 = 80m
. Diameter of container	D_m = 19.20m
. Curvature of sphere	R = 14,00m
. Thichness of dome	t = 0,54m
. Concrete quality (cube strength)	f_{ck} = 45^N/mm^2
. Reinforcement (yielding ")	fy = 400 "
. Impact loading coefficient	γ_f = 1,05
. Material cofficient steel	γ_{ms} = 1.00
. Material cofficient concrete	γ_{mc} = 1,30

The data of the falling objects are listed in figure 4.1. Approximately they have a shape like a bar, sphere or cube.

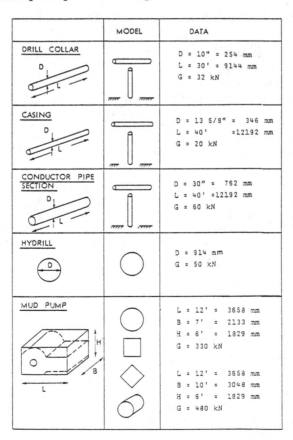

	MODEL	DATA
DRILL COLLAR		D = 10" = 254 mm L = 30' = 9144 mm G = 32 kN
CASING		D = 13 5/8" = 346 mm L = 40' =12192 mm G = 20 kN
CONDUCTOR PIPE SECTION		D = 30" = 762 mm L = 40' =12192 mm G = 60 kN
HYDRILL		D = 914 mm G = 50 kN
MUD PUMP		L = 12' = 3658 mm B = 7' = 2133 mm H = 6' = 1829 mm G = 330 kN L = 12' = 3658 mm B = 10' = 3048 mm H = 6' = 1829 mm G = 480 kN

Figure 4.1.   Falling objects.

The results of the numerical studies can be summarised in the
following way:

- By free fall from the platform deck, the objects reach the
  water surface with the velocity of ~ 25 $\frac{m}{sec}$.

- In the case of the impact of the objects with water, the energy
  loss and the change in velocity have been considered.

- Every object which is falling in water has its special terminal
  velocity v_t, which depends on the weight, volume and shape of
  the object. Edged objects reach their terminal velocity at a
  depth of 10-20 m, and spherical objects reach terminal velocity
  at a depth of 40-60 m. Bar-like objects of the type "Drill Collar"
  are shooting through the water surface and need a long distance
  to reach the terminal velocity. All objects examined **retard** by
  passing over from air into water.

- The objects hit the structure at a velocity close to the
  terminal velocity of each object. The velocity of different
  objects through air and water is illustrated in Fig. 4.2.

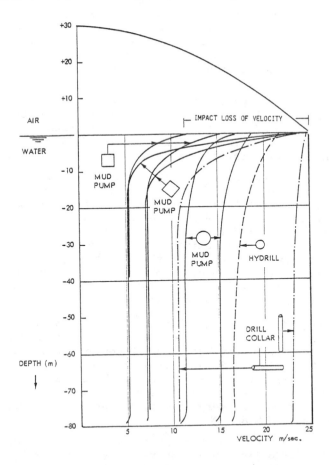

Figure 4.2. Velocities of the falling objects

The velocity of the different objects can roughly be estimated as follows: "Mud Pump" v = 7 m/sec, "Hydrill" v = 16 m/sec and "Drill Collar" v = 22 m/sec.

- The objects hit the structure and elastic, as well as inelastic, impact have been examined. The magnitude of the impact load, time of impact and possible loss of energy by impact are calculated at the same time as possible local damage in the structure surface is estimated.

- The time of impact of objects which strike the concrete surface varies from ca. 5-12 millseconds. Through covering the domes with a lightweight concrete cover, possible damping effects and prolonging of impact time, can be attained. In this case the impact lasts about 10-40 milliseconds.
  For the final analysis the time of impact has been assumed as a duration of 10-30 milliseconds, dependant on the impact objects and a possible lightweight concrete cover.

- On impact, local damage of the concrete surface is estimated to be of a depth of 40 mm in normal cases.
  In exceptional cases, it can be up to 120 mm for the "Drill Collar" object. In the case of possible lightweigt concrete cover the concrete surface will be protected while the local damage in the lightweight cover is estimated to ca. 80 mm.

- The loss of energy, caused by local crushing of the concrete, is calculated to the magnitude of 15-20% of the kinetic energy. The loss of energy caused by plastic deformations of the falling objects is only considered for the "Mud Pump" object and is, in the analysis, estimated at 10% of the kinetic energy.

- The magnitude of the impact loads is calculated on the basis of the impulse of the falling objects and the upper mentioned time of impact. A triangular impulse shape is assumed. Energy, loss of energy, impulse and the maximum impact force are summarized for different objects in figure 4.3. It should be mentioned that the idealization of a "Mud Pump" into a sphere is rather too unfavourable with respect to the impact load and this has to be kept in mind in later comparisons. On the other hand this case is valuable for judging the scatter of the results and as an upper limit case.

- To judge and control the computed impact loads, a simplified analysis, based on an "impact factor analysis" modified for shell structures, has been done. Dependant on the analysis model, i.e. elastic impact, inelastic impact and inelastic impact on cracked cross-sections of the shell, the impact forces have been computed. A possible magnitude, neither the very higest nor the very lowest, is estimated to be of P = 14,000 - 20,000 kN.

- The moment capacity of the spherical shell was calculated by a simple yield line model, where the acting normal stress in the shell under hydrostatic loading has been taken into

	"Drill Collar"	"Hydrill"	"Mud Pump"			Dim.
v	22,8	16,6	10,8	7,0	5,60	m/sek
m^*	3,6	5,4	47,5	47,5	47,5	t
$E=\frac{1}{2}mv^2$	935,7	744,0	2770	1163	744,8	kNm
$\Delta E_{pl.def.}$	0	0	10	10	10	%
ΔE_{crush} C	18	15	18	18	18	%
ΔE_{crush} L	25	25	25	25	25	%
$E_{d\ concr.}$	767	632	1994	837	536	kNm
$E_{d\ lighw\ c}$	701	558	1800	755	484	kNm
$I_{concrete}$	74,3	82,6	435,2	281,9	225,0	kN sek
$I_{lighw.c}$	71,0	77,6	413,5	267,8	214,4	kN sek

$P_{impact\ c}$	7430	16520	43520	28190	22500	kN
$P_{impact\ 1}$	4733	10346	27566	17853	14293	kN

Figure 4.3.   Energy, loss of energy, impulse and impact loads of the different falling objects.

account, as well as the rotation capacity of the cross-section having been checked. By a reasonable choice of reinforcement, a moment collapse can be avoided.

- The kinetic energy of the falling objects can be absorbed by the proposed yielding line model. Depending on on a prescribed degree of plasticity, the degree of reinforcement can be chosen. (Fig. 4.4)

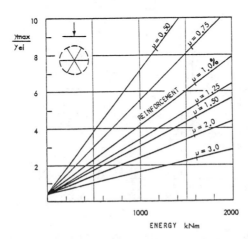

Figure 4.4.   Energy absorbtion of the yield line model as a function of the degree of plasticity and reinforcement.

- The natural period T of the spherical shell structure was computed to be of the magnitude of T = 0.020 - 0.030 sec. by assuming cracked cross-sections and concidering a possible added mass of surrounding water. The natural period of the shell structure and the probable time of impact are close to each other.

- A dynamic response of a one degree of freedom and elastic-plastic system imposed to impact loads has been carried out. The results are illustrated in Fig. 4.5. By a correct choice of reinforcement, the degree of plasticity can be kept on a reasonable level. A limit for a reasonable level of plasticity of β = 3.5, is proposed.

- Among the falling objects, the case "Mud Pump" as a sphere is the most unfavourable object, and, referring to the above comments, it is more realistic to consider the edged "Mud Pump" model. Objects such as "Hydrill" and "Drill Collar" are not decisive with respect to the moment capacity.

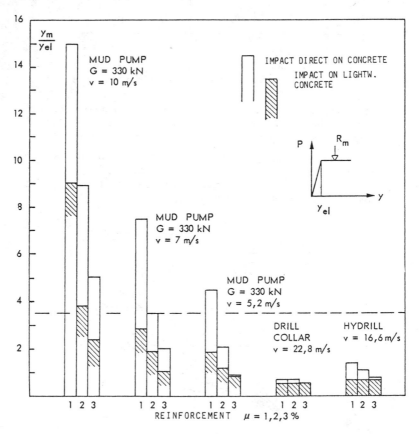

Figure 4.5. Dynamic response of impact loads. Relationship between degree of plasticity and reinforcement.

- In general, it can be concluded that the moment capasity for the falling objects can be ensured by reinforcement.

- A proposed protection cover of lightweight concrete can act as damping and prolong the time of impact, which results in a reduction of the momentary top of the impact force. By impact taking place on a dome covered with lightweight concrete, the moment capacity of impact loads can be ensured by a lower degree of reinforcement than in the case of impact direct on the concrete surface.

- The shear capacity of the domes against impact loads with respect to punching depends on the general stress situation, the loading time, the loading area as well as the degree of reinforcement and material quality.

- It has been turned to account that the shear capacity increases strongly by a two-dimensional stress situation, and that, the shear capacity also increases normally under rapid dynamic loading.

- A dynamic impact analysis on the elastic-plastic one-degree-of-freedom system has been carried out with respect to the shear loading capacity. The results are presented in Fig. 4.6. In the case of shear, strong restrictions have to be applied to the degree of plasticity, which causes the brittle character of a shear failure and a degree of plasticity of 1.5. has been proposed.

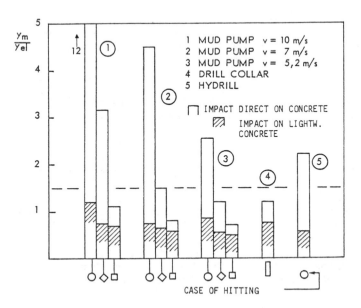

Figure 4.6.   Dynamic shear response of impact load. Relationship between degree of plasticit. and hitting case of object.

- The results indicate that the falling objects, such as "Mud Pump" and "Hydrill", cause the most serious cases for the shear failure.

- The effect of a lightweight concrete cover to protect the domes against punching failure is considerable, as all the examined objects have a degree of plasticity lower than 1.0 or 1.5.

The investigation has shown that the spherical domes of the Condeep platform can be ensured against failure of falling objects by a correct choice of reinforcement and a possible lightweight concrete cover.

ACKNOWLEDGEMENTS

The presented investigation was carried out for the Norwegian Contractors in March 1976, and the author wish to thank the Norwegian Contractors for their permission to publish this paper.

REFERENCES

| 1 | Schmieden, C.
"Der Aufschlag von Rotationskörpern auf eine Wasser-oberfläche". Z. Anger.Math. Mech. Bd. 33, Nr. 4, 1953.

| 2 | Fabula, A.G. et al.
"Vertical broadside water impact of circular cylinder". Growing circular arc. approx. U.S. Naval Ordnance Test-otion, Cinna Lake, California, Oct. 1955.

| 3 | Shess-Lun Chuang.
"Investigation of impact of rigid and elastic bodies with water". Naval Ship Research and Development Center, Washington DC, 1970.

| 4 | Lamb, H.
"Hydrodynamics" Dower Publications, New York, 1945.

| 5 | Schmidt B.
"Kontaktkraft und Biegespannungen im quergestossenen Balken" . Diss. Darmstadt 1966.

| 6 | Lener, C. and Feshbach, H.
"A Method of Calculating Energy Losses During Impact" Journal of Applied Mechanics, June 1939.

| 7 | Hunter, S. C.
"Energy Absorbed by Elastic Waves During Impact". Journal of the Mechanics and Physics of Solids 1957.

| 8 | Johnson, W.
        "Impact strength of materials".
        E. Arnold Limited, London 1972.

| 9 | Moore, C. V.
        "The design of barricades for hazardous pressure systems"
        Nuclear Engineering and Design, 5. 1967.

|10| Richart, F. E. Brandtzæg A. and Brown, R.L.
        "A study of the failure of concrete under combined
        compressive stresses. Eng. Exp. Sta, University of
        Illinois, Urbana, 1978.

|11| Biggs, J. M.
        "Structural Dynamics". Mc Graw-Hill 1964.

|12| Jensen, J. J., H. Svardal A.V.
        DYNBET - A computer program for dynamic analysis of
        frames in reinforced concrete taking elastic and non-
        elastic behaviour into account. (FCB-report STF65
        A78001 1978 (in Norwegian).

|13| Moe, J.
        "Shearing Strength of Reinforced Concrete Slabs and
        Footings Under Concentrated Loads". Development
        Department, Bulletin D47, PCA Shokie, Illineis, April
        1961.

|14| Langan, D. and Garas, F.K.
        "The failure of concrete under combined action of high
        shearing forces and biaxial restraint". Proceedings
        of the Southhampton 1969 Civil Engineering Materials
        Conference. John Wiley & Sons Ltd. 1971.

|15| Criswell, M. F.
        "Static and Dynamic Response of Reinforced Concrete
        Stab-Column-Connections" ACI, Special Publication
        SP42 1974.

TIME-DEPENDENT STRESS REDISTRIBUTION IN CONCRETE OIL STORAGE STRUCTURES

G.L. England
A. Moharram
K.R.F. Andrews

Civil Engineering Department,
King's College, University of London,
Strand, London, WC2R 2LS, England.

SUMMARY

The paper draws attention to the nature of the time-varying stresses in concrete oil storage structures under normal working conditions. They result from the combined effects of creep, spatially non-uniform and time-varying temperatures. Calculation procedures for determining the limiting stress states due to creep under regular cyclic temperature behaviour, are described, and it is concluded that design consideration should be given to both the initial thermo-elastic stresses at the time a structure first enters service, and the limiting states towards which stresses tend during the operational lifetime of an oil storage structure. Reference is made to non-periodic temperature variations, and the results of a creep analysis are presented for a single cylinder which is periodically filled and emptied of hot crude oil.

INTRODUCTION

Concrete ocean structures for the storage of crude oil at sea are often of a multi-cellular form or of a single cell type. In either case the process of storing oil and the discharge of it to tankers at sea is of a similar form. Periodically hot crude oil and cold sea water ballast are interchanged within the containment. This process causes immediate thermal stress changes within the walls of the containment and some longer term alteration to the stresses due to creep of the concrete. The initial state of stress is readily calculated from conventional thermo-elastic analyses. It is also possible to evaluate the limiting states of stress, which are quasi-steady-state stresses (1), from a single direct calculation provided a regular cyclic pattern of the temperatures exists.

1.234

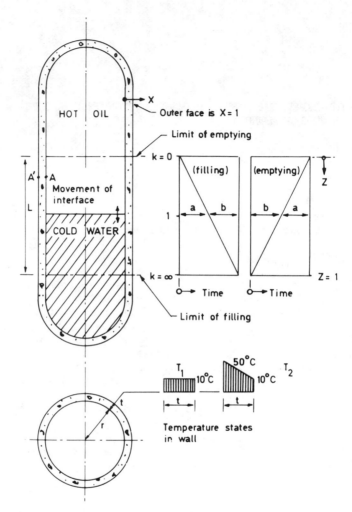

FIGURE 1. Long thin cylindrical containment subjected to
regular filling and emptying cycles, with hot oil
over central portion. There are no 'hold' times
in either the full or empty condition. Ordinates
'a' represent time in cold condition. $a:b = k_1:k_2$
and $a/b=k$. Total cycle period is $\tau = 2(a+b)$.
Data used in analysis are: prestress, f=7 MN/m² in
longitudinal and circumferential directions;
$r/t = 50$; $L/r = 1.8$; modulus of elasticity, E = 34
GN/m²; Coefficient of thermal expansion,
$\alpha = 12.10^{-6}/$ C

Theory is presented here, in the form of an 'initial' strain
elastic-type calculation procedure, for the determination of
these long-term stress states. A full account of the theory
and its analogous form to an 'initial' strain formulation in
elasticity is given in references (2) and (3).

The problem analysed is that of a single, vertical cylindrical
containment which is subjected to storage and pump-out cycles
of hot oil as defined in Figure 1. The analysis relates to
the central portion of the cylinder away from the ends, and
it is assummed that filling and emptying takes place over this
portion only. There are no 'hold' times in either the full
or empty condition. Other modes of operation cause no difficulty in calculation.

The problem is simplified to the extent that the temperature
states in the wall of the cylinder, correspond to steady-
state heat flow conditions and these change abruptly in time
from a linear gradient in the 'hot' condition to a uniform
temperature state in the 'cold' condition. No attempt is
made to represent the real heat flow and conduction properties
of the concrete.

The results of the analysis have been differentiated into
three categories for convenience. They are:

(i) The thermal stresses which result from the application
of the temperature crossfall only, through the wall of the
cylinder. These stresses are similar to those which result
from a plate calculation when a through-the-plate temperature
crossfall exists and the plate is restrained to remain flat.
These stresses are denoted as $\sigma_{\alpha n}$

(ii) Additional thermal stresses, which are caused by the
radial thermal incompatibility at the junction of the 'hot'
and 'cold' zones, i.e. at the level of the hot-oil/cold-
water interface. These are referred to as the perturbation
stresses and are denoted by, $\sigma_{b\alpha}$

(iii) The limiting steady-state-cyclic stresses which are
caused by creep and the cyclically varying temperatures
during the periodic filling and emptying of the cylinder.
These stresses are denoted by $\sigma*$ in the 'hot' condition and
by $(\sigma* - \sigma_{\alpha})$ in the 'cold' state. Here, σ is the total
thermal stress state, namely, $\sigma = \sigma_{\alpha n} + \sigma_{b\alpha}$

The thermal stress components are shown in Figure 2, and the
steady-state-cyclic stresses for the heated condition are
shown in Figure 5.

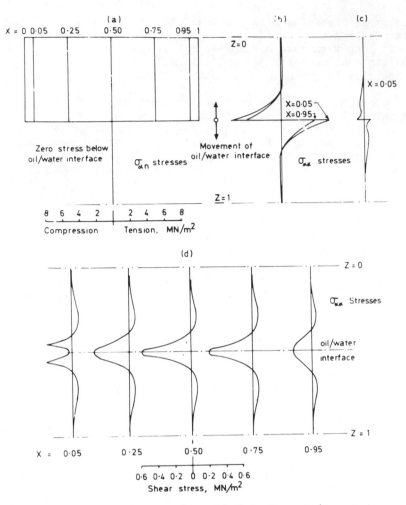

FIGURE 2. Thermal stresses in cylindrical containment.
(a) Longitudinal and circumferential stresses due
to curviture restraint,
(b) Circumferential stress perturbations close to
oil/water interface; slight variation through wall
thickness,
(c) Longitudinal stress perturbations close to oil/
water interface. Variation across wall thickness is
approximately linear with zero stress at mid radius.
(d) Shear stress perturbations through wall, to an
enlarged scale.
The total elastic state of stress initially is the
sum of the mechanical prestress, f, and the appropriate thermal stresses, i.e. in the heated region
of the cylinder, the total stresses are,
$$\sigma = f + \sigma_{\alpha n} + \sigma_{\alpha \alpha}.$$

STRESS-STRAIN LAW FOR CONCRETE

Although the creep behaviour of concrete shows a characteristic ageing form with time, it is possible to approximate the time-dependent strain behaviour to that of a Maxwell material, provided a suitable time transformation is adopted (4). In pseudo-time, the total strain equation in three dimensional stress is then,

$$D[\mathcal{E}] = \left(\frac{D}{E} + \phi(T) \right) [V][\sigma]$$

where $[\sigma]$ and $[\mathcal{E}]$ are the normal six component stress and strain vectors; D is the differential operator $d(\ )/dt'$ where t' is pseudo-time; $\phi(T)$ is the normalising creep-temperature function (4) and behaves as the reciprocal of viscosity in the dashpot element of the Maxwell model; E is Young's modulus and [V] is a Poisson's ratio matrix linking the stress and strain components.

$\phi(T)$ is usually a simple polynomial equation in the temperature, T, and is frequently taken as $\phi(T) = T$, in degrees Celcius: this form is used in the example of this paper. The uniaxial stress/strain equation then becomes,

$$D(\mathcal{E}) = \frac{D(\sigma)}{E} + \sigma T \qquad (1)$$

In the steady-state stress situation, after all redistribution due to creep has taken place, $D(\sigma) = 0$ and the steady-state creep strain rate is simply,

$$\dot{\mathcal{E}} = \sigma T \qquad (2)$$

Equation (2) is valid for any situation in which the temperatures, T, are time-invariant. σ then represents the steady-state stresses. Uniaxial stress-strain theory is used in what follows.

CYCLIC TEMPERATURE BEHAVIOUR

In the simplest cyclic temperature problem temperatures may be taken to change periodically between two states, T_1 and T_2, say, where each may be a spatially varying state. It is assumed that the form of the temperature changes, everywhere in the structure, are as defined in Figure 3, where the relative durations in each temperature state are in the ratio, $k_1:k_2$. This represents homogeneous cyclic temperature behaviour. When the cyclic periods are of short duration compared to the overall time scale of the problem and when temperature transients are not significant compared to the 'hold' times in each state, the average stresses over each part of the

1.238

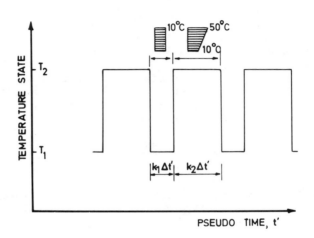

FIGURE 3. Nature of temperature cycles and states of temperature through wall of cylindrical containment of Figure 1.

interval are related by the equation,

$$\sigma_2 = \sigma_1 + \sigma_\alpha \tag{3}$$

where σ_α represents the thermo-elastic stress change caused by the temperature change from state T_1 to T_2.

After a long period of cycling the stresses of equation (3) tend towards repeating states in successive time intervals. These repeating states may be regarded as creep shake-down limits or quasi steady-state stresses. They are referred to simply as steady-state-cyclic stresses, σ_1^* and σ_2^*, and are related in a similar manner to σ_1 and σ_2, thus,

$$\sigma_2^* = \sigma_1^* + \sigma_\alpha \tag{4}$$

The corresponding creep strain rates during any single temperature cycle in the steady-state condition, are,

$$\dot{\varepsilon}_j^* = \sigma_j^{*T} j \qquad \text{for } j = 1,2 \tag{5}$$

The steady-state cyclic stresses, σ^*, and strain rates, $\dot{\varepsilon}^*$, may be determined from analyses based on minimum average power formulations for a time interval spanning one complete temperature cycle (5). These formulations may be of either the 'flexibility' or 'stiffness' type.

Flexibility Approach
The average power dissipated in creep over one temperature cycle is,

$$P = \frac{1}{\sum k_j} \sum k_j \int_{volume} (\sigma_j^{*T} j) \, \sigma_j^* \, dV, \text{ for } j = 1,2$$

For problems in which supports are not subjected to time-dependent movements, P may be minimised with respect to any free stress parameter to yield a solution. Thus, $\delta P = 0$, gives,

$$\frac{1}{\sum k_j} \sum k_j \int_{volume} \sigma_j^{*T} j \, \delta\sigma_j^* \, dV = 0 \tag{6}$$

When support displacement rates are specified as $\dot{u}_s \neq 0$ the general equivalent of Equation (6) must be used (5). This involves the support reactions and the power dissipated by them, together with one half of the internal power dissipation in creep.

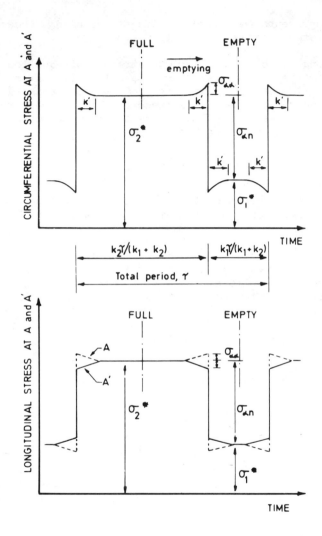

FIGURE 4. Diagramatic representation for the variation of the circumferential and longitudinal stresses with time, in the quasi steady state, at locations A and A' of Figure 1. The steady-state-cyclic stresses in the hot and cold conditions differ by the thermal stresses $\sigma_{.\alpha n}$. k' is a constant for regular filling and emptying.

From Equation (4) it may be noted that $\delta\sigma_2^* = \delta\sigma_1^*$. It then follows that when σ_1^* is defined as a series of self-equilibrating stresses, σ_{1i}, each with a different weighting parameter, a_i, together with at least one further distribution which is in equilibrium with the boundary loading to the problem, σ_{1o}; $\delta\sigma_1^*$ has the following meaning,

$$\delta\sigma_1^* = \frac{\partial\sigma_1^*}{\partial a_i} \tag{7}$$

where,

$$\sigma_1^* = \sigma_{1o} + \sum_{i=1}^{i=N} \sigma_{1i}a_i \tag{8}$$

Thus, Equation (6) may be used to generate a set of N algebraic equations from which the weighting parameters, a_i, are determined. This solution technique is possible whenever suitable self-equilibrating stress distributions, σ_{1i}, may be specified. Automated procedures for developing such stresses are available (6) and have been used successfully in generating approximate solutions of fair accuracy in both simple and complex problems, for as few as five terms in Equation (8).

The stresses in the steady-state may be derived from an alternative formulation of a 'stiffness' type. In this, the solution takes the form of solving initially for a set of displacement rates.

Stiffness Approach

Corresponding to Equation (6), a power formulation in terms of displacement rates exists; its variation may be written,

$$\int_{volume} \sigma^* \delta\dot{\varepsilon}^* \, dV - \int_{surface} P_e \delta\dot{u}_e^* \, dS = 0 \tag{9}$$

where the '*' refers to quantities in the steady state. The surface integral of Equation (9) is an essential part of the stiffness formulation. P_e represent the surface loads, which are usually time-invariant, and $\dot{u}_e^*$ are the corresponding surface displacement rates, which are unknown.

Under cyclic temperature conditions as defined by Figure 3 the integrals of Equation (9) need to be related to each part of the temperature cycle and an average power functional developed. The surface displacement rates are by necessity average values and are defined as,

$$\dot{u}_e^* = \frac{\sum k_j \dot{u}_j^*}{\sum k_j} = \dot{u}_{av}, \text{ say} \tag{10}$$
$$\text{for } j = 1,2$$

It then follows that the consistent set of internal strain rates is,

$$\dot{\varepsilon}_{av} = \frac{\sum \dot{\varepsilon}_i^{*k} k_1}{\sum k_j} \tag{11}$$

From Equations (11), (4) and (5)

$$\dot{\varepsilon}_{av} = \frac{1}{(k_1 + k_2)} \left[\dot{\varepsilon}_1^{*k} k_1 + \dot{\varepsilon}_2^{*k} k_2 \right]$$

$$= \frac{1}{(k_1 + k_2)} \left[(\sigma_2^* - \sigma_\alpha) T_1 k_1 + \sigma_2^* T_2 k_2 \right]$$

And hence,

$$\sigma_2^* = \frac{1}{T_{av}} \left[\dot{\varepsilon}_{av} + \frac{k_1 T_1 \sigma_\alpha}{(k_1 + k_2)} \right] \tag{12}$$

The form of Equation (12) suggests that the stresses σ_2^* may be derived from an 'initial' strain calculation using $1/T_{av}^2$ to represent the analogous elastic modulus and the right hand term in the brackets to represent the analogous initial strain. To reveal the complete analogy it is necessary to formulate the volume integral of Equation (9) in terms of the average strain rates, $\dot{\varepsilon}_{av}$, and one of the stresses, σ_2^* say. Equation (6) is used to determine the average power dissipated in creep, within the structure, as a density component; it is,

$$\int \dot{\varepsilon} d\sigma = \frac{1}{\sum k_j} \sum \int k_j \sigma_j^* T_j \, d\sigma_j^* = \frac{1}{2 \sum k_j} \sum \sigma_j^{*2} T_j k_j \tag{13}$$

The right hand term of Equation (13) defines one half of the 'complementary' average power. For a stiffness solution it is required to find simply one half of the average power. This corresponds to the integral $\int \sigma d\varepsilon$. Equation (13) may then be written in terms of σ_2^* only, after substitution of σ_2^* from Equation (4). A further part substitution of σ_2^* from Equation (12) allows Equation (13) to be represented thus,

$$\frac{1}{2 \sum k_j} \sum \sigma_j^{*2} T_j k_j = \frac{\sigma_2^*}{2} \left[\dot{\varepsilon}_{av} - \frac{k_1 T_1 \sigma_\alpha}{(k_1 + k_2)} \right] + \frac{\sigma_\alpha^2 k_1 T_1}{2(k_1 + k_2)} \tag{14}$$

By appealing to the elastic initial strain analogy and knowing that subsequently the first variation of the average power is required, it may be observed that this variation has the form,

$$\int \sigma_2^* \delta \dot{\varepsilon}_{av} \; dV \;\; = \delta \int \left\{ \frac{\sigma_2^*}{2} \left[\dot{\varepsilon}_{av} \; + \; \frac{k_1 T_1 \overline{\sigma_\alpha}}{(k_1+k_2)} \right] \; + \; const \right\} dV \qquad (15)$$

Substitution of σ_2^* from Equation (12) then leads to,

$$\int \sigma_2^* \delta \dot{\varepsilon}_{av} \; dV \;\; = \int \frac{1}{T_{av}} \left[\dot{\varepsilon}_{av} \; + \; \frac{k_1 T_1 \overline{\sigma_\alpha}}{(k_1+k_2)} \right] \delta \dot{\varepsilon}_{av} \; dV \qquad (16)$$

The right hand side of Equation (16) now defines the left hand term of Equation (9). The resulting 'stiffness' formulation is then,

$$\int \frac{1}{T_{av}} \left[\dot{\varepsilon}_{av} \; + \; \frac{k_1 T_1 \overline{\sigma_\alpha}}{(k_1+k_2)} \right] \delta \dot{\varepsilon}_{av} \; dV \; - \; \int P_e \delta \dot{u}_{av} \; dS \qquad (17)$$

volume   surface

The analogous initial strain term is now readily identified as

$$- \frac{k_1 T_1 \overline{\sigma_\alpha}}{(k_1+k_2)}$$

and $1/T_{av}$ replaces the normal elastic modulus.

Finite element analyses, of the stiffness type, may thus be employed to evaluate the steady-state-cyclic stresses, σ_2^*, by using Equation (17) to determine $\dot{\varepsilon}_{av}$. Back substitution of $\dot{\varepsilon}_{av}$ into Equation (12) then reveals σ_2^*.

The average strain rates, $\dot{\varepsilon}_{av}$, and boundary displacement rates, $\dot{u}_{av}$, have little engineering significance since strains and strain rates continue to develop even though stresses have reached stationary values with respect to time during each portion of the temperature cycle. They thus serve simply as suitable unknown parameters in the problem which allow the stresses to be evaluated.

Extension of Equation (17) to any number of temperature states causes no difficulty. An additional initial strain term appears for each additional temperature distribution included. The strain rates in each temperature state are related through a set of equations similar to Equs.(4,5).

For the problem of Figure 1, an additional consideration is necessary and must be included in the foregoing theory. It relates to the knowledge that the ratio, $k_1 : k_2$ is not constant and depends upon the vertical location in the cylinder, i.e. the problem is non-homogeneous in k.

Non-homogeneous cyclic temperature behaviour. When the ratio $k_1/k_2 = k$, say, varies in space, the initial strain term of Equation (17) is non-homogeneous with respect to both this ratio and temperature.

Frequently when k is a space variable, additional thermal stresses result from thermal displacement incompatibilities. In the cylinder example of Figure 1 the radial displacement incompatibility at the level of the oil/water interface (OWI) creates additional stresses there. These stresses decay to zero at sections remote from the OWI. Figure 2 shows the perturbation stresses, $\sigma_{\alpha\alpha}$, for the thin cylinder analysed. During the filling and emptying cycle these perturbation stresses, as they traverse the length of the cylinder, influence the creep strains and hence the values of the steady-state-cyclic stresses.

It has been shown (7) that the perturbation stresses give rise to an additional 'initial' strain term which forms an addition to Equation (17). The additional terms have the form,

$$\frac{2}{\gamma}\left\{ \int_0^{k'} \sigma_{\alpha\alpha} T_2 dt' + \int_{\gamma-k'}^{\gamma} \sigma_{\alpha\alpha} T_1 dt' \right\} = Q, \text{ say} \qquad (18)$$

where k' and γ are defined in Figure 4. $\sigma_{\alpha\alpha}$ represents the normal six components of stress in a three-dimensional situation.

The resulting variational equation from which the values of σ^*_2 have been derived for the thin cylinder example, is,

$$\int_{\text{volume}} \frac{1}{T_{av}} \left\{ \dot{\varepsilon}_{av} + \frac{k_1 T_1 \sigma_{\alpha n}}{(k_1 + k_2)} - Q \right\} \delta\dot{\varepsilon}_{av} \, dV - \int P_e \delta\dot{u}_{av} \, dS = 0$$

$$\text{surface} \qquad (19)$$

Here, $\sigma_{\alpha n}$ refers to the thermal stresses caused by complete

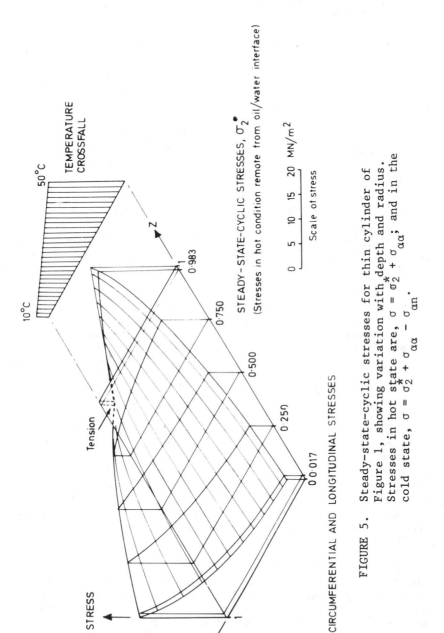

FIGURE 5. Steady-state-cyclic stresses for thin cylinder of Figure 1, showing variation with depth and radius. Stresses in hot state are, $\sigma = \sigma_2^* + \sigma_{\alpha\alpha}$; and in the cold state, $\sigma = \sigma_2^* + \sigma_{\alpha\alpha} - \sigma_{\alpha n}$.

curvature restraint in the circumferential and longitudinal
directions and together with the perturbation stresses constitute the total thermal stresses. Thus,

$$\sigma_\alpha = \sigma_{\alpha n} + \sigma_{\alpha \alpha}$$

Equation (19) has been used in conjunction with a finite element stiffness analysis to solve for the long-term stresses
in the thin cylinder example. These stresses are σ_2^* and
relate to the 'hot' condition of the containment wall. The
stresses in the 'cold' condition are then, $(\sigma_2^* - \sigma_{\alpha n})$. These
stresses represent the complete states of stress at sections
remote from the OWI. In regions where the perturbation stresses are present, the corresponding total states of stress in
the long term are, $(\sigma_2^* + \sigma_{\alpha \alpha})$ and $(\sigma_2^* - \sigma_{\alpha n} + \sigma_{\alpha \alpha})$.

DISCUSSIONS OF RESULTS FOR THIN CYLINDER EXAMPLE

The analysis of the cylinder of Figure 1 for periodic filling
and emptying of hot oil has revealed a number of important
features regarding creep and non-uniform states of temperature.

At sections close to the top of the cylinder, Z = 0, stress
redistribtuion through the cylinder wall is the most severe.
The initial high compressive stress at the inner face, X = 0,
has been replaced by low compressive stress in the long term
with consequent tensile stresses becoming possible during
cooling, i.e. $\sigma_2^* - \sigma_{\alpha n} < 0$ at Z=X=0. These stresses are increased further in the tensile sense by addition of the perturba-
tion stresses, $\sigma_{\alpha \alpha}$.

At the lower end of the cylinder, Z = 1, creep has least
effect on the stresses because temperatures there change little
during operation. The steady-state-cyclic stresses at this
section correspond closely to the normal homogeneous elastic
solution with the thermal stresses superimposed. This section
thus experiences its highest compressive stresses at the inner
face, X = 0, and possible tensile stresses at the outer face,
X = 1. At other levels in the cylinder stress variations are
intermediate between the two limits described. Their variation
is shown in Figure 5 for the ranges, $0 \leqslant X = Z \leqslant 1$.

The stress states in the wall cylinder, in the absence of the
thermal stress perturbations, are essentially of an equal
biaxial compressive nature. This has enabled a check to be
made on the influence of Poisson's ratio (elastic and creep)
on the stresses. Comparison with the solution to a simple beam
problem for which the same temperature crossfalls are imposed
and complete restraint to curvature changes exists, are made in
Table 1 for the longitudinal and circumferential stresses. The
beam solution corresponds to $\nu = 0$ and has been shown to be in

good agreement with a cylinder analysis when this condition is imposed in the axisymmetric analysis (7). The comparisons show the expected trends, namely that Poisson's ratio has an increasing effect as the time in the 'hot' condition, as a fraction of the total filling and emptying cycle, is reduced. The influence of the thermal stress perturbations, $\sigma_{\alpha\alpha}$, on the determination of the steady-state-cyclic stresses, σ_2^*, is also included in the tabulated results for the cylinder analysis. However, it has been shown (7) that their effect is small only on σ_2^* and that they are of importance mainly as additional short-term superimposed stresses on the creep solution in regions close to the moving oil/water interface.

CLOSING REMARKS

It is evident that creep combined with non-uniform temperature can cause considerable stress redistribution to take place with time. The extent to which the limiting stress states here are approached in reality depends upon the grade of concrete used, the temperatures to which it is elevated, and the life duration and modes of operation of the structure. Transient analyses however, suggest that stress redistribution of the order of 75% or more towards the limits calculated here, can be expected during a twenty or thirty year operational lifetime*. The results presented here relate to regular but different cyclic behaviour at each section of the cylinder. Non-regular cycling affects the long-term solution to some extent, but provided the time-averaged k values over the whole period of cycling can be determined, a good estimate of the long-term stress state can be made (8) for this average value.

Other indications are that tensile cracking is a possibility, either initially at the outside face or in the long term at the inner face at the upper end. To overcome these tensile stresses by increasing the mechanical prestress can lead to unacceptably high compressive stresses elsewhere in the wall section. Design should thus take account of both the initial and long-term states of stress as outlined here. Simple methods of calculation are available when finite element techniques are employed. Both the elastic and steady-state-cyclic stresses due to creep may be evaluated using conventional elastic stiffness methods of analysis. A simple analogy between the parameters in the creep problem and the normal elastic parameters exists for the evaluation of the latter stresses.

---

* For internal cells of multicellular structures this figure may be exceeded in situations where reversals of the temperature crossfall through the common containment wall take place.

z	1/60		1/4		1/2		3/4		59/60	
k	0.017		0.333		1.000		3.000		59.00	
X	P	B	P	B	P	B	P	B	P	B
0.05	3.68	3.68	4.68	4.53	6.29	5.91	9.16	8.36	15.39	13.67
0.15	4.01	4.01	4.93	4.80	6.38	6.05	8.83	8.15	13.59	12.24
0.25	4.40	4.40	5.23	5.12	6.48	6.21	8.46	7.92	11.77	10.79
0.35	4.88	4.88	5.59	5.49	6.60	6.39	8.04	7.66	9.92	9.32
0.45	5.47	5.47	6.03	5.97	6.75	6.61	7.58	7.36	8.05	7.83
0.55	6.24	6.24	6.58	6.55	6.92	6.88	7.04	7.03	6.15	6.33
0.65	7.26	7.26	7.30	7.31	7.14	7.21	6.43	6.64	4.23	4.80
0.75	8.68	8.68	8.25	8.33	7.41	7.62	5.72	6.20	2.29	3.25
0.85	10.80	10.80	9.61	9.78	7.76	8.17	4.89	5.67	0.32	1.68
0.95	14.33	14.33	11.67	11.97	8.25	8.91	3.90	5.04	-1.68	0.09

(a)

X	σ_z	σ_θ	σ_z	σ_θ	σ_z	σ_θ	σ_z	σ_θ	σ_z	σ_θ
0.05	3.68	3.74	4.68	4.74	6.29	6.33	9.16	9.27	15.53	15.48
0.15	4.01	4.07	4.93	4.98	6.38	6.42	8.83	8.92	13.70	13.65
0.25	4.40	4.45	5.23	5.29	6.48	6.51	8.46	8.53	11.86	11.80
0.35	4.88	4.92	5.59	5.63	6.60	6.62	8.05	8.09	9.99	9.92
0.45	5.48	5.52	6.03	6.06	6.75	6.75	7.58	7.59	8.09	8.04
0.55	6.24	6.27	6.58	6.60	6.92	6.91	7.05	7.03	6.18	6.12
0.65	7.27	7.28	7.30	7.30	7.14	7.11	6.44	6.39	4.23	4.19
0.75	8.69	8.68	8.26	8.24	7.41	7.36	5.73	5.65	2.25	2.23
0.85	10.82	10.79	9.61	9.57	7.76	7.68	4.89	4.78	0.25	0.27
0.95	14.35	14.27	11.67	11.60	8.25	8.13	3.90	3.75	-1.77	-1.73

(b)

X	σ_z	σ_θ	σ_z	σ_θ	σ_z	σ_θ	σ_z	σ_θ	σ_z	σ_θ
0.05	3.59	3.59	4.58	4.56	6.15	6.11	8.95	8.94	15.17	14.96
0.15	3.95	3.94	4.86	4.82	6.28	6.22	8.70	8.66	13.47	13.25
0.25	4.36	4.34	5.18	5.15	6.47	6.35	8.38	8.30	11.74	11.51
0.35	4.88	4.82	5.58	5.53	6.58	6.50	8.03	7.94	9.97	9.74
0.45	5.49	5.45	6.04	5.99	6.77	6.68	7.61	7.52	8.15	7.98
0.55	6.26	6.25	6.63	6.57	6.96	6.89	7.12	7.04	6.30	6.19
0.65	7.31	7.30	7.35	7.33	7.21	7.16	6.51	6.47	4.37	4.35
0.75	8.74	8.77	8.27	8.33	7.49	7.48	5.83	5.85	2.30	2.54
0.85	10.87	10.96	9.67	9.76	7.83	7.91	4.98	5.08	0.39	0.66
0.95	14.38	14.58	11.70	11.94	8.30	8.51	3.96	4.19	-1.63	-1.21

(c)

TABLE 1. Comparison of circumferential stresses, σ_θ, and longitudinal stresses, σ_z, in thin cylinder of Figure 1, in quasi-steady-state condition, σ_z^*. Poisson's ratio for creep, $\nu = 0.20$; other data as in Figure 1.

(a) Analytical solution for uniaxially stressed and flexurally restrained beam, columns 'B'; and equally biaxially stressed plate constrained to remain flat, columns 'P'.
(b) Finite element solution using Equation (21) with Q=0; no thermal stress perturbations included.
(c) Numerical solution using Equation (21) with Q≠0; i.e. solution contains thermal stress perturbations.

REFERENCES

1. England, G.L. Steady-state stresses in concrete structures subjected to sustained and cyclically varying temperatures. Nuclear Engineering and Design, 44, pp 97-107
   (October 1977)

2. Andrews, K.R.F. and England, G.L. Elastic analogy to
   steady-state stresses for creep and cyclic temperatures –
   A stiffness approach. Proc. of Seventh Canadian Congress
   of Applied Mechanics – CANCAM '79 – Sherbrooke, Quebec.

3. Andrews, K.R.F., Moharram, A., and England, G.L. Shake-
   down stresses due to creep and cyclic temperatures in
   concrete structures. Proc. of Conference on Environmental Forces on Engineering Structures. Imperial College
   London, (July 1979).

4. England, G.L. and Jordaan, I.J. Time-dependent and steady-
   state stresses in concrete structures with steel reinforcement, at normal and raised temperatures. Magazine
   of Concrete Research, 27, No. 92, pp 131-142. (September
   1975).

5. England, G.L. Temperature-creep stresses in concrete
   structures – minimum power formulations. Proc. of Conference on Numerical Methods in Thermal Problems, University
   College, Swansea. (July 1979)

6. Moharram, A. Creep analysis of concrete structures subjected to raised and time-varying non-uniform temperatures.
   Ph.D. thesis of University of London, 1979.

7. England, G.L., Andrews, K.R.F., Moharram, A. and Macleod,
   J.S. The influence of creep and temperature on the
   working stresses in concrete oil storage structures.
   Proc. of 2nd Conference on the Behaviour of Offshore
   Structures – BOSS '79 – London (August 1979).

8. England, G.L., Moharram, A., and Macleod, J.S. Designing
   for creep and temperature in concrete offshore structures.
   Proc. of Oceanology International '78 Conference, Brighton
   England. Paper A3 pp 25-31. (March 1978).

THERMAL STRESSES IN CONCRETE GRAVITY PLATFORMS

J.L. Clarke

Senior Research Engineer, Cement and Concrete Association, England

INTRODUCTION

Most current concrete gravity platforms are subjected to thermal stresses due to the differential temperature between the hot oil or gas and the surrounding sea water. The areas affected by heating and the severity of the imposed stresses will depend on the platform design and the way in which it is operated. Figure 1 shows a platform design typical of those used in the North Sea in which the conductors pass through the caisson and then through the sea water to the deck. This will lead to some heating of the centre of the caisson. In other designs the conductors are enclosed in one of the towers. In this situation the steady temperature reached in the concrete will depend on the insulation round the conductors, but may be about $45^{\circ}C$.

In both situations the concrete close to the conductors is likely to reach a steady temperature fairly quickly. It will remain in that condition for long periods with only occasional reductions during shutdown of the platform. The induced temperature regime is similar to that in a concrete chimney or in a concrete pressure vessel for a nuclear reactor. Much experimental and theoretical work has been carried out over the years to study the influence of creep upon the distribution of temperature induced stresses in pressure vessels (for example, Montcrieff and Waggott, 1967) and there is considerable experience of the design of large concrete structures subjected to steady temperature differences.

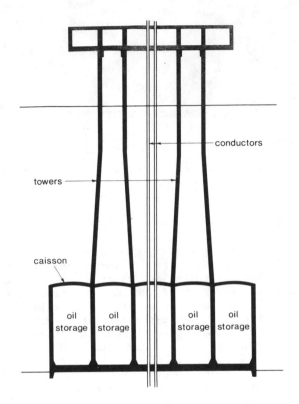

FIGURE 1   TYPICAL CONCRETE GRAVITY PLATFORM

The most severe thermal loadings are likely to occur when the caisson is used for the storage of oil which will be at about 50°C, having been cooled from an initial temperature of about 100°C. Generally the oil will be pumped out of the caisson at regular intervals, to a tanker or pipeline, being displaced by cold sea water. Thus the walls of the storage cells will be subjected to cyclic temperature differentials with the inside temperature alternating between 50°C and 5°C while the outside will be at a steady 5°C. The duration of the heating and cooling periods will depend on the operating characteristics of the platform but typically may lead to a cycle time of a week or so.

Heating and cooling will influence the structure in a number of ways. Filling an individual cell will lead to stresses due to the constraint of neighbouring cold cells. Also, during the filling process a cell will be hot at the top and cold at the bottom; the top will try to expand radially but will be restrained by the bottom. These two loading situations have

been examined analytically by Richmond (1976). Thirdly there
are local stresses due to the differential temperatures through
the walls of the oil storage vessels. Take the simple case of a
ring of concrete wall, initially at a uniform temperature. The
inside is then heated, causing this face to expand and putting
the outside face into tension, possibly leading to cracking.
This is illustrated on the left hand side of Figure 2. When the

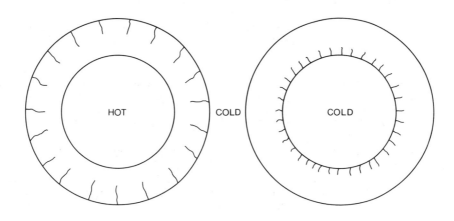

FIGURE 2   POSSIBLE CRACKING OF RING DUE

TO HEATING AND COOLING

inside face is cooled the middle of the wall will still be hot,
leading to tension on both faces and the possibility of additional
cracking (right hand side of Figure 2). From consideration of
symmetry the only possible net deformations for an element of wall
under a temperature difference are an elongation and a radial
displacement. Similarly in the vertical direction there will be
tensile strains on the inside surface which could lead to circumferential cracks.

This paper describes a three-year series of tests carried out on
large prestressed concrete beams to look at local temperature
effects. The work was carried out as part of the "Concrete in
the Oceans" programme, a series of projects funded by the
Department of Energy and a number of British Companies. The
paper also describes a further series of tests, which have just
been started - thin walled hollow cylinders subjected to cyclic
temperature differences. This work is a direct consequence of
the results obtained from the large scale tests.

EXPERIMENTAL INVESTIGATION

Test Specimens
The test specimens, which were designed to simulate a section of
prototype wall, were 600mm thick by 1m deep with an overall
length of 2.8m. High tensile reinforcement was provided on each
face.

When cells are used for oil storage it is general practice to
maintain a differential hydrostatic pressure between the outside
and the inside to prevent oil spillage in the event of major
cracks forming in the walls. This induces in-plane forces in the
walls which were simulated in the test specimens by longitudinal
prestress.

The concrete, using granite aggregate, had a water:cement ratio
of 0.45:1 and an aggregate:cement ratio of 4:1. This gave a
mean cube strength at test of 70 N/mm^2, a modulus of rupture of
5.5 N/mm^2 and a coefficient of thermal expansion of $9 \times 10^{-6}/^{\circ}C$.

Each specimen was instrumented with vibrating wire strain
gauges cast into the concrete in pairs, one vertically and one
horizontally, at three locations on a line running through the
centre of the block from the heated face to the cold. A number
of embedded thermocouples were used to record the temperature
profiles through the block.

The variables considered in the tests were the amount of prestress, the amount of reinforcement provided and the duration
of the heating and cooling cycles. Details are given in Table 1.

Test Method
The test rig is shown schematically in Figure 3 and a general
view of a specimen under test is given in Figure 4.

The requisite surface temperatures were obtained by circulating
water through Perspex tanks clamped against the faces of the
concrete. A simple optical system consisting of a theodolite,
mirror and scale was used to monitor the curvature set up by
the temperature gradient. The restoring moment necessary to
keep the specimen straight, simulating the behaviour of an
element in a cylindrical wall, was applied by means of the system
of jacks and cables. The whole test assembly was mounted on a
hemispherical bearing and system of rollers so that it was free
to elongate and rotate.

The testing on all specimens started at about 3 months after
casting. After the block had been stressed to the required level,
cold water was applied to both faces for sufficient time to cool
the specimen to a uniform temperature of $10^{\circ}C$. This usually took
about a week, and ensured that the specimen was fully saturated.
The water was then drained away from one face and the tank

Specimen	Reinf %	P.S. N/mm^2	Cross-fall °C	Heating Programme days							
				H	C	H	C	H	C	H	C
1	0.45	2	45	7	7	7	7	7	7	7	7
2	0.28	5	45	35	7	1					
3	0.28	O	45	7	7	7	7	7	7	7	2
4	0.28	5	45	3	11	3	11	3	11		
5	0.28	5	45	11	3	11	3	11	3		
6	0.28	5	±45	7	7	7	7	7	7		
7	0.28	2	60	7	7	7	7	7	7		
		O	60		7	7	2				
8	0.07	O	45	7	7	7	7	7	7	7	7
9	0.28	O	60	7	7	7	7	7	7	7	7

TABLE 1   DETAILS OF TEST SPECIMENS

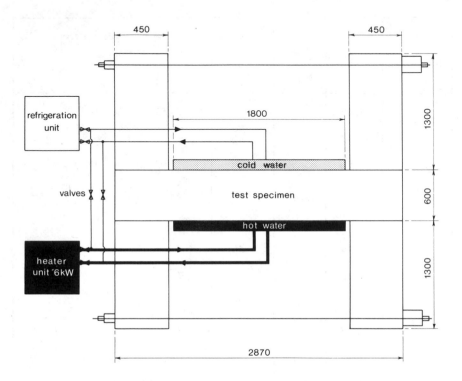

FIGURE 3   SCHEMATIC VIEW OF TEST RIG

FIGURE 4 VIEW OF SPECIMEN UNDER TEST

refilled with hot water at the required temperature. This is a
more rapid change in temperature than would occur in the real
structure where there would be some heating of the concrete wall
in advance of the oil-water interface and also some cooling of
the oil itself.

TEST RESULTS

The detailed results have been published elsewhere (Clarke and
Symmons, 1979). Those that follow are typical results with some
general overall conclusions.

Temperature Profiles
The internal concrete temperatures were measured at frequent
intervals while the specimen was being heated and cooled. The
measured profiles agreed closely with those obtained from standard heat flow theory and showed that an approximately linear
temperature gradient was obtained at 24 hours after the start of
heating. On cooling, a uniform temperature was not reached until
about 48 hours.

Restoring Moments
Figure 5 shows the restoring moments measured on a typical prestressed specimen subjected to a temperature crossfall from 55°C
to 10°C for periods of a week, interspersed with week long periods
at a uniform temperature of 10°C. The peak restoring moment
occurred at about 12 hours after the heat was applied, significantly before a linear temperature profile was established. The
Figure shows that creep reduced the moment during the week that
the cross-fall was maintained, by about 30%. On cooling the
specimen down to a uniform 10°C it was necessary to apply a
restoring moment in the opposite direction, because most of the
creep strain that had occurred during the heating phase was
irrecoverable. The range of moment was approximately equal to

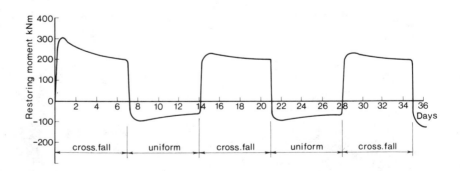

FIGURE 5   TYPICAL RESTORING MOMENTS

the moment initially applied. Some slight reduction of the moment took place during the 7 days when the specimen was maintained at 10°C. On reapplying the cross-fall at 14 days the moment returned to approximately the same level as before cooling. On subsequent cycles the reduction in moment during the 7 day heating period was less pronounced.

A number of points are significant. Firstly the peak moment recorded was about 20% below the moment that would be calculated from simple theory assuming the cross-fall to be applied instantaneously and taking the short term elastic modulus measured at ambient temperature. The reduction is explained by the fact that elasticity is a function of temperature and also a function of the rate of loading, as the concrete starts to creep as soon as the load is applied. In practice the change in temperature may be less rapid than that in the test specimen. This will lead to a further reduction in the peak moment. The second significant point is the very rapid fall in moment that occurred during the first heating cycle. This shows the influence of transient thermal creep, that is the creep that occurs when the concrete is raised to a higher temperature than it has achieved before.

The specimens tested without prestress showed a similar response except that the restoring moments under the temperature cross-fall were only about half those of the specimens with prestress. On removing the cross-fall the moments in the opposite direction were similar for all specimens.

Only one specimen was subjected to a complete reversal of the temperature cross-fall, simulating an internal wall between two storage tanks. Figure 6 shows the restoring moments measured.

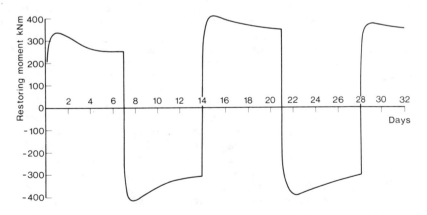

FIGURE 6   RESTORING MOMENTS UNDER
CROSS-FALL REVERSAL

It may be seen that in this case the maximum moment occurred when the temperature was reversed for the first time, and not during the first cycle of heating. In this instance the creep that took place during the early stages of heating increased the maximum moment.

Cracking

The simplest method for determining the likelihood of cracking is to assume that a linear temperature profile is applied instant- aneously, thus removing any effects of creep. This will be a conservative approach as the peak moment is reduced by creep during the time taken to reach a steady state. As the specimen was constrained to remain straight, cracking would be expected to occur when the net tensile stress on the cold face, i.e. the bending stress less the prestress, exceeded the tensile strength of the concrete. For a temperature difference of $45^{\circ}C$ the cri- tical prestress level was about 1 N/mm^2.

As anticipated the prestressed specimens showed no signs of cracking, but the specimens without prestress showed a greatly reduced stiffness when tested, but no visible cracks were formed. However, when the specimens were removed from the rig and treated with fluorescent flaw detector, a pattern of very fine vertical cracks could be seen under ultra-violet light. These were only about 30mm apart, closer than anticipated, implying that the crack width under load had been about 0.006mm. The cracks would not appear to have been influenced by the reinforcement.

DISCUSSION OF RESULTS

The tests demonstrated the important role that creep plays in the behaviour of walls subjected to temperature gradients. As was pointed out earlier, the peak bending moments recorded were only about 80% of those that would be calculated from simple elastic theory using the short term modulus. As the peak occurred before a steady cross-fall was achieved, it is likely that the maximum moments achieved in service will depend on the filling rate: a slow filling rate is likely to lead to further reductions in the peak moment.

No cracks were observed during testing on any specimens, but the specimens without prestress showed a pronounced reduction in stiffness. Using theories of cracking normally applied to members in bending would have predicted cracks at a spacing of about 100mm but those observed under ultra-violet light were much closer, at about 30mm. This behaviour is somewhat at variance with what little experimental work that has been carried out on members subjected to a temperature cross-fall.

A number of reinforced beams have been tested at the CEBTP Laboratories in France (Kavyrchine, 1978). These were 300mm thick and 600mm wide cooled on one face with water and heated

with electric mats on the other. Four point loading was applied
to the beams to give a constant moment in the test zone. As with
the tests described earlier the beams were kept straight under
the thermal gradient. The reinforcement percentage varied
between 0.13 and 0.35. In all specimens cracking occurred at a
cross-fall of about 25°C, with a single major crack forming. A
second crack formed at higher cross-fall, anything between 45°C
and 70°C. The tests were all of relatively short duration, up
to about 1½ days. The specimens were not subjected to cyclic
cross-falls.

Castellani and Fontana (1975) tested relatively thin concrete
cylinders with a temperature difference between the inside and
outside. First cracking appears to have occurred at a temperature difference of about 32°C. Two significant facts emerge.
The first is that the number of cracks that formed depended on
the amount of reinforcement, ranging from 3 cracks for an
unreinforced section up to 13 with 2% reinforcement. The second
point is that, apart from the unreinforced case, the number of
cracks increased with increasing temperature cross-fall: at 97°C
there were about 40 cracks, irrespective of the reinforcement
percentage which varied from 0.5% to 2%.

Some additional information can be obtained from the behaviour
of concrete chimneys. Arthenoor (1975) reported cracks in a
chimney with a wall thickness of 160mm and a diameter of about
6m. The reinforcement details and the temperature cross-falls
are unclear but again 3 vertical cracks formed, at about 120°
round the circumference.

In the light of the test evidence outlined above, it would
appear that rings subjected to temperature cross-falls tend to
form a few large cracks well spaced round the circumference.
Thus a single large crack would have been anticipated in the
Concrete in the Oceans tests.

One possible explanation for the absence of cracking is that
the true stress-strain curve for concrete in tension displays
plasticity and a falling branch, similar to that in compression
(Orr, 1970). If the concrete on the tension face of the large
test specimens behaved similarly it would reach a maximum
tensile stress and then continue to strain without cracking,
at a gradually reducing load. This would lead to a reduced stiffness. In addition, creep of the concrete in tension will play
an important role as the rate of loading is slow, leading to
higher strains prior to cracking.

TESTS ON HOLLOW CYLINDERS

In an attempt to explain some of the differences between the
results of the tests described in this paper and those carried
out elsewhere, a further investigation has been started at the

Cement and Concrete Association on small, thin walled hollow
cylinders heated internally. The specimens are 700mm in diameter
with a wall thickness of 70mm and a height of 680mm. Initially
the major variable will be the amount of reinforcement provided,
which will vary between about 0.07% and 1%. The cylinders are
heated by circulating hot water through the inside and cooled
externally by water running down the face from a distribution pipe
at the top to a collecting tray at the bottom, see Figure 7.

FIGURE 7   CYLINDER UNDER TEST

The specimens are subjected to alternate periods of heating and
cooling, as were the main specimens, but the duration is much
less, about a day for each phase. The preliminary specimens,
with 0.3% reinforcement, have behaved in a manner similar to the
hollow cylinders tested elsewhere, with a few longitudinal cracks
forming, as shown in Figure 7. In addition they developed a
single circumferential crack at mid-plane. The cracks did not
all form on the first application of heat but rather they
developed gradually with successive cycles. There is some evidence that the crack widths were reduced by the formation of
subsequent cracks. Further specimens will be tested to study the
influence of the reinforcement percentage on the number and
distribution of cracks.

ANALYTICAL WORK

The tests described in this paper were of short duration, a
maximum of about 10 weeks. In reality an oil storage vessel is
likely to be subjected to cyclic heating for the full life of the
platform, say 20 years. To get some idea of the long term

behaviour of prestressed members under these conditions, a computer program was developed, based on the method of analysis
proposed by Arthenari and Yu (1967). Details of the approach
adopted are given in Clarke and Symmons (1979).

The program is somewhat limited as it does not allow for cracking; thus it can only handle situations in which the permissible
tensile stress is not exceeded. In addition it requires a
detailed knowledge of the material properties of the concrete,
i.e. the modulus of elasticity, the coefficient of thermal
expansion, and the creep characteristics, which are divided into
recoverable creep, irrecoverable creep and transient thermal
creep. On the basis of measured material properties and the best
data available from published work, the program predicts values of
the internal strains and restoring moments which agree well with
the measured values. It may then be used, with some confidence,
to predict the behaviour in the longer term. Figure 8 shows
predicted bending moments at different ages for a specimen heated
for periods of 2 weeks at a 45°C cross-fall, alternating with 2
weeks at a uniform 10°C. Also shown is the simple elastic
solution based on the short term elastic modulus. It may be seen
that the moment under the cross-fall gradually decreases with
time while the moment in the opposite sense increases, but more
rapidly. Thus the range of moments increases with time, due to
the fact that the elastic modulus is steadily increasing. At 5

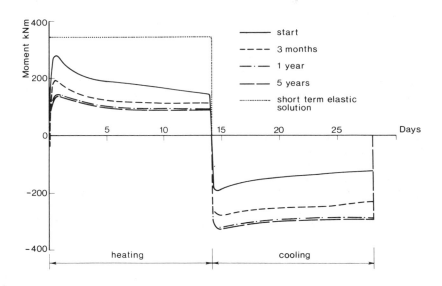

FIGURE 8   THEORETICAL RESTORING MOMENTS

years the restoring moment required on cooling is approximately
equal to the moment from elastic theory, but of course in the
opposite direction.

CONCLUSIONS

The experimental work described in this paper was intended to look
at the specific problem of cracking due to local temperature
effects and not to form the basis for a comprehensive design
method for the whole structure. To this end the results will
have to be considered in conjunction with analyses that consider
the global effects of thermal loading. Only one type of concrete
was considered but there is no reason why the results should not
be similar for other concretes.

For the wall thicknesses considered a linear cross-fall was
achieved after about 24 hours. The maximum moments occurred at
about 12 hours, these peak moments being appreciably less than
those calculated from simple theory. In practice the peak
moments are likely to depend on the rate at which the vessel is
filled with oil, a slow filling rate leading to a further
reduction in the peak moment.

Under current operating conditions with a realistic level of
drawdown, cracking due to local temperature effects is unlikely
to be a problem. Thus it may be possible to increase operating
temperatures in future designs.

The lack of visible cracking in the unstressed specimens was at
variance with the results of tests carried out by other
investigators. Further work is required to clarify the
situation. However it is obvious that, if there is a chance of
cracking, sufficient steel must be provided such that the cracks
are reasonably distributed.

ACKNOWLEDGEMENTS

The work described in this paper was carried out in the Design
Research Department of the Cement and Concrete Association. The
Author wishes to thank Dr. G. Somerville, Director of Research
and Development, for his permission to publish this paper.

REFERENCES

Arthenari,S. and Yu, C.W. (1976) An analysis of the creep and
shrinkage effects upon prestressed concrete members under temperature gradient and its application. Magazine of Concrete
Research, Vol 19, No. 60, Sept. 1967, pp 157-164.

Arthenoor, V.A. et al (1975) Repairs to a reinforced concrete chimney by the crack injection method, Indian Concrete Journal, Vol 49, No. 4, April 1975.

Castellani, A. and Fontana, A. (1975) Thermal cracking in reinforced concrete containment structures, 3rd International Conference on Structural Mechanics in Reactor Technology, London, Sept. 1975.

Clarke, J.L. and Symmons, R.M. (1979) Effects of temperature gradients on walls of oil storage structures, Concrete in the Oceans Technical Report No. 3, CIRIA/UEG, Cement and Concrete Association, Department of Energy, London (IN COURSE OF PREPARATION)

Kavyrchine, M. (1978) Fissuration du beton sous gradient thermique, Chapter 2 of "Recherches sur les structures en beton" Annales de l'Institut Technique du Batiment et des Travaux Publics, Paper 177, No. 360, April 1978.

Montcrieff, M.L.A. and Waggott, J.G. (1967) Time, temperature, creep and shrinkage in concrete, Conference on Prestressed Concrete Pressure Vessels, London, May 1967.

Orr, D.M.F. (1970) Deformation and strength of concrete in tension, Civil Engineering Transactions, Institution of Engineers, Australia, April 1970, pp 26-29.

Richmond, B. (1976) The time-temperature dependence of stresses in offshore concrete structures, Conference on "Design and Construction of Offshore Structures", Institution of Civil Engineers, London 1976.

INVESTIGATION, IDENTIFICATION AND CLASSIFICATION FOR OFFSHORE
GEOTECHNICAL ENGINEERING

Victor F. B. de Mello*
Luiz Guilherme F. S. de Mello*
Mario Cepollina*

* Victor F. B. de Mello & Associados S/C Ltda.

INTRODUCTION

One of the crucial problems involved in Offshore Geotechnical
Engineering is that of investigation, identification and clas
sification. The mechanical difficulties involved in setting -
-up fixed or floating platforms, or pneumatic bathychambers,
and of sampling from various depths of submergence, have been
repeatedly mentioned in specialty conferences and papers. On
the other hand three points of no lesser importance do not ap
pear to have been emphasized: firstly, the fact that the testing and interpreting is of much greater responsibility and
risks of dispersions and errors, because of the fact that the
underwater sediments are so close to conditions associated
with zero (resistance) that innate variabilities of conventio
nal geotechnical testing routines are proportionally very
great; secondly, the recognition that at present, and within
the foreseeable near future, it will be impossible to avoid
leaning on the "experience" associated with routine geotechni
cal engineering for solving ground engineering problems in a
scale of much higher subsoil competence; and thirdly, the frus
trating realization that even within the spectrum of such over
land problems on which attentions have been concentrated
through the past 40 years, one would conclude that standardized geotechnical testing towards identification and classification presents severe limitations.

Attention must urgently be drawn to some of these problems,
and it appears appropriate to attempt a synthetic appraisal,
partly historical, of the current practices and failings in
geotechnical identification and classification. These practices are simultaneously all-embracing and continually covered
or implicit in every single paper published, as well as in
every single problem of our professional activity. So the effort seems to lie at the extremes of the histogram of viable

tasks, either as a very simple one (of merely summarizing the would-be "accepted routines"), or as extending towards the impossible one of reflecting the ever-present manifold questions, on many of which the data gathered and agathering are already infinitely numerous and exponentially growing. (Fig.1)

The intent is of an examination of conscience within an historical process of purposefulness: and the feasibility may draw assurance from the ontological evolutionary principles of nature.

We need not detain ourselves in examining the proportion of the early efforts (e.g. First International Conference of Soil Mechanics and Foundation Engineering, Harvard 1936) occupied with the problems of identification and classification of soils, yielding place to testing: but it is definitely rele - vant today to repeat Terzaghi's statement of the closing ad - dress: "To be successful in their work they need first of all a thorough grounding in physics, and second, an inquisitive attitude towards the ultimate purpose of their tests. Otherwise investigation degenerates into a habit, comparable to the pious act of an old peasant woman who was found absorbed in prayer while kneeling in front of a milestone on a mountain road. When a passing tourist asked her which saint this stone represented, she replied 'I dont know, but he is certainly good for something'."

Although natural phenomena occur with such myriads of varia - tions that a stochastic rather than a deterministic system definition is inexorably necessary as realistic, we cannot

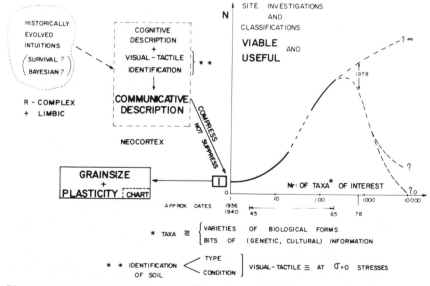

FIG. I - SCHEMATIC PAST AND FUTURE OF INVEST. AND IDENT. ASSOCIATED WITH CLASSIFICATION

FIG 2 - DUALISTIC SEPARATION (YES - NO) BASED ON SALIENT APPARENT FEATURES

SANDS (PURE)	– CLAYS ("PURE") (CF BELOW)
COHESIONLESS	– COHESIVE ($s=c$, $\phi = 0°$!)
PERVIOUS	– IMPERVIOUS
NON-PLASTIC	– PLASTIC
INCOMPRESSIBLE	– COMPRESSIBLE
"INSTANTANEOUS" DEFORMATIONS	– SLOW LONG-TERM DEFORMATIONS
(NO)	– SHRINKAGE / EXPANSION] ON [DRYING / WETTING
NON - SWELLING	– SWELLING
ERODIBLE	– NON-ERODIBLE (?)
NON - COLLAPSIBLE (?)	– COLLAPSIBLE
TRANSPORTED	– RESIDUAL
MICACEOUS	– (NO)
ORGANIC	– (NO)
NORMALLY CONSOLIDATED	– PRECONSOLIDATED

CLAYS   FAT — LEAN
   EXPANSIVE — (NO) ?

ACTIVITY (SKEMPTON)	INACTIVE AC < 0.75	NORMAL 0.75 < AC < 1.25		ACTIVE AC < 1.25
SENSITIVITY (SKEMPTON)	INSENS. S < 1	LOW 1 < S < 2	MEDIUM 2 < S < 4	SENS. 4 < S < 8 · HIGH S < 8
DISPERSIVITY (SHERARD)	DISPERSIVE ZONE A	C	(NO) B	

fail to observe the curious natural fact that at any early stage of evolution from ignorance, the intuitive system of guaranteeing usefulness of information, prediction and deci - sion, is associated with dualistic yes-no cognitive tasks on the most salient parameters.

It appears that in the same way as biologically, neurological- ly, and culturally, we repeat ontologically all of "our past", each new soil engineer, and/or any experienced engineer in the face of each new problem must in some way retrace the same ba- sic steps. Presumably, important evolutionary change must needs be accomplished by superposing new systems on top of old ones, reminescent of Ernst Haeckel's doctrine called "recapitu lation". Evolution by addition and the functional preservation of the preexisting structure seems to be imposed by good rea - sons, such as: either the earlier function is required as well as the new one, or there is no way of bypassing the old sys - tem that is consistent with the survival that we ourselves re- present.

PSEUDO-HISTORICAL RECAPITULATION

From a cursory survey of the Proceedings of the First International Conference, Harvard 1936, and of the Purdue Conference
1940, a neat pattern emerges essentially as summarized by the
very titles of papers, culminating in the paper by Terzaghi.
It is not surprising that at a visual-tactile degree of observation prevalent, a considerable lack of homogeneity in sedimentary deposits should be recognized, with "variations (that)
depend on the geologic history of the deposit", and that the
dictum should ensue for first-order working decisions of early
Soil Mechanics (Terzaghi, 1940 p.151): "in order to apply a
theory to a soil problem we are compelled to replace the real
soil profiles by simplified ones consisting of a small number
of homogeneous layers, and to assign to each one of these
layers a single set of soil constants to be derived from the
results of the soil tests by means of some process of avera -
ging".

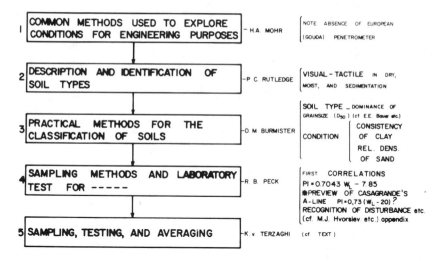

Fig. 3- TITLES OF PRINCIPAL PAPERS IN FIRST SOIL MECHANICS
CONFERENCES

Steps 2 and 3 of Fig.3 have remained as foster children. Regar
ding step 3, Casagrande (1947) in his classic paper began by
denominating "soil classification, the most confused chapter"
and well emphasized the "art of soil classification", the "
need to know thoroughly not only but all classification sys -
tems important in civil engineering" and the usefulness of the
"tool with which the engineer can fashion, if necessary, a new
classification to fit his needs in applying soil mechanics to
a particular problem". The difficulty in adjusting those postu
lations to later statistical and probabilistic reasonings is
patent. Moreover, it transpires that the facility at classi -

fying by any system whatever (and not merely by the textural ones singled out by Casagrande) arises from the felicity of ignorance, dating "back to the time when it was not realized that the physical properties (of apparently similar soils) can be widely different". Indeed, it is fortunate that "fools rush in where angels fear to tread", and whilst we proceed to deplo re the growing confusion of the subject, let it not be said of each of us that he be "scorning the base degrees by which he did ascend".

Mention must yet be made of the Symposium on the Identifica - tion and Classification of Soils (ASTM 1950) which essentially coincides with a milestone of dominant thinking and procedures of the subsequent 20 years of soil engineering routines, re - presenting considerable assurance of cause-effect correlative ability and satisfactory discriminative identification of im- portant geotechnical behavioral patterns and parameters. Bur- mister reaffirms that "classification of soils is probably the most confused aspect of soil mechanics" but in insisting that "the confusion need not be perpetuated" offers as the prop the intent that "soil investigations... provide the most accurate

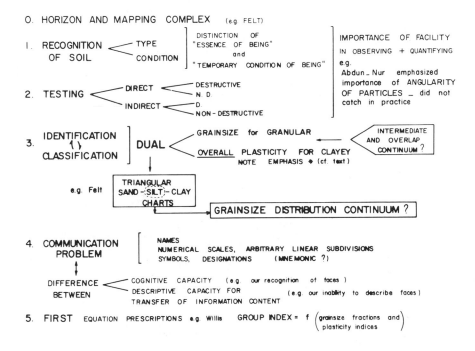

Fig. 4 - KEY PAPERS AND CONCEPTS, ASTM SYMPOSIUM 1950

and complete information on soil character and soil behaviour
...", and definitely implies that the knowledge has been "dominated" the sole culprit persisting as the "varied control -
ling conditions encountered in natural situations and in cons
truction practices".

Fig.4 has been prepared to attempt to summarize the key
thoughts that were thereupon handed over as the inheritance
of the second-generation soil mechanics. Important germs of
upheaval simultaneously sown were:
(a) the indication, associated with the grainsize distribution curves, that no matter what property was employed,
inexorably a continum (histogram) would be at play;
(b) the urge to substitute CORRELATIVE EQUATIONS for
PRESCRIPTIVE EQUATIONS (boundaries, etc..);
(c) the gradual honest recognition that it would be
too much to hope that crudely and intuitively devised INDEX
TESTS and coefficents could hit upon being the most significant, and fully satisfactory;
(d) the likelihood that arbitrary independent "inven-
tion" of such tests would automatically damage many inter-re-
lationships that might be sought.

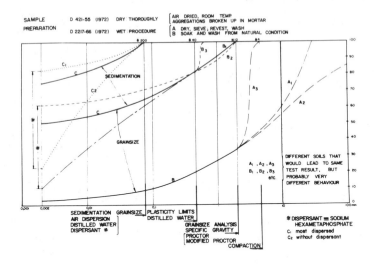

Fig. 5- DIFFERENTIATIONS IMPOSED ON SOIL IN ROUTINE TESTS;
        ASTM STANDARDS

Fig.5 has been prepared summarizing some of the basic requirements standardized for routine concomitant tests (as an exam -
ple, ASTM 1972 Standards). One notes the widely differentiated
grainsize components permitted into the separate tests. For
instance, Burmister's (1950) emphasis on the OVERALL PLASTICI-
TY "in contrast to an arbitrary definition of plasticity on
the basis of the material passing the nº 40 sieve" was set a-
side.

Another point of grave concern is the (very frequent) use of
drying and pulverizing of the material in preparation for index testing: no practice could have been more detrimental to
Soil Mechanics, since in most clayey soils major irreversible
changes occur upon drying, considerably reducing the plastici
ty indices of the soil in situ. Fig.6 taken from Carrillo (
1969) is purposely used to configurate the extremes to which
such influences can interfere in natural soils, Mexico City
clay having been used as a well-known clay of exceptionally
high plasticity. Casagrande's (1947) single plotted values is
also shown. Regarding the sedimentation tests it should be re-
called that the erst-
while interest in disper
sing the fines, and the
requirement of trying
out (visually, in test
tubes) the distinct opti
mized deflocculant for
each soil, aimed at in-
dicating the minimum
unit-particles capable
of participating in geo-
technical behaviour. The
use of a single defloccu
lant surely thwarts the
early intent: with what
gain? On the other hand,
if the colloidal activi-
ty of the clay fraction
must be enhanced by de-
flocculant, what   merit

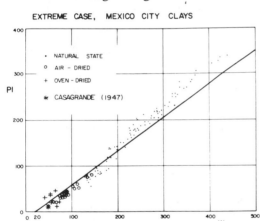

EXTREME CASE, MEXICO CITY CLAYS

• NATURAL STATE
○ AIR - DRIED
+ OVEN - DRIED
✳ CASAGRANDE (1947)

FIG6 - PLASTICITY CHARTS; EFFECT OF AIR AND OVEN DRYING
ON THE ATTERBERG LIMITS

can there be in comparing the Plasticity Index (and Limits) in
distilled water, with the percent clay fraction (colloidal Activity index, AC) as deflocculated?

Is it not time for us to revise significantly many of our routine testing standards and definitions? Should we not recognize that it is with correlations (statistical) and varying degrees of behaviour of continua that we are dealing? If and
when we honestly face up to it, will it not be preferable to
coin new parameters, coefficients, and names, so as to begin
using them side-by-side with the existing ones, without argu-
mentation, ... and thus let the test of natural selection play

its traditional role on the mutations? It is very important to emphasize at this point that in submarine sediments the va - rying types and concentrations of chemicals, both precipitated and in interstitial solutions, affect very significantly the in situ properties and the wide differences between index tests under different routines.

VISUAL-TACTILE IDENTIFICATION AND CLASSIFICATION: APPRAISAL OF PRESENT, AND POSSIBLE FUTURE.

In most fields of scientific endeavour the technological advances of the past 20 years have clearly demonstrated that for many a purpose much better "sensory equipment" can be developed than that represented by our visual-tactile manipulation: the field of the biosciences may be one of the best examples. Moreover, certain new fields of engineering (e.g. ocean engineering, lunar soil investigations, etc..) have made it quite imperative to rely greatly or solely on indirect manipulation by specially devised sensory equipment. And, at least one intrinsic disadvantage to the sensory perceptions of the visual-tactile manipulation of soils must be emphasized: under routine conditions such manipulation and its observations are, ipso--facto, under $\sigma = 0$ conditions and do not include detection of other influences such as chemical, etc..; the most transparent distinction between the intuitions of the trained soil mechaniciam and of the lay, centers around the latter's inability to visualize behaviours of the specimens when confined under external pressures, even light to moderate.

Thus, two candid questions arise that must be faced and answered objectively:

(1) To what extent is it really valid to claim "expe - rience and judgement" on the basis of identification and classification, in sufficient precisions to permit valid engineering decisions (employing predictions of what bounds will not be exceeded in a given behaviour... an implicit probability formulation)?

(2) To what extent is it worthwhile "playing-back" to the visual-tactile sensory basis for first-degree approxima - tion?

In the first question it is obvious that the practical validity of any such classification systems based on index observa - tions and tests persists longer in such fields as transporta - tion engineering (cf. Liu, 1970 or Ueshita and Nonogaki, 1971, etc..) dealing with minimum common denominator solutions over considerable variability of terrain, and with effects more clo sely associatable with surficial assessments.

But one should not fail to recognize that even in foundation and ocean engineering of the greatest locally concentrated res ponsibility, the very first phase of assessment of subsoil pro

blems must begin by similar visual-tactile observations and
probable inferences. It is again a question of efficiency
whereby within a principle analogous to "recapitulation" it is
best for us to see only overall predominant problems first,and
to focus in on details gradually at will.

It is the authors's experience (and observation of the stated
conviction of many highly experienced colleagues with whom
they have had the priviledge of working jointly) that the
answer to question (1) above has three parts:
          (a) experience and judgement in visual-tactile identi-
fication and classification are so highly prized (in direct as
sociation with anticipated behavior) that frequently a stack
of reports of geotechnical investigations and results are ra -
pidly brushed aside, overt preference being for the manipula -
tion of a soil specimen;
          (b) seldom is any presently acknowledged formal classi
fication system adhered to as a necessary link between identification and estimates of geotechnical parameters for design
computations;
          (c) finally, the attempt to quantify geotechnical para
meters is frequently very poor indeed, even by great specia -
list consultants, and when well covered by routine index tests and visual-tactile manipulation, if somewhat peculiar regio
nal soils are involved, situated beyond the specific context
of experience of the specialist: in other words some of the
present index observations can be misleading if there is no
context of visual correlation with the results of fundamental
tests and prototype behaviour.

As a consequence, the answer to question (2) follows automatically: it is highly profitable to "play-back" from good tests
to a good visual-tactile form of association and identifica -
tion. On the other hand, apparently the usefulness of such a
procedure cannot but remain extremely subjective and egoistic:
unfortunately it is part of our neurological and cultural inhe
ritance that our cognitive capacity is many many times better
than the capacity to describe and communicate the cognizance
acquired (Fig.4 item 4).

A striking example of the apparently contradictory situation
may be taken from Rock Mechanics and the elaborate routines
employed for the presentation of a core boring log, Fig.7, packed with information on parameters that have been reasoned a-
cademically to be of great importance. With the exception of
the data extracted from the water loss tests, which are in situ tests, to most civil engineers and rock mechanics specia -
lists, the colored photographs of Fig. 8 really furnish much
more of the meaningful and desired information content.

Fig. 7-TYPICAL PRESENT DAY CORE BORING LOG WITH INFORMATION
     PRESUMED IMPORTANT AND ABSORBABLE

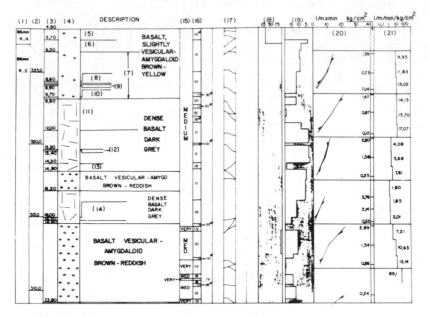

(1)Diam.,perf.;(2)elev.m;(3)depths,m;(4)lithology key;(5)frac-
tured;(6)very frac.;(7)fractures with altered faces,silty-clay
ey yellow and white veneer;(8),(9) and (10)fractures with
shear striations;(11),(12) and (13)fractures as in (7)   and
with shear striations;(14)fractures with white powdery infil-
ling;(15)degree of weathering;(16)rock quality classification
assessing both fracturing and weathering GRADES I best, to V
worst;(17)cracks sketched;(18)% core recovery;(19)n[r] of joints
per m;(20),(21) water loss pressure tests.

It appears of great interest to this conference to ponder on
the evidence exposed by Hynes and Vanmarcke (1977) possibly
confirming the impression, based on professional activities,
that "experience may not act merely on the input parameters,
but most frequently on the output", and "frequently experience intuitions are better and easier in connection with the com
plex lumped-parameter end result" (de Mello, 1975) because we
notice and remember the end results that affects us more signi
ficantly. In civil engineering we are not dealing with absolu-
tely new fields such as neurology, biochemistry, genetics, and
so forth, of unexposed experimentation, results, and possible
associations of tests and behaviour: there is a considerable
past of experience on the complex end-results, and therefore
there should be much to gain from tying the future to the past.

The point in question however is whether or not the somewhat
better intuitive prediction achieved by the audience in merely answering the questionnaire distributed (Hynes and Vanmarcke, 1977), would likewise have reached a modestly satisfacto
ry histogram of estimates if the data put forward had   been

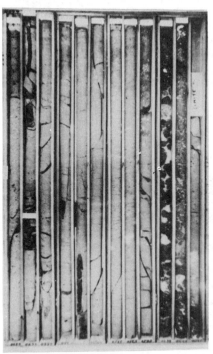

merely the classification and i - dentification information on the subsoil. The negative answer ap - pears obvious, suggesting that e- xisting identifications and clas- sifications hardly permit quanti- fied predictions. It is only when there have been many experiences at closing the cycle of analysis- -synthesis computation that the complex interpretation-prediction becomes viable. Apparently the early aims of classification and identification would be met within deterministic dualism, in permit - ting the decision as to (a) there being a problem to be further de- veloped, or (b) it being accepta- ble to forego further efforts on the less worthwhile avenues. Once the problem area has been accepted, the complex computed result may be more strikingly driven into our me mory (for Bayesian prior formula- tions) because of association with visual effects or importance.

In all respects therefore, emphasis must be placed not only on the appropriate choise of index parameters, but also on a man- ner of representation that may improve the visual impact of significant differentiation. And it is the authors's conten - tion that for some years to come we shall yet have to keep (or gain much from) tying back to the simple visual-tactile cog

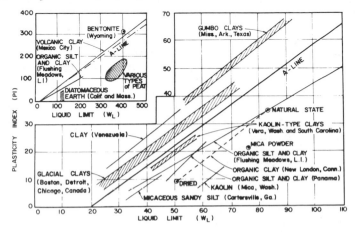

Fig. 9- ORIGINAL PLASTICITY CHART APUD CASAGRANDE (1947).

1.278

nitive and descriptive efforts. Although submarine geotechnical engineering must rapidly try to free itself from such a
cultural inheritance and shackle in a manner similar to what
was attempted in the lunar soil investigation, it appears
that we will yet be obliged to lean on evolution rather than
revolution.

Just as an example one might consider the Plasticity Chart pro
posed as a fundamental part of Casagrande's (1947) classification, Fig.9. Thirty years have gone by and the authors's have
seldom found any specialist drawing any significant inferences
based on the soil's plotted position in that chart. Might not
the reason be to some extent the fact that by having compressed all possible soils within the angle contained roughly
between 15º and 40º, the chart is not designed to provide any
visual discriminating capacity between what would presumably
be different soils of differentiatable behaviours?

The original chart appears to have been somewhat dominated by
the desire to evidence the essentially linear variations of
P_I versus W_L in each clayey stratum, as the percentage of i-
nerts mixed with the clay suffers its inevitable variations.
In comparison, Fig.10 has been prepared to exemplify one possible representation that would enhance the distinction
between soils representing "zones" as related to the A-line.
An obvious expedient is to rotate the A-line to become the
abscissa, and thereupon to plot (in expanded scale, chosen as
found convenient) the ΔP_I with reference to the A-line. If the
positions of plasticity parameters of soils relative to the
A-line (approximate average) really prove significant, such a
chart should emphasize the distinctions, increase soil en -
gineering's curiosity in investigation the influences, and,
hopefully, develop the experience to be associated with the
desired interpretative chart. Obviously it would be desirable
to begin by revising the very test procedures of the liquid
and plastic limits, to be somewhat more objective and reprodu-
cible, (cf. for instance Wroth and Wood 1978, Wood and Wroth
1978). Moreover, a further adaptation of such a chart may result even more interesting, if we incorporate the recognition
that P_I values include firstly a portion proportional to the
w_L or w_P and then a positive or negative complement: thus, some incorporation of a Plastic Ratio parameter (e.g. Saito and
Miki, 1975) in a chart similar to our Fig.10 may yield the
most useful presentation.

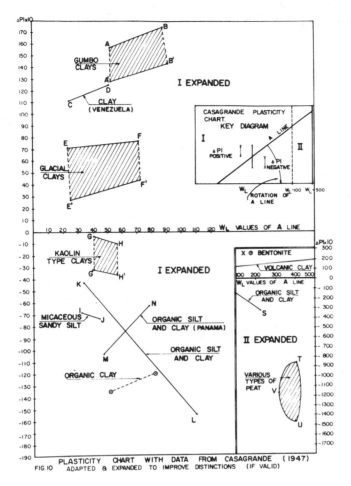

FIG.10 PLASTICITY CHART WITH DATA FROM CASAGRANDE (1947)
ADAPTED & EXPANDED TO IMPROVE DISTINCTIONS (IF VALID)

NECESSARY CRITICAL ANALYSIS OF MANY A PRESCRIPTION OR CORRE -
LATION.

The fundamental intent and purpose in site investigation and
soil classification is furnishing prescription or correlations
for analyses in first-degree aproximation. Whereas early ef -
forts in these directions were strongly empirical but tempered
by intuitions on physical behaviour of soils, and within a
transition period the advancement was introduced of fitting
statistical regressions to such intuitions, the recent and
growing trend has been to apply statistical treatments as self
-sufficient foolproof analytical tools to determine the presumed most appropriate regressions, even if they have no plausible association with the existing body of theorization, or,
worse still, even if they go contrary to such theorization.
The senior author however, has decried what he termed statis-

tics at random, under the reasoning that if existing theoriza- tion suggests a certain type of function for the relationship sought, the regression should firstly be sought with such a function as a prior imposition. How far is it valid to go a - long either of these alternate avenues?

The question poses to the authors a rather challenging problem of conditional probabilities within our context of Bayesian advancement of knowledge (decreasing uncertainties); they thus prefer to defer it to statisticians. If we impose a given func tion obviously we would inhibit discovery of truly new facts, trends, theories. On the other hand, quite evidently statis - tics at random cannot be accepted. How does one employ the weight of conditional probabilities implied in "theory" in or- der to permit new data to impinge on old data in a Bayesian approach?

When analysing a specific function, such as, for instance, the relationship of $C_C = F(w_L)$ we well know how to establish a prior probability based on existing knowledge, and thereupon apply the formula of Bayes' theorem to obtain the weighted im- pact of the new data. Some similar procedure might already exist in quantifiable form for establishing the "prior" that a theory represents: if it does, however, the authors are not aware of it, and have never seen it used. Theory represents basically a PRIOR of several sets of laws (correlations) duly interwoven into crosslinkages that should weigh heavily a- gainst any easy attempt at revision, since the impact of the change should be cross-examined not merely against the single function but against the many indirect consequences.

Regretably almost all the papers on statistical applications of soil parameters, and particularly of index parameters and correlations, have been developed as independent pieces of in- formation, without a broader analysis or the theoretical im -

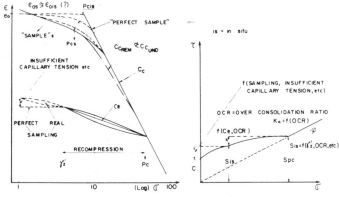

FIG II — CLASSIC KEY FOR SEEKING INDICATIONS ON COMPRESSIBILITY AND RESISTANCE PARAMETERS.

plications, prior and posterior. The practice derives partly
from rushing information to publication piecemeal, and partly
from some divorce between those closely interested in statistics, and those particularly preoccupied with the theory of
soil behaviour. At any rate, one must correct the trend: for
instance, when one discusses statistical correlations on compressibility of undisturbed clays, it is not merely the Bayesian prior probability postulation on similar undisturbed
clays, or even on all undisturbed clays, that is at stake,
but also,with heavy weight of conviction, all the results of
research on the consolidation behaviour of clay slurries and
remoulded clays, clays remoulded with different salt solu -
tions, etc..

If with a correlation coefficient of more than 0,7 one has a
right to be satisfied within an assumed random set of data,
the following sequence of questions may be posed:
    1. What minimum correlation coefficient would be re -
quired if it be merely to concede to a certain theoretically
anticipated function between X and Y, since a greater or lesser part of the variance may merely be associated with the cru
deness of the data and not with challenging the theoretical
function?
    2. How much higher would the coefficient have to be
for credence if the function goes contrary to a prior degree
of direct certainty of the specific function of X and Y (to a
point that one may have claimed the said function to be theoretically backed)?
    3. Finally, how much higher yet would the coefficient
have to be if the function does not align with what the claimed theoretical knowledge, wherein such "knowledge" establi -
shes a function not merely adequate for the direct relation -
ship between X and Y, but also for a number of important in -
direct relationships X-M-Y , X-M-P-Y , X-A-B-C-Y , and so on?
If some set of data, W, Y, do establish the required satisfac
tory coefficient for such a function contrary to theoretical
formulation, is it not incumbent on the proponent to examine
on the spot the impact of the finding on such other direct
and indirect relationships?

The authors do not mean these questions to be rhetorical, but
earnestly request of staticians an authoritative report indicating procedures for such cross-examination of the applicability of presumed regressions, and for establishing varying
acceptance levels of correlation coefficients.

In exemplifying the problem from the viewpoint of soil behaviour, the authors submit herein an inquiring discussion on
merely one of the two most commonly used index test correlations (cf. Peck, 1974), oft quoted as $C_c \approx 0,009(w_L-10)$ and
similar, and $c/p_c \approx 0,11 + 0,0037$ PI. {N.B. For the sake of
brevity the example of similar enquiry into the second said
correlation (cf. de Mello,1979) is avoided}. It will be assu-

med that the test values are truly representative, cleared of the suspicions raised in the first part of the paper.

Obviously the fundamental interest of the engineer would be for C_c values indicative of in situ behavior of the clay strata. It is nevertheless comprehensible, though regretable, that because of the much greater access to purely laboratory data, most papers on the subject have concentrated only on regressions between laboratory tests, without an iota of discussion of effects of sampling, disturbance, etc..

Two principal factors of sample disturbance are partial remoulding in high sensitivity clays, and the problem with pore water capillary tensions in the sample. Some index to such capillary tensions may be obtained by comparing unconfined compression tests routinely conducted, and upon rapid submersion of the specimen during the start of loading. Regarding capillary tensions the two problems are, one the one hand, insufficient capillary tension to maintain the sample at constant volume (either because of high consolidation pressures or because of coarder pore sizes and corresponding menisci), and, on the other hand, the release of dissolved gases as capillary tensions increase, (for bases of detailed treatment cf. for instance, Bishop and Hight, 1977). In ocean engineering the problem of release of dissolved gases upon significant decompression of the pore liquid further affects the standard "constant volume" assumptions of undisturbed samples. The basic inescapable knowledge therefore is that there is a definite bias in certain test data on "undisturbed samples", which makes it misleading to promote some regressions in lieu of others. Further, from a purely pragmatic sense if reasonable correlations may be established merely for $C_c \approx F(w_L)$, there is the advantage that the only test employed is not dependent on the sample being at in situ physical properties.

Conventional theorization regarding clay compressibility and shear strength is schematically summarized in Fig. 11 merely to establish the key to the symbols used below, and to indicate the inevitable trends associated with sample remoulding and swelling. Such fundamentals were backed by a very considerable body of experimentation notwithstanding its non-statistical treatment. Thus we are bound to accept that sedimentary clays consolidate from slurries of initial water contents analogous to their liquid limits and following approximately the e vs. log p straight lines of C_c values related to the respective w_L: in the case of offshore sediments it should be of interest and need to question and improve (under different appropriate salt solutions) the confidence limits on such an intuitive assertive, experimentally confirmed in first degree approximation. Sampling disturbance tends to increase e_0' and generally decreases both the C_c (remoulding) and the preconsolidation pressure p_c indicated. Sampling disturbances tend to

be least with clays of intermediate w_L values, increasing
with the high w_L clays that tend to be more Sensitive, and al
so with clays of very low plasticity and w_L. The regression
might thus improve of one substitutes the classic linear rela
tionship by a flat curve concave down. Disturbance is also
obviously affected by consolidation pressure, tending to increase with the latter.

At any rate it should be transparent that if the mental model
of e vs. log p curves is used together with the corresponding
essentially straight-line compression indices distinguishing
sharply between compressions and recompressions, it should
be:

a- impossible to pool together within the same cor
relations the pre-consolidated and normally consolidated
clays;

b- similarly, in preconsolidated conditions it is
impossible to achieve correlations between C_c and initial
specimen physical properties (e_0 void ratio, and the like),
and even if they did exist, they would be of no practical use
since the settlements under first pressure increments would
be along recompression;

c- in normally consolidated clays the very e_0 is a
function of C_c' and therefore correlations of C_c vs. e_0
should be obvious, although subject to greater errors and
dispersions;

d- recognizedly C_c depends on the clay structure:
therefore, under normally consolidated conditions which permit using interchangeably either e_0 or w_L' in many a soil the
better correlation may depend on which one of the two parameters is less damaged by obvious error. The w_L test cons-
ciously destroys clay structure totally, being run on the remoulded material, and therefore the correlation $C_c = F (w_L)$
assumes that structure exists proportionally to w_L: in many a
soil (e.g. peaty, highly sensitive, etc.) the e_0 may thus pro
ve to be a parameter with less obvious error. Needless to emphasize the preference for e_0 if the w_L test was done with
drying and pulverizing (cf. Fig. 6). On the other hand, in so
me peaty soils the "undisturbed sample" may be very far from
the $\Delta V = 0$ condition, which might yet not affect the laborato
ry correlations $C_c = F(e_0)$ if special care is exercised in
the determination of sample physical indices, but such correlations would be grossly in error for field estimates. On the
other hand, the water content determination may include a con
siderable error upwards due to burning off material at the
standard 104^0C drying temperature, which would impair correla
tions $C_c = F(e_0)$. In short, therefore, the papers favouring
one or other of the regressions should very carefully and com
pletely qualify the test results used.

e- in indiscriminate statistical treatments of a
great number of test data, if the proportions of normally con
solidated cases are high in comparison with unsuspected pre-

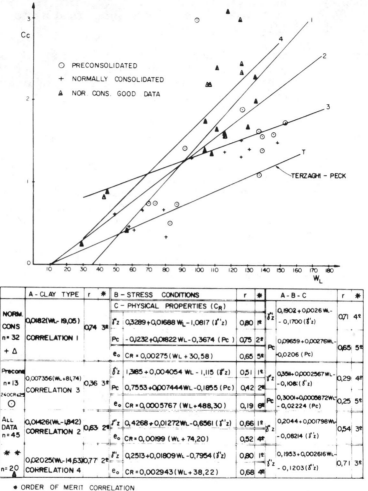

	A - CLAY TYPE	r	*	B - STRESS CONDITIONS	C - PHYSICAL PROPERTIES (C_R)	r	*	A - B - C	r	*
NORM. CONS n=32 +Δ	0,0182(W_L-19,05) CORRELATION 1	0,74	3ª	$\sigma'z$	0,3289+0,01688 W_L-1,0817 ($\sigma'z$)	0,80	1ª	$\sigma'z$ 0,1902+0,0026 W_L -0,1700($\sigma'z$)	0,71	4ª
				Pc	-0,1232+0,01822 W_L-0,3674 (Pc)	0,75	2ª	Pc 0,09659+0,00276W_L -0,0206(Pc)	0,65	5ª
				e_o	C_R=0,00275(W_L+30,58)	0,65	5ª			
Precons n=13 24OCR425 ○	0,007356(W_L+81,74) CORRELATION 3	0,36	3ª	$\sigma'z$	1,3185+0,004054 W_L-1,115 ($\sigma'z$)	0,51	1ª	$\sigma'z$ 0,351+0,002567W_L -0,108($\sigma'z$)	0,29	4ª
				Pc	0,7553+0,007444W_L-0,1855 (Pc)	0,42	2ª	Pc 0,300+0,0005872W_L -0,02224(Pc)	0,25	5ª
				e_o	C_R=0,0005767 (W_L+488,30)	0,19	6ª			
ALL DATA n=45 **	0,01426(W_L-1,842) CORRELATION 2	0,53	2ª	$\sigma'z$	0,4268+0,01272W_L-0,6561 ($\sigma'z$)	0,66	1ª	$\sigma'z$ 0,2044+0,001798W_L -0,08214 ($\sigma'z$)	0,54	3ª
				e_o	C_R=0,00199 (W_L+74,20)	0,52	4ª			
n=20 Δ	0,02025(W_L-14,63) CORRELATION 4	0,77	2ª	$\sigma'z$	0,2513+0,01809W_L-0,7954($\sigma'z$)	0,80	1ª	$\sigma'z$ 0,1953+0,002616W_L -0,1203($\sigma'z$)	0,71	3ª
				e_o	C_R=0,002943(W_L+38,22)	0,68	4ª			

* ORDER OF MERIT CORRELATION

* * NORM CONS RECENT SPECIALLY CAREFULL DATA FROM 32 TESTS OF CORREL

FIG 12 - BRIEF INVESTIGATION OF C_c , C_R CORRELATIONS IN COMPARISON WITH THEORETICAL EXPECTATIONS

consolidated ones, the coefficients of correlation may still be good on general regressions, and yet individual cases will continue to be too widely erratic for use in engineering. One does not improve credence by increasing the number of checks (Pearson, Kendall, Spearman, Kolmogorov-Smirnov, etc.) for coefficients of correlation.

  f- one should not confuse the above statements

with the published indications of a possible general correlation between compressibility de/dp and e_o, wherein no attempt is made to distinguish between the normally consolidated and preconsolidated conditions, (e.g. Janbu 1963, etc.). Such a generalized function merely related to porosities, for all materials of mineral compositions, is but a rough first approximation.

g- from the equation used for idealized calculations of settlements of normally consolidated clays, $\Delta H = = (C_c/1 + e_o)$ H log (pf/pi), it would appear that the most useful correlation in a given deposit would be referred to $(C_c/1 + e_o) = C_r$. Theoretically however it should vary significantly with depth and suffer more significantly from the bias due to disturbance, since C_c decreases and e_o frequently increases by swell.

The subject has been much debated, and will continue to be so (e.g. Krizek et al, 1977, Mohan and Bhandari, 1977, Croce et al, 1969, Kogura and Ohira, 1977, Dascal and Larocque, 1973 etc.). In the hope of confirming some theoretical preferences the author resorted to some select data furnished by the Instituto de Pesquisas Tecnologicas of São Paulo, and submitted them to linear regressions, Fig. 12. Most questions persist, but the following theoretically expected trends appear to be vindicated:

(1) correlations result much poorer in preconsolidated cases than in normally consolidated ones;

(2) the inclusion of the preconsolidation pressure as a parameter is significant, but is better included as the average value extracted from the subsoil profile, than as individually determined p_c values from the specimens themselves;

(3) the inclusion of the e_o parameter only retains acceptability (with no improvement, however) in normally consolidated cases, but leads to the expected absurd results in preconsolidated cases.

Is it not questionable to employ greater numbers of undiscriminated data in lieu of fewer, new, select data, expurgated of well-known sources of error? Should not all interlaced correlations with varying positions on the plasticity charts be investigated, in order to judge on probable inferences? For instance, using the candidly simple calculation of the consolidation pressures P_c required to densify different clays to their plastic limits (cf. Fig. 13) how would such indications confer with wroth and Wood's (1978) values of about 1,5 kg/cm^2 at w_p and with the classic but much debated c/pc relationships F(PI)?

Such exercises could not hope to elucidate the important questions on the subject (e.g. Karlsson and Viberg 1967, Matsuo and Asaoka 1977, Ladd et al 1977, etc.). One would inquire,

1.286

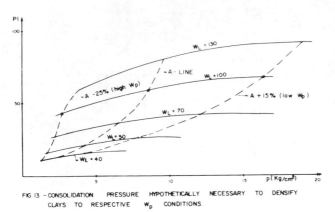

PI

*Note how wide
ly different
should be such
consolidation
pressures for
the same w_L
but different
positions
around the
A-line.

FIG 13 – CONSOLIDATION PRESSURE HYPOTHETICALLY NECESSARY TO DENSIFY CLAYS TO RESPECTIVE W_p CONDITIONS

however, why the separate interferences of w_L and PI should not have required concomitant investigation. The soil's abili ty to retain capillary tension should decrease with low w_L and PI values: but with soils of high w_L and PI the difficul- ty begins with the requirement of high p_c values in order to reach the s_{is}; thus the likely regressions should be concave downward. Moreover, it is frequently preferable to investiga- te variations, such as $\Delta u/\Delta p_c$ (cf. Lumb, 1977).

It may be hinted that if the plasticity chart had emphasized the importance of distances from the A-line (as in Fig. 10) the very first correlations would not have been proposed in connection with only one or the other of the two plasticity parameters. In a similar vein it is feared that many a pro- blem may be generated for the future of soil engineering by such multiple regressions as have easily come into vogue ra- ther unconditioned by theorization (e.g. Camargo and Salvoni 1978, Penna 1978, Teferra 1975, etc.) and unfettered to the interest in visual experience crystallization.

BRIEF THOUGHTS ON REEXAMINING NEEDS REGARDING IDENTIFICATION AND CLASSIFICATION TESTS.

Firstly, for purposes of identification and classification, testing should not necessarily aim at direct determinations of some of the principal fundamental design parameters since frequently these are not sufficiently discriminating from soil to soil (for instance, the modest variation of drained ϕ' values from clays to sands), and in other instances may not create the necessary impact of cognitive perception or of descriptive capacity (for instance, the existing methods of describing angularity of grains). Often such direct determi- nations are much better substituted by indirect tests that measure the symptom rather than the cause, especially if such indirect tests have been devised to amplify the distinctions. A good example of the first type is the w_L parameter which makes it unnecessary in an engineering sense to determine the clay-mineralogy content: for instance, if montmorillonite is effectively present, to the extent to which it would influence fundamental engineering parameters it should begin by influencing the w_L and PI indices. The cone penetrometer has already been mentioned as an example of the desirable amplification of distinctions.

Secondly, there are many "lumped parameter" problems on which at present the existing prescriptions and correlations are seriously lacking and in pressing engineering demand. Among such parameters one might list rippability, groutability, drainability, erodibility, liquefaction potencial, disintegration of grainsizes, susceptibility to piping erosion, seismic coefficients, and so on. There may be tendencies to attempt short cuts in the road to the solution, by devising new index tests, hopefully scientific, for each problem. The author would rather recommend a patient scientific examination of each case, to avoid as far as possible the multiplication of basic tests: one should preferably deploy revised versions of existing index tests by analysis-synthesis and suitable correlations, to compose the desired conclusions on the complex lumped parameter. Einstein is reported to have said that "the most incomprehensible thing about Nature is that it is so very comprehensible", which might be more of a truism than a truth, because that is so to ourselves, who presumably grew within the limits of her toleration of our incomprehensions. At any rate, we should not forget how few are the basic words from which languages developed, nor the persistent desire (and need) for a "unified theory".

Thirdly, in the choise of parameters for testing and for definition of appropriate indices, one should be careful to avoid behaviours dominated by extreme value conditions, and to check for outliers (cf. Lumb 1971, etc.) without excluding outer histogram behaviours that really incorporate different laws. Such an index as the relative density automatically invites difficulties because of the extreme values implicit, especially in the minimum density condition. Tests on erodibility also frequently degenerate into extreme conditions. Meanwhile some ratio indices such as the clay Activity can easily run into wide dispersions.

Thirty years have gone by during which identification tests and classification systems have remained unaltered. The multitudinous data collected in the interim may hint at some of the more pressing questions and basic principles for revisions and complementations of those early intuitions.

Preeminent importance must be retained by the description of the solid structure and components. The value of visual communication is well illustrated by the results of some of the high resolution seafloor scanning devices of modern applica-

tion, as herein reproduced in Fig. 14, from Carlson and Molnia (1977), Fig. 4. Fabric is very important and should be as
sessed: is it likely that sophisticated direct viewing of fabric will be incorporated into classification testing? It is
felt that indirect tests will concomitantly have to be devised to measure and differentiate between the consequences of
fabric: and if such consequences cannot be made striking, interest in the matter will not grow. The grainsize components
must continue to be dominant in classification: but because
of many soils there should be considerable interest in how
different the grainsize distributions will result under two
or three specially differentiated treatments (physical disintegration in varying degrees such as used by Annamalai et al
1975, colloidal dispersion, and even purposely strong chemical alteration). In coarse granular materials the grain shapes
and resistance to crushing are known to be most important:
the trouble is that no satisfactory index tests and presentations have been developed. The standard grainsize distribution curve has not favoured visual perception of the very important problem of skip-grading, affecting piping: if the
grainsize composition were presented as histograms on the se-
milog plot, the gap grading would cause immediate visual
impact. Moreover, special treatmentes of grainsize and grain-
-shape distributions (e.g. Rousseau 1960, Matsuura 1963, Ro-
man Alba 1973, etc.) may lie unheeded even when technically better, if but slightly more difficult to apply and not visually communicative.

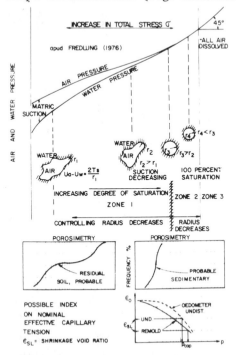

Secondly there has been growing recognition of the importance of poro-simetry (e.g. Kezdi 1968, Sridharan and Ven katappa Rao, 1975, Auvi net, 1977, etc.). In the behaviour of resi-dual soils and lateri-tes the existence of a certain percentage of macropores appears to influence greatly, as schematically shown in Fig. 14. It appears that in some seafloor sediments the existence of macropores of orga-nic origin or of special colloidal flocculations

Fig. 14- IMPORTANCE OF POROSIMETRY
AND SHRINKAGE VOID RATIO INDEX

cannot be disregarded. However, once again, it may be that in
direct indices to such fabric and porosimetry may be more
practical than direct determinations. For instance, shrinkage
limit, or, more generally, a shrinkage void ratio (starting
from undisturbed conditions), and especially its comparison
with the respective index after remolding at constant water
content may be a good indirect index of nominal effective capillary tensions: so also one might investigate the relevance
of the sudden loss of strength in unconfined compression tests
upon different rapid submersions of the specimens. Such classification indices would in no way supplant the tests for the
properties directly at stake, such as the psychometers etc.
(cf. Richards 1977, etc.).

Finally, the influence of colloid chemistry and dissolved che
micals in pore water, or even of different pore fluids, has
long since been recognized (e.g. Genevois 1977, Lumb 1977,
etc.). What is necessary is to devise index testing that
would force such chemical influences to maximum discrimination
conditions, reminiscent of the Atterberg Limit tests forcing
water contents to their limiting influences on clays: most
functions are better assessed if saliently evidenced as exten
ded to fairly extreme conditions.

TOWARDS AN OBJECTIVE SYSTEM OF SITE INVESTIGATION

It has been postulated that site investigations will probably
progress towards indirect determinations of significant index parameters, and acceptance of vertical profiling as a con
tinuum of varying degrees of occurrence of specific symptoms.
In a sense the Dutch cone penetration test was a beginning in
this direction. We shall not delve into discussions of the
degree to which sediments include vertical or horizontal discontinuities in comparison with vertical or horizontal continua: geologic, hydrologic, and meteorological factors justify
both the more frequent continuum condition and the occasional
discontinuity condition. At any rate, a discontinuity reveals
itself automatically when a medium is investigated as a continuum, since a discontinuity is observed as a break in a
continuum. The developments of specialized sensory equipment
have begun but recently and show great promise (e.g. Schwab
and Broms, 1977, Baguelin et al, 1977, Jones, 1977, Windle
and Wroth, 1977, Sanglerat, 1976, Gielly, 1976, Wissa, 1975,
Torstensson, 1975, Baguelin and Jézéquel, 1975, etc.).

The only thought that the author can offer in this connection
is that there has been a comprehensible but regretably atro-
phying tendency for each inventor or developer of an equipment
and technique to embrace and promote his development as singled out and self sufficient. Moreover, the unsatisfactory
present situation lies in the fact that in attempting to confirm a specific new technique the usual simplest recourse is

to compare with results of the selfsame conventional tests
that we have just shown to be fraught with difficulties and
errors.

In fact, any soil that we have subordinated into a highly sim
plified category has already been emphasized to embody a mul-
titude of interplaying information taxa,from which the visual-
-tactile multivariate cognitive ability of the professional
(developing or possessing experience) draws a vast cognitive
content. We should not allow ourselves to be fooled by the ve
ry limited descriptive content of our phraseology and/or index parameters. Thus, we shall only begin to substitute ade
quately, and even with significant gain, our visual-tactile
perceptions if and when our profiling will be simultaneously
on multiple differentiated parameters. Begemann's (1965) suggestion for classifying soils (by the friction jacket cone pe
netrometer on the basis of the interplay of two simultaneous
equations for two parameters), embodies the first step in the
direction that the author presumes to be required, inevitable,
and fruitful (cf. Sanglerat 1976, etc.). Fig. 15 exemplifies
schematically what may be the results of multiple sensory pro
filing and computorized statistical interpretation by multivariate correlative techniques (e.g. Alonso and Krizek, 1975,
Muspratt 1972, etc.). Once again one emphasizes that one need
not seek (in fact should preferably not) direct determinations of known index or fundamental parameters. Generally it
is much better to develop new indices of high discriminating
power and high capacity for resolution of the simultaneous
equations and regressions: a first suggestion and request in
this direction has long since been made (de Mello, 1971) with
regard to interpretation of SPT results towards estimating
the interconnected (c, ϕ) parameters layer by layer in a subsoil profile. Classic geophysical testing and in situ tests

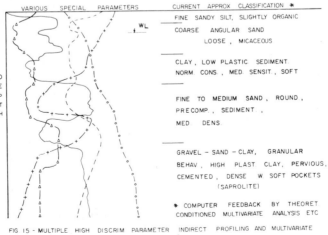

FIG. 15 - MULTIPLE HIGH DISCRIM. PARAMETER INDIRECT PROFILING AND MULTIVARIATE
ANALYSIS CLASSIFICATION FOR FUTURE ?

to determine moduli of elasticity or shear strength are examples of solutions poorly fitted for classification and identification. The cone penetrometer based on point resistances at depth has already been mentioned as an example of a highly sensitive parameter. The author recognizes that such a recommendation goes contrary to what is most generally accepted as appropriate (e.g. Arman et al, 1975) which is the search for "test results compatible with present design methods and theories": as already mentioned, for purposes of identification and classification it seems to the author that emphasis should be on amplification of distinctions and classification in order to simplify an idealized subsoil profile is generally a priority requisite; the in situ tests for parameters applicable in design should constitute a second stage of investigations.

The question of breadth and intensity of a particular site investigation will doubtless be judged by Bayesian approaches or such proposed methods as the Minimum Akaike's Information Criterion (MAIC) procedure (cf. Matsuo and Asaoka, 1977 etc.).

Finally one should remember that although it is necessary to tie back any new tests with reference to experience with those being superseded, one must not fall into criticising the new test results on the basis of such comparisons, which would imply validity of the old ones (cf. Baguelin et al, 1975, etc.). The basic test of validity is with regard to prototype behavior, and is inexorably necessary sooner or later, directly or indirectly even though much more expensive and time consuming.

CONCLUSIONS

Soil classifications have remained a rather confused chapter because of arbitrary test standards that cause such obvious alterations in the feel of the total soil that the experienced professional gradually sets aside test results and relies mostly on his visual-tactile inferences. Moreover, the identifications and descriptions have inexorably fallen into egocentric practices, fostered further by the same insufficiently striking descriptive indices and visual presentations. Test and parameter revisions can be suggested: possibly they have not merited much attention because of the egocentrism of each specialist in solving his problem. Indirect subsoil profiling with multiple highly discriminating sensory equipment appears to lie ahead with promise, associated with multivariate analyses. Possibly a part of the yet modest success is due to the confusion between classification index testing and in situ tests for fundamental parameters: the latter seldom have the desired highly discriminating power for effectiveness towards identification and classification. It is comprehensible that older more experienced professionals may be pessimistic regar ding any proposals that do not center no visual-tactile manipulation of specimens: but it is certain that sensory devices and interpretative correlations and indices will be developed to supplant the visual-tactile cultural background, since in most attempts hitherto it may be said that absence of evidence is not evidence of absence. Surely geotechnical investigation of ocean sediments is one area where necessity will mother satisfactory inventions for such indirect sensory classi fication, once the profession has taken conscience of the unquestionable deficiencies in current practices prematurely crystallized from the important early steps of conventional soil mechanics.

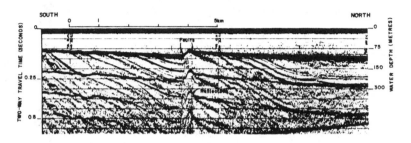

Fig. 16 - Minisparker profile showing older faulted and folded strata (Tertiary-Pleistocene) cropping out at the seafloor. Vertical exaggeration (VE) ~ 10 X. (From Carlson, Paul R. and Molnia, Bruce F.(1977) Submarine Faults and Slides on Continental Shelf, Northern Gulf of Alaska-Marine Geotechnolo gy).

REFERENCES

1- Abete, L.A. and Sanchez, M. (1968) "Relacion entre las cons tantes de Atterberg y su estimacion rapida mediante el ensayo de expansion libre". Memoria 1a. Reunion Argentina SMFE, La Plata, p. 241
2- Alonso, E.E. and Krizek, R.J. (1975) "Stochastic formulation of soil properties". 2nd ICASP, Aachen, vol.2, p.9
3- Arman, A. (1969) "Adefinition of organic soils (an engineer ing identification)". Louisiana State Univ. Engineering Research Bulletin n° 101
4- Arman, A. et al. (1975) "Study of the vane shear". ASCE conf. In situ measurement of soil properties, vol1, p.93
5- ASTM (1972) Annual Book of Standards, Part 11, April.
6- Auvinet, G. (1977) "Structure des milieux pulverulents". 9th ISSMFE Conf. Tokyo, vol.1, p.109
7- Azzouz, A. et al. (1976) "Regression analysis of soil compressibility". Soils and Foundations, vol. 16, n.2, p.19
8- Baguelin, F. and Jézéquel, J.F. (1975) "Further insights on the self-boring technique developed in France". ASCE Conf. In situ Measurement of Soil Properties. vol.2, p.231

9- Baguelin, F. et al. (1977) "Le penetrometre latéral autofo̲
reur" 9th ISSMFE Conf., Tokyo, vol.1, p.27
10- Bcgemann, H.K.S.Ph. (1965) "The friction jacket cone as an
aid in determining the soil profile". 6th ISSMFE Conf., Montreal, vol.1, p.17; also, discussion, vol.3, p.294
11- Bishop, A.W. and Hight, D.W. (1977) "The value of Poisson'
s ratic in saturated soils and rocks stressed under undrained
conditions". Geotechnique vol.27, n.3, p.369
12- Camargo, T.A.M.B.H. and Salvoni, J.L. (1978) "Correlações
entre alguns parametros para os solos da cidade de São Paulo".
6th Congress Brasilian SMFE, Rio de Janeiro, vol.2, p.21
13- Carlson, P.R. and Molnia, B.F. (1977) "Submarine faults
and slides on the continental shelf, Northern Gulf of Alaska",
Marine Geotechnology, vol.2, p.275
14- Casagrande, A. (1947) "Classification and identification
of soils". ASCE Trans vol. 113, 1948, p.901
15- Croce, A. et al. (1969) "Compressibility and strength of
stiff intact clays". 7th ISSMFE Conf., Mexico, vol.1, p.81
16- Dascal, O. and Larocque, G.S. (1973) "Caracteristiques de
compressibilité des argiles du complexe Nottaway-Broadback-Ru̲
pert (Baie James)". Canadian Geotechnical Journal, vol.10,1,
p.41
17- de Graft-Johsons J.W.S. et al. (1969) "The engineering
characteristics of the laterite gravels of Ghana". Proc. Specialty Session Eng'g Properties of Lateritic Soils, 7th ISSMFE
Conf. Mexico, Spec. vol., p.117
18- de Mello, V.F.B. (1971) "The Standard Penetration Test",
State-of-the-art Report, 4th Panam Conf. S.M.F.E., vol.I, p.1
19- de Mello, V.F.B. and Souto Silveira, E.B. (1975) "The phi̲
losophy of statistics and probability applied in soil engineer̲
ing". 2nd ICASP, Aachen, vo.3, p.65
20- dos Santos, M.P.P. (1953)"A new soil constant and its applications". 3rd ISSMFE Conf. Zurich, vol.1, p.47
21- Edil T.B. et al. (1975) "Effect of grain characteristics
on packing of sands". Istambul Conf. SMFE, vol.1 p.46
22- Esrig, M.I. and Kirby, R.C. (1977) "Implications of gas
content for predicting the stability of submarine slopes" Mari̲
ne Geotechnology, vol.2, p.81
23- Field, W.G. (1963) "Towards the statistical definition of
a granular mass". 4th Australia-New Zealand Conf. SMFE, p.143
24- Fredlund, D.G. (1976) "Density and compressibility of
air-water mixtures". Canadian Geotechnical Journal, vol.13,
n.4, p.386
25- Genevois, R. (1977) "Chemical interaction on the compressi̲
bility of remoulded
26- Hynes, M.E. and Vanmarcke, E.H. (1976) "Reliability of em̲
bankment performance predictions". ASCE-EMD, preprint, Mecha̲
nics in Engineering, Univ. of Waterloo Press, 1977
27- Janbu, N. (1963) "Soil compressibility as determined by
oedometer and triaxial tests". European Conf. SMFE, Wiesbaden,
vol.1, p.19 ·
28- Kogure, K. and Ohira, Y. (1977) "Statistical forecasting

of compressibility of peaty ground". Canadian Geotechnical Journal, vol.14, n.4, p.562

29- Liu, T.K. (1970) "A review of engineering soils classification systems". ASTM STP 479, p.361

30- Lumb, p. (1971) "Precision and accuracy of soil tests". 1st ICASP, Hong Kong, p.329

31- Lumb, P. (1977) "The marine soils of Hong Kong and Macau". Geotechnical as pects of soft clays. Bangkok, Int. Symposium, p.45

32- Matsuo, M. and Asaoka, A. (1977) "Probability models of undrained strength of marine clay layer". Soils and Foundations vol.17, n.3, p.53

33- Matsuo, S.I. and Kamon M. (1974) "Engineering properties of inferior clayey soil material and its improvement". 1st Australian Conf. on Eng'g. Materials, Sydney, p.385

34- Matsuura, Y. (1963) "Statistical measures concerning the grading of sand". Soils and Foundations, vol.3, n.2, p.24

35- Mohan, D. and Bhandari, R.K. (1977) "Analysis of some Indian marine clays". Geotechnical aspects of soft clays. Bangkok, Int. Symposium, p.59

36- Mohr, H.A. and other papers as in Fig.3 Proc. of the Purdue Conf. on Soil Mechanics and its Applications. 1940, p.118--173 and appendix. Terzaghi, K.p.151

37- Muller-VonMoos, M. (1965) "Determination of organic matter for the classification of soil samples". 6th ISSMFE Conf. Montreal, vol.1, p.77

38- Muspratt, M.A. (1972) "Numerical statistics in engineering geology". Engineering Geology, Elsevier, vol.6, n.2, p.67

39- Nabor Carrillo (1969) "El hundimiento de la ciudad de Mexico, Proyecto Texcoco".

40- Peck, R.B. (1974) "2nd Nabor Carrillo Lecture". 7th Nat. Meeting of the Mexican Society of Soil Mechanics.

41- Penna, A.S.D. (1978) "Comportamento dos solos argilosos da cidade de São Paulo". 6th Congress Brazilian SMFE, Rio de Janeiro, vol.1, p.261

42- Perrin, J. (1974) "Classification des soils organiques". Bull. Liaison de Labor. Ponts et Chaussées, n.69, p.39

43- Ramalho Ortigão, J.A. (1978) "Efeito do preadensamento e consolidação anisotropica em algumas propriedades da argila da baixada Fluminense". 6th Congress Brazilian SMFE, Rio de Janeiro, vol.1, p.243

44- Roman Alba, R. (1973) "I. Propositions pour une nouvelle classification". Bull. de Liaison des Labor. Ponts et Chaussées, n.65, p.142

45- Rousseau, J. (1967) "L'apport de l' analyse texturale a l' étude des propriétés mécaniques des milieux granulaires". Annales ITBTP, Sols at Fondations 60

46- Saito, T. and Miki, G. (1975) "Swelling and residual strength characteristics of soils based on a newly proposed 'Plastic Ratio Chart'". Soils and Foundations, vol.15, n.1, p. 61

47- Sanglerat, G. et al. (1976) "Classification directe des

sols a l' aide du pénétromètre statique avec manchon de mesure
de frottement latéral". Annales ITBTP Sols et Fondations 132,
p.25
48- Symposium on the identification and classification of
soils ASTM, STP 113, 1950 All papers, specifically by Burmister, D.M.; Abdun-Nur, E.A.; Abercrombie, W.F.; Willis, F.A.;
and Felt, E.J.
49- Teferra, A. (1975) "Relationships between angle of internal friction, relative density and penetration resistances of
non-cohesive soils with different grainsize distributions".
Forschungsberichte aus Bodenmechanic und Grundbau FGB1, Aachen
50- Terzaghi, K. (1936) "Closing address". Harvard, 1st ICSMFE,
1936
51- Torstensson, B.S. (1975) "Pore pressure sounding instrument" ASCE Conf. In situ measurement of soil properties. vol.2
p.48.
52- Tsotsos, S.S. (1977) "A new relation between compressibili
ty and other soil parameters". loc.cit. p.301
53- Whelan III, T. et al. (1977) "Acoustical penetration and
shear strength in gas-charged sediment", Marine Geotechnology
vol.2, p.147
54- Wissa, A.E.Z. et al. (1975) "The piezometer probe"- ASCE
Conf. In situ Measurement of Soil Properties, vol.1, p.536
55- Wood, D.M. and Wroth, C.P. (1978) "The use of the cone pe
netrometer to determine the plastic limit of soils". Ground
Engineering, vol.11, n.3, p.37
56- Wroth, C.P. and Wood, D.M. (1978) "The correlation of index properties with some basic engineering properties of
soils". Canadian Geotechnical Journal, vol.15, n.2, p.137

ON THE EVALUATION OF SOIL PARAMETERS FOR THE FOUNDATION DESIGN OF OFFSHORE STRUCTURES

F. Bogossian   Sergio F. D. de Matos

Geomecânica S.A.   Petrobrás

ABSTRACT

A soil investigation was carried out for two nearby areas offshore southeast Brazil. From each of these areas, two sounding boreholes and the two corresponding C.P.T. tests were selected to furnish the soil data used in the present paper. These data are the results obtained from " in situ " " down the hole " cone penetrometer testing and from laboratory testing on recovered samples.
A comparative analysis was performed on these results in the trial to establish a pattern of disturbance for the sampling process over the explored depth.

INTRODUCTION

In this paper the authors try to evaluate the degree of disturbance imposed to the soil samples during the whole process of investigation, i.e., from the extraction of the samples , the testing on board, transportation and testing ashore.
The evaluation of the degree of disturbance tends to establish a basic criterion for the assessment of the soil parameters to be used in the foundation design, based on laboratory testing results.
For this purpose, undrained shear strength (S_u) obtained on the several stages of the investigation were compared, resulting in an index called " disturbance ".
The S_u values obtained indirectly from the C.P.T. results and from the "Atterberg" limits were called "natural in situ strength". The undrained shear strength measured in the laboratory testing were called "natural laboratory strength" and were divided into "on board" and "ashore", according to the place where the laboratory tests had been executed.

INVESTIGATION PROCEDURES

The methods used in the investigation were basically the following:

i. Boreholes drilled with a heave-compensated drilling rig mounted over a centre-well installed through the hull of a vessel, positioned by means of a dynamic positioning system (Bogossian and McEntee, 1978; Bogossian, Lopes and Lima,1978) Undisturbed soil samples were obtained by using a wire-line sampling technique (Mc Clelland, 1972).

i.i. On board laboratory testing including:
   - water content
   - unit weight
   - pocket penetrometer
   - laboratory vane
   - unconfined compression
   - triaxial compression (UU)

i.i.i. Ashore laboratory testing including:
   - Atterberg limits
   - hidrometer analysis
   - sieve analysis
   - fall cone test
   - triaxial compression(UU)

i.i.i.i."In situ" C.P.T. tests with the "down the hole" equipment and heave compensator. The Vandenberg type cone has standard dimensions with a conical tip with $60°$ apex angle and 10 cm^2 cross-sectional base area. The standard sleeve area is 150 cm^2 and the assembly is driven into the soil at a standard rate of cone penetration of $2.0 + 0.5cm/_s$ over a depth of 3.0 m in one stroke (Bogossian and McEntee, 1978).

THE RESULTS

The soil profiles based on the results obtained by the borings in the studied areas are shown in Fig. 1 to 4. Also disclosed are the natural water content, unit weight and the "natural laboratory strength" values from several types of tests, plotted versus depth.
The soils encountered in the two areas are primarily silty clays with fine sand, interbedded with thin sandy layers widely spaced. A superficial layer was found to occur in all borings, consisting of a silty calcareous fine to medium sand with biodetritic calcareous concretions and shell fragments. This layer extends to the maximum depth of 20m bellow seabed in borehole 2 of area 1.
In fig. 1 to 4, also shown are the C.P.T. results over the penetration explored.
The comparison between sleeve and cone resistance indicated friction ratios (R_f) of 0.5 to 1% for the upper layer and 2% for

the silty clay with fine sand, what is in good agreement with the existing correlations (Begemann, 1965; Schmertmann, 1975)

ASSESSMENT OF S_u VALUES

The assessment of undrained shear strength values was made as follows:

<u>Natural in situ strength</u> corresponds to the undrained shear strength of the soil as it is in the field. Assuming the silty clays as normally consolidated, the S_u values were evaluated from the measured cone resistance and from the PI and WL values

<u>From C.P.T. tests</u> The S_u values were evaluated on the basis of the following correlations

$$S_u = \frac{q_c - q_w - \sigma_{vo}}{8} \quad \text{(DNV, 1978)} \tag{1}$$

$$S_u = \frac{q_c - q_w - \sigma_{ho}}{14} \quad \text{(Baligh, Ladd and Vivatrat, 1977)} \tag{2}$$

The cone resistance (qc) values used above are average ones for each borehole, assuming a linear relationship between qc and depth. It should be stated that variations up to 25 % ocurred from the mean value to upper and lower limits.

<u>From PI and WL</u> In this case the undrained shear strengths were obtained by the expressions bellow:

$$\frac{S_u}{\sigma_{vo}} = 0.11 + 0.0037 \; PI \quad \text{(Skempton, 1954)} \tag{3}$$

$$S_u = 0.45 \; W_L \cdot \bar{\sigma}_{vo} \quad \text{(Hansbo, 1957)} \tag{4}$$

<u>Natural laboratory strength</u> corresponds to the undrained shear strength measured in the tests executed on "undisturbed" samples collected as previously described. These samples have probably been subjected to sample disturbance, which affected the strength determinations (Ladd and Lambe, 1963)

<u>On board natural laboratory strength</u> obtained from the tests aboard the vessel.
The S_u values were tentatively split into two groups:
 - "immediate strength" values acquired as soon as the samples were recovered (pocket penetrometer, lab vane).
 - "aged strength" values measured in samples that passed through period of storage (unconfined compression, triaxial UU) (George, 1976).
However, due to the scattering of values and mainly to the limited amount of "aged strengths" it was decided to disregard this subdivision.

Ashore natural laboratory strength obtained from the tests
executed in the on-shore laboratory. In this case, besides
the storage period, the samples suffered "handling and
transportation" to the on-shore lab.
All "natural in situ strength" and "natural laboratory
strength" values are disclosed in Fig. 5 and 6.
Figures 7 and 8 show the agreement of measured S_u to the
correlation expressed by Equation 3.

THE DISTURBANCE APPROACH

In the trial to determine the amount of disturbance of the
samples, an index called "disturbance" (D), non-dimensional,
was established and defined as the quotient of two undrained
shear strengths.
The following indices were considered: $D_{s/b}$ (disturbance in
situ / on board), $D_{b/1}$ (disturbance on board /ashore) and
$D_{s/1}$ (disturbance in situ /ashore).

The $D_{s/b}$ and $D_{b/1}$ values are plotted in Fig. 9 to 12, together
with the sensitivity as defined by Skempton, versus depth.
The $D_{s/b}$ values shown were calculated considering the natural
in situ strength obtained from Equation 1.

CONCLUSIONS

The authors think that from this paper on, more detailed
studies should be undertaken in the attempt to establish a
basic criterion for the evaluation of soil parameters to be
used in the foundation design of offshore structures.
Considering the present status of the analysis the authors
found it beneficial to pose the following questions:

1) is the disturbance of the soil samples a function of the
depth ?

2) does the disturbance depend on the sensitivity or could
it be related to any other soil property (e.g.,water content,
Atterberg limits, etc.) ?

3) which laboratory test furnishes S_u values that best agree
with those evaluated by correlations from the C.P.T. results
and which correlation is best fitted to that laboratory test?

4) is the disturbance in situ / on board significantly larger
than the onboard /ashore ?

5) does the disturbance in situ /ashore correspond to the
adding of in situ / on board to onboard / ashore disturbance?

6) is the silty clay normally consolidated or could it be
under consolidated ?

7) is it possible to identify any behaviour tendency from the
disturbance plots or is the scattering random ?

At this point, the authors intend only to release the first data collected and the questions that have arisen during the study, to avoid coming to untimely conclusions.

The authors also believe that, once positive answers are found to the questions raised, the approach herein presented gives an option to lessen the cost of "in situ" offshore investigations.

ACKNOWLEDGEMENTS

The authors wish to express their gratitude to their organizations for assistance in writing this paper and especially to PETROBRAS, for permitting its publication.

REFERENCES

A.S.T.M. (1972) Underwater Soil Sampling, Testing and Construction Control S.T.P. 501

A.S.T.M. (1975) Annual Book of A.S.T.M. Standards Part 19 - Soil and Rock; Building; Stones; Peats.

Baligh, M.M., Ladd, C.C. and Vivatrat, V. (1977) Exploration and Evaluation of Engineering Properties of Marine Soils for Foundation Design of Offshore Structures, Sea Grant Project RT-3, M.I.T.

Begemann, H.K.S. (1965) The Friction Jacket Cone as an Aid in Determining the Soil Profile. Proc. 6th ICOSOMEF, Vol. 1, pp. 17-20, Montreal.

Bogossian, F. and McEntee, J.M. (1978) Marine Site Investigations in Exposed Deep Water Locations Offshore Brazil. Proc. VI COBRAMSEF, Vol. 3, pp. 49-60, Rio de Janeiro.

Bogossian, F., Lopes, P.C.C. and Lima, S.A. (1978)"Considerações para Análise e Interpretação de Estudos Geotécnicos Executados em Águas Profundas para Fundação de Estruturas Offshore".Proc. VI COBRAMSEF, Vol. 3, pp. 39-48, Rio de Janeiro.

DNV (1978) Technical Report.

George, P.J. (1976) Notes on Site Investigation with Respect to the Design of Offshore Structures. Offshore Soil Mechanics Course held at Cambridge Univ., pp. 101-116, London.

Hansbo, S. (1957) A New Approach to the Determination of the Shear Strength of Clay by the Fall-Cone Test. Swed. Geot. Inst. Proc. No. 14, pp. 7-47.

Ladd, C.C. and Lambe, T.W. (1963) The Strength of Undisturbed

Clay Determined from Undrained Tests. A.S.T.M., S.T.P. 361, pp. 342-371.

McClelland,B. (1972) Techniques Used in Soil Sampling at Sea Offshore, Vol. 32, No. 3 pp. 51-57.

Schmertmann, J.H. (1975) Measurement of In Situ Shear Strength. Proc. ASCE Spec. Conf. on In Situ Measurement of Soil Properties, Vol. 2, pp. 57-138.

Skempton, A.W. (1954) Discussion of the Structure of In-norganic Soil. J.S.M.F.E., ASCE, Vol. 80, No. 478, pp. 19-22.

NOTATIONS

S_u = undrained shear strength

q_c = cone resistance from C.P.T..

q_w = mudline correction to account for the water (or drilling mud) pressure at mudline level.

σ_{ho} = total vertical overburden pressure

$\bar{\sigma}_{vo}$ = efective vertical overburden pressure

σ_{vo} = total lateral pressure

PI = plasticity index

W_L = liquid limit

W_P = plastic limit

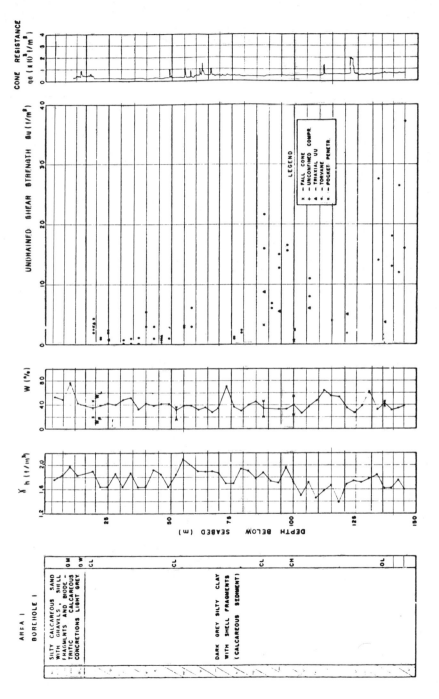

FIGURE 1

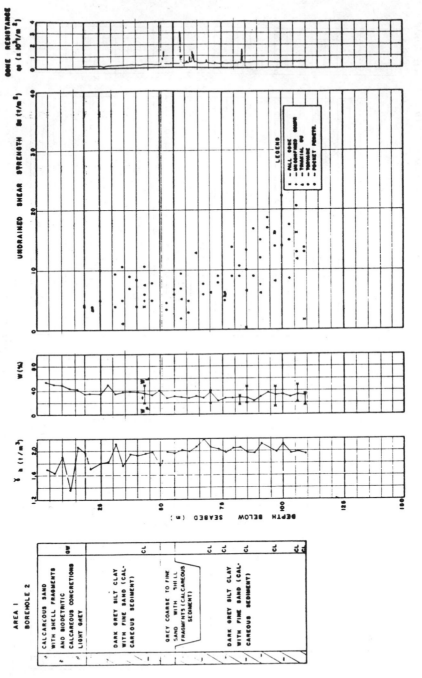

FIGURE 2

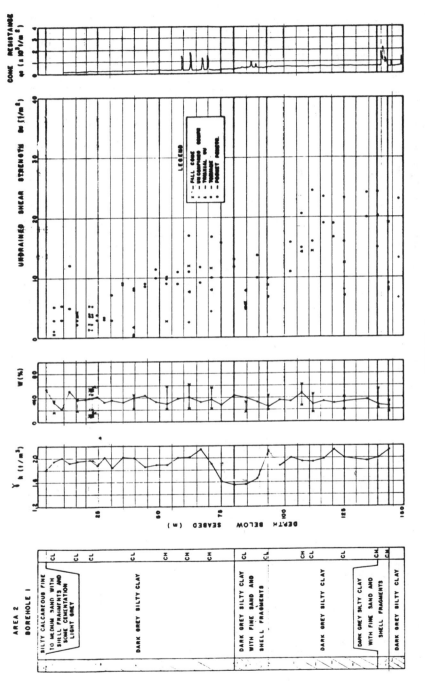

FIGURE 3

1.306

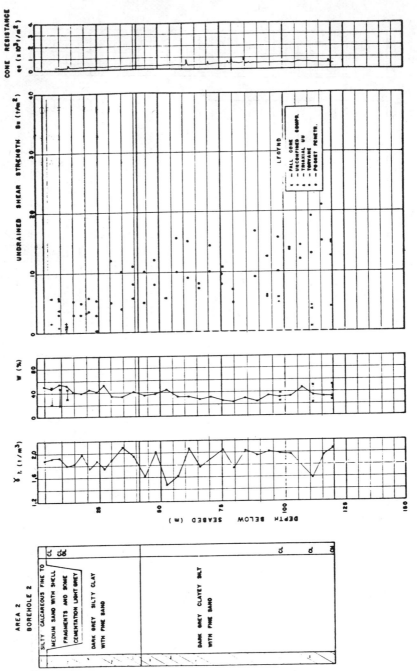

FIGURE 4

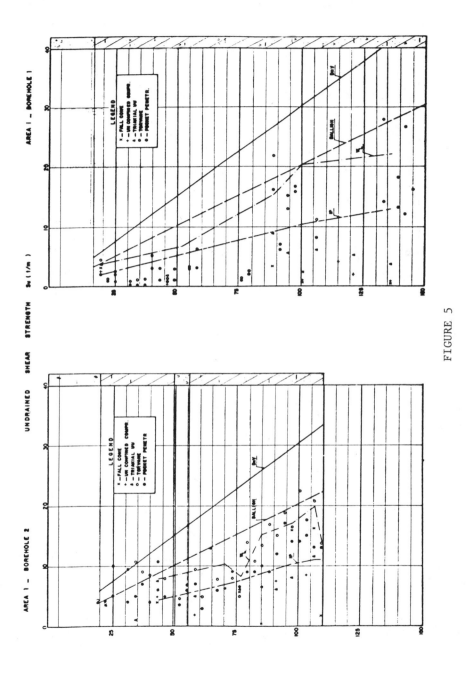

FIGURE 5

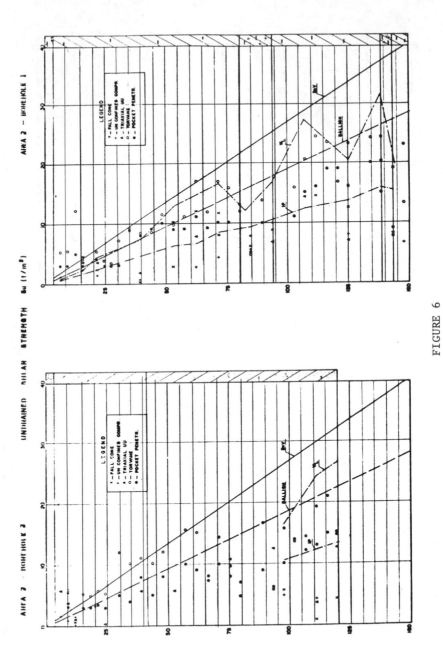

FIGURE 6

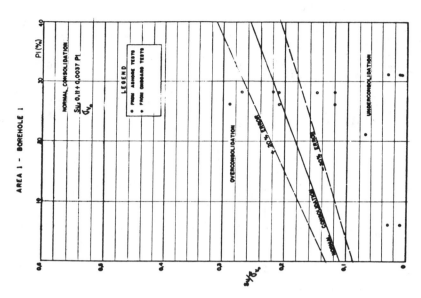

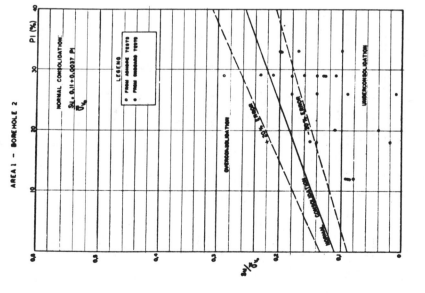

FIGURE 7

1.310

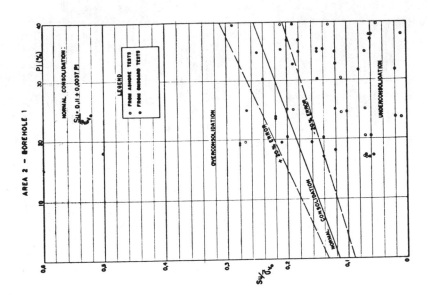

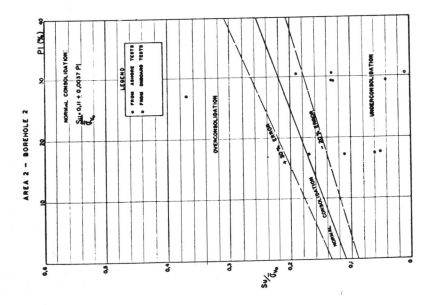

FIGURE 8

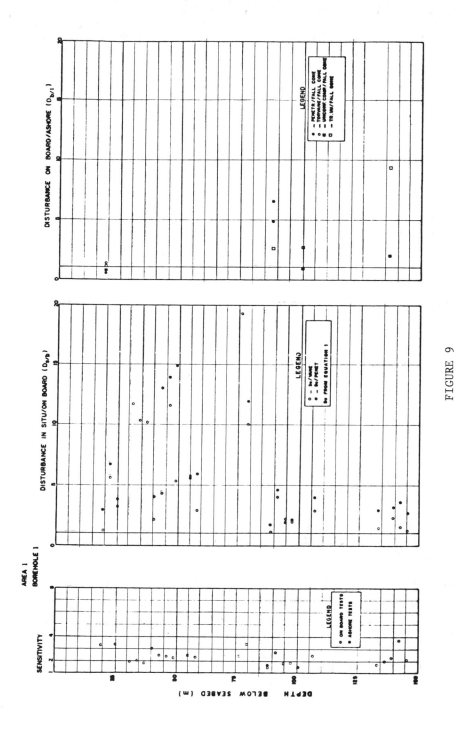

FIGURE 9

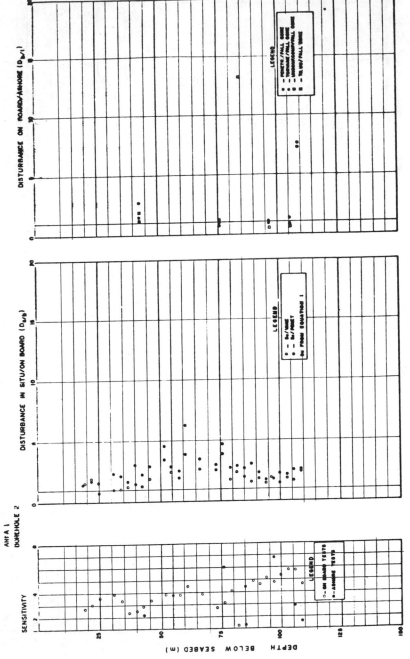

FIGURE 10

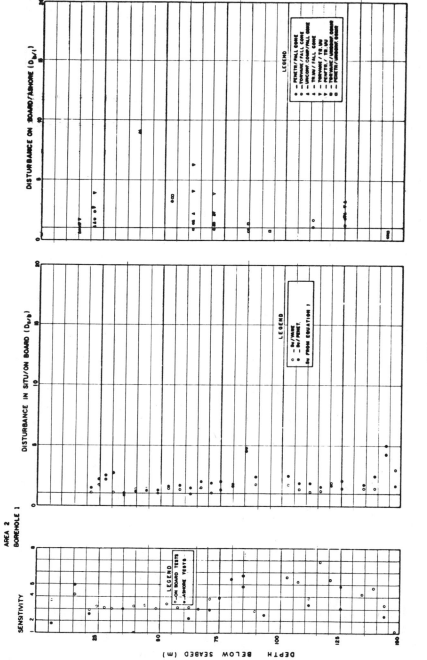

FIGURE 11

1.314

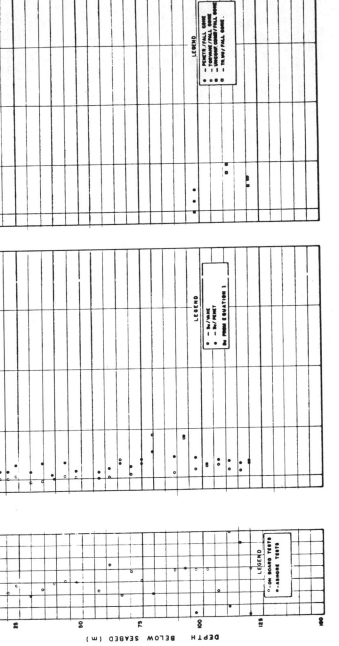

FIGURE 12

ETUDE THEORIQUE ET EXPERIMENTALE DE LA PENETRATION DES BECHES
EN BETON

BERTHIN, Jean-Claude   LE TIRANT, Pierre

LELARGE, Jean-Pierre   MONTARGES Robert

SEA TANK COMPANY   BECUE Jean-Pierre

                            INSTITUT FRANCAIS DU PETROLE

1 - Résumé

La plupart des plates-formes comportent des bêches qui doivent
s'enfoncer dans le sol de manière à améliorer leur résistance
au glissement, à permettre les opérations d'injection et à
constituer une protection contre les affouillements.

Il est très difficile de prévoir avec précision l'enfoncement
des bêches en béton dans le sol au cours de la mise en place
d'une plate-forme. Le programme de recherche présenté a pour
but de proposer une méthode de calcul qui utilise les résultats
obtenus à partir d'essais pénétrométriques.

L'étude expérimentale a été effectuée au moyen de bêches en
béton à l'échelle 1/10 . La pénétration des bêches et des
pénétromètres a été mesurée simultanément pour des sols de
caractéristiques différentes : argiles compactes, sables et
argile à "blocaux" (choisis en fonction des dimensions de la
bêche).

A partir d'un programme aux différences finies des calculs ont
également été réalisés. Le programme a été adapté de manière à
simuler la pénétration progressive de la bêche conique, prenant
en compte la rupture et la plasticité des sols.

Les résultats théoriques et expérimentaux ont été comparés pour
établir la corrélation entre les valeurs caractéristiques des
différents paramètres pour le modèle théorique et pour ceux
déduits des essais pénétrométriques.

Le comportement des bêches au cours de la mise en place de
plates-formes en Mer du Nord est présenté. Les valeurs prévues
et mesurées sont comparées avec celles déduites des résultats de
cette recherche.

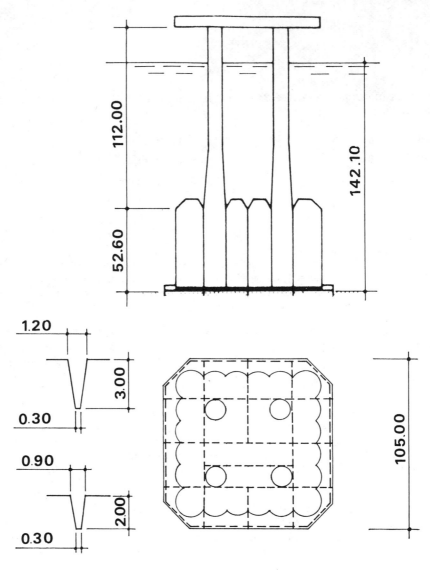

BRENT C

Disposition des bêches

Fig. 2_1

2. STABILITE D'UNE PLATE-FORME POIDS.

Une plate-forme poids comprend essentiellement trois parties:
- un pont métallique qui supporte les équipements pétroliers et qui constitue une surface de travail au-dessus du niveau de la mer à l'abri des plus hautes vagues.
- des colonnes cylindriques qui supportent le pont en offrant une faible résistance à la houle de surface.
- un caisson en béton dont le rôle est triple:
  a) grâce à sa flottabilité, il permet de remorquer la plate-forme depuis le site de construction jusqu'à sa destination finale.
  b) il forme un réservoir utilisable pour le stockage du pétrole.
  c) il forme une gigantesque semelle de fondation raidie par les parois des cellules.

Cette semelle doit transmettre au sol les différents efforts supportés par la plate-forme (poids propre, efforts de houle, vent et courant).

Une plate-forme poids est posée sur le sol sans aucune préparation de celui-ci, aussi pour assurer une bonne assise, le caisson est muni à sa base de bêches dont la longueur est déterminée, à la fois en fonction des irrégularités du terrain ou de la pente générale à corriger, et en fonction de la présence éventuelle à la surface du sol d'une couche de caractéristiques mécaniques insuffisantes.(fig. 2.1.)

Au cours de la mise en place de la plate-forme, les bêches pénétrent dans le sol sous l'action du ballastage du caisson qui permet d'augmenter progressivement le poids apparent de la structure. L'ouvrage est maintenu horizontal grâce à des ballastages différents dans les compartiments, ce qui permet de compenser les différences de réaction du sol sur les bêches.

A la fin de l'opération, le fond du radier touche le sol en quelques points, et radier, sol et bêches constituent une enceinte fermée. Une injection dans cette enceinte (l'eau emprisonnée s'échappant par les évents disposés à travers le caisson) permet alors d'assurer un repos uniforme du radier sur le sol.

La structure exerce sur ce plan d'appui un effort de compression permanent, dû à son poids apparent après le ballastage définitif, et des efforts aléatoires, dus aux effets de la houle sur la structure. L'effort de compression et la surface d'appui sont déterminés de telle façon qu'en aucun point le sol ne sorte du domaine de sécurité sous les effets, instantanés ou cumulatifs, des efforts aléatoires. Les calculs comportent d'abord les calculs classiques de fondation sous une semelle. Suivant la nature des couches superficielles, les effets déterminants sont

en général le moment et le risque de décompression sous une
arête pour les sables, l'effort horizontal et le risque de
glissement pour les argiles.

Les bêches jouent ainsi un rôle très important dans la stabilité
de la structure. Elles doivent être dimensionnées pour assurer
la stabilité permanente de la structure et pour transmettre au
sol une partie des efforts horizontaux. Le poids apparent
minimum et les procédures de ballastage sont en partie déterminés par l'enfoncement des bêches. Il était donc important de
disposer d'une méthode de calcul permettant de prévoir avec
précision les efforts de pénétration des bêches dans le sol.

3. ETUDE EXPERIMENTALE DE PENETRATION DES BECHES.

L'étude expérimentale de pénétration des bêches en béton, effectuée
en laboratoire sur modèle réduit, avait pour objet le calage du
modèle numérique de calcul de la pénétration à partir notamment
des résultats d'essais pénétrométriques.

L'expérimentation a été conduite sur différents massifs de
sols reconstitués, compactés à des densités en teneurs en eau
comparables à celles rencontrées couramment en mer.

Le programme expérimental réalisé comprend:
- d'une part, des essais de pénétration du modèle réduit de
  bêche (à l'échelle 1/10 environ) dans l'argile compacte
  et relativement homogène, dans l'argile à blocaux (de
  dimensions choisies en fonction de l'échelle du modèle de
  bêche.)
- d'autre part, des essais pénétrométriques permettant d'examiner notamment l'influence de la vitesse de pénétration, du
  diamètre et de l'état de surface du pénétromètre.

3.1. <u>Conditions expérimentales.</u>
On décrit successivement le matériel d'expérimentation utilisé,
les massifs de sols compactés et les dispositions expérimentales
avec les mesures effectuées.
3.1.1. Matériel d'expérimentation   Le matériel de laboratoire
utilisé comprend notamment la cuve de compactage des massifs
de sols, le modèle de bêche en béton et la presse de chargement
(Fig. 3.1.)

La cuve de compactage, de dimensions approximatives
 1m x 0,60m x 0,45m (soit un volume de sol d'environ $0,25m^3$),
est suffisamment rigide pour éviter les déformations latérales
en cours de compactage du massif comme des essais de pénétration de la bêche.

Le modèle de bêche en béton, de section trapézoïdale, est à
peu près homothétique, à l'échelle 1/10, aux bêches disposées
sous les radiers des plates-formes.

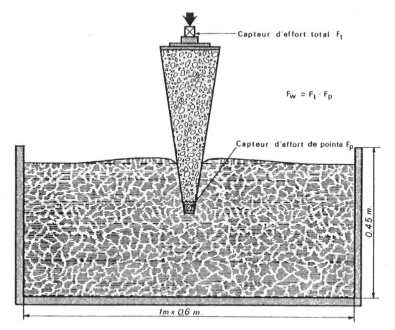

Capteur d'effort total F_t

$$F_w = F_t - F_p$$

Capteur d'effort de pointe F_p

0.45 m.

1m x 0,6 m.

Fig. 3_1

VUE DE L'ECHANTILLON DE SOL APRES L'ESSAI

Fig. 3_2

Les dimensions du modèle sont :
- largeur au sommet (pointe) B = 3cm
- largeur à la base   18 cm
- hauteur   50 cm
- angle au sommet   18°
- longueur (sensiblement équivalente à la largeur de la cuve
  d'essai)   60 cm.

La presse d'essai, à vitesse d'avancement réglable, est
utilisée d'une part, pour le compactage des massifs de sols,
d'autre part, pour l'application de l'effort de pénétration
de la bêche et des pénétromètres aux vitesses désirées.
3.1.2. Caractéristiques des massifs de sols   Les essais ont
été effectués sur plusieurs massifs d'argile, et d'argile à
blocaux.

Le compactage des massifs d'argile a été opéré par couches en
autorisant le drainage :
- les caractéristiques obtenues sont assez voisines de celles
  des argiles surconsolidées de Mer du Nord.
- les graviers de granulométries comprises entre 2,5 et 4cm
  représentent à l'échelle du modèle ($\sim$ 1/10) les
  dimensions des blocaux (boulders). Le pourcentage en volume
  de graviers est d'environ 10% de celui de l'argile.

Les caractéristiques moyennes des différents massifs de sols
compactés sont résumés dans le tableau 1.

Tableau 1 : Caractéristiques des massifs de sols.

Nature des sols	Caractérist. d'ident.	Teneur en eau W%	Poids spec. t/m^3	Résistance au cisaillement
Argile compacte	W_ℓ $\sim$ 110 I_p $\sim$ 80	30	1,95	Cohésion non drainée c_u $\sim$ 7t/m^2
Argile à blocaux	W_ℓ $\sim$ 110 I_p $\sim$ 80 10% en volume de graviers 25 - 40 mm	30	2	Cohésion non drainée c_u $\sim$ 5,3t/m^2

3.1.3. Expérimentations et mesures effectuées L'expérimentation opérée sur chaque massif comprend l'essai de pénétration de la bêche et des essais pénétrométriques.

La pénétration de la bêche a été effectuée:
- à une vitesse de 2mm/mn, correspondant à la vitesse moyenne de pénétration dans le sol des bêches réelles de 3 mètres de hauteur en 24 heures, durée approximative de mise en place d'une plate-forme;
- avec enregistrement de l'effort total et de l'effort de pointe et mesure du profil de déformation du massif de sol en surface. Toutes les dispositions ont été prises pour éliminer le frottement aux deux extrémités de la bêche.

Les nombreux essais pénétrométriques ont permis de préciser l'influence:
- de la vitesse de pénétration, notamment dans les cas des argiles à blocaux,
- des dimensions relatives de la pointe et des graviers (blocaux),
- de l'état de surface de la tige, significatif de la rugosité de la bêche en béton.

Diverses mesures et des contrôles sur chaque massif, après enfoncement de la bêche et des pénétromètres, avaient pour objet:
- d'observer la déformation des couches et des lignes de rupture du massif;
- de contrôler l'homogénéité du massif (teneur en eau, poids spécifique),
- de mesurer en divers points la résistance au cisaillement de l'argile au moyen du scissomètre (torvane).

3.2. Pénétration de la bêche dans les argiles et l'argile à blocaux.
Les résultats d'essais de pénétration de la bêche dans les massifs de sols supposés identiques sont parfaitement reproductibles. Il est donc possible de présenter des conclusions générales pour chaque type de sol.

La forme des lignes de rupture observées (fig. 3.2.) sur les différents massifs est conforme à celle prévue par la théorie de la butée.

Les déformations de la surface du massif en cours de pénétration de la bêche correspondent sensiblement au volume pénétré de la bêche.

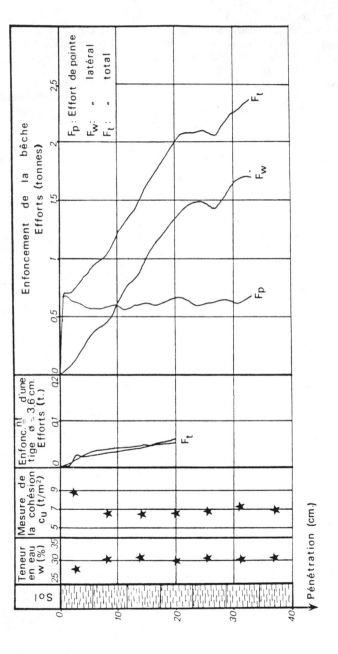

Fig. 3_3

3.2.1. La résistance de pointe q_p demeure sensiblement constante en cours de pénétration (fig. 3.3. et 3.4.), en bon accord avec la relation :

$$q_1 = C_u N_c$$

où C_u cohésion non drainée de l'argile (mesurée au scissomètre)

$N_c \simeq 5$ (valeur du coefficient de portance des argiles au voisinage de la surface du sol.

Le tableau 2 résume les valeurs moyennes obtenues sur les différents massifs.

Tableau 2 - Résistance de pointe q_p

	Résistance de pointe q_p (t/m^2)	Cohésion non drainée (t/m^2)	
		$\overline{C_u} = \dfrac{q_p}{5}$	C_u mesuré au scissomètre
Argile compacte	34	6,8	7
Argile à blocaux	31	6,2	5,3

D'après ces résultats on observe:
- un très bon accord entre la cohésion moyenne non drainée C_u mesurée sur les massifs et la cohésion $\overline{C_u}$ déduite de la résistance de pointe dans les massifs d'argile compacte,
- une valeur $\overline{C_u}$ supérieure à C_u dans l'argile à blocaux: tout se passe comme si les blocaux rencontrés par la bêche et entraînés par celle-ci en augmentait sensiblement la section de pointe (cette explication est confirmée par l'observation de l'empreinte de la bêche dans les massifs.

3.2.2. L'effort latéral par unité de longueur F_w varie à peu près linéairement avec la profondeur jusqu'à une pénétration équivalente à 6 ou 7 B (fig 3.3. et 3.4.) où la rupture des couches de sol intervient. L'effort latéral s'exprime donc par la relation :

$$F_w = a C_u z = A z$$

où : a coefficient sans dimension déduit de l'expérience,
      A pente de la droite $F_w(z)$ exprimée en tonnes par mètre de longueur de bêche et par mètre de pénétration dans le sol (supposé homogène).

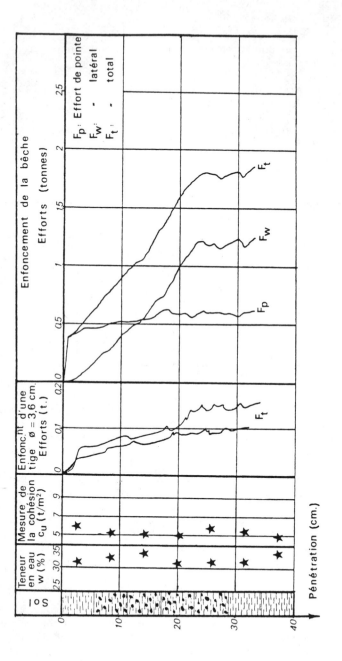

Fig. 3 _ 4

Les valeurs de A et de $a = \dfrac{A}{C_u}$ sont reportées dans le tableau 3.

Tableau 3 - Valeurs de A et a

	Cohésion non drainée C_u (t/m^2)	Pente A= $\dfrac{F_w}{2}$ A (t/m/m)	$a = \dfrac{A}{C_u}$
Argile compacte	7	11,7	1,65
Argile à blocaux	5,3	9	1,64

Le coefficient de proportionnalité a , fonction de la rugosité du béton et de la cohésion de l'argile, est pratiquement indépendant de la présence ou non de blocaux (tout au moins dans la limite de 10% en volume du sol).

Au-delà de la rupture du sol visible en surface, l'effort latéral croît beaucoup plus lentement (ceci peut être dû aux conditions aux limites rigides du massif).

3.2.3. Application aux bêches réelles Dans le cas de l'argile étudiée, on déduit que pour une bêche réelle de largeur en pointe B = 0,30 mètre et de hauteur 3 mètres, l'effort de pénétration par mètre de longueur serait:

- effort de pointe $F_p \simeq$ 10 t/m
- effort latéral $F_w \simeq$ 35 t/m

soit,

   $F_t \simeq$ 45 tonnes par mètre.

3.3. Essais pénétrométriques.

Les essais pénétrométriques effectués parallèlement aux essais de pénétration du modèle de bêche avaient pour objet d'examiner l'influence :

- de la vitesse de pénétration,
- des dimensions de la pointe,
- de l'état de surface de la tige,

sur la résistance de pointe et le frottement latéral.

Il convient en effet de rappeler que:

- la vitesse d'exécution des essais pénétrométriques est normalisée à 2cm/seconde alors que la pénétration des bêches s'effectue approximativement à 2mm/mn (3m/24h), soit dans un rapport de vitesse de 600 fois environ,

1.326

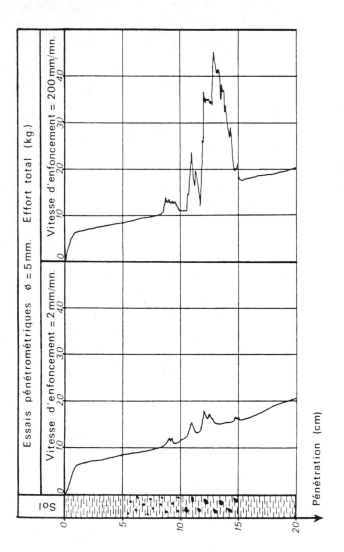

Fig. 3 _ 5

- les dimensions du pénétromètre et des bêches ne permettent pas une comparaison simple des caractéristiques mesurées, en particulier dans le cas des blocaux,
- les différences d'état de surface du pénétromètre et des bêches pourraient également modifier les résultats.

3.3.1. Influence de la vitesse de pénétration et des dimensions
Dans les argiles relativement homogènes, la vitesse d'enfoncement du pénétromètre dans les limites de 2 à 200mm/mn n'a pratiquement pas d'influence sur la résistance de pointe et le frottement latéral mesurés.

Dans les argiles à blocaux par contre, la rencontre de graviers au cours de la pénétration se traduit par des "pics" d'autant plus accusés que la vitesse de pénétration est élevée (fig.3.5.) Il apparaît donc que les "hauteurs de pics" ne caractérisent pas significativement les argiles à blocaux mais dépendent essentiellement :
- des dimensions relatives bêche/blocaux ou pénétromètre/ blocaux,
- de la vitesse d'enfoncement du pénétromètre très supérieure à celle de la pénétration des bêches.

En définitive, les "pics" des enregistrements pénétrométriques n'ont pas d'influence significative sur les efforts observés en cours de pénétration des bêches du fait:
- des phénomènes d'échelle pénétromètre/bêche,
- de la vitesse très lente de pénétration des bêches (de 500 à 1.000 fois plus faible que celle du pénétromètre standard).

3.3.2. Influence de l'état de surface de la tige   Le frottement latéral s'accroît légèrement avec la rugosité de la tige pénétrométrique mais les écarts n'apparaissent pas réellement significatifs. Le frottement latéral, mesuré au pénétromètre standard, dans les argiles s'applique donc au calcul des efforts de pénétration des bêches en béton plus rugueuses que la tige du pénétromètre.

4. ETUDE THEORIQUE

4.1. <u>Méthode utilisée</u> : choix des paramètres.
Pour cette étude de pénétration, nous avons dû utiliser une
méthode qui prenne en compte le comportement totalement non
linéaire du sol. Le premier problème fut donc de définir une
loi de comportement du matériau "sol", ainsi qu'une loi de
frottement sol-bêche ou sol-pénétromètre suivant les cas.
Bêche et pénétromètre ont été supposés indéformables.

La loi de comportement retenue est celle de Von Mises limitée
par une cape de traction (voir fig. 4.1.); les paramètres à
définir sont au nombre de quatre:
-   le paramètre K et la résistance à la traction,
-   le module d'Young et le coefficient de Poisson.

Il apparaît que les coefficients d'élasticité ne sont pas
critiques dans les problèmes d'équilibre plastique; ils ont
donc été figés pour toute l'étude.

La résistance à la traction a été prise égale à Cu/2 (Cu= résistance au cisaillement non drainé).

Ces hypothèses faites, les deux paramètres retenus pour caler
le modèle numérique sont donc K, fonction de Cu, qui a été
déterminé d'après les essais pressiométriques, et f le
frottement qui dépend de la nature de l'interface sol-béton
ou sol-métal et de Cu.
4.2. <u>Caractéristiques du programme.</u>
Une fois choisies les lois de comportement le programme doit
intégrer les équations de la mécanique avec les conditions
particulières suivantes:
-   le calcul doit être valide en grand déplacement et en
    grande déformation;
-   il doit pouvoir tenir compte des glissements sol-bêche et
    éventuellement de surfaces de rupture;

Ces calculs ont été confiés à la société ESI qui possède un
certain savoir-faire dans ce genre d'étude. Elle a utilisé
le programme HEMP/ESI qui utilise la méthode des différences
finies.

Ce programme possède en effet les propriétés précédemment
requises: notamment le remaillage qui tient compte des
glissements élément sur élément est automatique.

Enfin ce programme traite aussi bien les problèmes
axisymétriques (pour l'enfoncement des pénétromètres) que
bidimensionnels (pour celui des bêches.)

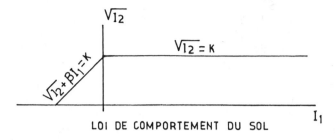

LOI DE COMPORTEMENT DU SOL

Fig. 4-1

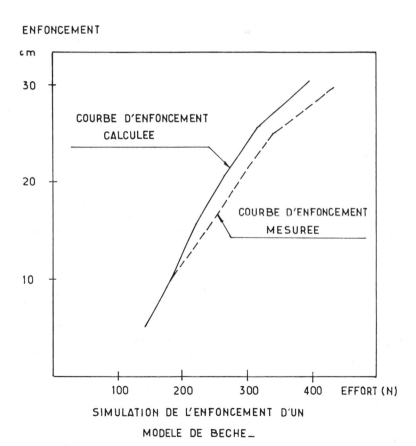

SIMULATION DE L'ENFONCEMENT D'UN

MODELE DE BECHE_

Fig. 4-2

4.3. Programme de l'étude

Ce programme a été décomposé en trois parties.

4.3.1. Phase de validation Cette première phase avait pour but de vérifier la validité des hypothèses faites dans le para. 4.1. et d'établir la fonction K(Cu) et le frottement latéral.

Un premier test a été conduit sur la pénétration d'un disque plat circulaire dont on connait la solution théorique (test de Prandth). La valeur limite calculée est de 5,22 Cu à comparer à 5,1416 Cu pour la solution théorique.

Deux séries de tests sur des enfoncements pénétrométriques et de bêches ont permis de caler les 2 paramètres K et f.

4.3.2. Simulation de l'enfoncement d'un modèle de bêche (essai no. 4).

Ce calcul a été réalisé à partir des résultats de l'enfoncement de pénétromètres. La valeur du frottement latéral f=0,05MPa a été déterminée au cours de l'essai de validation. Les résultats sont donnés en fig. 4.2.

4.3.3. Simulation de l'enfoncement d'une bêche réelle.

Connaissant la courbe d'enfoncement des bêches de la plate-forme Brent 'C', nous avons voulu la comparer à celle que l'on obtient en partant d'une courbe moyenne de cohésion non drainée. Les résultats sont donnés sur la figure 5.1.

4.4. Résultats et conclusion.

On peut tout d'abord faire une remarque sur le mode opératoire. En effet dans les premiers calculs l'enfoncement de la bêche a été entièrement simulé, puis on s'est aperçu qu'on pouvait réduire sensiblement les temps de calcul en se contentant d'étudier l'équilibre à des niveaux différents. Avec cette dernière méthode on a bien entendu perdu la forme de la déformée de surface, mais les forces portantes obtenues n'ont guère été perturbées.

On notera également que la courbe d'enfoncement de la bêche réelle donnée au paragraphe 5.1. est moins satisfaisante. La raison est sans doute qu'elle a été obtenue à partir de la courbe de cohésion non drainée du champ de Brent , et que, compte tenu de la similitude des phénomènes il aurait été préférable de faire le calage du modèle directement à partir des essais pénétrométriques et non de leur interprétation.

5. INTERPRETATION DES MESURES EFFECTUEES AU COURS DE
   L'INSTALLATION DE LA PLATE-FORME BRENT 'C'.

La plate-forme Brent 'C' est équipée de bêches de deux hauteurs
différentes:
- les unes de 3 mètres (longueur totale: 793 mètres).
- les autres de 2 mètres (longueur totale : 263 mètres).

5.1. Méthode de calcul de l'effort de pénétration des bêches
déduite de l'expérimentation.
D'après les résultats expérimentaux de pénétration du modèle
de bêche dans les argiles, on constate que l'effort de
pénétration est donné par la relation:

$$F_t = CuNc\ B + az\ Cu = F_p + F_w$$

où

$N_c \simeq 5$ pour des pénétrations relativement faibles
de la bêche (le rapport $\dfrac{z}{B_{min}}$ ne dépasse pas

10 et le rapport $\dfrac{z}{B_{moy}}$ est au maximum de 4)

$a \simeq 1,65$ pour les argiles compactes avec ou sans
blocaux, ce qui correspond à un coefficient
de frottement sol-bêche $f \simeq 0,4$.
Suivant l'état de surface des bêches le
coefficient a resterait compris entre 1,3 et 2
environ.

La cohésion non drainée Cu de l'argile est:
- soit mesurée en laboratoire,
- soit déduite de la résistance de pointe R_p mesurée au
  pénétromètre: $Cu = \dfrac{R_p}{N_k}$

avec N_k facteur de forme, voisin de 10 à 20 (suivant la
valeur de Cu)

Dans la détermination de Cu à partir des diagrammes pénétrométriques, on fait abstraction des "pics",non significatifs
de l'effort de pénétration des bêches. Cette hypothèse est
parfaitement justifiée par les résultats:
- de pénétration du modèle réduit de bêche dans l'argile à
  blocaux,
- des essais pénétrométriques à différentes vitesses de
  pénétration et avec des pointes de différents diamètres.

5.2. Application à Brent 'C' de la méthode de calcul. Comparaison des résultats.
A partir des divers diagrammes pénétrométriques enregistrés
à l'emplacement de la plate-forme Brent 'C', on a estimé les
profils de cohésion non drainée de l'argile pour
$N_k = 10$ et 15.

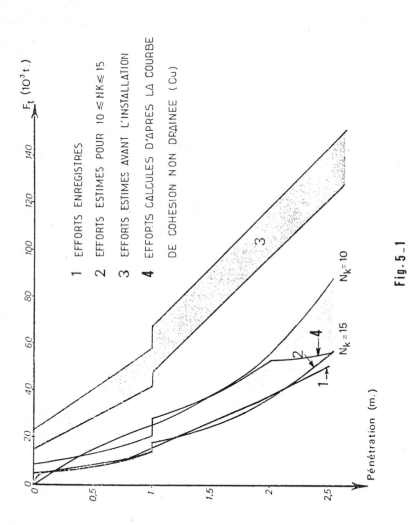

F_t (10³ t.)

1 EFFORTS ENREGISTRES
2 EFFORTS ESTIMES POUR 10 ≤ NK ≤ 15
3 EFFORTS ESTIMES AVANT L'INSTALLATION
4 EFFORTS CALCULES D'APRES LA COURBE
DE COHESION NON DRAINEE (Cu)

Pénétration (m.)

Fig. 5 _ 1

La figure 5.1. représente les efforts de pénétration des bêches dans le sol jusqu'à 2,50 mètres de profondeur:
- observés lors de l'installation de la plate-forme,
- calculés au moyen de la méthode indiquée ci-dessus, en admettant N_k = 10 et 15,
- initialement prévus avant l'installation de la plate-forme

On constate un très bon accord entre les efforts observés et ceux calculés d'après les diagrammes pénétrométriques pour N_k = 15.

A noter que la valeur relativement élevée de N_k (=15) pour des argiles compactes peut s'expliquer par l'appréciation des phénomènes de rupture:
- interférence entre les surfaces de rupture sous la pointe et les surfaces de ruptures latérales,
- remaniement du sol travaillant en butée sur les surfaces latérales du fait des ruptures sous la pointe.

6. CONCLUSIONS

Comme on l'a vu précédemment les organismes de contrôle ont fortement surestimé ces efforts de pénétration de bêches sur les premières plates-formes, les prévisions se sont avérées de 2 à 3 fois trop pessimistes. On évitera dans le futur les répercutions de ces hypothèses trop prudentes en notant les points suivants révélés par l'étude:
- le phénomène physique est répétitif et l'effet d'échelle ne se fait pas sentir;
- les efforts de pénétration peuvent être déterminés directement à partir des diagrammes de résistance de pointe du pénétromètre sans passer par leur interprétation usuelle au terme de Cu. Les "pics" de ces courbes sont préalablement écrétés, car comme on l'a vu pour les argiles à blocaux ces pics n'affectent pas sensiblement la résistance du sol pour les vitesses de pénétration utilisées;
- le calcul peut être fait aussi bien par une formule du type "portance" avec les paramètres appropriés, que par un programme similaire à celui qu'on a utilisé si la complexité du sol ou l'importance de l'enjeu le justifie.

GEOLOGIC AND GEOTECHNICAL ANALYSIS OF GOLFO TRISTE: ITS IN-
FLUENCE ON OFFSHORE STRUCTURES AND DRILLING OPERATIONS.

Jean Paul Barbot
Jorge Butenko
Juan I. Rodríguez
INTEVEP - Venezuela

INTRODUCTION

Exploratory drilling in offshore areas is usually exposed to
several geological hazards such as shallow gas traps, soft
muds in paleochannels, hard and uneven seabottom, seabed instability etc. The knowledge of geotechnical properties of submarine soils in a wide area of interest for oil exploration
can be very helpful in the early stage of oilfield developments to define the type of foundation, hazardous seabottom
and subbottom features for placement of permanent facilities
and the general behaviour of seafloor materials in the short
and long term that can assure better planning, safe and economical production development.
With this objective in mind, INTEVEP (Instituto Tecnológico
Venezolano del Petróleo) has conducted since May 1978 a
comprehensive general geotechnical investigation in the Golfo
Triste area.
Field work has been carried out with the assistance of McClelland Engineers Inc. who have provided and operated the following seismic equipment:
A Sparker with an output energy of 10 KJ, a frequency band of
10-500 Hz, analog recording on tape, and a graphical display
on a 1 sec scale.
An Acoustipulse with an output energy of 1.5 KJ, a frequency
band of 200-10.000 Hz, and analog graphical recording on a
1/4 sec-scale.
A Tuned Transducer with an energy up to 2J and a frequency of
3,5 or 7 KHz to obtain the bathymetry and the thickness of
soft mud on the seabottom.
A Side Scan Sonar of high frequency (105+ 10 KHz) to provide an
acoustic picture of the seafloor out to 250m. to each side
of the vessel trackline.
A Maxidart gravity sampler to recover seabed samples (Geotechnical tests were performed on the samples at the U.C.A.B. soil
mechanics laboratory).

1.336

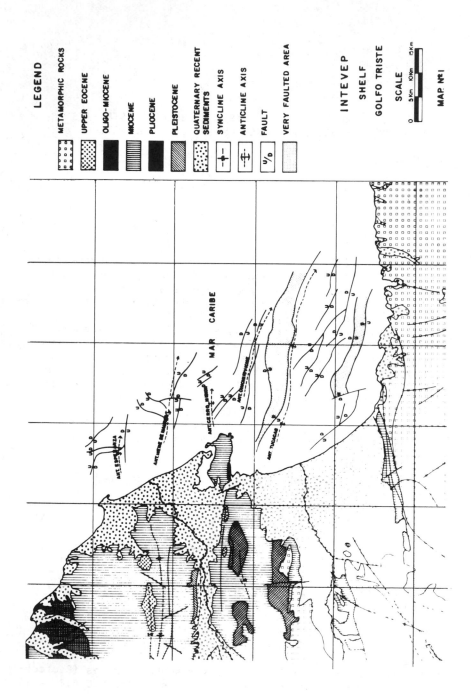

LEGEND

METAMORPHIC ROCKS
UPPER EOCENE
OLIGO-MIOCENE
MIOCENE
PLIOCENE
PLEISTOCENE
QUATERNARY RECENT SEDIMENTS
SYNCLINE AXIS
ANTICLINE AXIS
FAULT
VERY FAULTED AREA

INTEVEP
SHELF
GOLFO TRISTE
SCALE

0   5Km   10Km   15Km

MAP Nº1

MAR CARIBE

A Motorola Miniranger system was used to assure accurate positioning. All the information was analysed and integrated with
a geological hydrocarbon prospecting report provided by Maraven and the data obtained by McClelland Engineers, in a program of six geotechnical borings conducted in the area in 1974
for the stability analysis of a jack up rig and general pile
behaviour.

GEOLOGICAL FRAMEWORK

The area of interest (indicated in Map N° 1), lying on the
shelf of Golfo Triste within a wide bay open towards the Nor-
theast, corresponds to the Eastern extension of the Falcon
Basin and is limited on its Southern border by a coastal range
of Cretaceous metamorphic rocks, locally interrupted by acid
intrusives and basic effusives.
The Cretaceous basement of this basin is filled by a sequence
of sediments ranging from the upper Miocene up to the Pliocene;
locally the total thickness can reach 5.000m. Massive outcrops
of Tertiary sediments can be followed on land towards the Northwest.
The actual physiographic features of the Falcon Basin were
developed during the Tertiary Orogenic movements. Important
tectonic activity probably occured till the Holocene. Contemporary active faults can be traced on the seabed. Outstanding
folding both on land and seabed is represented by a sequence
of anticlines and synclines with paralell East-West trending
axis. Examples of this folding are the anticlines of Chichiri-
viche and Tucacas and the heights of Cerro Mision. The regional
fault pattern has its maximum expression in the Boconó fault
along the Yaracuy graben. An important paralled fault system
trending in a Southeast-Northwest direction can be followed in
the ocean and locally on land. This system is crossed by less
important faults trending East-West and North-South.
Quaternary deposits are confined to the wide and most important
river valleys such as the Yaracuy, Aroa and Tocuyo, which
reach the sea, discharging the actual sediments on the shelf.
Due to the sea level variations associated with the glaciations
and interglaciations starting during the Pleistocene, several
erosion-sedimentation periods have affected the shelf of Golfo
Triste. The last Holocene Transgression has played a main role
in the development of recent sedimentation in Golfo Triste.
Coral reefs now submerged in deep waters, carbonate cemented
sand and silt layers and paleochannels filled with soft sediments are some features that can be explained in association
with this sealevel oscillation.

SEA FLOOR MORPHOLOGY AND SHALLOW STRATIGRAPHY

Bathymetry and seafloor topography
As indicated on Map N° 2, the seabed in the Golfo Triste dips
gently towards the East-Northeast to the edge of the Continental Slope. The average slope of the seafloor is about 0.25%,

1.338

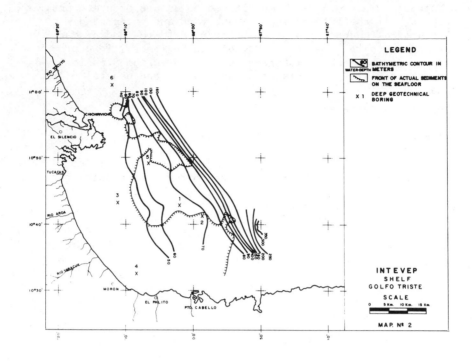

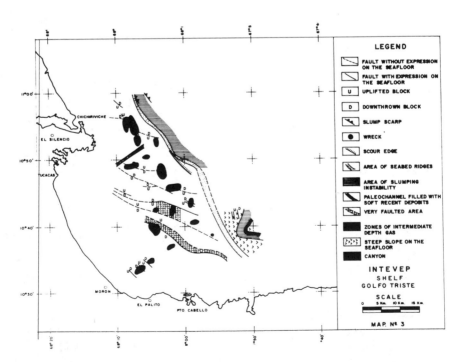

except in the Northern part of the area where it reaches 1%.
At the beginning of the continental slope, the seabed dips
more steeply towards the Bonaire Basin with an average slope
of 2%. The Side Looking Sonar shows a smooth seafloor over
most of the area investigated. This general tendency of the
bathymetry presents several local anomalies. In the central
Eastern part of the investigated area, the seabed has an
abrupt fall of about 9m, forming a slope of approximately 30
degrees.
Another outstanding feature corresponds to a submarine canyon,
located in the Southeastern part of the area, where the water
depth increases very rapidly down to 396m. The slope at the
edges of the canyon towards the central axis reaches 15%. A
Northwest-Southeast trending band of seabed ridges was identified both on the Tuned Transducer and on the Side Looking
Sonar. These ridges are generally between 2 and 3m. high and
their sides have apparent slopes between 2 and 10 degrees;
they appear to be formed on compacted and partially cemented
materials. Some small seabed depressions, about 10 or 15 m.
across and 1,5m, deep, probably due to water currents, were
also recognized with the Side Looking Sonar. The origin and
nature of all these features will be discussed in the following sections.

Seafloor materials
Most of the surveyed area on the gently-sloping shelf is covered by very recent sediment that can be penetrated by the
7 KHz Tuned Transducer (See Fig. 4). The thickness of this
loose/soft material varies between 1m and 4m. Where these sediments are not present, older consolidated materials appear
on the seafloor. In some localized zones the thickness of this
recent sedimentary layer is greater, such as near the slump
edges where it reaches approximately 9m, and in the buried
channel (indicated on Map N$^{\circ}$ 3) where a penetration of 18m.
has been achieved by the Tuned Transducer.
As seen on Map N$^{\circ}$ 2, the accumulation of these very recent
sediments increases towards the shore line and in the vicinity
of the major drainage network that discharges into the Golfo
Triste. A re-distribution of sediments on the seafloor is due
to the action of waves and the prevailing North-Northwest
current that pushes the sediments towards the mangrove area
in front of Tucacas.
As observed from the seabed samples, the very recent sediments
consist of soft clays, silty fine sands and clayed fine sands;
the underlying and locally outcropping sediments consist of
compacted partially cemented sands and stiff clays with dispersed small old coral formations.

Shallow stratigraphy

In the whole area, the shallow stratigraphy generally consists
of 3 different units that have been recognized on the Acoustipulse records (See Fig. 5):
- Unit 1: Horizontally bedded recent sediments between 0 and
  24 m. thick.
- Unit 2: Sediments dipping Eastwards, between 20 and 80 m.
  thick.
- Unit 3: Horizontally bedded more competent deposits below
  unit 2.
Unit 1, which probably consists of Holocene deposits, is
abruptly interrupted where the seafloor falls of approximately
9 m. (See Fig. 1, and Map Nº 3). A penetration of about 11 m.
in the sediments forming this steep slope (approximately 30
degrees) has been achieved by the Tuned Transducer, which indicates that they are soft or loose and probably water-satu-
rated.
The presence of this scarp, which interrupts the horizontal
continuity of the Holocene sedimentation and marks the appearance on the seabottom of unit 2, formed by older sediments
probably associated with the remains of a Pleistocene shelf,
can be explained by 3 hypotheses:
- strong currents that have swept away the loose sediments.
- massive creep movements of Holocene sediments towards the
  slope.
- old dispersed coral reefs that have retained the recent sedimentation forming the scarp.
The most likely answer is the action of strong currents.
The top of the sedimentary Unit 2 seems to be unconformable
with the overlaying layers and probably represents an old
erosion surface that could be correlated with the low sea
level at the end of the Pleistocene. The sediments of Unit 2
present current bedding features characteristic of a prograding shelf. The dip of the layers varies between 0.4 and 5.0
degrees. These layers show a gradational contact with Unit 3
characterized by multiple stages of prograding sedimentation
and erosion features. The Sparker records show that this sedimentary sequence continues to a great depth.
A correlation has been made between 6 geotechnical borings
that were drilled between 76 m. and 98 m. bellow the seafloor
in the area (See Map Nº 2 and the geophysical profiles). In
order to get a good correlation, two different velocities of
seismic compressional waves have been used to calculate the
depth to the interface between units 2 and 3. In the Southern
part of the investigated area a velocity of 1.550m/sec. has
been used and, in the Northern part, it has been increased
to 1.820m/sec. In the Central part of the area, the correlation was done with a transitional continuous velocity. This
change is based on the fact that, according to the boreholes,
the Northern part of the Golfo Triste presents a greater predominance of stiff clay in the upper sedimentary sequence,

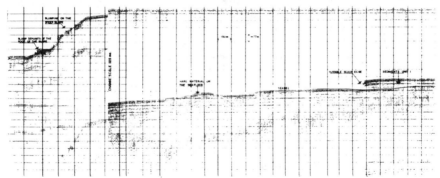

Fig.1   Acoustipulse Profile showing Slump Deposits, Slumping
on a Slope, Ridge of Hard Material and the Possible
Scour Edge

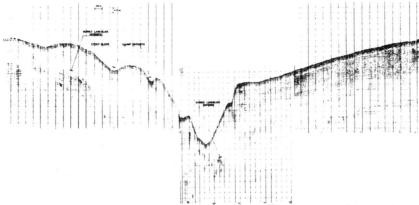

Fig.2   Acoustipulse Profile showing the Steep Slope, the
Slump Deposits and the Submarine Canyon

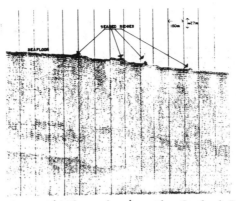

Fig.3   Acoustipulse showing the Seabed Ridges

which would tend to raise the velocity of propagation. Using these 2 velocities, the base of Unit 2, which can be traced throughout the area, has been correlated with the top of a grey, siliceous, silty, fine-sand layer with shell fragments and gravels. The contact between units 1 and 2 is mainly an acoustic reflector associated with an unconformity; however, there is no clear lithological interface and the reflector lies in the middle of a sandy, silty layer. According to the geotechnical borings, Unit 1 consists mainly of silty fine sand, sandy silt, and locally cemented sand and layers of stiff clay; some shell fragments and coral fragments were also found in these materials. The predominant sediments of Unit 2 are also silty fine sand, sandy silt, siliceous fine sand and stiff to very stiff clay layers predominating in the Northern portion of the area. In the extreme North of the area the Acoustipulse records are of poor quality, showing a significant lack of penetration due to a partialy cemented silt layer about 10m thick that lies approximately 1m below the seafloor.

GEOLOGICAL HAZARDS RELATED TO DRILLING AND CONSTRUCTION

The large amount of data gathered in the study area was also used to identify the most important geological features that might be hazardous for drilling and construction in Golfo Triste. We will give here a general overview of these hazards. As seen on Map Nº 3, there is a Northwest-Southeast trending band of seabed ridges that crosses the whole area close to the shelf edge. Those ridges (Fig. 3) are generally uneven and dispersed and emerge 2 or 3m. above the seabed. They are formed by cemented or consolidated materials and locally by coral. Seabottom foundations of gravity structures or pipeline routes in this area would require a very detailed survey for precise localization of the ridges and probably an extensive and costly operation for seabed leveling. Piles would hardly penetrate in this material. If possible this band of ridges should be avoided for production operations. Floating exploration equipment might have anchoring problems through anchors failing to embed themselves deep enough in the sediments to provide adequate uplift capacity. Uneven seabed topography could result in instability of guide bases for well re-entry. Location of Jack-up rigs should be carefully selected to avoid rough topography and possible differential settlement of legs. Eastward from this ridge-band in the Northeastern border of the shelf a zone of massive ancient and possibly active slumps was identified on the Acoustipulse profiles (See Fig. 1). The upper part of the slump deposits consists of soft and loose material that may be part of a still active movement down to the slope. As seen on the Acoustipulse record, a considerable thickness of sediments has been affected. Another zone of slumping has been recognized in the Southeastern part of the survey area in the border of a submarine canyon (Fig. 2). A thickness of about 30m. of sediments has been affected by the movements. Prior to exploratory drilling these potentially unstable areas would require a careful survey focussing on an assessment of present seabed stability. Side Scan and shallow seismic records should detect features that might show recent movements. Fixed production facilities should not be placed in these zones, for this could result in loss of support or abnormal lateral loading on foundation members or pipe lines. If there is no alternative location, a seabed stability analysis based on good quality boring samples and in situ testing should be done. Down to the slope of the canyon exploration or production activities are probably not feasible.

The slope of the seafloor reaches 4% in the zone that lies between the band of ridges and the canyon. Though no slumping has been recognized, the sediments of this slope may be subjected to failure, which represents a risk to the installation of pile-structures. The potential instability of this slope may also preclude the use of gravity production structures.

The scour edge that marks the limits of the Holocene sedimentation (See Map Nº 3 and Fig. 1) represents a seabed stability problem if overloading is generated by the placement of a structure. A zone of at least 300m on each side of the scour edge is potentially dangerous for production or exploration activities.

Though most of the faults identified in the study area do not reach the seabed, a few of them have affected the whole sedimentary sequence and movements have occurred very recently (Fig. 6). These faults can be considered as active. All the regional fault pattern appears to be generated by tectonic movements; none of them can be qualified as being caused by consolidation or shallow movements.

Drilling and placement of production facilities should avoid the faults mainly because the risk of the fault itself, but also due to the fact that sediment properties may differ from one side to the other, which could result in differential movements of foundation members. As the offshore area of interest is close to a fairly active seismic region, rupture along faults or soil displacement have to be considered as a serious risk during installation of platforms. Also some high amplitude reflectors have been observed along the faults (Fig. 7); this anomalous reflection is usually asociated with trapped gas. Gas migrating along faults from deep reservoirs can be under high pressure and become a serious hazard during drilling operations. The Sparker records show some dispersed gas trapped in sediments ranging between 50m. and 450m; locally the gas has reached the surface and can be detected in the water column (See Fig. 8). Some Acoustipulse records also show features that can be interpreted as gassy sediments; however this gas is not under pressure and probably comes from organic decomposition in the shallow layers. It does not represent a real direct hazard for drilling, but can affect

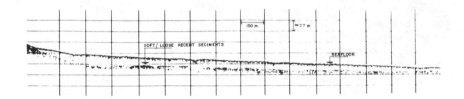

Fig.4 Tuned Transducer Recent Sediments on the Sea Floor

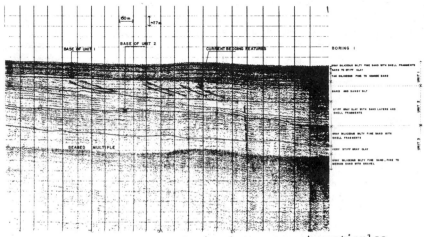

Fig.5 Example of Correlation between an Acoustipulse
Profile and a Geotechnical Boring

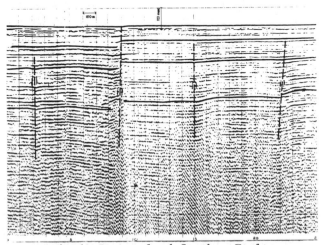

Fig.6 Deconvolved Sparker-Faults

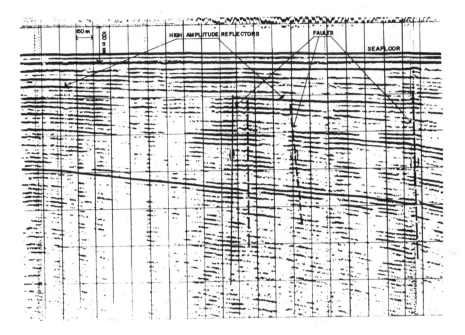

Fig.7   Deconvolved Sparker High-Amplitude Reflectors and Faults

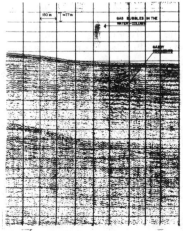

Fig.8   Acoustipulse Gas in the Water-Column and Dispersed in
        the Sediments

engineering properties of soils for foundation purposes.
A Southwest-Northeast trending buried paleochannel, about 25m.
deep, filled with soft recent deposits was identified in the
Northwestern part of the area. The thickness of soft sediments
is approximately 18m and the base of the channel seems to be
filled by coarser or more cemented material. Drilling problems
such as loss of mud circulation may occur within these deposits. Abrupt lateral and vertical variations in the strength
properties may also occur within the sediments filling the
channel, which represents a problem for foundation members.
The granular materials, such as gravel, may cause pile-driving
to be difficult. Jetting or predrilling may be necessary to
aid pile driving.
Another hazardous feature was recognized on a Side Scan Sonar
record. It is a wreck, that lies in approximately 75m of water
and appears to project about 9.5m above the seafloor. The
length of the vessel, estimated from the shadow on the record
is about 60 m.

GENERAL ENGINEERING CONSIDERATION FOR EXPLORATORY DRILLING AND PERMANENT CONSTRUCTION

Based on all the information presented previously and gathered
during this survey, and on the existing data, mainly those
obtained by McClelland Engineers in 1974, we will develop general ideas to evaluate behaviour of permanent and temporary
equipment placed on the seafloor, and of pile foundation for
offshore structures.

Exploratory drilling
Anchor behaviour   The Golfo Triste seabed presents a wide
range of marine deposits, and no single type of anchor is most
suitable for all of them. Assuming the average type of anchor
used for offshore exploration, the holding capacity of which
not only depends on size but also on its depth of embedment
and the nature of the sediments, we can infer that a typical
30.000 lbs. Danforth anchor will penetrate the widespread soft
layer which is between 1 and 4 m. thick and covers most of the
area. The anchor will get its holding capacity from more
compacted material that lies under the soft soils and has an
undrained shear stregth of 5 T/m^2.
Anchoring should be avoided in areas of hard bottom where
anchors will fail to embed themselves, and also in the paleochannel filled with very soft mud, due to the problem of obtaining reasonably secure holding capacity.

Guide base   The guide base that is placed on the seafloor to
provide well re-entry is usually supported like a shallow
footing. In zones of soft materials on the seafloor, the size
of the guide base should be large enough to prevent excessive
penetration into the soil. An ultimate bearing capacity of
1 T/m^2 should be used to estimate base plate foundation. Seabottom topography has to be taken into account in locating

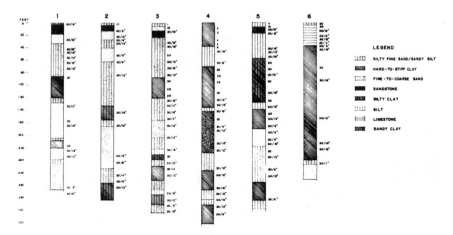

Fig.9   Geotechnical Borings Description and Blow Counts

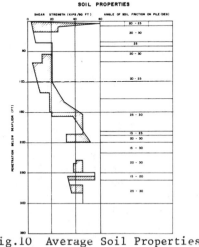

Fig.10   Average Soil Properties
for 6 Borings

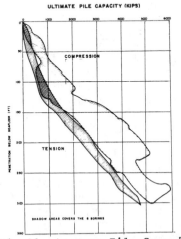

Fig.11   Average Pile Capacity
Curves 42 in.od Pipe
Piles

the base plate; areas of steep slopes, ridges and scour edges
will pose a problem for the installation of the guide base on
the seafloor.

Conductor installation   A conductor pipe is usually installed
during spudding operations. According to the nature of the
shallow sediments several procedures can be used for its installation. With the conditions encountered in the Golfo Triste, the conductor pipe could be easily jetted through the
soft sediments except in the areas where a more compacted material outcrops. Through the denser horizons beneath the soft
materials the conductor pipe should be driven with a pile
hammer or installed in a pre-drilled hole and grouted.

Jack Up legs penetration   Based on standard procedures for
offshore sampling and testing and using current engineering
formulas for footing foundation, Jack Up leg penetration for
a Rowan-Houston type of rig was estimated to be between 1.5
and 4m in most of the area covered by the shallow mud layer
with underlying compacted soil. This range of penetration is
applicable to areas correlated with borings 1-2-3-5-6 (See
Fig. 9). Boring 4, located close to the shore where the very
recent soft sediment layer is thick (See Fig. 9) has a predicted value for leg penetration of 13m. In general the whole
area, except for the hazardous zones, pointed out before,
can be explored using a Jack-Up drilling rig. To check the
real penetration of platform legs into the seabed and there-
for to improve predictions we are proposing the use of a
closed hydraulic device developed by the Norwegian Geotechnical Institute that is able to measure the relative movement between the legs and the seabed.

Pile foundation
Soil conditions that will be encountered in the area and that
will influence pile foundations are shown in Fig. 8 which
presents a detailed description of the 6 borings available
and the blow count of a 79,5 kg. weight to drive a wire line
sampler approximately 1,5m. into the sediment.
In general most of the soils will be interbedded layers of
sand, silts and mixtures of clay, silt and sand. Wedge deposits of cohesive clays that range from very soft to very stiff
and hard thin layers of soils locally lithifield or overconsolidated are also present. Cemented sands and silts, shell
deposits and overconsolidated clays due to desication, lying
right below the very recent sediments on the shelf, can be
explained by association with lower sea levels during the
Holocene Transgression.
The average design soil strength for the 6 borings is shown
in Fig. 10. The left hand side shows the maximum and minimum
shear strength for the scatter of clay layers, while the
right hand side shows the angle of friction between soil and

pile wall versus depth of pile penetration.
The available data based on disturbed samples gives very little information on the relative density of sands which is the
most important parameter governing their engineering properties.
The ultimate compressive (axial) load capacity of piles was
assessed using the static method of analysis. Fig. 11 summarizes the values obtained by McClelland Engineers; the shaded
area covers the average ultimate compression and tension pile
capacities for the 6 borings. The method was utilized to compute axial pile capacity for cohesive soils. In granular materials the calculations were made based on the recommended
practice of the A.P.I. The ultimate compressive and tensile
capacities computed for a 42 inch diameter open end pipe driv-
en to penetration of 300 ft. do not exceed 6000 and 5000 kips
respectively. An approximate working capacity of 3000 kips
per pile in a possible design for a platform was obtained by
Tera Inc. We recommended a factor of safety of 1,5 over the
ultimate capacity to absorb possible storm loading.

Additional future survey to complete a general geotechnical
analysis of Golfo Triste
Standard procedure for boring and sampling offshore has proven
to be unsatisfactory to cope with all geotechnical problems
in Golfo Triste. We are starting a state-of-the-art research
project, and expect to present some of the results at the conference. Since sands represent more than 50% of the soils in
Golfo Triste, in situ testing with the Dutch Cone will be
performed. Sample disturbance should be minimized by using a
push sampler instead of wire line hammering. In situ shear
strength of clays will be measured using. Remote Vane Shear
equipment. Eventually if a detailed seabed stability analysis
is required in the slumping areas, in situ pore pressure
measurements will be performed in the clayed deposits using
a device developed by the Massachusetts Institute of Technology.
Pipeline routes crossing hazardous zones, pointed out previously, especially soft mud in paleochannels, should be surveyed in detail by geophysical equipment and shallow, subbottom, in situ soil-testing devices.

ACKNOWLEDGEMENTS

The authors wish to express their gratitude to Petróleos de
Venezuela S.A. for the authorization to publish the results
contained in this paper.
They wish also to express their thanks to INTEVEP (Instituto
Tecnológico Venezolano del Petróleo) for the help and indul-
gence extended during the preparation of the paper and to
Maraven S. A. who has provided the funds for this investiga-
tion.

1.350

REFERENCES

- C.V.P-I.F.P. Sintesis paleogeografica y petrolera del Occi-
  dente de Venezuela.
- Garrison L.E, Tatum T.E, Boath J.S. and Casby S.M. (1977).
  Geologic hazards of the upper continental slope of the Gulf
  of Mexico O.T.C. 1977 Vol. 1.
- McClelland Eng. Inc. (1974) Soil and foundation investigat-
  ion Gulf of Triste Report to C.V.P. Maracaibo, Venezuela
- McClelland Eng. Inc. (1978) Offshore site evaluation Report.
- L. Rodríguez S. (1978) Golfo Triste y áreas adyacentes.
  Primera evaluación geológico-geofísica Maraven S.A.
  Caracas - Venezuela.
- Vásquez E. and Dickey P. (1972)
  Major faulting in Northwestern Venezuela and its relation
  to global tectonics. Trans Caribbean Geol. Conf.
  Margarita - Venezuela.

FOUNDATION CONDITIONS FOR PILED STRUCTURES OFFSHORE BRAZIL

F. Spatz   F. Bogossian   N.F. Braathen•R. Dahlberg

Petróleo   Geomecânica S.A.   Det Norske Veritas
Brasileiro S.A.
(PETROBRÃS)

INTRODUCTION

About ten years ago the first wildcat was drilled in Brazilian
waters. In 1974, oil was struck in what is now known as the
Campos Basin (Figure 1),about 90 km off the coast of the state
of Rio de Janeiro. Later several oil strikes have been made
within this area. With the discovery of oil and the decision to
extract it,the need for large structures in the area became
apparent. Since the foundation conditions are of decisive
influence in the choice of the structure to be placed in these
waters, Petrobrás (A Brazilian Company of mixed economy) had to
conduct soils investigations in the main areas of interest
areas. This was done in several steps. The first phase consisted
of coarse grid seismic surveys and soil borings to determine,
the general nature of foundation conditions. As the type of
structure was selected, more detailed site investigations were
performed to provide design parameters and,finally, a specialized survey to fill gaps in earlier investigations and to
confirm assumptions based on interpretation of available data.

The fixed platforms planned for the Campos Basin are jacket
types for water depths of 100 to 160 meters. Results of the
detailed site investigations and some of the experience
gained, will be presented in this paper together with some of
the considerations behind the assessment of the soil parameters.
This includes the choice of relevant investigative methods as
well as selection of relevant correlation between measured
parameters and design parameters.

FOUNDATION CONDITIONS

In research on foundation conditions on the Brazilian Continental Shelf considerable complications are to be encountered
due to the presence of large quantities of calcareous soil in
many areas.

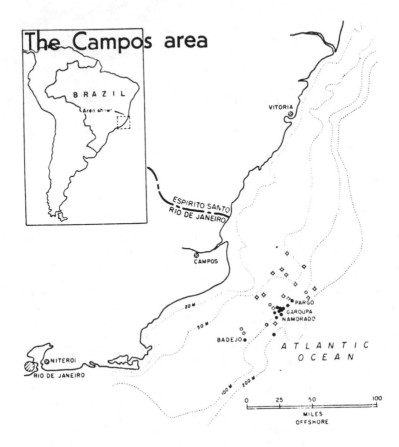

Figure 1. The Campos area.

At the Campos Basin a rather thick layer of differentially cemented conglomerations of sand, shell and coral fragments is overlying a medium silty clay. Thicknesses of this top layer have been measured in the range of 15 to more than 150 meters.

Tests on this calcareous soil yield higher angles of shearing resistance than quartziferous sands due to greater mineral frictional resistance (see Horne and Deere, 1962). The selection of skin friction parameters for pile design must, however, consider breakdown of cementation, high void ratio and water content resulting in low lateral pressures against the sides of a driven pile (McClelland, 1972 and Angemeer , Carlson, Stroud and Kurzema, 1975).

Explanation for the low skin friction values may also be
found in the fact that the mineral hardness of these grains
are 2-3 as compared to 6-7 for siliceous materials on Mohs'
scale of hardness.

Due to the limited knowledge of the engineering behaviour of
calcareous sands, the selection of design parameters is very
much based on judgement. This judgement is in turn
based on the results from field and laboratory investigations
at the actual site. The adequacy of such investigations
will to a large extent determine the conservatism used in
selection of design parameters.

The underlying silty clay layers contain only a small
amount of calcareous materials (about 5 percent) and is
therefore expected to behave more or less like "normal"
clays. However, the silt and fine sand contents is so high
in certain layers, that recovery of reasonably undisturbed
samples should be very difficult.

SITE INVESTIGATION

After the selection of the type of fixed platform to be used
and the determination of the best location for that structure, detailed site investigations were performed. Bathymetry, sea bed observations and shallow seismic profiles
where collected first by a finegridded geophysical survey.
As these results indicated rather uniform soil layering
across the site the soil sampling was limited to three 50 m
borings and one boring exceeding 120 m depth of penetration,
carried out from a specialty vessel. After completion of
the laboratory investigations and the preliminary design, it
was decided to perform additional site investigations. Su-
spiciously low undrained shear strengths were measured on
samples from 60 m depth and deeper. This raised questions
about axial capacity and installation resistance of the long
foundation piles (penetrations of 80 to 100 m).

To provide the necessary information, it was decided to perform another site investigation. This time both "in situ"
testing and sampling were done. In three holes, downhole cone
penetration tests were performed down to about 150 m. For
correlation with the CPT tests and with earlier investigations,
wireline sampling were done in 2 deep and 2 shallow
borings at comparable locations. The results are discussed
below.

INTERPRETATION OF RESULTS

Seismic profiling

The results of the investigations are summarized in Figure 2.
When comparing the seismic reflectors with the soil profile ,
as defined by the initial wireline sampling survey,one arrives
at very little correlation between the layer boundaries and
the depths of the reflectors. However, the general, trends in
slope and thicknesses of the layers are the same in the seismic
and the soil sampling profiles. Examining the results of the
cone penetration testing and the seismic profiling, we find a
rather good correlation between peaks on the CPT profile and
the depth of the measured reflectors. The reasons for the
discrepancies can be a) missed layers as the CPT is not
continuous b)not entirely correct estimation of the sound velocity in the layers and c) slight differences in positioning
of the profiling versus CPT boring location. The conclusion
must, however, be that the correlation is rather good.

Laboratory investigation

Examining the undrained shear strength results in Figure 2, one
finds that samples from 30 to 50 meters depths yield $c_u/\bar{\sigma}_{vo}$
ratios of about 0.2 which is within the range usually
encountered for normally consolidated clays. However,below 60m
the ratio drops down to 0.1 which is well below what could be
expected. Water content and Atterberg limits do not indicate
any significant difference in the layer from 20 to 60m and
that below 80m. From 60 to 80m the samples clearly contained
a much higher fraction of silt and fine sand which is reflected
in lower plasticity. It was noticed that samples from this
layer had lenses and/or pockets of fine sand/silt. This sand/
silt appeared to be disturbed and moist, i.e. the material had
been "liquefied" either during hammering of the sample tube
into the soil or banging against the sides of the drill pipe
during retrieval. Although such disturbance was not obvious on
the samples from the layers below 80m depth it is believed
that similar sensitivity to disturbance has caused the low
strengths measured in the laboratory tests. On comparison of
these results with the cone resistance profile_ ,there are no
indications of a similar reduction in the c_u/σ_{vo} ratio. It is
consequently concluded that push sampling must be tried if
reasonably undisturbed samples are to be recovered from deeper
clay layers.

Cone penetration tests

The nearly continuous profile recorded in the separate CPT
borings, gives a much better concept of the variations in the
soil deposits than the examination and testing of soil samples.
This is easily seen by comparing the two left hand diagrams in
Figure 2 with the cone resistance diagram in the same figure.
In addition to this it has been a pratice of long standing in

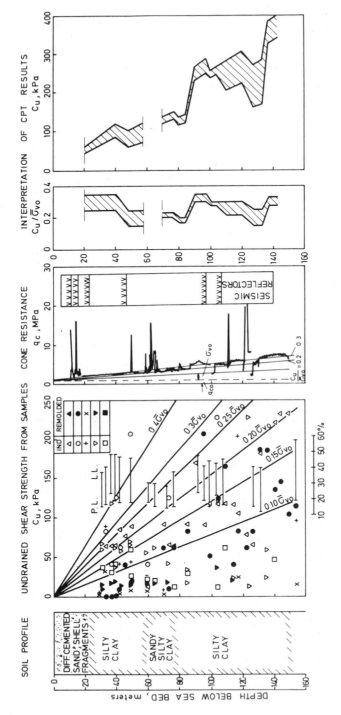

Figure 2. Measured and interpreted soil properties.

Europe to use the ratio of sleeve friction versus tip resistance to identify the soil type (ref. Sanglerat, 1972).
A more practical problem with using the downhole cone penetrometer equipment is the need for 6 to 10m penetration of the drill pipe, before sufficient reaction is established to permit the penetration of the cone. Consequently, alternative methods have to be employed to investigate the in situ properties in this upper region, important in the design of lateral support of the piles and the jacket stability prior to piling.

Test in clay - a literature review. Theoretically, cone resistance can be predicted, based on the bearing capacity theory which gives a bearing capacity factor of N_c = 11. From the cavity expansion theory, N_c factors in the range of 7 to 12 are obtained. Baligh's theory (Baligh, 1975) combines bearing capacity and cavity expansion theories to calculate the work q_c (know as cone resistance) done per unit area to push the cone a unit distance. Assuming frictionless pushing rods (f_s =0) this work is split in two parts.

$$q_c = w_1 + w_2 \qquad (1)$$

where w_1 is the work per unit area to push the cone tip a unit distance, assuming incompressible material.

w_2 is the work per unit area per unit distance to produce the cylindrical space allowing for the penetration of the pushing rods.

A cone factor N_k may then be defined for conversion of cone resistance to undrained shear strength

$$N_k = \frac{q_c - \sigma_h}{c_u} \qquad (2)$$

where σ_h = total lateral pressure at test level.

The factor given in Equation (2) is expressed as a function of cone apex angle (θ) and the rigidity index (I_r) of the soil (ref. Baligh, 1975 or Vesic, 1977). For θ = 60° and I_r = 10 - 300 Equation (2) yields N_k = 16 ± 1.7.

A more common expression for q_c incorporates the total vertical overburden pressure σ_{vo} instead of σ_h.

$$N_k = \frac{q_c - \sigma_{vo}}{c_u} \qquad (3)$$

Still other definitions are found in the litterature, e.g. use of effective instead of total overburden pressure or simply neglecting the overburden pressure completely. This only leads to confusion and misunderstandings.

Of course there is no theory that takes into account all influencing factors. Factors which are normally neglected, are effects of clay anisotropy, imperfect saturation, differences in strain rates and non-linear stress-strain behaviour of the soil. Still, these factors affect the measured cone resistance and consequently shear strength and the N_k values derived from the measurements.

In order to calibrate the models, it has thus become necessary to revert to empiricism, i.e. to carry out cone penetration tests in well-documented soil deposits and feed the data into the model. Such calibrations are done all over the world, but the reported N_k factors are difficult to compare due to highly variable testing conditions. The main uncertainties are related to refferred-to undrained shear strength which may have been derived from in situ vane tests, plate-loading tests, backcalculated embankment failures or from laboratory tests on recovered soil samples. Other factors of importance for the N_k value are the cone penetrometer characteristics (electrical or mechanical, cylindrical or "necked" cone) and the clay properties (Ip, St, OCR, etc.). In an attempt to compare some of the N_k factors reported in the litterature, it was found necessary to use one single definition of the N_k factor, see Equation (3). To comply with this definition some N_k factors were converted. According to this definition, assuming a c_u/σ_{vo} ratio of 0.2 (probably lower limit for NC clays), a soil bulk density $\gamma = 18.5$ kN/m^3 and a coefficient of earth pressure at rest $K_o = 0.5$, the N_k factor proposed by Baligh (Equation (2)) varies between 11.8 and 15.2 for $\theta = 60°$ and $I_r = 10-300$. It is also evident from Equation (2) that N_k increases with increasing soil density, shear strength and coefficient of earth pressure at rest.

Schmertmann (1975) proposed $N_k = 10$ for cylindrical electrical cones, provided the referred-to undrained shear strength was obtained from high quality borehole sampling in young non-fissured, not highly sensitive clays with OCR<2 and Ip >10 percent. For mechanical "necked" cones (friction jacket type) a higher cone factor ($N_k = 16$) was proposed.

Lunne, Eide and DeRuiter (1976) correlated results from vane shear tests and cone penetration tests (Fugro electrical cylindrical cone) carried out in soft to medium stiff marine clay (5 sites) and in a soft brackish clay (1 site). The depths of penetration ranged from 12 to 35 m. The vane strengths c_u, vane were converted to field strengths c_u,field based on a relationship proposed by Bjerrum (1973) for

Scandinavian clays, see Figure 3.

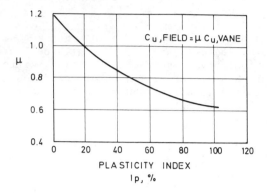

Figure 3. Bjerrum's (1973) correction chart..

With this conversion N_k factors in the range 15 to 19 were obtained for marine clays and in the range 11 to 13 for the brackish clay .

Niccolai, Colombo, Jamiolkowski, Meardi and Tornaghi (1974), reported results from cone penetration tests in normally consolidated and slightly overconsolidated cohesive soils in the eastern part of the River Po Valley and the Venice area which were compared with undrained shear strength c_u from unconsolidated undrained triaxial and unconfined compression tests. In this case N_k was derived from the expression

$$N_k = \frac{q_c - \bar{\sigma}_{vo}}{c_u} \tag{4}$$

Which differs from Equation (3) in the use of effective overburden pressure $\bar{\sigma}_{vo}$ instead of total overburden pressure. Equation (4) yielded N_k = 15-25, the lower values referring to normally consolidated clays. A value of N_k = 15 based on Equation (4) is comparable with N_k = 9.2 according to Equation (3) using an assumed average soil bulk density of 18.5 kN/m^3 and a ratio of undrained shear strength to effective overburden pressure ($c_u/\bar{\sigma}_{vo}$) of 0.20. Still lower N_k values would have been obtained, had the referred-to shear strength been derived from laboratory tests carried out for representative effective stress levels.

Appendino (1974) compared the results of electrical cone penetration tests (Fugro type) with undrained shear strength from vane tests. The tests were carried out in an inorganic clay (I_p = 20-30 percent) in the north eastern part of Italy to a depth of about 30 m. The results were expressed in terms of effective overburden pressure, i.e. $c_u = 0.288\,\bar{\sigma}_{vo}$ and $q_c = 3.84\,\bar{\sigma}_{vo}$ yielding $q_c/c_u = 13$. Transforming these results to Equation (3) will give $N_k = 5.5-6.0$ for an assumed average soil bulk density of 18.5 kN/m^3 and $\mu = 0.9-1.0$ according to Figure 3.

In a recent paper by Semple and Johnston (1979) the experience with downhole cone penetration testing with Stingray (Ferguson et. al., 1977) is presented. In this kind of testing the borehole is advanced by alternating drilling and testing, each cone penetration test extending only a short distance (1 to 5 m depending on type of penetrometer) below the level of the drill bit. Semple and Johnston neglect the overburden pressure in correlating the cone resistance with laboratory strength measurements, but in so doing, the N_k values derived will, in the authors' opinion, be too high.
However, there must be some difference in the response of two cones, one penetrating from the ground level or the sea floor and the other from the bottom of an open (water filled) borehole. This could be considered in the latter case by using as overburden correction the hydrostatic water pressure for initial penetration increasing to the full (total) overburden pressure at a certain depth of penetration. A conservative interpretation would, however, be to use correction for the full overburden pressure for the whole depth range.

Semple and Johnston (1979) reported N_k values in the range of 13 to 30 from tests with the Stingray penetrometer in soft to very stiff North Sea clays, using zero overburden pressure in the correlation with c_u from unconsolidated undrained triaxial tests. They express the opinion that, theoretically, $N_k = 13$ would be appropriate for normally consolidated clays. The North Sea cone records presented in their paper allow for a reinterpretation, where the full overburden pressure is subtracted from q_c before dividing by c_u. Assuming a bulk density of 18.5 kN/m^3, a correted N_k becomes 14.9 instead of $N_k = 17$ for the northern North Sea site (OCR$\approx$5) and $N_k = 11.8$ (instead of $N_k = 15$) for the central North Sea site (OCR$\approx$3). The overconsolidation ratio was derived by assuming a preconsolidation pressure $p_c = 5\,c_u$. Extrapolation to OCR = 1 gives $N_k = 9$ (provided a linear variation is used).

From the above review of existing literature , it is apparent that the basis for establishing the referred-to undrained shear strength is important for the results of the correlation. The attempt has been made in this paper to transform all N_k values to comply with the definition given by Equation (3). For normally consolidated clays then the N_k factors derived are summarized in Table 1.

Table 1. Summary of "corrected" N_k values for N_c clays

Source	N_k	Correlation assumptions
Baligh (1975)	11.8-15.2	$c_u/\bar{\sigma}_{vo} = 0.2$, $\gamma = 18.5$ kN/m^3 $K_o = 0.5$
Schmertmann (1975)	10	
Lunne et.al. (1976)	15-19 11-13	c_u, field $= \mu.c_u$, vane
Niccolai et.al.(1974)	9.2	$c_u/\bar{\sigma}_{vo} = 0.2$
Appendino (1974)	5.7-6.3	c_u, field $= \mu.c_u$, vane
Semple and Johnston (1979)	9	σ_{vo} considered using $\gamma = = 18.5$ kN/m^3, OCR assumed based on $P_c = 5c_u$ and extrapolated to OCR = 1

The most relevant and reliable use of cone penetration tests
in the above respect is for an actual site to establish a
statistical "local" correlation between q_c and c_u. The shear
strength should be derived from high quality (push) samples
consolidated to original in situ effective stress conditions
before sheared undrained. The "local" relationship thus
established is then used to determine c_u profiles from cone
resistance records within the area supplemented with a minimum
of sampling and laboratory testing.

Interpretation of CPT results from Campos. In offshore projects
reliable undrained shear strength determinations are not
always possible to get, generally due to a high degree of sample
disturbance and especially when percussive sampling techniques
are employed. For the Campos investigations the percussive
sampling resulted in very low laboratory shear strengths,
especially for greater depths, see Figure 2. Due to this lack
of reliable reference, shear strength, the interpretation of
the CPT results has been based on general experience of the
kind referred to above and engineering judgement. Based on the
assumption that the clays are normally consolidated with $c_u/\bar{\sigma}_{vo}$
ratios greater than 0.20, a value of $N_k = 9$ was chosen. Further
more, the cone resistance reading was corrected for the water
(or drilling mud) pressure at mudline level, q_{co}, which changes
Equation (3) into

$$N_k = \frac{q_c - q_{co} - \sigma_{vo}}{c_u} \tag{5}$$

The mudline correction incorporated in Equation (5), was
derived from the difference between the electrical cone
readings at deck level ("deck-zero"), before lowering the
assembly down the drill string and at latching level, just
before starting the test ("latch-zero"). The difference
"latch-zero" minus "deck-zero" was recorded for each test
level and plotted against "height of drilling mud". The
intercept at mudline level was taken as the mudline correction.

A typical result from interpretation of a set of three downhole cone penetration tests carried out by Wimpey Laboratories
in water depth of 163m in the Campos area is given in Figure
2. The condensed plot of the cone resistance versus depth
shows an almost linear increase in q_c with depth, typical for
normally consolidated clays. The c_u/σ_{vo} ratio varies from
slightly less than 0.2 to slightly more than 0.3 based on an
average soil bulk density of 18.5 kN/m^3 and $N_k = 9$. The mudline correction q_{co} for the actual water depth was 1040 kPa.

The derivation of angles of shearing resistance from CPT results is affected by many uncertainties, and the methods
available give very different results. A review of the most
common methods was presented by Mitchell and Lunne (1978).
For the Campos investigations, a method proposed by Vesic
(1977) was employed which considers the compressibility of
the soil. Due to the high ambient stress levels encountered
in offshore testing, the non-linear stress-strain characteristics of the soil and the grain crushing strength have a
marked effect on the soil response upon loading.

RECOMMENDATIONS AND CONCLUSIONS

The quality of a site investigation is very much dependent
on the characteristics of the survey vessel, such as limiting
sea-state for operation, type of heave compensation, positioning system, manoeverability of ship and survey equipment.
It is also especially important when the investigation is
carried out in a relatively uninvestigated area, that a
trained geotechnical engineer is on board the vessel to evaluate the results in the course of the investigation and to
change or extend the original site investigation program
if necessary.

However, a firm base program has to be established prior to
start of the soil survey. From the experience to date, it is
the authors' opinion that a reasonable geotechnical program
for piled foundations at Campos could be:

Two deep borings near the center of the foundation for the pro
posed plataform. The depth should exceed the maximum expected
pile penetration. The first hole is to be used to obtain a near
continuous CPT profile. Based on the results, soil sampling is
to be performed in the second boring, i.e. in dense/cemented
sands driven samples are to be taken, but in "softer" soils,
push sampling is to be attempted in order to recover less
disturbed samples.

Three shallow borings to about 40 m depth and located about
50 meters from the platform center, distributed equally around
the foundation area. The cone penetration tests and push
samplings are to be performed alternately to full depth. In
dense sand or stronger cemented layers, driven samplers may be
permitted.

The surface layers are to be investigated by a combination
of gravity cores and light, over the side remotely operated
penetrometer or vane equipment. About 15 to 20 locations
are to be tested.

ACKNOWLEDGEMENT

The authors wish to express their gratitude to their
organizations for assistance in writing this paper and to
PETROBRÁS for permitting it's publication.

REFERENCES

Angemeer, J., Carlson, E.D., Stroud, S. and Kurzema, M.
(1975) Pile Load Tests in Calcareous Soils Conducted in 400
Feet of Water From a Semi-Submersible Exploration Rig. Proc.
Offshore Techn. Conf., Paper No. OTC 2311, pp 657-669.

Appendino, M. (1974) Interpretation of Results of Static Penetration Tests. General Discussion, Proc. European Symp. on
Penetr-Testing, Vol. 2, pp 113-115, Stockholm.

Baligh, M.M. (1975) Theory of Deep Site Static Cone Penetration Resistance. Publ. No. R75-56, Order No. 517, Mass. Inst
of Technology.

Bjerrum, L. (1973) Problems of Soil Mechanics and Construc-
tion on Soft Clays. State-of-the-Art Rep. 8th Int. Conf. on
Soil Mech. and Found. Engng., Proc. Vol. 3 pp 111-159,
Moscow.

Horn, H.M. and Deere, D.U. (1962) Frictional Characteristics
of Minerals. Geotechnique, Vol. XII, No. 4, pp 319-335.

Lunne, T., Eide, O. and DeRuiter. J. (1976) Correlations
between Cone Resistance and Vane Shear Strength in some
Scandinavian Soft to Medium Stiff Clays. Canadian Geot. J.,
Vol. 13, No. 4, pp 430-441.

McClelland, B. (1972) Design of Deep Penetration Piles for
Ocean Structures. Journal, Geot. Engng. Div., ASCE, Vol.
100, No. GT7, pp 709-747.

Mitchell, J.K. and Lunne, T.A. (1978) Cone Resistance as
Measure of Sand Strength, Journal, Geot. Engng. Div., ASCE,
Vol. 104, No. GT7, pp 995-1012.

Niccolai, C., Colombo, P., Jamilkowski, M., Meardi, G. and
Tornaghi, R. (1974) Penetration Testing in Italy. State-of-
the-Art Report, Proc. Europ. Symp. on Penetr. Testing, Vol.
1, pp 69-78, Stockholm.

Sanglerat, G. (1972) The Penetrometer and Soil Exploration.
Elsevier Publishing Company.

Schmertmann, J.H. (1975) Meaurement of In Situ Shear Strength
State-of-the-Art Report, Proc. ASCE Specialty Conf. on In
Situ Measurement of Soil Properties, Vol. 2, pp 57-138.

Semple, R.M. and Johnston, J.W. (1979) Performance of
"Stingray" in Soil Sampling and In Situ Testing. To be
presented to Conf. on Offshore Site Investigation, London
6-8 March 1979, Preprint.

Vesic, A.S. (1977) Design of Pile Foundations. National
Cooperative Highway Research Program, Synthesis of Highway
Practice, Report No. 42. Transp. Research Board, Wash, D.C.

PART 2   DESIGN METHODS FOR OFFSHORE
STRUCTURES

SENSITIVITY ANALYSIS FOR STEEL JACKET OFFSHORE PLATFORMS

S. Shyam Sunder and J.J. Connor

M.I.T., Massachusetts, U.S.A.

INTRODUCTION

This paper is concerned with the significant uncertainties and their influence on the predicted response of steel jacket offshore platforms. A simplified numerical model for carrying out sensitivity analyses is outlined and
results for two operating platforms with natural periods of 1.15 and 1.73 seconds
respectively under rigid foundation conditions are included. The sensitivity
analysis is focussed on assessing response to (i) variations in wave height, (ii)
uncertainties in wave period to be associated with wave height, (iii) choice of
hydrodynamic force coefficients C_M and C_D particularly in the presence of marine
growth, (iv) changes in deck mass and hysteretic structural damping. Detailed
discussion of the various uncertainties is presented first, followed by the
numerical comparisons.

Spectral Representation of Waves

Sea waves are generated by several mechanisms. It has long been felt that
wind generated waves occur most often, although one of the major findings of the
Joint North Sea Wave Project (JONSWAP) experiment was that on the average 60 - 70
percent of the observed wave growth can be attributed to non-linear wave-wave
interactions [1]. There is still a diversity of opinion in this respect and
research efforts are currently being directed towards understanding the wave generation mechanisms more completely.

Due to the lack of a generally accepted wave generation model, empirical
models which rely on recorded observations of sea-state characteristics are applied. Typically, one uses records describing the variation of the wave surface
elevation with time. Such records show irregular and random behavior and this
has led to a generally accepted view that a seaway can be properly modelled only
as a stochastic process [2].

A study carried out by McClenan and Harris questions the validity of such
models [3]. They found that aerial photos of coastal regions generally showed
complex but well organized wave patterns. The use of the concept of a random
sea was, in their view, the result of making most wave observations from too
low an elevation, and thus with too limited a field of view. However, they do
not preclude the possibility that storm waves, which could not be photographed
because of low cloud cover, are more chaotic and less well organized.

Most wave observations, nowadays, consist of continuous records describing
completely the wave motion at the point of observation, but with no information
on the wave direction. As a conservative estimate, therefore, all the waves are
assumed to propagate in the same direction. If one assumes that the irregular
and random observed records represent this unidirectional wave flow, the use of

stochastic models is justified. In the following, attention is restricted to the one-dimensional spectral representation of waves.

Many parametrized wave spectra have been proposed in the literature and it is usual for different spectra to produce different dynamic structural responses. Typically ,these spectra are expressed in terms of short-term sea-state descriptors such as a characteristic wave height, characteristic wave period, etc. The Pierson-Moskowitz spectrum, used in this study,is defined in terms of the significant wave height,H_s, and zero crossing period,T_z [4,5],

$$G_{\eta\eta}(\omega) = H_s^2 \frac{B}{4\omega^5} \exp(-B/\omega^4) \quad (\omega \geq 0) \tag{1}$$

where

$$B = 16\pi^3 T_z^{-4} \tag{2}$$

The units for H_s are arbitrary. Reference [4] describes some of the other spectra and traces the genealogy of the different representations. Ochi and Bales have studied the effect of various spectral formulations in predicting responses of marine vehicles and ocean structures [6].

Although the use of the sea spectrum in engineering problems is well estab-lished, as pointed out by St.Denis, it is important to recognize its scope and limitations [2]. One of the fundamental basis for the spectral representation is that the phase angles are independent random variables. Any harmonic coupling between them would suggest non-linearity. The JONSWAP study concluded that in no case did a strongly significant coupling occur [1]. These results immediately question the use of Stokes theory (or other high order theory) for describing the wave particle kinematics since it assumes a coupling of frequencies.

The JONSWAP results appear, however, to conflict with the views of St. Denis who has commented on the validity of the different sea-state spectrum represen-tations due to non-linearities of the sea system [2]. St. Denis noted that when the sea-state is light, it can validly be described in principle by the spectral distribution of its energy or variance, but that empirical formulations of the shape of the spectrum are not fully satisfactory although there is a strong convergence toward a definite basic shape. When the sea grows to moderate in-tensity, the variance spectrum begins to lose validity due to the appearance of asymmetries which manifest themselves as cusps and haunches and white-caps and breakers, but adjustments can be made so that it remains usable, although with lessened confidence. When the intensity of the sea rises to such a level that it manifests an appearance of mountains in turmoil, no theory, linear or quasi-linear, is adequate for its description, and clearly, therefore, the variance spectrum cannot be depended upon to describe the sea. Heavy seaways, in his opinion, can be regarded only as the surface manifestation of turbulence, a phenomenon of considerably greater complexity than that of the propagation of seaways of lesser intensity. In such a situation, the prediction of the extreme characteristics of the sea waves will suffer from serious uncertainty.

A second problem arises due to the linearization of the spectral analysis process, since the method is valid only when linear superposition is ap-plicable [7]. The implication is that non-linear loads, such as drag forces, must be small in comparison to the linear loads such as inertia forces, and that the offshore structure-foundation system responds linearly. Hogben roughly defines the various loading regimes for the predominance of individual forces such as drag, inertia and lift by relating them to two ratios: D/W and π/K [8], where D is a member diameter, W is an orbit width parameter, and K is the Keu-legan-Carpenter number. The definitions for W and K are

$$W = \frac{H}{\tanh kh} \tag{3}$$

$$K = \frac{UT}{D} \tag{4}$$

where H is wave height, h is water depth, k is the wave number, U is the fluid particle velocity and T is the zero-crossing period. The regimes are defined as follows:

$D/W \simeq \pi/K > 0.2$ Inertia increasingly important

$D/W \simeq \pi/K < 0.6$ Incipience of lift and drag

$D/W \simeq \pi/K < 0.2$ Drag increasingly predominant

Wave Height and Wave Period

For carrying out sensitivity analyses using the Pierson-Moskowitz spectrum, the wave environment is characterized by two parameters: significant wave height and mean zero-crossing period. Although, the significant wave height is a random variable, generally considered to follow the three-parameter Weibull distribution [9], for purposes of this study it was decided to select five discrete values (4,12,20,28 and 36 feet respectively) which adequately cover the range of sea states that an offshore platform might normally encounter.

There is considerable uncertainty in the choice of wave period to be associated with wave height since the relationship between the two is stochastic rather than deterministic. Draper and Squire present a scatter diagram (Figure 1) of significant wave height versus T_z for the North Atlantic which clearly demonstrates the stochastic interdependence of H_s and T_z [10]. Houmb and Overik have proposed the following two-parameter conditional Weibull distribution [11] (based on 3925 samples of instrumental data from Utsira):

$$P(T_z|H_s) = 1 - \exp\left[-\left(\frac{T_z}{T_c(H_s)} \right)^{\gamma(H_s)} \right] \tag{5}$$

with

$$T_c(H_s) = 6.05 \exp(0.07H_s) \tag{6}$$

$$\gamma(H_s) = 2.35 \exp(0.21H_s) \quad (H_s \text{ in meters}) \tag{7}$$

Due to the lack of reliable and adequate wave data such long-term conditional distributions are not commonly available and one resorts to the use of a deterministic relationship between the two variables. Figure 2 shows a relationship between significant wave height and characteristic wave period proposed by Wiegel in 1961 and recently updated [12,13]. An analytical approximation is

$$H_s = 0.378 \, T^{1.788} \quad (H_s \text{ in feet}) \tag{8}$$

where T can be selected from the several characteristic periods represented in Figure 2.

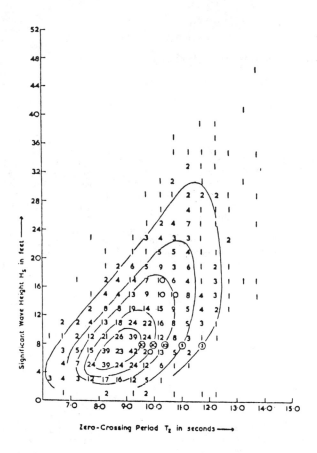

Figure 1   Scatter Diagram of Significant Wave Height
            and Mean Zero-Crossing Period for a Whole
            Year in the North Atlantic [10]

2.7

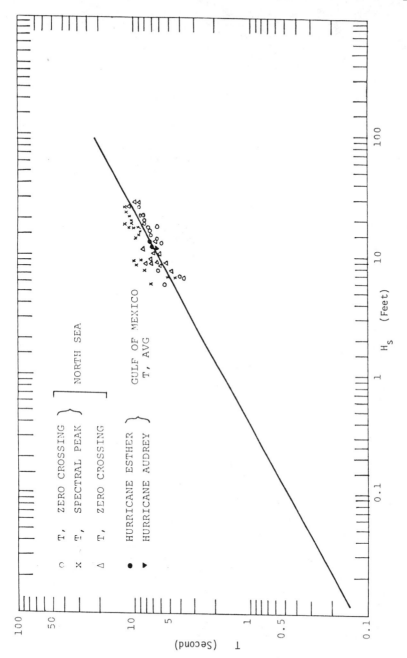

Figure 2 Characteristic Wave Period Versus Significant Wave Height [12]

For purposes of sensitivity analyses, five values of T_z have been selected for each value of significant wave height. These correspond to the upper extreme of wave period for any given H_s from Draper and Squire's scatter diagram, T_{DS}; periods corresponding to a cumulative probablity of 0.05 and 0.95, and the average of the mean and median from Houmb and Overik's expression, $T_{0.05}$, $T_{0.95}$, and T_{HO}; and finally, the period given by Wiegel's relation, T_W. The periods are listed in Table 1.

Estimation of Fluid Loading Using Morison's Equation

In a realistic response assessment of offshore structures it is necessary to identify and improve our understanding of the assumptions and uncertainties that go into the prediction of fluid loading, given the description of the wave and current environment. Hogben et al emphasize in their state-of-the-art paper that although data on fluid loading are plentiful, there are still many serious uncertainties and gaps in knowledge [14].

Several studies have shown that the mathematical form of the Morison equation, which is widely used for calculating wave loads, is satisfactory but the difficulty with its application to offshore structures has been the choice, from a wide range of published values, of the empirical coefficients C_M and C_D appropriate to both the structure and its design sea states [14]. The least well understood wave loading regime, hence the one with the least accurate description, is the regime wherein both drag and inertia forces are important [15]. Unfortunately, this is the regime in which Morison's equation is generally assumed to be applicable. An an approach, Hogben et al recommend using average values of C_M and C_D with functional dependence on Reynolds number and Keulegan-Carpenter number [14]. The Keulegan-Carpenter number represents the relative importance of drag over inertia forces and can be shown to be proportional to their ratio.

Ramberg and Niedzwecki point out that there are uncertainties in the estimation of C_M and C_D from measured force records of experiments and tests [15]. Different estimation techniques will produce different pairs of coefficients for the same force record unless the wave force is identically given by Morison's equation. This identity rarely occurs even in one-dimensional oscillating flow [32]. Another uncertainty lies in the accuracy with which the phase between the wave force and the wave cycle is known. Incorrect phasing has the effect of trading one force component for another.

Effects in the real sea situation, such as orbital motion of the fluid particles, directional and spectral properties of the flow sea waves, and orientation of the orbits with respect to the axis of the structural member are not normally accounted for. Sarpkaya's one-dimensional experiments have also pointed to the importance of the vortex-generated lift or side force which is not included in Morison's equation and can render the local peak wave force much larger than that predicted by Morison's equation [33,34]. However, the total wave forces obtained by integrating over the member lengths are far more reliable than the local forces [14].

Extensive tests with smooth and rough cylinders subjected to flow in wind tunnels and to waves in one of the National Maritime Institute (UK) ship tanks have provided strong evidence that roughness comparable with the expected level for North Sea structures can cause large increases (150% or more locally) in drag coefficient at high Reynolds number. This results in a loading increase which is greater than the increment corresponding to the increased diameter [14]. Experimental work also shows that with the rise in drag coefficient, there is a decrease in the inertia coefficient [16]. It should be noted that experimental programs have studied only the effects of hard fouling or rigid marine growths caused by rust, scale, barnacles and mussels. The effects of soft fouling or flexible growths caused by seaweed and sea anemones on C_D remain unquantified [16].

The values of C_M and C_D as functions of Reynolds number, relative roughness (ratio of roughness height to cylinder diameter) and Keulegan-Carpenter number

	$H_s=4'$	12'	20'	28'	36'
T_W	3.74	6.92	9.20	**11.11**	12.79
T_{HO}	5.87	7.23	8.82	10.66	12.80
$T_{0.05}$	2.48	4.35	6.52	8.91	11.50
$T_{0.95}$	9.46	9.71	10.55	11.88	13.66
T_{DS}	11.25	12.75	12.75	13.75	13.75

Table 1   Values of Mean Zero-Crossing Period to be Associated with Specified Significant Wave Heights

	$H_s=4'$	12'	20'	28'	36'
Top Node Displacement,σ_u(in.)	0.008	0.060	0.118	0.183	0.266
Base Shear,σ_F(kips)	12.0	111.5	242.3	394.8	591.1
Base Moment,σ_M(kip-ftx10^{-3})	3.5	27.3	55.2	86.9	127.4
Base Force Period,T_{FM}(sec.)	4.7	9.1	11.1	12.8	14.4
RMS Rel.Vel. just above SWL(in/s)	0.010	0.040	0.064	0.087	0.112
RMS Rel.Vel. just below SWL(in/s)	3.26	15.12	24.84	33.34	41.48

Table 2   Influence of Wave Height on Response for Platform A

Period Used	$H_s=4'$	12'	20'	28'	36'
T_W	1.00	1.00	1.00	1.00	1.00
T_{HO}	1.57	1.05	0.96	0.96	1.00
$T_{0.05}$	0.66	0.63	0.71	0.80	0.90
$T_{0.95}$	2.53	1.40	1.15	1.07	1.07
T_{DS}	3.01	1.84	1.39	1.24	1.08

Table 3   Mean Zero-Crossing Period as a Ratio to Wiegel's Value

predicted by Sarpkaya et al's work [17] seem to be the most appropriate data for predicting the effect of different heights of surface roughness on C_M and C_D and the corresponding hydrodynamic force [16]. Figure 3 shows the variation of C_M and C_D with Reynolds number and relative roughness for a Keulegan-Carpenter number equal to 30. The fact that Sarpkaya's data was obtained in two-dimensional harmonic flow suggests that such an approach would lead to a conservative design. Sarpkaya does not report the cycle-to-cycle variations in C_M and C_D. At low Reynolds numbers, according to Hogben et al, the wave force coefficients depart significantly from a mean value over a wave cycle only for Keulegan-Carpenter numbers in the region of 15.

The present study utilizes Sarpkaya's results to assess the sensitivity of response of an offshore platform to constant versus flow dependent hydrodynamic force coefficients and to variations in relative surface roughness. However, one should keep in mind that there remains some doubt as to the direct applicability of Sarpkays's results to wave flows. Heaf has shown that the modification of the dynamic response of the offshore structure by the increased mass and added mass arising from marine growth is not so significant as the direct increase in loading due to the same thickness of marine growth. These effects have been ignored in this study.

Hogben et al report that the presence of a current seems to influence C_D and not C_M. Dalrymple's conservative approach for deep water calculates the drag force by adding vectorially the current velocity to the wave particle velocity (for a current approximately in the wave direction) both for the definition of Reynolds number and for use in Morison's equation [18]. As waves are rarely steeper than $H/\lambda = 0.1$ in the open ocean (λ being wave length), slamming due to impulsive pressures caused by impact between the members and the free surface is predominantly a vertical force. However, under breadking wave conditions horizontal slamming is significant [14]. The effects due to current, slamming and impulsive buoyancy (sudden application of buoyancy loads as the member is submerged) have also been neglected in the sensitivity analyses.

Finally, it remains to select an appropriate wave theory to describe the fluid particle kinematics. Dean has discussed the relative validities of water wave theories [19]. It has been found that in deep water, prediction of loading using Airy theory but with integration of the forces upto the actual water surface (not as in strict linear theory to still water level) give results which do not differ greatly from prediction based on Stoke's fifth order theory [14]. The use of linear wave theory with integration of forces upto still water level is usual for carrying out frequency domain analysis, and has been adopted in this study.

THEORETICAL MODEL AND COMPUTATIONAL SCHEME

A simplified frequency domain model for the analysis of a fixed offshore platform has been developed at the Massachusetts Institute of Technology [4,20]. A brief description of the model outlined in the references is given here, highlighting various simplifications and assumptions that have been made.

Structural Idealization

The platform is modelled as an "equivalent planar beam" with lumped masses for the dynamic response. The structural geometry and pile configuration are assumed to be doubly symmetric with one of the symmetry axes coinciding with the direction of wave propagation. An approximate two-dimensional model is generated by lumping the masses at the various panel nodes and simulating the stiffness with an equivalent planar beam. Figure 4 illustrates this discretization. There are two displacement measures per node, the horizontal translation and the rotation of the equivalent beam cross-section. Rotatory inertia is neglected.

The tower, a complex assemblage of tubular elements is first modelled as a pin-jointed truss. This approximation neglects the rotational restraint at the joints. Rigidity coefficients for the equivalent beam are then generated with

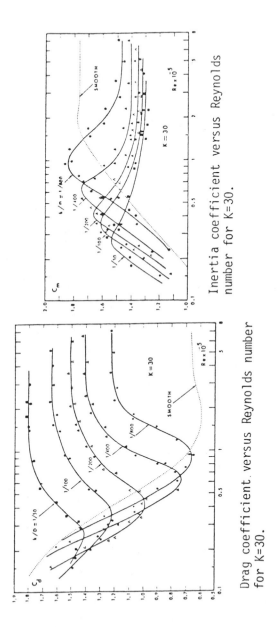

Inertia coefficient versus Reynolds number for K=30.

Drag coefficient versus Reynolds number for K=30.

Figure 3 Sarpkaya's Curves for C_M and C_D [17]

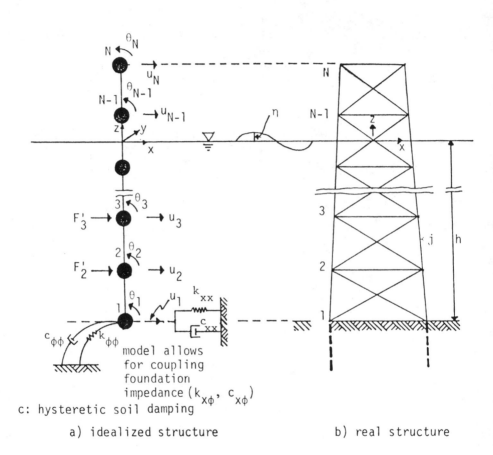

a) idealized structure   b) real structure

Figure 4 System Idealization

a complementary energy argument. One applies self-equilibrating force systems to a typical panel, evaluates the complementary energy and then by differentiating with respect to the shear force and bending moment obtains the flexural and shear rigidities. Equivalent flexural and transverse shear rigidities for X and K bracing systems are listed below (Figure 5).

(a) X-brace

$$(EI)\ eq\ =\ \frac{1}{2}\ h^2 A_c E_c \tag{9}$$

$$(GA)\ eq\ =\ \frac{\ell h^2}{L^3}\ 2A_d E_d \tag{10}$$

(b) K-brace

$$(EI)\ eq\ =\ \frac{1}{2}\ h^2 A_c E_c \tag{11}$$

$$(\frac{1}{GA})\ eq\ =\ \frac{\ell^2}{2h^2 A_c E_c}\ +\ \frac{h}{\ell}\ \frac{1}{4A_h E_h}\ +\ \frac{2L^3}{\ell h^2 A_d E_d} \tag{12}$$

These results are based on perpendicular sides, i.e., the outside verticals are perpendicular to the horizontal members. This approximation has been found to yield acceptable results for structures normally encountered.

The illustrated derivation of the equivalent rigidities is based on only one frame in planar motion parallel to the flow direction. The total equivalent rigidity coefficients are obtained by summing the contributions of all the frames in the structure. Inherent in this structural model is the assumption that the displacement of all parallel frames at each panel level are identical.

Equations of Motion

The equations of motion for the system are expressed as

$$\underset{\sim}{M}\ \ddot{\underset{\sim}{U}}\ +\ \underset{\sim}{C}\ \dot{\underset{\sim}{U}}\ +\ \underset{\sim}{K}\ \underset{\sim}{U}\ =\ \underset{\sim}{P} \tag{13}$$

Vector $\underset{\sim}{U}$ contains the nodal displacements,

$$\underset{\sim}{U}\ =\ \{\ u_1, \theta_1,\ u_2, \theta_2, \ldots u_N,\ \theta_N\ \} \tag{14}$$

where u_i and θ_i are the horizontal translation and rotation for node i.

The stiffness matrix $\underset{\sim}{K}$ is generally complex; the real parts, K_R, contains the stiffness associated with the structure and the soil, and the imaginary part, K_I, contains the hysteretic damping associated with the structure and also with the soil. The soil stiffness is represented by means of three springs having stiffnesses $k_{xx}, k_{\phi\phi}$ and $k_{x\phi}$. The hysteretic damping is written as

$$\underset{\sim}{K}_I\ =\ Im\ \underset{\sim}{K}\ =\ \pm\ (2D_S \underset{\sim}{K}_1\ +\ \underset{\sim}{K}_2) \tag{15}$$

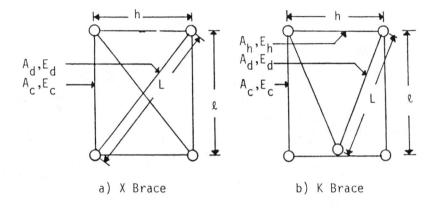

a) X Brace   b) K Brace

Figure 5   Bracing Systems

where K_1 is the stiffness matrix of the structure, D_s is the hysteretic damping coefficient for the structure, and K_2 contains the hysteretic damping terms c_{xx}, $c_{\phi\phi}$ and $c_{x\phi}$ for the soil. They form a 2 x 2 submatrix in K_2; the remaining terms in this matrix are zeros. The choice of a plus or minus sign is governed by the form of the proposed solution. For hydrodynamic loading, it is convenient to assume a solution which is in phase with and proportional to the term $e^{i(-\omega t + \psi + \zeta)}$. Since the hysteretic damping must be in phase with the velocity and proportional to the displacements, a minus sign is required.

The matrix C represents the viscous damping of the structure. This may be expressed by a Rayleigh type damping:

$$C = \alpha_1 K_1 + \alpha_2 M + \alpha_3 M_a \qquad (16)$$

where M is the lumped mass matrix of the structure and M_a is the added mass matrix of the structure, to be described later in this section.

Hydrodynamic Forcing

Hydrodynamic forcing is evaluated on the original three-dimensional structure applying a modified form of Morison's equation which attempts to account for relative motion between the fluid and structure. The forces are lumped at the nodes. The equations derived for evaluating the wave forces are based on certain idealizations. Although the velocity of the fluid decays non-linearly with depth (exponentially in the case of deep water conditions), the variation is considered to be step wise; the value at a node level is assumed constant over the tributary segments extending to the mid-points of adjacent panels. The force on each member is calculated with the "undisturbed" fluid velocity assuming that there is no interference to the the fluid flow due to closeness of the members. There are no published data on flow interference in waves, although certain thumb rules do exist [14]. Only the wave particle motion in the x-direction is considered, assuming no variation in particle motion in the other horizontal direction. Wave forces in the z-direction are not considered as they do not excite horizontal motions. Members that are inclined in the direction of flow present a problem since Morison's equation yields the force only on a vertical member. To get over this problem, the vertical projected length of inclinded cylinders are used for calculating the force. Forces on members which lie in the direction of the wave are neglected, since they contribute little to forces in the direction of flow. The net moment created by the forces about a node level is neglected, as it will be relatively small.

The wave force for node "i" is the sum of the forces for the members "j" of the real structure which lie in the tributary segment associated with the node. Using (ij) to denote such combinations, and applying Morison's equation, the nodal hydrodynamic force, F_i', is given by

$$F_i' = \sum_j [\rho(C_{Mij}-1)\frac{\pi}{4} D_{ij}^2 \ell_{ij}(\dot{v}_{ij}-\ddot{u}_i) + \rho\frac{\pi}{4} D_{ij}^2 \ell_{ij}\dot{v}_{ij}$$

$$+ \frac{1}{2}\rho C_{Dij}D_{ij}\ell_{ij}|v_{ij}-\dot{u}_i|(v_{ij}-\dot{u}_i)] \qquad (17)$$

where C_{Mij}, C_{Dij} are the inertia and drag coefficients which are, in general, dependent upon the flow and structural response characteristics; D_{ij}, ℓ_{ij} are the diameter and projected length of the member (ij); $\dot{v}_{ij}$ and v_{ij} are the water particle acceleration and velocity; $\ddot{u}_i$ and $\dot{u}_i$ are structural acceleration and velocity at level i.

The last group of terms in (17) is non-linear. A linearization of these terms is required for carrying out spectral analysis which employs a linear superposition over the frequencies describing the sea-state. The assumption of stationarity is implicit in the use of the spectral techniques. Although the sea-state is not stationary, for short-intervals of time lasting one to several hours, the free surface elevation, $\eta(x,t)$, from the still water level can be approximated as a stationary process [21,22,23]. If the excitation is a zero-mean, Gaussian process and the linearized forcing applies to a linear structure (iteratively linear soil), the output u_i and the relative velocity $\dot{r}_{ij} = v_{ij} - \dot{u}_i$ are also Gaussian with zero mean. Minimizing the error of the linearized form in a least squares sense [24,25] results in

$$|v_{ij} - \dot{u}_i| \, (v_{ij} - \dot{u}_i) = \sqrt{8/\pi} \, (v_{ij} - \dot{u}_i) \, \sigma_{\dot{r}_{ij}} \qquad (18)$$

where $\sigma_{\dot{r}_{ij}}$ = root mean square relative velocity.

For a stationary random process, the probability distribution of the instantaneous realizations is time-invariant and often symmetric about the mean. In the case of waves, for which the mean is likely to be zero, as assumed, it is convenient to take this distribution as Gaussian However, as pointed out earlier, asymmetries are introduced under moderate and severe sea-states, and the Gaussian assumption is not valid. Such asymmetries have actually been noted by Kinsman, Longuet-Higgins and others. For practical purposes, one might retain the normality assumption based on the following justifications offered by Nordenstrom: (1) the departures from the normal distribution found by Kinsman and others were not very large, and (ii) the influence of such departures on the response of marine systems is not known [23]. The latter justification is really not appropriate. However, results of the North Sea Environmental Study Group also support the Gaussian hypothesis [26].

The least squares linearization of the flexible cylinder **Morison wave force** introduces uncertainty in the representation of the drag force component. The linearization introduces conservation in the drag component when water particle velocities are less than $\sqrt{8/\pi} \approx 1.6$ times the root mean square velocity values (which correspond to a 88% probability) but underestimates it for higher velocities. The magnitude of the uncertainty depends on the importance of the drag component, the C_D employed in the analysis and increases with the intensity of the stationary sea-state in question. In addition, regular drag forces linearization methods currently in use, like the one above, underestimate high frequency force components on the structure which are associated with structural resonance and therefore important to the fatigue design of the structure [27]. A typical difference between predicted and observed force spectral density functions is that there are local maxima in the force spectral density function at frequencies twice and three times the peak frequency of the wave spectral density function which are not predicted by the linearized theory. In most cases, the natural period of fixed structures is located in the range of these frequency peaks and the structure can be more severly excited at this higher frequency.

Now, rearranging (17) with the objective of separating response dependent and flow dependent terms, and introducing the definitions:

$$M_{ai} = \rho \frac{\pi}{4} \sum_j (C_{M_{ij}} - 1) \, D_{ij}^2 \, \ell_{ij} \qquad (19)$$

$$C_{di} = \frac{1}{2} \rho \sum_j C_{D_{ij}} D_{ij} \ell_{ij} \sqrt{8/\pi} \, \sigma_{\dot{r}_{ij}} \tag{20}$$

results in

$$F_i' = - M_{ai} \ddot{u}_i - C_{di} \dot{u}_i + F_i \tag{21}$$

$$F_i = \rho \frac{\pi}{4} \sum_j C_{M_{ij}} D_{ij}^2 \ell_{ij} \dot{v}_{ij} + \frac{1}{2} \rho \sum_j C_{D_{ij}} D_{ij} \ell_{ij} \sqrt{8/\pi} \, \sigma_{\dot{r}_{ij}} v_{ij} \tag{22}$$

The terms M_{ai} and C_{di} are called added mass and hydrodynamic drag damping respectively. They lead to two diagonal matrices $\underset{\sim}{M}_a$ and $\underset{\sim}{C}_d$ with the above terms occupying the diagonal positions associated with the translational degrees of freedom.

Finally, substituting for F_i' in the system force vector,

$$\underset{\sim}{P} = \{F_1', 0, F_2', 0, \ldots, F_N', 0\} \tag{23}$$

and noting (21), the equations of motion are transformed to

$$(\underset{\sim}{M} + \underset{\sim}{M}_a)\ddot{U} + (\underset{\sim}{C} + \underset{\sim}{C}_d)\dot{U} + \underset{\sim}{K} \, U = \underset{\sim}{F} \tag{24}$$

$$\underset{\sim}{F} = \{F_1, 0, F_2, 0, \ldots, F_N, 0\} \tag{25}$$

Next, the orbital wave velocity and acceleration for member (ij) are expressed as functions of the one-sided wave spectral density function of the free surface elevation, $G_{\eta\eta}(\omega)$, with the ω axis discretized into M segments, $\Delta\omega$. The resulting expression for force using linear wave theory is

$$F_i = \sum_{n=1}^{M} A_n F_{in} \sin(-\omega_n t + \Psi_n + \gamma_{in}) \tag{26}$$

where

$$A_n^2 = 2G_{\eta\eta}(\omega_n)\Delta\omega \qquad \omega_n = n\Delta\omega$$

$$F_{in}^2 = B_{in}^2 + C_{in}^2 \qquad \tan\gamma_{in} = C_{in}/B_{in}$$

$$B_{in} = \sum_j [R_{ijn}^{(1)} \cos(k_n x_{ij}) - R_{ijn}^{(2)} \sin(k_n x_{ij})]$$

$$C_{in} = \sum_j \left[\overset{(1)}{R_{ijn}} \sin(k_n x_{ij}) + \overset{(2)}{R_{ijn}} \cos(k_n x_{ij}) \right]$$

$$\overset{(1)}{R_{ijn}} = \rho \frac{\pi}{4} C_{M_{ij}} D_{ij}^2 \ell_{ij} \omega_n^2 G_{in}$$

$$\overset{(2)}{R_{ijn}} = \frac{1}{2} \rho C_{D_{ij}} D_{ij} \ell_{ij} \sqrt{8/\pi} \sigma_{\dot{r}_{ij}} \omega_n G_{in}$$

$$\omega_n^2 = g k_n \tanh k_n h$$

$$G_{in} = \frac{\cosh k_n(z_i+h)}{\sinh k_n h} \tag{27}$$

Ψ = random phase angle uniformly distributed between 0 and 2π
g = gravitational acceleration
h = depth to still water level
z_i, x_{ij} refer to the coordinate system fixed at the still water level. Note that both B_{in} and C_{in} are independent of time. Phase shift due to the finite width of the structure is accounted for in the $k_n x_{ij}$ terms.

The hydrodynamic drag and inertia coefficients may either be assumed constant for all members or adapted according to Sarpkaya's results. The Reynolds number and Keulegan-Carpenter number are defined for wave flows in the following manner:

$$(Re)_{ij} = \text{Reynolds number} = \frac{\sigma_{\dot{r}_{ij}} D_{ij}}{\nu} \tag{28}$$

$$(K)_{ij} = \text{Keulegan-Carpenter number} = \frac{\sigma_{\dot{r}_{ij}} (T_0)_{ij}}{D_{ij}} \tag{29}$$

where ν is the kinematic viscosity and $(T_0)_{ij}$ is the mean zero-crossing period of relative velocity on member (ij).

$$(T_0)_{ij} = 2\pi \sqrt{\frac{(m_0)_{ij}}{(m_2)_{ij}}} \tag{30}$$

$$(m_\lambda)_{ij} = \int_0^\infty \omega^\lambda G_{\dot{r}_{ij}}(\omega) d\omega \tag{31}$$

and by definition

$$\sigma_{\dot{r}_{ij}}^2 = (m_0)_{ij} \tag{32}$$

A five parameter expansion was fitted to each of Sarpkaya's curves, i.e., for the five values of relative roughness indicated in Figure 3 and Keulegan-Carpenter numbers 20,30,40,60 and 100. Interpolation is used to estimate the parameters corresponding to intermediate values of relative roughness and K. Forward extrapolation based on the information at K=60,100 is used for K greater than 100. At the lower end, $15 < K < 20$, information at K = 20,30 is used for backward extrapolation. After the five parameters consistent with the Keulegan-Carpenter number (in the range > 15) and roughness are obtained, C_M and C_D are calculated from the expansion in terms of Reynolds number. Evaluation of C_M and C_D, for K < 15 is based on interpolation between $C_M = 2.0$, $C_D = 0$ at K = 0 and the values of C_M and C_D for the given Reynolds number at K = 15.

Solution Strategy

Since the system is linear, the nodal displacements can be expressed as a superposition of solutions corresponding to the M discrete frequencies.

$$\underline{U} = \text{Im} \left\{ \sum_{n=1}^{M} A_n \, \underline{\bar{U}}_n \, e^{i(-\omega_n t + \Psi_n)} \right\} \tag{33}$$

$$\underline{\bar{U}}_n = \{\bar{U}_{jn}\} = \{u_{1n} e^{i\beta_{1n}}, \theta_{1n} e^{i\delta_{1n}}, \ldots, U_{Nn} i\beta_{Nn}, \theta_{Nn} e^{i\delta_{Nn}}\} \tag{34}$$

where $\underline{\bar{U}}_n$ is determined from

$$[\underline{K} - i\omega_h(\underline{C} + \underline{C}_d) - \omega_h^2(\underline{M} + \underline{M}_a)] \, \underline{\bar{U}}_n = \underline{\bar{F}}_n \tag{35}$$

$$\underline{\bar{F}}_n = \{\bar{F}_{1n}, 0, \bar{F}_{2n}, 0, \ldots, \bar{F}_{Nn}, 0\} \tag{36}$$

The spectral density function for displacement at node m is $G(\omega_n) = (A_n u_{mn})^2 / 2\Delta\omega$. If the force F_i, (26) is written in complex exponential as

$$F_i = \text{Im} \left\{ \sum_{n=1}^{M} A_n F_{1n} e^{i(-\omega_n t + \Psi_n)} \right\} \tag{37}$$

then

$$\bar{F}_{in} = F_{in} e^{i\gamma_{in}} \tag{38}$$

Iteration on the hydrodynamic coefficients and linearized **drag term** requires the spectral density function for the relative velocity. Since from linear wave theory

$$v_{ij}(t) = \sum_{n=1}^{M} A_n \, \omega_n \, G_{in} \cos(-\omega_n t + k_n x_{ij} + \Psi_n) \tag{39}$$

one obtains using (33)

$$\dot{r}_{ij} = v_{ij} - \dot{u}_i = \sum_{n=1}^{M} A_n \omega_n H_{ijn} \cos(-\omega_{nt} + \zeta_{ijn} + \psi_n) \tag{40}$$

where

$$H_{ijn}^2 = G_{in}^2 + u_{in}^2 + 2G_{in}u_{in} \cos(k_n x_{ij} - \beta_{in}) \tag{41}$$

$$\tan \zeta = \frac{G_{in} \sin k_n x_{ij} + u_{in}\sin\beta_{in}}{G_{in} \cos k_n x_{ij} + u_{in}\cos\beta_{in}} \tag{42}$$

Noting that Ψ_n is random and uniformly distributed, the spectral density function reduces to

$$G_{\dot{r}_{ij}}(\omega_n) = \omega_n^2 H_{ijn}^2 G_{\eta\eta}(\omega_n) \tag{43}$$

The base shear and moment are evaluated with the stiffness coefficients for the equivalent beam. The general expressions are

$$F = Im \{(1 + 2D_s i) [S_{F_1} (u_1 - u_2) + S_{F_2} \theta_1 + S_{F_3} \theta_2]\} \tag{44}$$

$$M = Im \{(1 + 2D_s i) [S_{M_1} (u_1 - u_2) + S_{M_2} \theta_1 + S_{M_3} \theta_2]\} \tag{45}$$

where D_s is the hysteretic structural damping coefficient and S_{Fj}, S_{Mj} represent the equivalent beam stiffness coefficients which are taken here as

$$S_{F_1} = \frac{12EI^*}{\ell^3} \qquad S_{F_2} = S_{F_3} = - \frac{6EI^*}{\ell^2}$$

$$S_{M_1} = - \frac{6EI^*}{\ell^2} \qquad S_{M_2} = (4 + a) \frac{EI^*}{\ell} \qquad S_{M_3} = (2 - a) \frac{EI^*}{\ell}$$

$$a = \frac{12}{\ell^2} \left(\frac{EI}{GA}\right)_{eq} \qquad I^* = \frac{I}{1 + a} \tag{46}$$

Substituting for the complex nodal translation and rotation measures defined by (33), and taking the imaginary part of the resulting expressions, one obtains the general form,

$$F = \sum_{n=1}^{M} A_n F_{Bn} \sin (-\omega_{nt} + \Psi_n + \nu_n) \tag{47}$$

$$M = \sum_{n=1}^{M} A_n M_{Bn} \sin (-\omega_n t + \Psi_n + \mu_n) \tag{48}$$

The spectral density functions follow directly from (48).

In the present study the foundation has been assumed rigid. For a discussion on flexible foundation modelling and solution strategy refer to [4] and [28].

Computational Procedure

Initially a zero response is assumed and $\sigma_{\dot{r}_{ij}}$ and $(T_o)_{ij}$ are calculated with the relations presented already with the r_{ij} terms associated with the response dropped. Next, the coefficients $C_{M_{ij}}$, $C_{D_{ij}}$ (if Sarpkaya's curves are used), the hydrodynamic drag damping C_d $^{M_{ij}}$ and the forcing vector are determined. The equations of motion are then solved M times and the response is generated. Updated values of $\sigma_{\dot{r}_{ij}}$, $(T_o)_{ij}$ (now functions of the response) are used to determine new r_{ij} estimates for $C_{M_{ij}}$, $C_{D_{ij}}$ and the damping co-efficients. In each iteration the new value of M_{ij}, D_{ij} $\sigma_{\dot{r}_{ij}}$ is checked for convergence. Iteration is terminated when the following r_{ij} criterion is satisfied:

$$\varepsilon_{\sigma_{\dot{r}}} = \max \text{ all } i,j \left| \frac{(\sigma'_{\dot{r}_{ij}})^2 - (\sigma_{\dot{r}_{ij}})^2}{(\sigma'_{\dot{r}_{ij}})^2} \right| \leq \varepsilon_{\sigma_{\dot{r}}} \tag{49}$$

where the prime denotes the current value. Although iteration is required, the process converges rapidly.

PRESENTATION AND DISCUSSION OF RESULTS FROM SENSITIVITY ANALYSIS

Two steel jacket platforms, A and B, have been analyzed using the computer program POSEIDON developed for the model outlined in the earlier section. Platform A is a North Sea type structure of 404 feet height and has a fundamental period of 1.73 seconds under rigid foundation conditions. The water depth is 319.5 feet. Platform B is a smaller structure of 145 feet height and has a period of 1.15 seconds. The water depth for this structure is 104 feet. The salient features of both structures are indicated in Figures 6 and 7. In the following, results of the sensitivity analyses carried out for the cases indicated in the introductory discussion are presented. A brief discussion of the results for each case is also included.

Influence of Wave Height on Response

Platform A is subjected to the selected significant wave heights with zero-corssing periods being given by Wiegel's relation, i.e. T_W (Table 1). Constant values of $C_M=2$ and $C_D=1.4$ are used in the analysis. The response quantities of interest include the top node displacement, the base shear and moment along with its average zero-crossing period, and the root-mean-square relative velocity. Table 2 gives a summary of the results.

A number of interesting conclusions may be arrived at. First, the rms displacements are very small in all cases, including the case where $H_s=36'$ which corresponds to an extreme wave of approximately 72'. Figures 8 and 9 show the wave spectrum and the displacement spectrum for the two extreme cases, $H_s=4'$ and $H_s=36'$. The location of the natural frequency of the platform on the frequency axis has also been indicated. It is clear from the response spectral

2.22

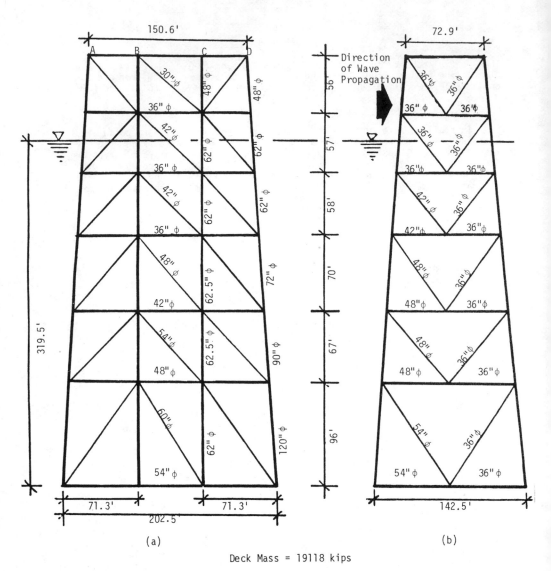

(a)   (b)

Deck Mass = 19118 kips

(i) Frames A and D are identical. Similarly, frames B and C are identical.
(ii) Dimensions on the left in Figure 6(b) correspond to frames A and D,
     whereas those on the right correspond to frames B and C.

Figure 6 General Characteristics of Platform A

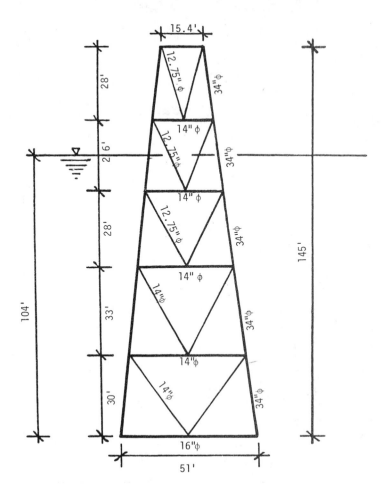

Deck Mass = 1434 kips

Platform is square in plan, doubly symmetric and has similar
properties about both symmetry axes.

Figure 7 General Characteristics of Platform B

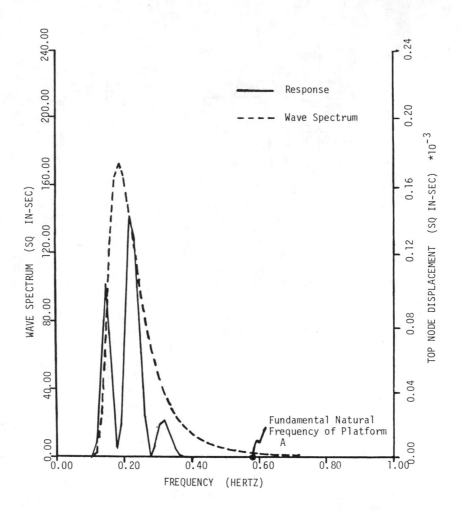

Figure 8   Excitation and Response Spectral Density
Functions for Platform A (H_s=4',T_z=3.74 sec)

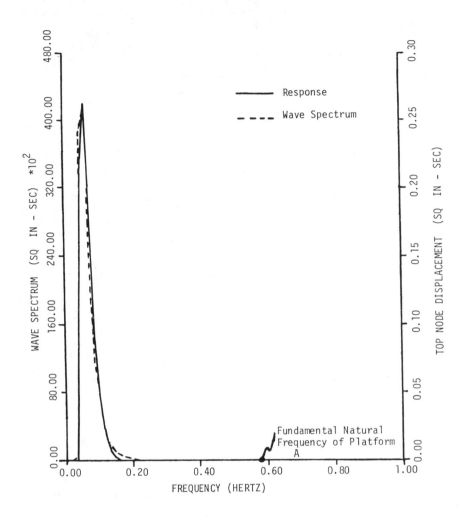

Figure 9 Excitation and Response Spectral Density
Functions for Platform A (H_s=36', T_z=12.79 sec)

density functions that there is no dynamic amplification and that, in fact, a quasi-static analysis procedure would have yielded identical results. The multiple peak response spectral density of Figure 8 requires some explanation. The zeros (or valleys) in the spectrum are due to the possible occurrence of out-of-phase harmonics in the load effects. While the overall (global) displacement response prediction is always accurate, in some cases, the true wave-induced stress state may be underestimated. This corresponds to the condition where certain force harmonics are associated with wave lengths which are whole number fractions of the distance separating column planes of the platform. This effect is a function of the distance between the major column planes of the structure and the bandwidth of the wave spectral density function. Therefore, it is more prominent in the response to the lower to moderate sea states, which are associated with smaller wave lengths. In order to accurately account for the out-of-phase load effects, a more complex structural model should be used, such that the behavior of the major column planes can be studied separately. Similar conclusions apply to the base shear and base moment spectral density functions.

Second, there is a definite relationship between base shear and base moment for a given structure. Figure 10 plots $h = \sigma_M / \sigma_F$ versus σ_F, where h is a measure of the location of centre of force. Such relations are useful in developing simple models for assessing stiffness degradation of soil, etc. [4,28]. The base force period listed in Table 2 is the average of mean zero-crossing periods computed from the base shear and base moment spectral density functions. In all cases, the base force period is larger than the corresponding wave zero-crossing periods, T_W. This occurs because the high frequency components of excitation, and hence response, attenuate faster with depth. In addition, the high frequency wave energy was observed to contribute little to force.

Third, the motion of the structure is negligible compared to the fluid motion, and this reduces the uncertainty associated with the use of (17). This is discernible from the last two lines of Table 2. The rms relative velocities listed in the table correspond to nodes just above and below the still water level and to a position at the middle of the structure along the wave propagation direction. It was observed that the variation in rms velocities for different positions along the wave propagation direction is negligible. It should be noted that the rms relative velocity for the node above still water level is equal to the rms structural node velocity. However, the conclusion arrived at here does not preclude the possibility that, for more flexible platforms, structural motion might not be negligible.

Effect of Uncertainty in Wave Period to be Associated with Wave Height

Platform A has been subjected to the different H_s, T_z combinations indicated in Table 1. Table 3 lists the ratio of period used to Wiegel's period, T_W, for different values of significant wave height. Tables 4-7 list the corresponding response ratios. The actual values of response for Wiegel's period have already been given in Table 2. Figures 11 and 12 represent the same information in plot form.

Perusal of the results shows that uncertainty in T_z is large for small H_s, and small for large H_s. In addition, uncertainty in response is positively correlated to the uncertainty in T_z. One notes that, in general, at large H_s uncertainty in response is less than uncertainty in T_z. At low H_s, uncertainty in top node response is almost equal to the uncertainty in period, whereas uncertainty in base shear and moment is larger. It is significant that the uncertainty in base force zero-crossing period, T_{FM} is also positively correlated to the uncertainty in T_z.

Therefore, for extreme sea states, period uncertainty does not appear to be critical. However, for such sea states it is the adequacy of the wave spectrum in representing the sea surface that is questionable. For lower sea states, which are potentially important for fatigue assessment, the uncertainty in force

Period Used	H_s=4'	12'	20'	28'	36'
T_W	1.00	1.00	1.00	1.00	1.00
T_{HO}	2.02	1.03	1.00	1.00	1.00
$T_{0.05}$	0.71	0.53	0.86	0.99	1.00
$T_{0.95}$	2.50	1.09	1.00	1.00	0.99
T_{DS}	2.42	1.02	0.97	0.97	0.99

Table 4   RMS Top Node Displacement for Various H_s,T_z Pairs as a Ratio to that Predicted by Wiegel's Period

Period Used	H_s=4'	12'	20'	28'	36'
T_W	1.00	1.00	1.00	1.00	1.00
T_{HO}	2.45	1.05	0.98	0.98	1.00
$T_{0.05}$	0.67	0.43	0.75	0.91	0.96
$T_{0.95}$	3.76	1.26	1.05	1.03	1.01
T_{DS}	3.90	1.32	1.10	1.05	1.01

Table 5   RMS Base Shear for Various H_s,T_z Pairs as a Ratio to that Predicted by Wiegel's Period

Period Used	H_s=4'	12'	20'	28'	36'
T_W	1.00	1.00	1.00	1.00	1.00
T_{HO}	2.17	1.03	0.99	1.00	1.00
$T_{0.05}$	0.69	0.50	0.83	0.97	0.99
$T_{0.95}$	2.85	1.13	1.01	1.01	0.99
T_{DS}	2.81	1.10	1.00	0.99	0.99

Table 6   RMS Base Moment for Various H_s,T_z Pairs as a Ratio to that Predicted by Wiegel's Period

Period Used	H_s=4'	12'	20'	28'	36'
T_W	1.00	1.00	1.00	1.00	1.00
T_{HO}	1.72	1.03	0.97	0.97	1.00
$T_{0.05}$	0.77	0.64	0.79	0.85	0.92
$T_{0.95}$	2.40	1.26	1.10	1.05	1.05
T_{DS}	2.69	1.52	1.27	1.17	1.05

Table 7   Average Base Force Zero-Crossing Period for Various H_s,T_z Pairs as a Ratio to that Predicted by Wiegel's Period

	H_s=4'	12'	20'	28'	36'
Top Node Displacement,σ_u(in)	0.008	0.055	0.095	0.142	0.240
Base Shear,σ_F(kips)	11.9	103.1	203.6	309.4	498.0
Base Moment,σ_M(kip-ftx10^{-3})	3.4	24.9	44.9	67.4	112.4
Base Force Period,T_{FM}(sec.)	4.7	9.1	11.1	12.7	14.4
RMS Rel.Vel. just above SWL(in/s)	0.010	0.036	0.052	0.068	0.100
RMS Rel.Vel. just below SWL(in/s)	3.26	15.12	24.84	33.33	41.46

Table 8   Response of Platform A to Variable Hydrodynamic Coefficients with Relative Roughness 0.02

Zone	Average Diameter of Members(ins)				Distribution of Groups Within Zones(%)			
	Group 1	Group 2	Group 3	Group 4	Group 1	Group 2	Group 3	Group 4
1	77.71	54.00	33.00	-	41.2	23.5	35.3	-
2	76.25	50.57	33.00	-	23.5	41.2	35.3	-
3	67.25	47.14	33.00	-	23.5	41.2	35.3	-
4	62.00	42.00	33.43	-	23.5	35.3	41.2	-
5	62.00	42.00	34.20	-	23.5	17.6	58.8	-
6		48.00	34.20	-		41.2	58.8	-

Table 9   Analysis of Average Member Diameters in Platform A

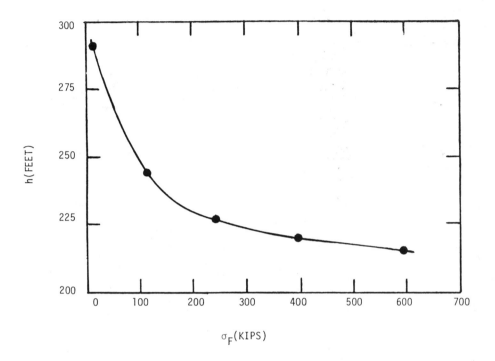

Figure 10 Plot of h versus σ_F for Platform A

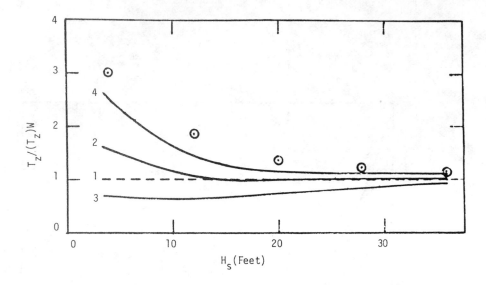

1. Wiegel T_W

2. Houmb and Overik $T_{0.05}$

3. Houmb and Overik T_{HO}

4. Houmb and Overik $T_{0.95}$

⊙   Draper and Squire T_{DS}

Figure 11 Plot of T_z/T_W versus Significant Wave Height

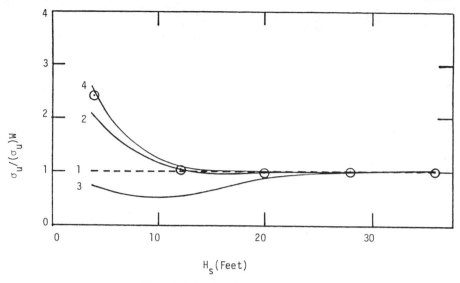

(a)   RMS Top Node Displacement

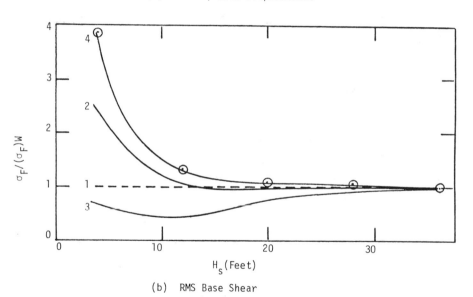

(b)   RMS Base Shear

Figure 12 a,b   Response Ratios   for Platform A

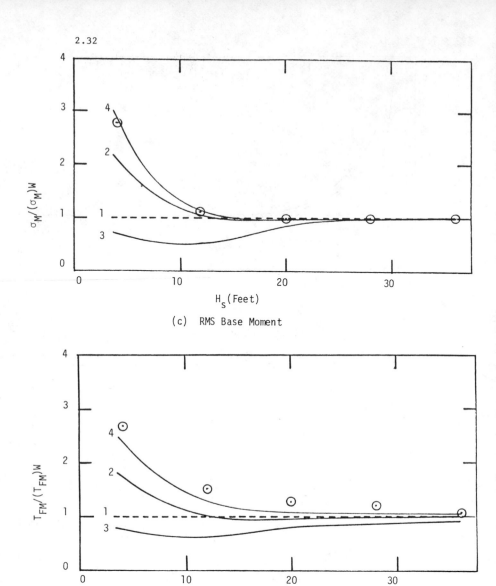

(c) RMS Base Moment

(d) Average Base Force Zero-Crossing Period

Figure 12 c,d Response Ratios for Platform A

is appreciable. An increase in force is partially compensated for by a reduction in effective number of loading cycles since the base force zero-crossing period increases at the same time. It would be interesting at this stage to look at the conclusions of a study on the fatigue behavior of a fictitious steel jacket platform with period 3.85 seconds [29]. An extract from the report follows:

> "...most of the cumulative fatigue damage comes from the higher sea states. The highest contribution corresponds to the largest slope (of the cumulative fatigue damage curve), which occurs about a 23 feet significant wave height. This result contradicts the common idea that fatigue in offshore structures is primarily due to lower to moderate sea states. As a matter of fact, the lowest six sea states considered, for which the degree of dynamic response is significant, do not contribute to the fatigue in the joint. Even though the probability of their occurrence is small, the higher sea states play the major role in inducing the fatigue process at the structural joints."

It thus appears that uncertainty in period, T_z is unlikely to significantly influence design or fatigue life assessment.

The response spectral density function for $H_s=4'$ and $T_{0.05}=2.48$ seconds requires some explanation for two reasons (i) there is no second peak due to dynamic amplification even though there is significant wave energy at the natural frequency of the platform, and (ii) the quasi-static response is negligible above a frequency of ~4OHz, although there is significant wave energy in that region (Figure 13). Equations (26) and (27) are the key to understanding this phenomenon. In (26), the term F_{in} is essentially the force transfer function. It is observed that this transfer function becomes very small for $\omega \geq 4OH_z$ and thus there is no response whether quasi-static or dynamic.

Influence of Hydrodynamic Force Coefficients and Marine Growth on Response

In the first instance platform A was analyzed for constant versus flow dependent hydrodynamic coefficients using the various H_s, T_z pairs identified through Wiegel's relation and a relative roughness of 0.02. The worst case, represented by relative roughness equal to 0.02, was chosen to see if there was any effect at all of flow dependent hydrodynamic coefficients on the structure. The usual upper bound design values $C_M=2$ and $C_D=1.4$ were used for the constant coefficients case. Table 2 gives a summary of results for the constant coefficients case and Table 8 gives results for the variable coefficients case. In order to present results for Keulegan-Carpenter number, Reynolds number, C_M and C_D in a convenient and systematic manner, the structure has been divided into four types of members by diameter:

GROUP 1   120" >DIA >60"
GROUP 2   60" >DIA >40"
GROUP 3   40" >DIA >20"
GROUP 4   20" >DIA > 0"

and further divided into horizontal zones (counted from bottom) corresponding to each vertical bay i.e., the region including and between adjacent nodes. For each group and zone, an average member diameter has been calculated and is given in Table 9. Table 10 lists the average values of K, Re, C_M and C_D for each of the groups in all zones, for the case $H_s=36'$, $T_z=12.79$ seconds. When $H_s=4'$ and $T_z=3.74$ seconds, the Keulegan-Carpenter number are all close to zero yielding $C_M \approx 2$ and $C_D \approx 0$ for all members.

The results show that the usual upper bound values of $C_M=2$ and $C_D=1.4$ give an upper bound response for all sea states. Table 10 shows that for this structure Keulegan-Carpenter numbers are all below 20, the lowest value for which Sarpkaya's data are available. The mean zero-crossing period of the wave, from the relative velocity spectrum, was found to increase with depth. This confirms

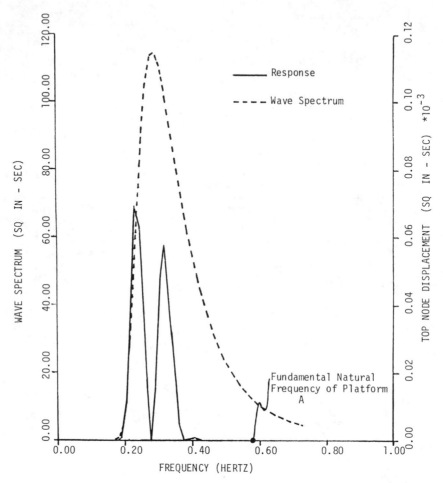

Figure 13 Excitation and Response Spectral Density
Functions for Platform A (H_s=4',T_z=2.48 sec)

Zone	Group	K	$Re(\times 10^{-6})$	c_M	c_D
1	1	4.23	0.9803	1.76	0.55
	2	5.61	0.6405	1.68	0.73
	3	9.01	0.4074	1.49	1.17
2	1	4.63	1.0660	1.74	0.60
	2	6.61	0.6981	1.62	0.86
	3	9.88	0.4629	1.43	1.28
3	1	6.02	1.1953	1.66	0.79
	2	8.46	0.7998	1.52	1.10
	3	11.51	0.5789	1.34	1.50
4	1	7.81	1.5225	1.55	1.02
	2	11.53	1.0312	1.34	1.50
	3	13.23	0.7681	1.24	1.72
5	1	8.49	1.7850	1.51	1.10
	2	12.53	1.2090	1.28	1.63
	3	15.20	1.0017	1.16	1.90

Table 10 Flow Parameters and Force Coefficients for Platform A.
Zone 6 is Outside Water. (H_s=36', T_z=12.79 sec., Relative
Roughness = 0.02)

	H_s=4'	12'	20'	28'	36'
Top Node Displacement, σ_u(in)	0.009	0.037	0.080	0.142	0.206
Base Shear, σ_F(kips)	2.8	13.2	30.4	56.0	82.7
Base Moment, σ_M(kip-ftx10^{-3})	0.23	0.95	2.08	3.71	5.40
Base Force Period, T_{FM}(sec)	5.0	7.7	10.0	11.8	13.0
RMS Rel.Vel. just above SWL(in/s)	0.011	0.030	0.050	0.074	0.097
RMS Rel.Vel. just below SWL(in/s)	7.0	22.4	36.1	48.4	58.4

Table 11 Response of Platform B to Constant Hydrodynamic Coefficients

the earlier finding that the high frequency components of excitation attentuate faster with depth from still water level.

An interesting feature of the results is the variation of the hydrodynamic force coefficients with wave height, wave period and depth below surface. It is reported that there is a trend for C_D to decrease with increasing wave height and period at all depths below the surface [30]. Pierson and Holmes suggest that variation in wave force coefficients with depth below the surface is significant, although results from the Gulf of Mexico data suggest that C_D is more or less constant, with possibly smaller values near the surface; C_M appears to increase significantly towards the surface [31]. Results from platform A, which is inertia dominant (ie, large member diameters), shows: (i) C_D increases and C_M decreases with increasing wave height and period, (ii) there is significant variation in wave force coefficients with depth below the surface as pointed out by Pierson and Holmes, (iii) C_D varies from 0.55 to 1.90, with larger values near the surface, and (iv) C_M varies from 1.16 to 1.76, with smaller values near the surface. Thus, these results are at direct variance with the findings of Evans from the Gulf of Mexico data [30].

Further investigation was carried out on platform B, a drag dominant structure, to assess effects of constant versus flow dependent hydrodynamic coefficients and marine growth. Significant wave heights and T_z identified through Wiegel's relation and a range of relative roughness values from 0.00125 to 0.02 were considered. Table 11 gives a summary of results for the constant coefficients case and Tables 12 and 13 list results for relative roughness 0.00125 and 0.02 for the variable coefficients case. Average member diameters within different groups are listed in Table 14, and average values of K, Re, C_M and C_D for the case $H_s = 36'$, $T_z = 12.79$ seconds and relative roughness 0.02 is given in Table 15. For the same excitation but relative roughness 0.00125, $C_M \approx 1.30$ and $C_D \approx 1.40$ for members in Group 3, and $C_M \approx 1.72$ and $C_D \approx 1.30$ for members in Group 4. There was almost no variation with depth. As before, $C_M \approx 2$ and $C_D \approx 0$ when $H_s = 4'$ and $T_z = 3.74$ seconds, irrespective of relative roughness values. It was observed that significant variation of the force coefficients with depth occurred for moderate sea states, and in these cases the trend was similar to that observed in platform A. For the higher sea states there was only a mild variation in the coefficients with depth, as observable in Table 15. This minimal variation unlike that for platform A, is similar to results reported by Evans on the basis of the Gulf of Mexico data [30].

Perusal of the results for platform B indicates that for relative roughness 0.02 and $H_s = 36'$, $T_z = 12.79$ seconds, the variable coefficients option yields rms response that are larger by ~25% over the constant coefficients case. In cases where variable C_M and C_D yielded larger response, it was found that the Keulegan-Carpenter number fell within those for which Sarpkaya's results are available. For relative roughness 0.02, the variable coefficients case response is larger for $H_s > 20'$. As relative roughness reduces, this limit for H_s increases to above 20'. This result is consistent with the fact that as relative roughness increases C_D increases, and that as H_s increases drag force starts dominating. For sea states below limiting sea states (i.e., 20' for 0.02), the constant C_M, C_D values are conservative, and the Keulegan-Carpenter number tends to fall outside Karpkaya's published curves. However, even in those cases where constant C_M and C_D yield conservative results, the results show that the choice of $C_D = 1.4$ is not necessarily an upper bound, although $C_M = 2$ most certainly is.

For drag dominant structures such as platform B, it is important to interpret results keeping in mind the simplification introduced by the linearization of the drag force term.

Influence of Deck Mass and Hysteretic Structural Damping on Response

Sensitivity of fundamental natural period to changes in deck mass, M of platform A is shown in Table 16 and Figure 14. For a single-degree-of-freedom system the fundamental natural period should be proportional to square root of

	H_s=4'	12'	20'	28'	36'
Top Node Displacement,σ_u(in)	0.009	0.028	0.063	0.132	0.194
Base Shear,σ_F(kips)	2.7	10.1	23.8	51.4	77.8
Base Moment,σ_M(kip-ftx10^{-3})	0.22	0.72	1.63	3.45	5.09
Base Force Period,T_{FM}(sec)	5.0	7.6	10.0	11.9	13.1
RMS Rel.Vel. just above SWL(in/s)	0.011	0.023	0.039	0.068	0.091
RMS Rel.Vel. just below SWL(in/s)	7.0	22.4	36.0	48.4	58.4

Table 12   Response of Platform B to Variable Hydrodynamic Coefficients and
Relative Roughness= 0.00125

	H_s=4'	12'	20'	28'	36'
Top Node Displacement,σ_u(in)	0.009	0.030	0.081	0.176	0.259
Base Shear,σ_F(kips)	2.7	10.5	30.3	68.7	103.9
Base Moment,σ_M(kip-ftx10^{-3})	0.22	0.76	2.09	4.59	6.79
Base Force Period,T_{FM}(sec)	5.0	7.7	10.2	12.1	13.2
RMS Rel.Vel. just above SWL(in/s)	0.011	0.024	0.049	0.090	0.120
RMS Rel.Vel. just below SWL(in/s)	7.0	22.4	36.0	48.4	58.4

Table 13   Response of Platform B to Variable Hydrodynamic Coefficients and
Relative Roughness= 0.02

Zone	Average Diameter of Members(ins)				Distribution of Groups Within Zones(%)			
	Group 1	Group 2	Group 3	Group 4	Group 1	Group 2	Group 3	Group 4
1	-	-	34.00	14.67	-	-	25.0	75.0
2	-	-	34.00	14.00	-	-	25.0	75.0
3	-	-	34.00	13.17	-	-	25.0	75.0
4	-	-	34.00	13.17	-	-	25.0	75.0
5	-	-	34.00	13.17	-	-	25.0	75.0

Table 14   Analysis of Average Member Diameters in Platform B

Zone	Group	K	Re($\times 10^{-6}$)	C_M	C_D
1	3	17.72	0.9902	1.16	1.93
	4	41.56	0.4201	1.30	1.77
2	3	18.68	1.0765	1.17	1.92
	4	44.92	0.4362	1.32	1.76
3	3	20.06	1.2610	1.19	1.90
	4	51.91	0.4725	1.37	1.74
4	3	20.70	1.3780	1.19	1.89
	4	53.24	0.5370	1.37	1.73

Table 15   Flow Parameters and Force Coefficients for Platform B. Zone 5 is Outside Water. (H_s=36',T_z=12.79 sec, Relative Roughness =0.02)

Mass	0.6M	0.8M	M	1.2M	1.4M
Fund. Period (sec)	1.42	1.58	1.73	1.87	1.98

Table 16   Fundamental Natural Period of Platform A for Various Values of Deck Mass

D_s	σ_u(in)	σ_F(kips)	σ_M(kip-ft$\times 10^{-3}$)	T_{FM}(sec)
0.05	0.00885	12.374	3.632	4.62
0.01	0.00892	12.402	3.642	4.61

Table 17   Response of Platform A to Two Different Values of Hysteretic Structural Damping

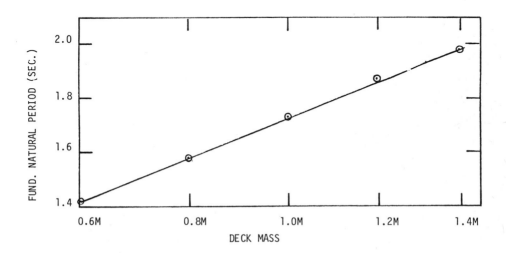

Figure 14   Variation of Natural Period with Deck
Mass for Platform A

mass,and this is. borne out by the plot in Figure 14 which shows period versus square root of mass. The plot is and should be a straight line for the above to be true. The proportionality constant yields the stiffness of the equivalent single-degree-of-freedom system. Results showed that even a mass of 1.4M, which makes the natural frequency move closer to regions of larger wave energy, yielded no dynamic amplification. Thus, large variations in deck mass do not affect lateral motions of the platform.

To check whether structural hysteretic damping, D_s influenced platform response, structure A was analyzed for the larger mass i.e., 1.4M, H_s=4' and T_z=3.74 seconds with D_s=0.05 and 0.01. Results are presented in Table 17. None of the results are different more than 0.8%, in addition, there is imperceptible dynamic amplification in both cases. Therefore, for the North Sea structure considered, quasi-static analysis procedures would suffice for both short and long-term response predictions as has already been pointed out.

CONCLUSIONS

One of the major objectives of this study has been to highlight the numerous uncertainties that go into the characterization of the environment and the offshore system, and the effect that these uncertainties are likely to have on short and long-term response. Thus, results of any analysis should be accepted only after field verification and calibration of the model.

Some of the major conclusions of the sensitivity analyses are summarized below:

(i) For the platforms considered, rms displacement even under extreme sea conditions, are small. There is negligible or imperceptible dynamic amplification irrespective of the hysteretic structural damping. Quasi-static analyses procedures are therefore likely to be adequate.

(ii) A definite functional relationship was observed between rms base shear and rms base moment.

(iii) The zero-crossing period of the relative velocity spectrum increases with depth below still water level. The zero-crossing period of base shear and moment are larger than the wave zero-crossing period.

(iv) Structural motion is negligible compared to fluid motion for the structures considered. However, for flexible structures this might not be so.

(v) Uncertainty in zero-crossing period to be associated with significant wave height is unlikely to influence design or fatigue life assessment.

(vi) Constant hydrodynamic force coefficients equal to C_M=2 and C_D=1.4 yield conservative results for inertia dominant structures. For drag dominant structures, the flow dependent C_M and C_D from Sarpkaya's experiments are conservative for large values of relative roughness and significant wave height.

(vii) It was observed that C_M decreases and C_D increases with increasing wave height and period. C_M and C_D vary significantly with depth below still water level, especially for moderate sea states,with smaller C_M and larger C_D near the water surface in these cases.

(viii) Large variations in deck mass do not affect lateral motion of the platform since the change in period does not induce perceptible dynamic amplification.

This investigation has ignored sensitivity of response to finite foundation impedances and changes in hydrodynamic drag damping. The phasing effect, which causes multiple peaking of the response spectral densities, leads to the neglecting of the breathing mode which may be of importance in fatigue life assessment, especially of horizontal members. For correcting the phasing problem a more complex structural model is warranted.

ACKNOWLEDGEMENTS

This work was funded by the Instituto Tecnologico Venezolano del Petroleo, Caracas, Venezuela. We are most appreciative of their support. The contribution of Dr. D.C.Angelides in the development of the computational strategy for the computer code POSEIDON is most gratefully acknowledged.

REFERENCES

1. Barnett, T.P. (1972) "Observations of Wind Wave Generation and Dissipation in the North Sea: Implications for the Offshore Industry", Paper No. 1516, Proc. Offshore Technology Conference, Houston, TX.

2. St.Denis,M. (1973) "Some Cautions on the Employment of the Spectral Technique to Describe the Waves of the Sea and the Response Thereto of Oceanic Systems", Paper No. 1819, Proc. Offshore Technology Conference, Houston, TX.

3. McClenan, C.M. and D.L.Harris (1975) "Wave Characteristics as Revealed by Aerial Photography", Paper No. 2423, Proc. Offshore Technology Conference, Houston, TX.

4. Angelides,D.C. (1978) "Stochastic Response of Fixed Offshore Structures in Random Sea", Ph.D. Thesis/Research Report R78-37, Dept. of Civil Engineering, Massachusetts Institute of Technology, Cambridge, MA.

5. Proceedings of the Third International Ship Structures Conference (1967) Oslo.

6. Ochi,M.K. and S.L.Bales (1977) "Effect of Various Special Formulations in Predicting Responses of Marine Vehicles and Ocean Structures", Paper No. 2743, Proc. Offshore Technology Conference, Houston, TX.

7. Bea,R.G. and N.W.Lai (1978) "Hydrodynamic Loadings on Offshore Platforms", Paper No. 3064, Proc. Offshore Technology Conference, Houston, TX.

8. Hogben,N. (1974) "Fluid Loading on Offshore Structures, A State of Art Appraisal: Wave Loads", Maritime Technology Monograph No. 1, Royal Institute of Naval Architects,UK.

9. Shyam Sunder,S. (1979) "Stochastic Modelling of Ocean Storms", S.M.Thesis/ Research Report R79-7, Dept. of Civil Engineering, Massachusetts Institute of Technology, Cambridge, MA.

10. Draper,L. and E.M.Squire (1967) "Waves at Ocean Weather Ship Station India", Transactions of the Royal Institution of Naval Architects,UK.

11. Houmb,O.G. and T.Overik (1976) "Parametrization of Wave Spectra and Long Term Joint Distribution of Wave Height and Period", Proc. of the International Conference on the Behavior of Offshore Structures, Trondheim, Norway.

12. Wiegel,R.L.(1978), "Waves and Wave Spectra and Design Estimates", Paper for the Conference on Deep-Sea Oil Production Structures (Jan. 23-27), University of California, Berkeley, CA.

13. Wiegel,R.L.(1964) Oceanographical Engineering, Prentice-Hall, Inc., Englewood Cliffs, NJ.

14. Hogben,N. et al (1977) "Estimation of Fluid Loading on Offshore Structures", Part 2, Vol. 63, September, Proc.Institution of Civil Engineers,UK.

15. Ramberg,S.E. and J.M.Niedzwecki (1979) "Some Uncertainties and Errors in Wave Force Computations", Paper No. 3597, Proc. Offshore Technology Conference, Houston, TX.

16. Heaf,N.J. (1979) "The Effect of Marine Growth on the Performance of Fixed Offshore Platforms in the North Sea", Paper No. 3386, Proc. Offshore Technology Conference, Houston, TX.

17. Sarpkaya,T., N.J.Collins and S.R.Evans (1977) "Wave Forces on Rough-Walled Cylinders at High Reynolds Numbers", Paper No. 2901, Proc. Offshore Technology Conference, Houston, TX.

18. Dalrymple,R.A. (1974) "Models for Non-Linear Water Waves on Shear Currents", Paper No. 2114, Proc. Offshore Technology Conference, Houston, TX.

19. Dean,R.G. (1970) "Relative Validities of Water Wave Theories" Vol. 93, WW2, May, Journal of the Water Ways and Harbors Division of the American Society of Civil Engineers.

20. Shyam Sunder,S., J.Connor and D.Angelides (1979) "User Manual for POSEIDON: A Program for Evaluating the Frequency Domain Response of Offshore Steel Jacket Platforms", Research Report R79-15, Dept. of Civil Engineering, Massachusetts Institute of Technology, Cambridge, MA.

21. Cartwright,D.E. (1974) "Theoretical and Technical Knowledge", Paper 1, The Science of Sea Waves after 25 Years, The Dynamics of Marine Vehicles and Structures in Waves,London.

22. Kinsman,B. (1965) Wind Waves, Their Generation and Propagation on the Ocean Surface, Prentice-Hall Inc., Englewood Cliffs,NJ.

23. Nordenstrøm,N. (1972) "Methods for Predicting Long-Term Distributions of Wave Loads and Probability of Failure for Ships", Det norske Veritas Research Report No. 71-2-S.

24. Krylov,N. and N.Bogoliubov (1947) "Introduction to Non-Linear Mechanics: Approximate Asymptotic Methods", Vol. II, Princeton University Press.

25. Lin,Y.K. (1967) Probabilistic Theory of Structural Dynamics, McGraw-Hill, Inc., NY.

26. Bell,A.O. (1972) "North Sea Wave Spectra", North Sea Environmental Study Group,UK.

27. Mes,M.J. (1978) "New Studies Improve Wave Force Spectral Calculations", April Issue, The Oil and Gas Journal.

28. Angelides,D.C. and J.J.Connor (1979) "A Probabilistic Model for the Stiffness Degradation of Steel Jacket Structures", Proc. Second International Conference on the Behavior of Offshore Structures, London.

29. Bismut,P. and O.Buyukozturk (1979) "Fatigue Analysis of Offshore Steel Jacket Structures", Research Report R79-32, Dept. of Civil Engineering, Massachusetts Institute of Technology, Cambridge, MA.

30. Evans,D.J. (1969) "Analysis of Wave Force Data", Paper No. 2190, Proc. Offshore Technology Conference, Houston, TX.

31. Pierson,W.J. and P.Holmes (1965) "Irregular Wave Forces on a Pile", Vol. 91, WW4, November, Journal of the Water Ways and Harbors Division of the American Society of Civil Engineers.

32. Sarpkaya,T. (1975) "Forces on Cylinders and Spheres in a Sinusoidally Oscillating Fluid", Vol. 42, Number 1, Journal of Applied Mechanics, Transactions of the American Society of Mechanical Engineers.

33. Bidde,D.D. (1971) "Laboratory Study of Lift Forces on Circular Piles", Vol. 97, No. WW4, Journal of the Waterways, Harbors and Coastal Engineering Division of the American Society of Civil Engineers.

34. Isaacson,M.de St.Q. and D.J.Maull (1976) "Transverse Forces on Vertical Cylinders in Waves", Vol. 102, No. WW1, Journal of the Waterways,Harbors and Coastal Engineering Division of the American Society of Civil Engineers.

USE OF THE HYBRID ELEMENT METHOD IN THE ANALYSIS OF WAVE POWER EXTRACTION

Aranha, J.A., Sugaya, M., Martins, C.

INSTITUTO DE PESQUISAS TECNOLÓGICAS DO ESTADO DE SÃO PAULO S.A.

INTRODUCTION AND MATHEMATICAL MODEL

This work aims to explore some new results concerning wave power extraction by oscillating bodies. Specifically C.C. Mei (1976) and D.W. Evans (1976), have shown how to express the efficiency of systems properly tuned in terms of $m_a(\omega)$, $\mu(\omega)$ and $B_o^\pm(\omega)$, the apparent mass, the radiation damping and the wave amplitude as $x \to +\infty$, respectively. All these coefficients can be computed by solving the radiation problem associated with the oscillation of the body. Only by means of a numerical method we can determine $m_a(\omega)$, $\mu(\omega)$ and $B_o^\pm(\omega)$, when the body's geometry is arbitrary. In the context of this work the numerical method to be used is the one devised by Chen and Mei (1974) and called "Hybrid Element Method". The efficiency of this method has been numerically proved in several works (Chen and Mei (1974); Yue, Chen and Mei (1976) and some of its theoretical aspects have been studied by Aranha (1978). It is worthwhile to emphasize that the same method can be used as well to analyse harbors, off-shore structures, etc.

A body placed in sea water starts to oscillate due to the action of an incident wave. If associated with the body there is a generator that converts the kynetic energy in another form of energy, then power is extracted from the wave. An ideal generator can be thought of as a mass-spring-dashpot system. In this way the extracted power equals the power dissipated in the dashpot. The efficiency of the system is thus defined as the ratio between the extracted power and the power of the incoming wave.

Following C.C. Mei (1976) and D.W. Evans (1976) it

can be shown that the efficiency $E(\omega)$ for an incident wave from the left to the right, is given by:

$$E(\omega) = 4\rho\omega K_O \frac{\nu_c \omega^2 \mid B_O^-(\omega)\mid 2}{Q(\omega)}$$

$$Q(\omega) = \left[K_T - \omega^2 (m_c + m_a(\omega)) \right]^2 + (\nu_c + \mu(\omega))^2 \omega^2$$

$$\dots (1)$$

for a body with only one degree of freedom.

In the above expression ρ is the water density, ω and K_O the frequency and wave number of the incoming wave, m_c, ν_c and $K_c = K_T - K_b$ the mass, damping and spring constants of the generator, K_b being the buoyancy restoring coefficient. In the expression (1), $B_O^-(\omega)$ is the assimptotic value of the radiation potential as $x \to -\infty$. That is

$$\dots (2)$$

$$\phi_R(x,0) \sim \sqrt{2K_O} \; B_O^{\pm}(\omega) \; e^{\pm iK_O x} \quad \text{as} \quad x \to -\infty$$

where a deep water dispersion relation, $\frac{\omega^2}{g} = K_O$, has been assumed.

If the generator is properly tuned the efficiency can be maximized for a given frequency ω_0. In fact (see C.C. Mei (1976) and D.W. Evans (1976)) if:

$$\nu_c = \mu(\omega_0)$$

$$K_T = K_c + K_b = (m_a(\omega_0) + m_c)\omega_0^2 \qquad \dots (3)$$

then:

$$E(\omega,\omega_0) = 4\rho\omega K_O \frac{\omega^2 \mu(\omega_0)\mid B_O^-(\omega)\mid 2}{Q(\omega \; ; \; \omega_0)} \qquad \dots (4)$$

$$Q(\omega,\omega_0) = \left[(m_a(\omega_0) + m_c)\omega_0^2 - (m_a(\omega) + m_c)\omega^2 \right]^2 + (\mu(\omega_0) + \mu(\omega))^2\omega^2$$

Using the identity $\mu(\omega) = \rho K_O \omega \left(\mid B_O^+(\omega)\mid^2 + \mid B_O^-(\omega)\mid^2 \right)$ in the expression (4), the following relation can be obtained:

$$E_{max}(\omega;\omega_0) = E(\omega_0;\omega_0) = \frac{1}{1 + \frac{\mid B_O^+(\omega_0)\mid^2}{\mid B_O^-(\omega_0)\mid^2}} \qquad \dots (5)$$

For a more comprehensive analysis the reader is refered to C.C. Mei (1976), D.W. Evans (1976) or Ara nha, Sugaya, Martins (1979), where a detailed explanation concerning the underlying assumptions of this theory is given.

Expression (5) shows explicitly that the maximum efficiency for a symmetric body ($|B_o^+ (\omega_o)| = |B_o^- (\omega_o)|$) is 50%. If the body is non-symmetric in such way that waves generated to the left are bigger than waves generated to the right ($|B_o^- (\omega_o)| > |(B_o^+ (\omega_o)|$) then $E_{max} > 50\%$ for a left to right incoming wave. So far, bodies with only one degree of freedom have been analysed. If a body is symmetric and has two independent degrees of freedom (vertical and horizontal motion, for example) and two generators, each one of them tuned by means of expression (3), then $E(\omega_o;\omega_o)=100\%$.

A very efficient mechanism is the one proposed by S. Salter, called "Salter's cam" and sketched at figure (1). It can be shown both experimentally and theoretically (see D.D. Serman (1978)) that $E(\omega_o;\omega_o) \approx$ 90% for this mechanism.

It has been argued that the structure that sustains the Salter's cam is too complex and must be too stiff in order to keep this high efficiency. Also, that this mechanism, being placed at the free surface, would be severely loaded in a storm condition. Directed by these reasons an english firm, "Submerged Buoyant Structures Limited", has proposed another mechanism, called SWEEP and indicated at figure (2). They argue that the structure that sustains the SWEEP, being similar to the standard off-shore structures,is less complex than the one that sustains the "Salter's cam". Also, because it is submerged, SWEEP would be less affected by a storm condition.

The serious drawback of this mechanism is its low efficiency. In fact, due to its symmetry $E_{max} = 50\%$.

The objective of this work is twofold. In one hand, the efficiency curve, $E(\omega;\omega_o)$, will be determined as a function of ω. Observe that ω_o is the tuning frequency, $E(\omega;\omega_o) \leq E(\omega_o;\omega_o) = 50\%$, but the width of the curve $E(\omega,\omega_o)$ around the peak ω_o, $\Delta(\omega_o)$, can change with ω_o. It is also the intention of this work to explore non-symmetric mechanisms that would share the some engineering advantages of the SWEEP but that eventually would be more efficient, as a result of its non-symmetry.

The plan of this study is then the following: first some theoretical results about the assimptotic behaviour of $m_a(\omega)$, $\mu(\omega)$ and $E(\omega;\omega_o)$ will be presented. The objective is to clarify some obscure points, to

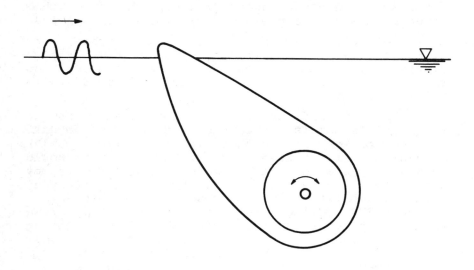

FIGURE 1

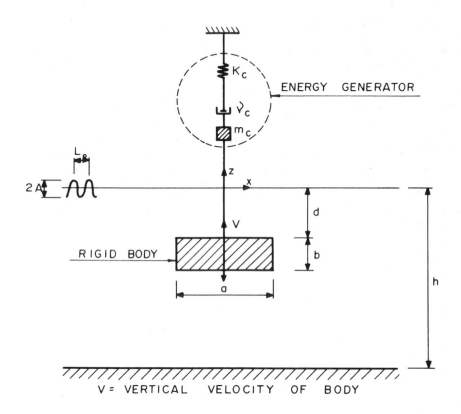

FIGURE 2

provide a better physical understanding and to build a sensibility about the numerical results to be obtained. Secondly, the basic idea about the "Hybrid Element Method" will be sketched and the round-off and discretization errors will be analysed. Lastly the analysis of the SWEEP will be presented together with some new mechanisms, with the same conception of the SWEEP but non-symmetric.

ASSIMPTOTIC BEHAVIOUR OF $m_a(\omega)$, $\mu(\omega)$ AND $E(\omega;\omega_0)$

From a general understanding of a wave-body interaction it can be expected that maximum efficiency should happen when $K_0a \sim O(1)$, where (a) is the characteristic dimension of the body. In this sense is somewhat amazing that $E_{max} = 50\%$, independent of K_0a.

In order to reconciliate these two apparently conflicting results it must be observed that a true measure of the efficiency should be the area and not its peak value. Since $\Delta(\omega_0)$ is the width of the curve $E(\omega;\omega_0)$, then the area is $\approx 1/2\ \Delta(\omega_0)$. In this section it is shown that $\Delta(\omega_0) \to 0$ when $\omega_0 \to 0$ or ∞, therefore the true efficiency goes to zero when the tuning frequency goes to zero or infinite.

For a body moving in the vertical direction the assimptotic values of $m_a(\omega)$ and $\mu(\omega)$ are given by the expressions below:

$$\lim_{\omega \to 0}\ m_a(\omega) = m_{a1} \neq 0$$

$$\lim_{\omega \to 0}\ \mu(\omega) = \frac{1}{2}\ \rho \sqrt{\frac{g}{h}}\ (\hat{L}_B)^2 \qquad \ldots(6)$$

$$m_a(\omega) = m_{a2} + O\left(\frac{1}{\omega^2}\right) \text{ for } \omega \gg 1$$

$$\mu(\omega) = O\left(\frac{1}{\omega^3}\right) \text{ of } \omega \gg 1$$

Where $\hat{L}_B$ is the "water line" ($\hat{L}_B = 0$ for a submerged body) and m_{a1}, m_{a2} are values that can be numerically computed. A derivation of expression (6) can be found in Aranha, Sugaya, Martins (1979) and a plot of $m_a(\omega)$, $\mu(\omega)$ as a function of ω is shown in figure (3), together with the assimptotic values m_{a1} and m_{a2}. It must be pointed out that $\mu(\omega) \to 0$ faster than $m_a(\omega) \to m_{a2}$ as $\omega \to \infty$, what is consistent with expression (6).

Using expression (6) into expression (4) with $\hat{L}_B = 0$,

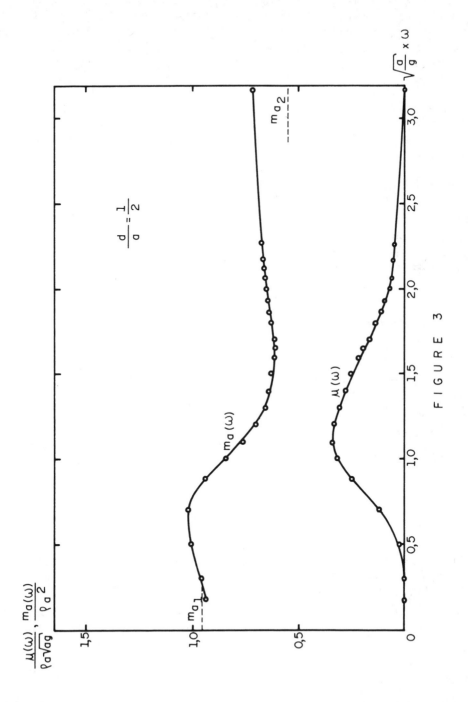

F I G U R E   3

it is possible to show that $\Delta(\omega_O) \to 0$ when $\omega_O \to 0$ or ∞. For bodies floating in the free surface $\hat{L}_B \neq 0$ and $\lim\limits_{\omega \to 0} \mu(\omega) \neq 0$, impling that we cannot show that $\Delta(\omega_O) \to 0$ when $\omega_O \to 0$ by means of the above reasoning. In this circunstances, however, the restoring coefficient due to buoyancy is given by $K_B = \rho g\,\hat{L}_B \neq 0$. The tuning $K_C = (m_a(\omega_O) + m_C)\omega_O^2 - \rho g\hat{L}_B$ can be satisfied only for $\omega_O \geq \omega_{O1}$, where $(m_a(\omega_{O1}) + m_C)\omega_{O1}^2 = \rho g\hat{L}_B$. When $\omega_O < \omega_{O1}$ we must take $K_C = 0$, $K_T = \rho g\hat{L}_B$. Using this value in the expression (1) we get for a symmetric body:

$$E(\omega_O;\omega_O) = 2 \frac{\mu^2(\omega_O)\cdot\omega_O^2}{\left[\rho g\hat{L}_B - (m_C + m_a(\omega_O))\omega_O^2\right]^2 - 4\mu^2(\omega_O)\omega_O^2} \qquad (\omega_O < \omega_{O1})$$

Letting $\omega_O \to 0$, $\mu(\omega_O) \to \frac{1}{2}\rho\sqrt{\frac{g}{h}}\,(\hat{L}_B)^2$ in the above

expression results: $E(\omega_O;\omega_O) \approx (\frac{1}{2}\frac{\hat{L}_B^2}{gh})\omega_O^2 << 1$.

That is: the true efficiency goes to zero as $\omega \to 0$ or ∞ for both submerged bodies and bodies floating in the free surface.

HYBRID ELEMENT METHOD

The basic idea of this method is the following: in the region where irregularities (scatter) are present the solution is obtained via finite elements. In the region where there are no irregularities the solution is sought by means of a serie expansion. The two types of solution are then matched at the common boundary. Specifically, it must be imposed that:

$$\phi_F(x_O^\pm, z) = \phi^\pm(x_O^\pm, z)$$
$$\phi_{F,X}(x_O^\pm, z) = \phi_X^\pm(x_O^\pm, z)$$

$$\ldots (7)$$

where ϕ_F is the finite element solution defined in the region $x_O^- < x < x_O^+$, $\phi^\pm(x,z)$ are the serie solutions defined in the regions $x > x_O^+$ and $x < x_O^-$, respectively. After the discretization the set of linear equations has the form

$$\left([K] - \frac{\omega^2}{g}[M] + i[G_O] + [G_1]\right)\{\phi_F\} = \{v\}$$

$$\ldots (8)$$

where $\{\phi_F\}$ are the nodal values of $\phi_F(x,z)$ and the matrices $[G_0]$ and $[G_1]$ come from the matching condition, expression (7). Theoretical details about the "Hybrid Element Method" can be found in Aranha (1978). There is one result that is worthwhile to be mentioned, namely: the global identities (energy theorem, Haskind's relation) are preserved by this method, no matter how coarse the discretization is. Then any discrepancies in these identities can only be caused by round-off errors. In all computations made in this work they are of order 10^{-6}.

CONVERGENCE

In all computations in this work it has been used a mesh with 106 nodes, 155 elements and 30 terms in the serie expansion for $\phi^{\pm}(x,z)$. A detailed analysis of convergence is presented in Aranha, Sugaya, Martins (1979).

The numerical result is correct up to the second decimal digit, what is fairly good once it is known that both $\mu(\omega)$ and $m_a(\omega)$ are of order one when $K_0 a \sim 0(1)$.

NUMERICAL RESULTS

Figure (4) presents the efficiency curve of the SWEEP for three diferent tuning frequency ω_0. It is quite clear that the width $\Delta(\omega_0)$ goes to zero as $\omega_0 \to 0$ or $\omega_0 \to \infty$. Figures (5) and (6) present the curves $m_a(\omega)$, $\mu(\omega)$ as a function of ω, for two different depths of submergence. It is not difficult to show that the wave-body interaction is bigger the bigger is the ratio $\mu(\omega)/m_a(\omega)$. In particular we must expect larger width $\Delta(\omega_0)$ for situations where $\mu(\omega_0)/m_a(\omega_0)$ is large. (see Aranha, Sugaya, Martins (1979). Since water waves are surface waves, it must also be expected that the closer the body is from the free surface the larger should be the wave effect. Figures (5) and (6) show clearly that the ratio $\mu(\omega)/m_a(\omega)$ is bigger the closer the body is from the free surface. In this sense the width $\Delta(\omega_0)$ should be larger the smaller the d/a is, where (d) is the depth of submergence. Figure (7) displays two efficiency curves for two differents d/a. It is quite clear that in fact $\Delta(\omega_0)$ is larger for the smaller d/a.

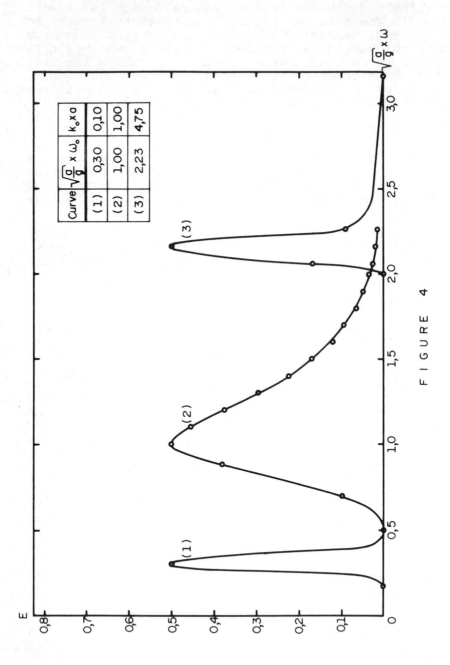

Curve	$\sqrt{\frac{a}{g}} \times \omega_0$	$k_0 x a$
(1)	0,30	0,10
(2)	1,00	1,00
(3)	2,23	4,75

F I G U R E 4

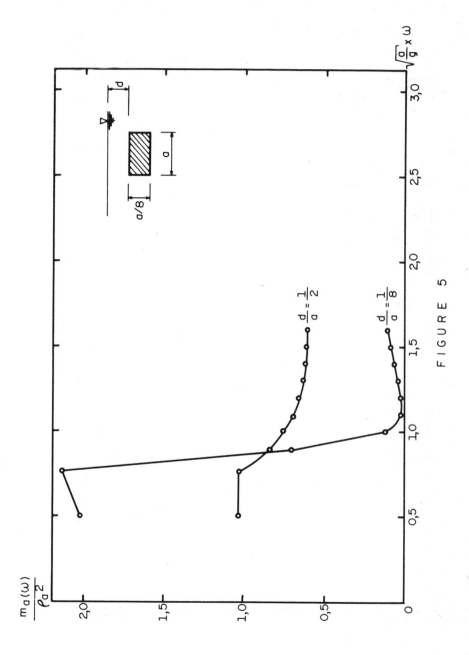

F I G U R E 5

2.56

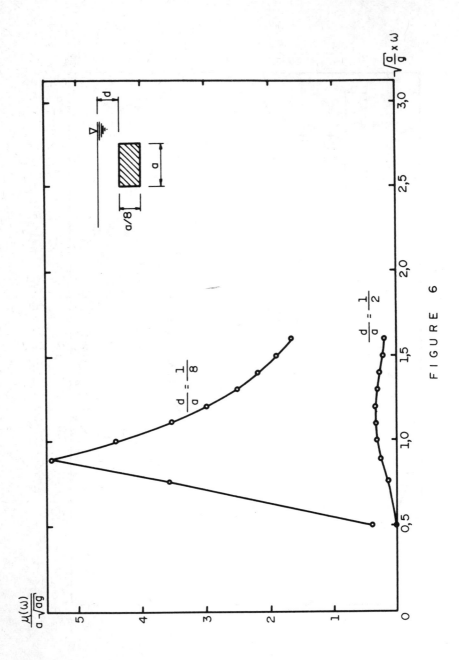

FIGURE 6

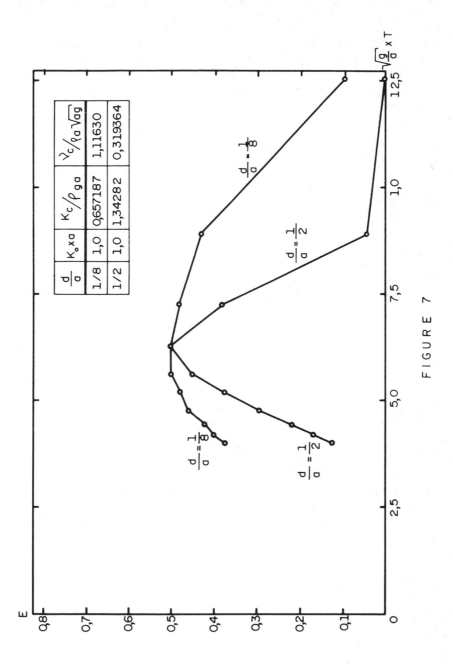

FIGURE 7

$\frac{d}{a}$	K_o x a	K_c/ρ_{ga}	$\gamma_c/\rho_a\sqrt{ag}$
1/8	1,0	0,657187	1,11630
1/2	1,0	1,34282	0,319364

This set of numerical results is in agreement with the theoretical results presented before. The main features of the SWEEP have been analysed. A more exhaustive parametric study can be done, the forces in the support structure can be determined and the friction loss can be estimated. It is not the intention of this work to proceed further in this direction.

The second objetive of this study is to explore the idea of non-symmetry (see expression (5)). To be more specific the intention is to devise bodies that would share the same engineering advantages of SWEEP but with greater efficiency, as a result of non-symmetry. This analysis, again, has not been exhaustive and figure (8) displays the non-symmetric bodies that have been analysed. Bodies (I), (II), (III) are those that most trivially would satisfy the two precondition, namely: to have a conception similar to SWEEP and to be non-symmetric in such a way that they can generate waves to the left with bigger amplitude than the ones to the right.

The body (IV), figure (8), has been devised following this reasoning: if the fixed part were very large (infinite) then no waves would be generated to the right due to the motion of the left part, and from expression (5) E_{max} = 100%. The only drawback of this body is that, being placed in the free surface, it is more affected by storm conditions.

The body (V), figure (8), has been devised by indirect means. The former intention was to submerge body (IV) but its efficiency, numerically computed, was less than 50%. Therefore the body (V), inverse of the body (IV), must have efficiency greater than 50%. The explanation of this behaviour is the following: if the water depth (h) and the fixed part of the body (V) were both infinite, then the oscillating part of the body (V) has to its right a sea with infinite depth and to its left a sea with depth (d). Clearly the shallow is the water the bigger will be the wave amplitude and so waves generated to the left must be bigger than waves generated to the right.

The table below presents the maximum efficiency (see expression (5)) for each one of the non-symmetric bodies.

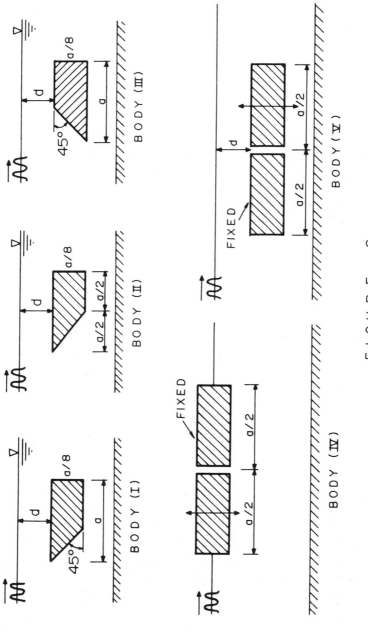

FIGURE 8

TABLE (1)

Maximum efficiency - non symmetric bodies

Body	$K_o a$	d/a	E_{max}
I	1	1/2	50,02%
I	1	1/8	50,17%
II	1	1/2	50,22%
III	1	1/2	50,07%
IV	0,75	*	61%
V	1	1/2	53,16%
V	1	1/8	64,26%

As it is clear from the above table the most promising body is body (V). For future reference it will be called SIPT.

The following table has been produced by the efficiency analysis of the SIPT (d/a = 1/8).

TABLE (2)

Maximum efficiency - SIPT

$K_o a$	E_{max}	$(\omega_o)/m_a(\omega_o)$
0,25	50,3%	0,05
0,50	52,0%	0,44
0,75	56,5%	1,49
1,00	64,3%	2,26
1,25	74,2%	2,1
1,50	82,2%	1,86
1,75	83,5%	1,82
2,00	78,0%	1,97
2,25	69,7%	2,22
2,50	67,6%	2,46

Notice that for $K_o a$ = 1,5; 1,75, Emax > 80%, that is: SIPT is 1,6 times more efficient than the SWEEP. The best SIPT's efficiency curve occurs when $K_o a$ = 1,5, although E_{max} is greater when $K_o a$ = 1,75. The point is that the width of the curve when $K_o a$ = 1,5 is greater. As it has been said before, the bigger is the ratio $\mu(\omega_o)/m_a(\omega_o)$ the bigger must be the width of the efficiency curve. Notice that $\mu(\omega_o)/m_a(\omega_o)$ is 1,86 when $K_o a$ = 1,5 and 1,82 when $K_o a$ = 1,75.

Bodies with two degrees of freedom have E_{max} = 100%. The SWEEP with freedom to move in the horizontal direction has two degrees of freedom and is called here by SW2D. Clearly this mechanism is a radical departure from the original conception of the SWEEP, but its efficiency curve will be ploted in order to be compared with the others efficiency curves.

In the table below it is presented the geometric dimensions of SALTER, SWEEP, SIPT and SW2D when all mechanism are tuned to a period of T = 10 sec.

TABLE (3)

Geometric dimensions

	$K_o a$	a(mts.)	Perimeter (mts)
SALTER	0,5	12,7	93
SWEEP	1	25,3	57
SIPT	1,5	38	85,5
SW2D	1	25,3	57

Figure (9) shows the efficiency curve for SALTER (see D.D. Serman (1978)), SWEEP, SIPT and SW2D. It must be noticed that SIPT has an efficiency worse than SALTER but much better than SWEEP.

Figure (10) shows the relative amplitude Z_A/A for the SWEEP and SIPT, where A is the wave amplitude and Z_A the amplitude of the vertical motion of these mechanism. Observe that $Z_A/A \sim 0(1)$.

CONCLUSION

The objective of this work was to use a relatively recent technique, the "Hybrid Element Method", and some new results obtained by C.C. Mei (1976) and D.W. Evans (1976), in order to explore mechanism for wave power extraction. In the author's opinion this kind of analysis, due its simplicity, must be done before a more exhaustive experimental analysis is carried out. It must be emphasized that the "Hybrid Element Method" can also be used in the analysis of off-shore structure, harbors etc.

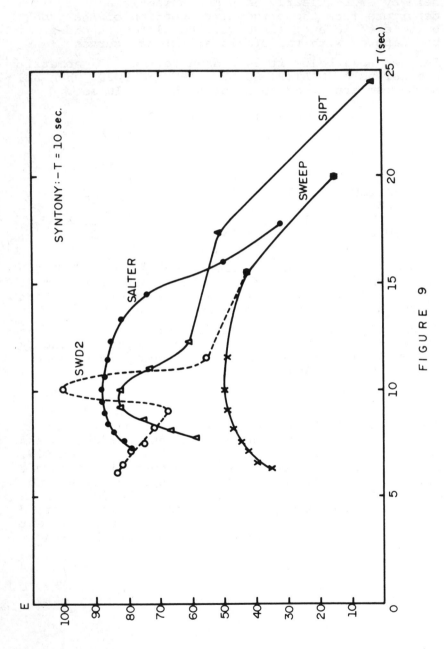

F I G U R E   9

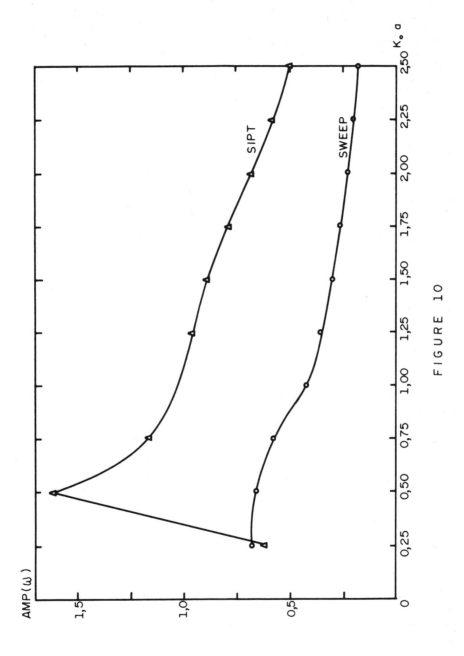

FIGURE 10

ACKNOWLEDGEMENTS

The authors acknowledge Dr. Carlos de Sousa   Pinto,
Head of Civil Engineering Division at IPT and   Engº
Luiz Emilio Soares de G. Horta, Head of the Structure
Sub-division, by their cooperation in this work; Mr.
José Luiz Maitan, Mr. Mauricio Pires Toledo and Miss
Hilda Barbosa da S. Lima by the drawings and typing.

REFERENCES

Aranha, J.A. (1978) - "Theoretical Analysis of the
    Hybrid Element Method in water wave problems", Ph.
    D. thesis, Part II, Dept. of Civil   Engineering,
    M.I.T.

Aranha, J.A., Sugaya,M., Martins, C. (1979) - "Apli-
    cação do "Hybrid Element Method" na análise   de
    mecanismos para aproveitamento energético das on-
    das do mar", Publicação IPT.

Chen, H.S., Mei, C.C. (August 1974) - "Oscillations
    and wave forces in an offshore harbor",   TR190,
    R.M. Parsons Lab., Dept. of Civil   Engineering,
    M.I.T.

Evans, D.W. (1976) - "A theory of wave power extraction
    by oscillating bodies", Proc. 11th Symp. on Naval
    Hydrodynamics, London.

Mei, C.C. (1976) - "Power extraction from water waves",
    Journal of Ship Researsch, Vol. 20, nº 2,pp.63-66.

Serman, D.D. (1978) - "Theory of Salter's wave energy
    device in Random Sea", master thesis, Dept.   of
    Civil Engineering, M.I.T.

Yue, D.K., Chen, H.S., Mei, C.C. (1976) -   "There-
    dimensional calculation of wave forces by a Hybrid
    Element Method", Proc. 11th Symposium on   Naval
    Hydrodynamics, London.

OFFSHORE SEISMIC RISK: REGIONAL SEISMICITY EVALUATION

J. Grases (IMME, UCV), E. Gajardo and
M. Contreras (INTEVEP) - Venezuela

****

INTRODUCTION

The earlier efforts on the evaluation of the seismic risk, at
a particular location, began around the fifties. The work
was mostly carried out by seismologists, who tried to synthe-
size historical data, geological information and other factors, ending with the earlier seismic risk maps. Later, these
maps were based on relations between Mercalli Modified Intensities, maximum probable intensities or maximum credible
intensities and the mean return period obtained from historical information.   Meanwhile, scientists began to make extensive use of the recurrences relation concept (Richter,
1958, 1959).

As the time of occurrence of an earthquake, its location, magnitude and other characteristics of the seismic activity, are
believed to be random, they need to be treated using probability theory.

Perhaps the first use of probabilistic models to obtain information to be directly used in engineering design, was done by
Cornell in 1968 (see references). He and Esteva (1969 and
others), are the pioneers in this field. The fundamentals
proposed in their research work are still used in more recent probabilistic models: Shah et al (1975), Liu and Fagel
(1975), Kiremidjian and Shah (1975), Wiggins (1975) Der
Kiureghian and Ang (1975, 1977), Mortgat (1976, 1977),
Mc Guire (1976, 1978) and Schumacker and Whitman (1978). The
model is based on: a) the evaluation of available seismic
information to obtain the parameters of the recurrence relation to be used (linear, quadratic, exponential, etc); b)
the definition of source zones and,based on the joint evaluation of the geology, tectonics and seismicity of the region,
the definition of the geometry, mean depth and seismicity of
each source zone;

c) mathematical expressed attenuation laws to adequately represent the propagation of the seismic wave from the epicenter to each site; d) the assumed type of energy release for
each source zone, originally taken as point sources, Cornell
(1968), Algermissen and Perkin (1972), and lately described
by the fault rupture theory, Der Kiureghian and Ang (1975,
1977); e) the events occurrence distribution, usually taken
as Poisson type, Cornell (1968), Algermissen and Perkins
(1972), Der Kiureghian and Ang (1975, 1977). Shah et al (1975)
and Schumaker and Whitman (1978). Other types of distribution are also used, as the Weibull (Lomnitz, 1974); f) the
analytical relations to quantify the seismic risk on a probabilistic basis.

The evaluation of the seismic risk for offshore structures
must bear in mind its long period characteristic. Therefore,
instead of a design criteria based on maximum ground accelerations, for intermediate period structures (2-4 sec), it
is more reliable to use the maximum ground velocity or the
spectral velocity. In the case of long period structures
(4 sec or greater), it is more convenient to use maximum
ground displacement. The previous considerations are based
on the better correlation existing between the above mentioned parameters and certain ranges of the periods scale (Cornell
and Vanmarcke, 1975).

The authors contributions to the seismic risk evaluation
methodology, include: a) the inclusion of historical data in
the recurrence relations, using the extreme value distribution (Gumbel 1954, 1950); b) the definition of source zones
based on the energy release distribution, hypocenter density
and spatial distribution of seismic activity, by means of a
graphic representation using computing facilities, and c)
the definition of attenuation laws based on assigned intensities (MMI), including the found uncertainties.

The example included, to illustrate the methodology, is the
evaluation of the seismic risk for a site located offshore of
the Orinoco River Delta and South of Trinidad Island.

SHORT DESCRIPTION OF THE AREA

Tectonically, the area corresponds to a platform whose development, within a geosyncline structure, started at the
mesozoic, and which now has a napped structure overriding it.
There is long term sedimentation, affected by several compressive and distensible tectonic cycles. The most remarka-
ble event was the growth of a cordillera at the early terci-
ary, defining an asymetric basin with torrential sedimentation from the north and slow sedimentation from the south,
until the middle of the eocene (Gonzalez de Juana, 1977).

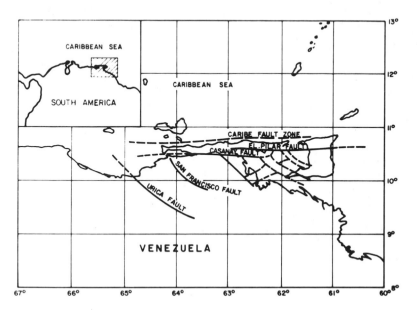

FIG. N⁰ 1 - Location and Tectonic of the area

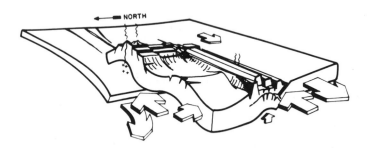

FIG. N⁰ 2 - Southeastern Caribbean Area
Simplified Tectonic Model.

The sea floor spreading mechanism transported southward the metamorphic and folded napped sediments in segments guided by major transcurrent faults, as Urica, San Francisco, etc. (Gonzales de Juana, 1977). The northern border of the basin was then folded and uplifted, forming the Serrania del Interior. Afterwards, as a result of gravitational adjustments, the normal faults were produced, some of which have derivated into right lateral faults (Gallardo, 1979), such as the El Pilar fault system.

The present principal morphostructural features are, from north to south; an interridge basin (Aves ridge and the Antilles Island arc), a block system (horst-graben) defined by Margarita Island, Paria-Araya peninsulas and the Northern Trinidad range, the Serrania del Interior and the plateau of the eastern Venezuela basin. There is no volcanic activity in this area, with the exception of a few hot springs and sulphur formations. The region is believed to correspond to a subduction and obduction model (Fig.2).

INSTRUMENTAL SEISMICITY EVALUATION

Due to the lack of an adequate seismological network in the area, most of the gathered information comes from events recorded with the worldwide seismic network. Therefore the lower threshold of magnitude for recorded earthquakes is generally higher than in other zones with more seismic instrumentation.

The data source used was the Venezuelan Seismic Catalogue (Gajardo, 1978) which includes up-to-date standard information from all other available data sources. The magnitudes defined for each source were converted into body wave magnitudes through a regression analysis to develop conversion formulae used for the zone.

Through the study of the frequency of occurrence of earthquakes at different depths it was possible to establish three well defined depth ranges, located at 0-27 Km., 28-70 Km. and 71-300 Km.

For a more objective expression of the seismicity of the area, epicentral density maps were prepared, evaluating the number of epicenters for each square of 0.5 x 0.5 geographic degrees. The resultant values were smoothed, taking into account the eight bordering squares weighted by a factor of 0.5 and obtaining the mean total value. These values were used to draw isolines of equal epicenter density for each depth range. All maps were drawn using Lambert conical projection with a scale of 1:2.000.000 in order to make them directly comparable with the geological and tectonics maps.

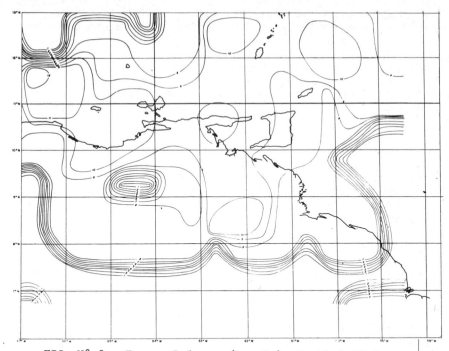

FIG. Nº 3 – Energy Release (Log E), Depth 0–27 Km.

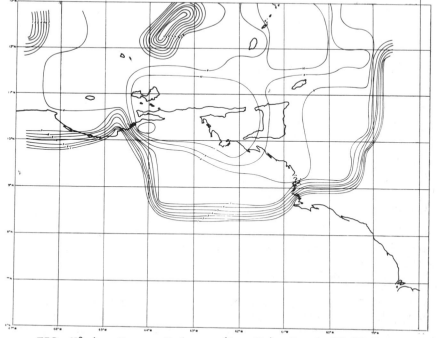

FIG. Nº 4 – Energy Release (Log E), Depth 28–70 Km.

Several vertical profiles with different directions were
used to obtain a better understanding of the depth distribution of hypocenters.

The general feature of hypocenter depth distribution was obtained through maps of mean depth of earthquake occurrence
for each depth range. These values were calculated and
smoothed for each square of 0.5 x 0.5 degrees and isolines
of equal depth were drawn.

Compared with severe earthquakes, low magnitude events have
little influence in the evaluation of seismic risk. The
seismic energy release is an exponential function of the phenomena of seismic activity since small events make little
contribution to the total energy release. The use of seismic
energy release, together with other variables such as the
epicentral density, mean depth feature, vertical profiles and
the tectonic correlation of the area, allows a more realistic
approach to the seismicity of the area, making possible a better definition of the seismic source zones.

No magnitude determinations exist for some of the reported
earthquakes. Minimum values were given to them. The values
selected were the minimum detectable magnitude for each
period.

Table 1

MINIMUM DETECTABLE MAGNITUDE IN EACH TIME PERIOD

Period	m_b
1900 – 1942	5.5
1943 – 1950	5.0
1951 – 1962	4.5
1963 – 1977	4.0

To obtain the energy release the following relation was used:

$$\text{Log } E = 5.8 + 2.4\ m_b \tag{1}$$

Total energy release maps were prepared by procedures similar
to those previously mentioned. The total energy release isolines represent the smoothed values of Log $\sqrt{E}$, for the three
studied depth ranges. (Figs. 3,4,5).

MACROSEISMIC DATA EVALUATION

The research on regional seismic activity was based on the
analysis of historical records of earthquakes, starting in
1530. The region of this study is shown in Fig 1 and includes
the northeastern section of Venezuela, the northwest of Guyana

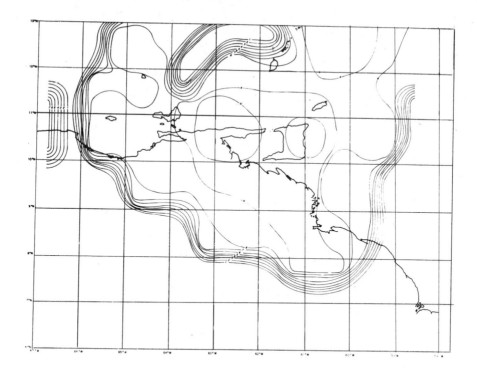

FIG. N⁰ 5 - Energy Release (Log E), Depth 71-300 Km.

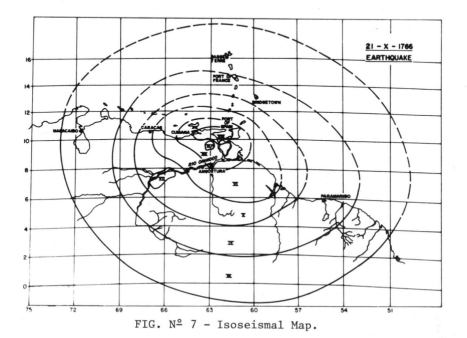

FIG. N⁰ 7 - Isoseismal Map.

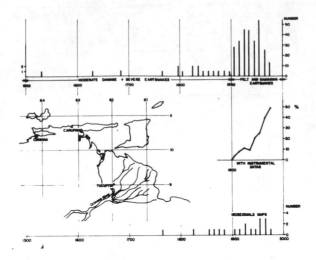

FIG. Nº 6 - Time Distribution of Macroseismic Data.

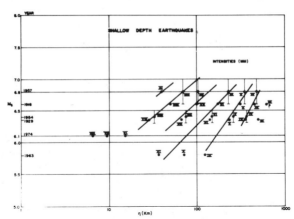

FIG. Nº 8 - Intensity Observed Values - Shallow Depth.

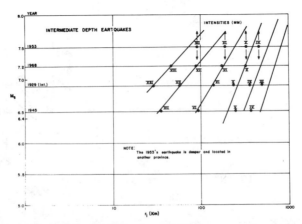

FIG. Nº 9 - Intensity Observed Values - Intermediate Depth.

and the islands of Trinidad, Tobago and Grenada. The surrounding offshore areas constitute about 50% of the total
area which is estimated to be 500.000 Km^2. Since the discovery of America, the history of the region with respect to
its politics and colonial activities was dominated mainly by
Spain, Great Britain and France, with some influence by
Holland. Therefore the search for information had to be made
in many different and various sources.

Two groups of data were considered, the events which occurred
after 1900 and the events which occurred in the previous century. Through the study of the contemporary instrumental
data, it was possible to correlate events with their known
effects. This procedure allows a better description of historical events based on their known effects. Attention was
focused on each damaging earthquake which occurred during
the last 4.5 centuries, and especially on those instrumental-
ly recorded events with macroseismic information. A catalogue, not contaminated by personal opinion, containing information about 305 felt or damaging earthquakes (94% correspond to this century) was prepared; those earthquakes felt
before 1900 without known hypocentral area and with little
engineering interest were excluded. Fig 6 shows the amount
of information gathered, the time distribution and the percent of felt or damaging earthquakes with known origin time,
location and magnitude.

Two-thirds of the most severe earthquakes, with MM intensity
of at least VII, took place before 1900. Fig 6 also shows
these events, 20 in total, for which it was possible to draw
isoseismal maps. Fig 7 shows an example of an isoseismal
map. It is believed that it would be possible to make about
10 to 13 additional maps for events which occurred after
1900, after a more detailed study of local source data.

If Ai is the area with assigned intensity equal to or greater
than I, the equivalent radius ri $=\sqrt{Ai/\pi}$ is an adequate parameter to use to compare the attenuation laws for differents
events. The contemporary events are of special interest
because they were used to enhance the evaluation of past
events. Figures 8 and 9 show observed intensity values and
the corresponding isoseismal lines. Shallow earthquakes
(h $\leq$ 70 Km) present a different attenuation feature compared
with intermediate events (70< h <150) (Grases 1979).

With r known from the study of other earthquakes in the
same epicentral area, and adjusting it, using the curves in
Fig 8 and 9, the values given in Table 2 were obtained. This
information has proven to be a useful complement to the
inferred instrumental record in evaluating the regional seismicity, since, with the degree of homogeneity obtained, time
intervals could be extended to several centuries.

Table 2

LARGE EARTHQUAKES IN NORTH-EASTERN VENEZUELA (XVIIIth AND XIXth CENTURY)			
Date (year)	Ms	Depth	Approximate Epicentral Area
1766	7.4 - 7.6	Sup.	Paria Peninsula
1825	6.1 - 6.3	Sup.	Dragon Mouth
1853	7.0	Int.	Cariaco Gulf
1865	6.6	Sup.	40 Km. North of Paria Peninsula
1874	5.9	Sup.	Near Yaguaraparo and El Pilar
1888	6.5 - 6.6	Sup.	100 Km. North of Paria Peninsula.

DETERMINISTIC DEFINITION OF SEISMIC SOURCE ZONES.

In those areas with well known recent tectonic activity, it is possible to obtain reliable seismic source zones and other seismicity parameters used in the evaluation of the seismic risk by use of the methodology developed by Molnar (1978).

Molnar states the relation between the frequency of occurrence of earthquakes and the slip rate of an important fault or the rate of deformation of a diffusely faulted area. Due to the fault slip and the finite strains produced by earthquakes, the relative sizes of earthquakes are best represented in terms of the parameter "seismic moment"(M_O) which is pro-portional to the fault slip and the areal extent of faulting.

M_O = Shear modulus x rupture area x average slip

(Aki, 1966,1967)

Using the plate tectonics theory it is possible to evaluate the long term average slip rate on major faults and plate boundaries. Neotectonic field work permits the definition of deformation rates in areas of complicated tectonics for short periods(some centuries) .

The frequencies of occurrence for events with different seis-mic moment are therefore related and can be determined from the estimated slip rate for a specific area.

The empirical Gutenberg-Richter relation (Log N = a-bM) re-lating frequency of earthquake occurrence with magnitude can be converted into a relation between frequency of occurrence and different values of the seismic moment by mean of other empirical relations. It is believed that a maximum possible

seismic moment exists for each region; the relation giving
the frequency of occurrence includes this maximum value as a
parameter.

$$N (M_o) = \alpha M_o^{-\beta} \mid 1 - H (M_o - M_o^{max}) \mid \qquad (2)$$

where $N(M_o)$ is the annual event number $H(X)$ is the Heaviside
function and M_o^{max} is the maximum possible seismic moment.

The total seismic moment in a faulted area is the integral of
all the seismic moments weighted according their relative
frequency of occurrence. The total seismic moment can be expressed as a function of the maximum feasible seismic moment:

$$N (M_o) = \int_{M_o}^{\infty} n (M_o) \quad dM_o \qquad (2a)$$

where $n (M_o)$ is a frequency density function of M_o.

Given the slip rate of a faulted zone, the rate of increase
of the seismic moment is obtained. Defining this value
through the tectonic plate movement theory or other methods
it is possible to estimate the frequency of occurrence of
events for different seismic moments. This can also be expressed as a mean repeat time for earthquakes of different
seismic moment.

The recurrence period and frequency of occurrence relations
are expressed in terms of three parameters: a) the exponent
β in the relative recurrence relation which corresponds to
the b value in the Gutenberg-Richter relation mentioned above,
b) the maximum possible seismic moment for a particular region, and c) the mean rate of change of seismic moment in
the area.

It is possible with geological and tectonic studies of qua=
ternary faulting to directly measure the slip rates and fre=
quency of occurrence in active faults and also to find out
what portion of the displacement is pure creep movement.

This methodology, applied when an adequate knowledge of the
recent tectonic exists, is an efficient complement to the
historical information in the evaluation of seismic risk,
especially when recurrence periods are relatively long.

SEISMIC SOURCE ZONES AND ATTENUATION LAWS

Two different methodologies for the definition of the sesmic
source zones are examined. The first is based on Molnar
(1978); the zones are obtained assuming fault rupture, where
the total seismic energy release occurs along a rupture or
slip line. The slip or rupture length is a function of magnitude, empirically represented by:

$$S = e^{a_s M - b_s} \tag{3}$$

where S is length of slip and a_s, b_s are coefficients dependent on the area and fault type. The assumed value for a_s is the world-wide average 1.15 Value of b were obtained from (3) by making assumptions of a maximum possible magnitude and a maximum rupture length for each source zone.

The source zones defined for eastern Venezuela are shown in Figs. 13 and 14.

The other approach to seismic source definition is based on an analysis of the spectral distribution of seismic parameters. Using the seismic energy release maps, (Figs.3,4 and 5), the epicentral density distribution, the everage depth value of each depth range and several vertical profiles to obtain a three dimensional view of the seismic activity, it is possible to make a realistic definition of seismic sources, especially if the previous information is complemented with tectonical and historical data. The evaluation of seismic risk using this second approach is now in progress.

It has been inferred from the isoseismal attenuation that: a) felt areas A differ for superficial events $(h \leqslant 70$ Kms.) and intermediate events $(70 < h \leqslant 300 km)$. The felt area can be approximately described by:

$$A = 10^{0,592(M_s + c)} - 150.000 \tag{4}$$

where: $C_{Sup.} = 3,76$ and $C_{Int.} = 3,46,$ Valid

for 2×10^5 Km$^2 < A < 3 \times 10^6$ Km^2. The above values overestimates felt areas for small magnitude events. (b) the modified Mercalli Intensity (MMI) attenuation for a set of 37 local earthquakes with known magnitude and foci is shown in Figure No. 10.
An empirical relation describing these observations is:

$$I = C_1 M_s - C_2 (\log_{10} \bar{\Delta} - \log_{10} C(_F)) \tag{5}$$

where: $C1 = 3,27 - 0.115 M_s$ $\hspace{2cm}$ (6)
$\hspace{1.5cm} C_2 = 4,9$

$$C(p) = 2(1-p) - 0,1M_s (1-2p) \tag{7}$$

The above formula means that, given an earthquake of magnitude M_s with local depth h, the Intensity I has been observed at a mean $(p = 0.50)$ hypocentral distance $\bar{\Delta}$; for a different confidence level p, between 0.90 and 0.10, the hypocentral distance is no more than $\bar{\Delta}$. $C(p)$, which is:

$$\bar{\Delta} = C(p) \cdot 10^{\frac{C1 \cdot M_s - I}{C_2}} \tag{8}$$

is valid for the following ranges:

$5.0 \leq M \leq 7,5$;   III $< I \leq$ IX ;

$0,1 \leq p \leq 0,9$ and $\bar{\Delta}$ greater than about 30 Km.

RECURRENCE EVALUATION FOR ONE OF THE SOURCE ZONES.

In their paper about the statistical prediction of maximum
regional earthquakes Yegulalp and Kuo (1974) concluded that
they can complement predictions based on deterministic physical processes very well . For this a useful tool commonly
used is the Extreme Value Theory which implies that: (a)
the observed seismic activity is representative of future
activity, and (b) the largest observed values are independent.
The first hypothesis is currently taken to imply the constan-
cy of the mean rate of occurrence of events with magnitude
equal to or greater than M_0. This can be expressed by:

$$\text{Log}_{10} \lambda = a - b (M - m_o) \tag{9}$$

or by means of any other relation that fits the seismological instrument available data. It is therefore accepted that
the mean rate λ defines the regional activity independently
of the time origin. It is generally accepted that the larger
observed magnitudes are independent and that the longer the
observation period is in relation to the interval of maxima,
the more reliable is the assumption of the independence of
the maxima.

The first asymptotic extreme value distribution studied by
Gumbel (1954), is unlimited in both directions and is given
by:

$$G_n (m) = e^{-e^{-\alpha_n (m - un)}} \qquad \alpha_n > 0 \tag{10}$$

where Gnm) is the probability that m is the largest of n
independent samples of a certain random variable:

$$G_n (m) = P \left[M_1 \leq m; \; M_2 \leq m; \; --; \; M_n \leq m \right] \tag{11}$$

Additionaly, u_n is the characteristic value, which means
$G (u_n) = 1/e$.

Equation (10) can be written in the form:

$$\ln \left[- \ln G_n (m) \right] = \alpha_n u_n - \alpha_n m \tag{10a}$$

from which:

$$b = \alpha_n / \ln 10 ; \; a\ln 10 = \left(\alpha_n u_n - bm_o \ln 10 \right) \tag{12}$$

In a previous paper, Grases (1974), a distribution similar to
(10) was adjusted for a given area in Central America (7°N –
16°N; 82°W – 93°W) by means of the annual maxima during a 40
year period (1934 – 1973 inclusive).

Using the Maxima in longer intervals would have led to the
prediction of mean rates of occurrences similar to shown in
Fig. 11 in determining i, use of hypothesis (a) has been
made, according to which the annual probability of nonexce-
dance is equal to:

$$\sqrt[T]{G_{T \ years}^{(m)}} \tag{13}$$

If the criteria applied to the evaluation of historical information are accepted, a set of homogeneus data extending
several centuries is available. In Fig 11 the results for
the period 1766-1975 are presented, using the maxima for 21
year intervals, expressed by:

$$G(m) = e^{-e^{-2,22(m-5.3)}} \tag{10b}$$

from which:

$$\log_{10} \lambda = 1,254 - 0.965 \ (m-4.0) \tag{9a}$$

or

$$\log_e \lambda = 2,886 - 2,222 \ (m-4.0) \tag{9b}$$

Slightly different coefficients correspond to the time period
1923-1976 (See Figure 11).

For the northeastern Venezuelan region, Molnar (1978) postu-
lates maximum magnitude earthquakes with $M_u = 7,9$, which is
greater than any of the larger known earthquakes during the
period 1530-1978. In this case it is convenient to write the
recurrence law in the form:

$$\lambda = \alpha_1 \ (e^{-\beta_1 \ m} - e^{-\beta_1 \ m_u}) \tag{14}$$

If earthquake occurrence is taken as a Poisson process, the
annual probability of nonexcedence is:

$$P \ (M < m) = (e^{-e^{-\beta_1 \ m}})^{\alpha_1} \cdot (e^{\alpha_1 \ e^{-\beta_1 m_u}}) \tag{15}$$

The last product factor tends to unity, therefore (15) is
nearly equal to

$$(e^{-e^{-\beta_1 \ m}})^{\alpha_1} \tag{15a}$$

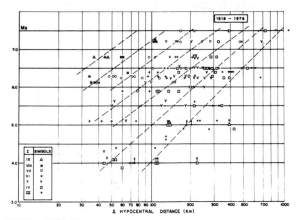

FIG. N°10 - MMI Attenuation Relations.

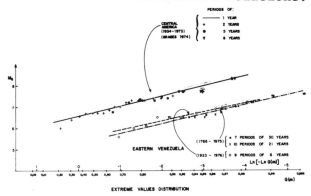

FIG. N°11 - Means Rates of Occurrence.

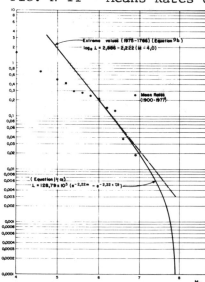

FIG. N°12 - Recurrence
Relations.

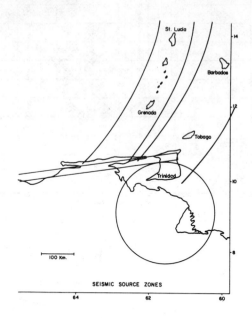

FIG. N°13 - (After Schumacker & Whitman, 1978)

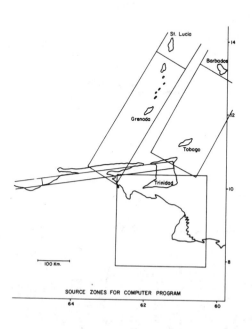

FIG. N°14 - (After Schumacker & Whitman, 1978)

Together with equation (10) this gives:

$$\beta_1 = \alpha_n \; ; \; \alpha_1 = e^{\alpha_n} \cdot u_n \tag{16}$$

With the coefficients given in (10b), equation (14) becomes

$$\lambda = 128,79 \times 10^3 \; (e^{-2,22m} -2,417 \times 10^{-8}) \tag{14a}$$

In figure 12 relations (9b) and (14a) are compared with observed mean rates derived from the regional instrumental catalogue compiled by Gajardo (1979)

APPLICATION AND PRELIMINARY RESULTS.

The methodology mentioned before will be applied to the Orinoco Delta River Offshore area to establish the potential seismic risk using a Probabilistic model RUPRISK developed through the Offshore Research and Development Agreement between the Massachusetts Institute of Technology and INTEVEP. Preliminary results has been obtained for a specific location southern of the Trinidad Island (9°56' N, 61°02'W) using different approaches for the modeling of the source zones, and also different mean annual rate values, Contreras (1978), Schumacker and Whitman (1978). The attenuation relationship used for these analysis was:

$$v \; (2\%, \; 1 \; sec) = 0.43 \; e^{0.88M} (R + 25)^{-0.587} \tag{17}$$

which is McGuire's relationship for Pseudo-velocity of 1-DOF oscillator with dampins of 2% and a period of 1 sec.

Results are shown in table 3:

Table 3

SEISMIC RISK PRELIMINARY RESULTS - LOCATION 9°56''N, 61°02'W

References	Pseudo-velocity (in/sec) (2%, 1 second		Spectral Acceleration (g)	
	50 yr.	100 yr.	50 yr.	100 yr.
Contreras (1978)	9.7	13.4	0.16	0.22
Schumaker and Whitman (1978)	14.0	18.0	0.23	0.29

CONCLUSIONS.

Due to the dispersion shown in table 3, for the same location when a different criteria is used, we consider necessary to look for a more realistic definition of seismic source zones using the seismic energy release concept. The evaluation of seismic risk for the Orinoco Delta River Offshore area is now in progress.

ACKNOWLEDGEMENTS.

The authors wish to express their gratitude to Petróleos de Venezuela S. A. for the authorization to publish the results contained in this paper.

They wish also to express their thanks to INTEVEP (Instituto Tecnológico Venezolano del Petróleo) and to IMME-UCV (Instituto de Materiales y Modelos Estructurales - Univ. Central de Venezuela) for the help and indulgence extended during the preparation of the paper.

REFERENCES

AKI, K. (1966) Generation and propagation of G Waves from the Niigata Earthquake of June 16, 1964, 2, Estimation of earthquake moment, released energy and stress strain drop from G-wave spectrum, Bull. Earth. Res. Int. Tokyo Univ. 44, 73-88.

AKI, K. (1967) Scaling law of seismic spectrum, J. Geophys. Res. 72, 1217 - 1232.

ALGERMISSEN, S.T. and PERKINS, D.M. (1972) A technique for Seismic zoning: general considerations and parameters. Microzonation Conference, Seattle, Washington.

CONTRERAS, M. (1978) Investigación sobre Riesgo Sismico Delta del Orinoco - Reporte de Avance-INTEVEP- Apartado 76343, Caracas, Venezuela.

CORNELL C.A. (1968) Engineering Seismic Risk Analysis Bull Seism. Soc. Am. 58, 1583-1606.

CORNELL C.A. and GRIGORIU, M. (1974) - Seismic Risk Analysis: Single Site Case a User's Manual, M.I.T.
- Seismic Risk Analysis: Multi-Site of Mapping Case a User's Manual.
- Correction/Modifications to "Seismic Risk Analysis Program Support Documents".

CORNELL C.A. and VANMARCKE E.H. (1975) Seismic Risk Analysis for Offshore Structures O.T.C. Houston, Texas.

DER KIUREGHIAN A. and ANG H.S. (1975) A Line source model for Seismic Risk Analysis Tech. Report for NSF. Grant GK-36378 Univ. of Illinois, Urbana.

DER KIUREGHIAN A. and ANG A.H.S. (1977) A line source model for seismic risk analysis. Bull Seism. Soc. Am. 67, 1173-1194.

ESTEVA L. (1968) Bases para la formulación de decisiones de diseño sísmico Doctoral Thesis Univ. Nac. Aut. de México.

ESTEVA L. (1969) Seismicity prediction: a bayesian approach IV WCWW Santiago, Chile.

ESTEVA L. and VILLAVERDE R. (1973) Seismic Risk, Design Spectra and Structural Reliability V WCEE, Rome, Italy.

ESTEVA L. (1974) Geology and Probability in the assessment of seismic risk. 2nd Int. Congress of the Int. Ass. Eng. Geol. Sao Paulo, Brasil.

ESTEVA L. (1976) Seismicity (Chapter 6). Seismic Risk and Engineering Decisions Editors C. Lomnitz and E. Rosenblueth Elsevier Scientific Publishing Co.

GAJARDO, E. (1978) Catálogo Sísmico de Venezuela, 1900-1977, Intevep, Venezuela.

GALLARDO, C. (1979) Estructuras de la Serranía de Paria en Relación con la Sismotectónica del Borde Suroriental del Caribe, IV Congreso Latinoamericano de Geología, Port of Spain, Trinidad - Tobago.

GONZALEZ DE JUANA, C. (1977) Tertiary Tectonics in the Caribbean and the Eastern Venezuela Basin Abs., 8th Carib. Geol. Conf., pp. 61-62

GRASES, J. (1974) Sismicidad de la Región Centroamericana asociada a la Cadena Volcánica del Cuaternario, Caracas, UCV, Vol. 1.

GRASES, J. (1979) Investigación sobre los sismos destructores que han afectado el oriente de Venezuela, Delta del Orinoco y regiones adyacentes. Intevep, Febrero 1979.

GUMBEL, E.J. (1954). Statistical Theory of Extreme Values and some practical applications. U.S. Dept. Commerce Appl. Math. Ser. 3, 51 pp.

GUMBEL, E.J. (1958) Statistics of Extremes Columbia University Press, 375 pp.

KIREDMIJIAN A.S. and SHAH H.C. (1975). Seismic Hazard Mapping of California, Technical Report No. 21, The John A. Blume Earthquake Engineering Center, Dept. of Civil Engineering, Stanford University.

LIU S, C. and FAGEL L.W. (1975) Seismic Risk Analysis-Comparison of Three Different Methods for Seismic Regionalization, Bull. of Seis. Soc. of America, Vol. 65, No. 4, pp. 1023-1027.

LOMNITZ C. (1974) Global Tectonics and Earthquake Risk. Elsevier Scientific Publishing Co.

MCGUIRE R. (1976) Fortran Computer Program for Seismic Risk Analysis U.S.G.S. Report 76-77.

MCGUIRE R. (1978) Frisk: Computer Program for Seismic Analysis Using Faults as Earthquake Sources. U.S.G.S. Open File Report 78-1007.

MOLNAR, P. (1-78) Earthquake Recurrence Intervals and Plate Tectonics, Report Submitted to Intevep.

MORTGAT C.P. (1976) A Bayesian Approach to Seismic Hazard Mapping: Development of Stable Design Parameters, Ph.D. Dissertation, Stanford University, California.

MORTGAT C.P. (1977) A Study of Seismic Risk for Costa Rica, Report No. 25, The John A. Blume Earthquake Engineering Center, Dpt. of Civil Engineering, Stanford University.

RICHTER C.F. (1958). Elementary Seismology W.H. Freeman and Co., San Francisco.

RICHTER C.F. (1959) Seismic Regionalization, Bull. Seism. Soc. Am. 49, 123-162.

SHAH H.C. and Others (1975) A Study of Seismic Risk for Nicaragua. Part I and II, The John A. Blume Earthquake Engineering Center. Dpto. of Civil Engineering, Stanford University.

SCHUMACKER B. and Whitman R. (1978) Preliminary Seismic Risk Study of Orinoco Delta and Computer Program for Seismic Risk. Research Report R78-39. Dpt. of Civil Engineering M.I.T.

WIGGINS J.H. (1975) Procedure of Determining Acceptable Risk Ground Motion Design Criteria. Technical Report No. 75-1229, J.H. Wiggins Company, Redondo Beach, California.

YEGULALP, T.M. and J.T. KUO. 1974. Statistical Prediction of the ocurrence of maximum magnitude earthquakes. Bull. Seism. Soc. of America. Vol. 64, No. 2. pp. 393-414.

SEA-STRUCTURE INTERACTION FOR TRIPOD TYPE STEEL GRAVITY PLATFORM

M.Berta, A.Blandino, D.Marcon, A.Paruzzolo

Tecnomare S.p.A., Venice, Italy

ABSTRACT

The present paper deals with a numerical integrated pro cedure to calculate the effects of the interaction between sea waves and a tripod-type steel gravity platform.
The main aspects to be taken into account for a reliable wave loading analysis of such a new type of platform will be empha sized. Among them, the field perturbation effect due to the large bodies presence will be analysed.
Finally some principal results in terms of structure global loads obtained by the numerical integrated procedure will be presented.

INTRODUCTION

Designers of recent offshore installations for the North Sea and similar waters face a number of exceptional demands especially with respect to the extreme environmental conditions, the great water depths and the soil conditions, the deck payload, the integrated and economical exploitation of new oil fields.
In response to this challenge, a rapid development of new design concepts has led to the emergence of new types of monoli thic and hybrid structures. These pose several difficult design problems and, in particular, are not generally amenable to conventional methods for computing wave loads. The main reason for this is their interaction with the surrounding fluid; this cannot be disregarded and therefore prediction me thods based on the diffraction theory are needed.

THE TRIPOD-TYPE STEEL GRAVITY PLATFORM

By monolithic or hybrid structures is meant a range of
structure types all having as general a characteristic the
large dimension of one or more of their components.
Among these several broad classes of structures (tension leg
and tethered platforms, storage tanks and so on) a major trend
already well established is for the emergence of gravity plat
forms.
The definitive feature of these types of platforms is that
they rest on the sea bed under their own weight without piling.
So far this new design philosophy and the relevant construction and installation techniques make fixed platforms still at
tractive for the development of offshore petroleum fields.
Our company has studied for many years the possibility of using a pileless fixed platform for mean-deep water drilling
and production operations.

The basic design philosophy for this type of structure was as
follows:
- To eliminate pile driving operations in order to simplify
  and shorten the installation procedure.
- To adopt three foundation bases in order to minimize the ef
  fects of possible initial soil unevenness and differential
  soil settlement.
- Extensive use of steel framed structures to minimize both
  total weight and wave forces.
- To use floatation tanks as an integral part of the structure
  to lessen weight and to make simpler and safer the installat
  ion.
- To adopt construction, transportation and installation procedures keeping the structure in a vertical position, in or
  der to minimize stresses and hazards in transition phases,
  and to have the possibility of transportation of equipment
  already installed on the deck.
- Possibility of storage capacity inside cylinders.
- Good seakeeping performances for possible long and safe tow
  ages as well as for installation on a cluster.
- Prefabrication in large structure components to facilitate
  assembly operations in order to permit a time saving modul-
  ar construction even in limited water depths. Together with
  the previous one, this platform feature assures the economic
  al advantages of utilizing for any case the most suitable
  construction facilities already installed.

As a result of the above mentioned premises the main elements

of a tripod-type steel gravity platform are three foundation ba
ses, three stabilizing cylinders, a triangular framed structu
re connecting the cylinders and a tower supporting the deck.
Three typical configurations are illustrated in Fig.1 together with the major design characteristics.
The shape and dimensions of the tower are designed according
to the deck characteristics.
The shape and dimensions of the foundation bases and of the
stabilizing cylinders are due both to the diverse soil proper
ties and to the amount of equipment to be transported on the
platform during tow. As a matter of fact payload presence requires an increase in cylinder dimensions to assure stability
during tow as well as during sinking operations.
In this way, greater built-in storage capacity is made availa
ble or, on the contrary, in case of storage capacity demand a
relevant payload transportation capability is assured.
For stability and safety reasons even in damaged conditions
during tow, each storage/stabilizing cylinder is compartment-
ed; each compartment works as a single storage unit which ope
rates on the water displacement principle.

The particular tripod-type arrangement and the high low
er horizontal bracing offer an "open" area to facilitate the
platform installation over a predrilled template and the access of the template itself for underwater work and maintenan
ce.
In addition the particularly favourable dynamic behaviour of
the platform assures its capability of reaching the very high
precision positioning.
This TECNOMARE patented concept, already developed as a research project, found its first application for the construct
ion of the four steel gravity platforms for the Loango Field
(Congo). Furthermore this platform design has now been proven
to be particularly suitable for the development of marginal
fields and has been selected for the above application in the
North Sea by a major Oil Company, from among a very large num
ber of solutions, for its technical merits and competitivity.

WAVE LOADING ANALYSIS PROCEDURES

In addition to the conventional engineering techniques
used in the design of jacket-type piled platforms or monolithic structures, this type of self-floating platform requires
the development of specialized and sophisticated design methods.

THREE CASES OF TECNOMARE STEEL GRAVITY PLATFORM

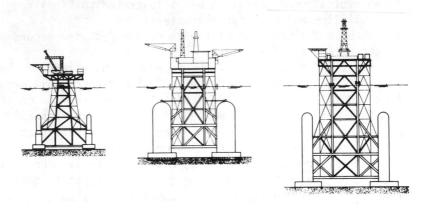

AREA	WEST · AFRICA	NORTH · SEA	NORTH · SEA
WATER DEPTH	90 m	100 m	140 m
PLATFORM STEEL WEIGHT	4,400 t	23,500 t	27,800 t
STORAGE CAPACITY	NOT REQUESTED	650,000 bbls	240,000 bbls
MAXIMUM WET PAYLOAD	3,500 t	16,000 t	19,000 t
TOWING PAYLOAD	DECK	10,000 t	6,000 t
EARLY PRODUCTION	POSSIBLE	YES	YES
POSITIONING ACCURACY			
OVER SEA · BED TEMPLATE	0,15 m	0,15 m	0,15 m

FIGURE No. 1

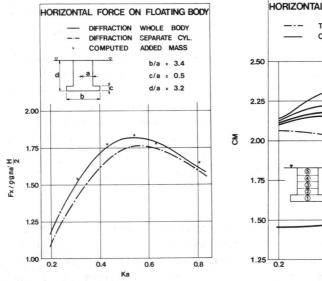

FIGURE No. 2

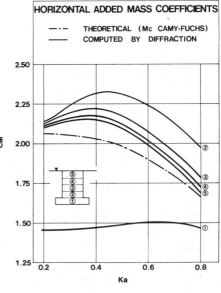

FIGURE No. 3

Among the several design procedures especially developed for a
complete and thorough analysis of such a type of platform, the
wave loading analysis procedure is to cover a completely new
area in the field of offshore engineering.
As a matter of fact, the proposed type of platform requires
both large floatation cylinders and foundation bases and a tu
bular framed structure.
As a result the determination of the wave forces acting on the
platform in floating as well as in stand-on-bottom condition
is not easily accomplished. The simplified theory based on Mo
rison's equation and conventional coefficients is indeed no
longer a suitable application and even the results given by
the diffraction theory are unsatisfactory.

The main reasons why the above theories are not completely sui
table may be summarized as follows:
- The conventional coefficients cannot be applied when calculating the wave loads acting on the large bodies.
- Linear diffraction theory based on the well established sink
  source techniques is able to compute wave inertia loads act
  ing on the large bodies but do not take into account any non-
  linear effect which in the present case cannot be disregard
  ed.
- The presence of the large components of the structure induces on the surrounding hydrodynamic field a disturbance
  which in some cases is not negligible when evaluating the
  local wave loads on tubular elements or trusses of the connecting framed structure.

Because of the above aspects the development of a new computer procedure was needed. It basically consists of an integra
tion of several computer programs based both on linear diffraction theory analysis of the large bodies and on non-linear
analysis of the framed structures in order to be able to take
into account the different requirements for a reliable wave
force evaluation.

MAJOR NEEDS FOR AN INTEGRATED PROCEDURE

        Before discussing the integrated procedure in detail
and presenting its main results, it may be useful to recapitu
late some earlier accounts already published about the salient
aspects which call for it.
As for load evaluation on platform large cylinders and bases
two main aspects are to be taken into account:

- For such a variously shaped body there is possibly a mutual interaction between its basic components (two diverse co-lùmns placed on top of each other) which depends mainly on the typical body dimensions and cannot be disregarded when computing total wave loads. This effect becomes particular ly significant when the platform is in floating conditions, as demonstrated in Fig.2 in which the global horizontal for ces acting on a single base and cylinder are compared with those calculated by the superposition of the loads acting on separate columns. The dots on the same figure represent the inertia loads evaluated by the Morison   formula and the large body actual added mass coefficients. These are demonstrated to be rather different from the theoretical ones. In Fig.3 the trend of the real added mass coefficients calculated by means of the diffraction theory along the ver tical axis of the body is compared with the theoretical ones derived from the McCamy and Fuchs theory. From the said fi-gures it is intended that a suitable evaluation of the act-ing loads on a single large member can be achieved only by a three dimensional approach, both through a direct calcu-lation or by a correct computation of the relevant added mass coefficients to be adopted in the Morison   formula. In the latter case Fig.2 clearly demonstrates that the ap-proximation with respect to the correct value supplied by the diffraction computation is no greater than some 2 per-cent within the full wave period   range considered.

- The large body presence modifies the incident field and the relevant wave kinematics within an area close to it. For multibody structure like that considered here, the ex-tent of this area of influence is of great importance due to the possible interaction of the large bodies between each other. In this. case, in fact, an approach based on the calculation of the added mass coefficients for a single body is no long er applicable.

Figs 4 and 5 show the perturbation of the hydrodynamic field in terms of wave horizontal velocity at mean sea level for two cylinder and base bodies 7a apart. The wave heading is along the direction of the two bodies.
The former figure is related to the velocity components in li ne with the incident wave direction.
The perturbation effects are shown in terms of lines connect-ing the equal value points of the actual velocity component

FLOATING FIXED BODIES V$_L$/V$_0$
AT MEAN SEA LEVEL   K$_a$= 0.5

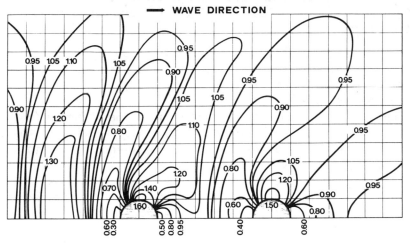

FIGURE No. 4

TWO FLOATING FIXED BODIES V$_T$/V$_0$
AT MEAN SEA LEVEL   K$_a$ = 0.5

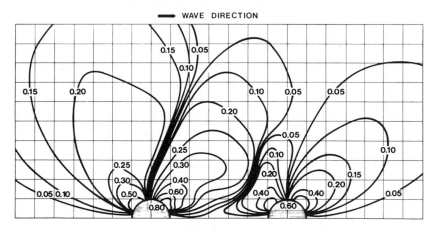

FIGURE No. 5

over the modulus of the incident wave horizontal velocity.
Perturbation ratios less than 5 percent are not indicated in
the figure.

From Fig.4 there is evidence of a strong perturbation in the
zones immediately downstream and upstream the two bodies; with
in these areas the modified hydrodynamic field is weaker than
the incident one.
Along the contour of the two bodies from the upstream to the
downstream zone as well as in the opposite direction , the va
lues of the amplitude ratios continuously increase up to a
maximum at the body middle part.
In the upstream zone of the first cylinder it is possible to
identify an alternative varying regime of the amplitude ratios
as function of the distance from the body along the incident
wave direction.
The area between the two bodies presents almost all the characteristics of the mutual interaction induced by the two cy
linders.
As for isolines pattern modifications it is for instance inte
resting to note how the outline of the 1.05 line derives from
the interaction of the lateral 1.05 line of the first cylinder and the upstream 1.05 line of the second one.

In Fig.5 the same equal-value line pattern is shown for the
transversal component of the total velocity; it should be emphasized that this component is originated by the interaction
between the fluid and the bodies and between the bodies themselves. Besides,the existence of inversion regions of this
component direction may be observed, in particular in the area
between the two bodies.

Figs 6 and 7 contain the same information relevant to a wave
heading perpendicular to the line connecting the bodies.
As a general comment on these figures, it can be noticed how
the line systems are more regular and smooth from a geometric
al point of view; this is because the mutual interaction effects are in the present case much weaker than in the previous
one.
Another peculiar characteristic of the same line pattern is a
larger extension of the perturbation area around the bodies.
It is mainly due to the significant influence on the phenomenon of the body interaxis distance.
Since the wave approaches considered are the more important
for a tripod-type structure, from Fig.4 and following the general hydrodynamic field pattern around the whole structure

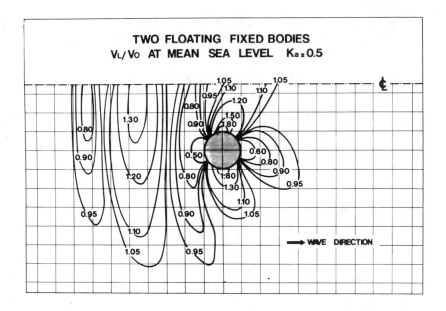

FIGURE No. 6

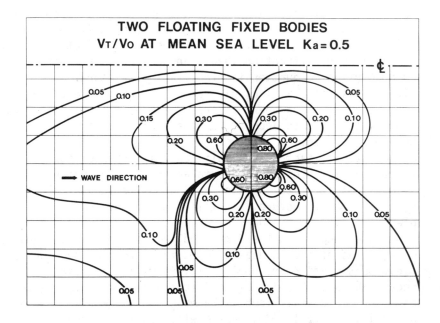

FIGURE No. 7

may be argued.
In particular the perturbation effect emphasized will lead to a diverse influence on the structure global load as function of different wave approaches.

As to the force calculation on the platform framed structure the following major effects are to be accounted for:

- As previously demonstrated the hydrodynamic field perturbation due to the large body presence determines a new wave kinematics; in some cases these modified pressure, velocity and acceleration fields are to be used in the Morison equation in order to accomplish a suitable wave loading analysis.

- Due to the significant non-linear effects consistent with a tubular framed structure piercing the free surface, a wave loading analysis based on a linear wave theory is possibly unsatisfactory. A non-linear wave theory (Stokes V° for instance) is indeed needed to fully describe the wave kinematics (modified or not) up to the time functional real elevat ion of the free surface.

THE NUMERICAL INTEGRATED PROCEDURE

On these bases a powerful procedure for a careful wave loading analysis would result from the integration of a correct evaluation of wave forces on large members actually based on the linear diffraction theory and a non-linear approach based on Morison's equation for the framed structure.
Fig.8 illustrates a block diagram of the procedure presented. Two different modus operandi are foreseen; they basically depend on the need to account for the field modification around the large bodies.
As a matter of fact if a significant disturbance caused by the big bodies presence leads to an interaction between these or modifies the total tension acting on the tubular elements of the framed structure, it will be mandatory to use the complete integrated procedure.
Otherwise, when both the large body mutual interaction and the differences of the tubular element total tension due to the field perturbation are negligible, it will be possible to disregard the wave kinematics modifications and to calculate both large and small members by means of the Morison equation utilizing the real added mass coefficients as calculated for the larger elements by the diffraction theory program.
These are cases in which the distance among the large struc-

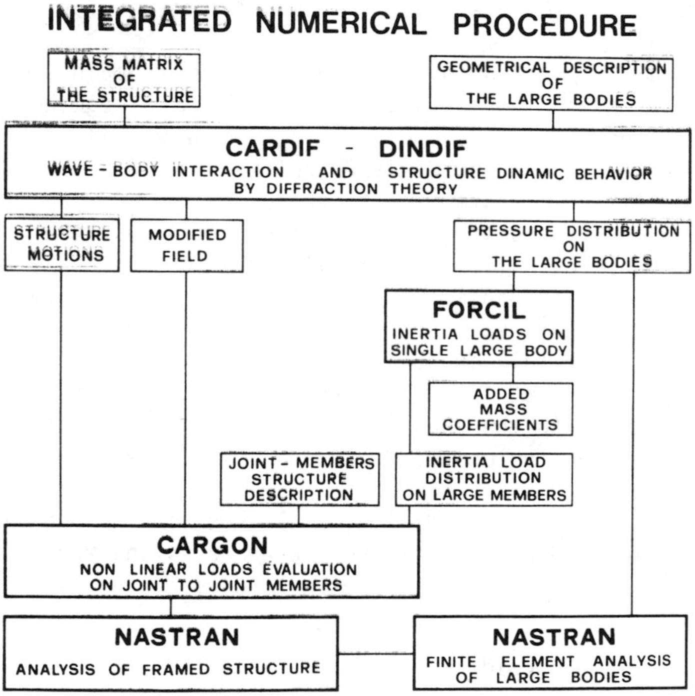
INTEGRATED NUMERICAL PROCEDURE
MASS MATRIX OF THE STRUCTURE
GEOMETRICAL DESCRIPTION OF THE LARGE BODIES
CARDIF - DINDIF
WAVE - BODY INTERACTION AND STRUCTURE DINAMIC BEHAVIOR BY DIFFRACTION THEORY
STRUCTURE MOTIONS
MODIFIED FIELD
PRESSURE DISTRIBUTION ON THE LARGE BODIES
FORCIL
INERTIA LOADS ON SINGLE LARGE BODY
ADDED MASS COEFFICIENTS
JOINT - MEMBERS STRUCTURE DESCRIPTION
INERTIA LOAD DISTRIBUTION ON LARGE MEMBERS
CARGON
NON LINEAR LOADS EVALUATION ON JOINT TO JOINT MEMBERS
NASTRAN
ANALYSIS OF FRAMED STRUCTURE
NASTRAN
FINITE ELEMENT ANALYSIS OF LARGE BODIES

FIGURE No. 8

ture components is greater than the extension of the mutual in
fluence zone and the total tension on tubular trusses is main
ly dictated by deck payload and by the environmental load on
the large bodies themselves, rather than by their local hydro
dynamic loads.
Then some of the lengthy and expensive computer calculations
required by the diffraction theory can be avoided. It is indeed sufficient to calculate for a single large body the added mass coefficient trend within the wave period range considered in order to compute the correct wave loads on the
whole structure for any design wave period.

INTEGRATED PROCEDURE APPLICATIONS

The above mentioned integrated procedure has been satisfactorily used to accomplish the wave loading analysis of
the production storage platform now under design for the
North Sea.
The overall dimensions of the platform and the main dimensions
of its bases and storage stabilizing cylinders together with
the floating and operational payloads on deck calls for a
wide utilization of the newly established procedure.
For the resting-on-bottom platform during the 100 years storm
survival conditions it has been demonstrated that the influen
ce of the hydrodynamic field modification on the total tension of the trusses adjacent to the large bodies can be disregarded and no interaction arises among the large bodies.
The reasons for this are basically:
- The major part of the total tension on framed structure ele
  ments is due to the deck operational payload and to the glo
  bal forces acting on the cylinders which affect the connect
  ing trusses.
- The wave kinematics modification is not very high because
  of the low diffraction of the longer waves and the high attenuation of the shorter waves according to the distance
  from the free surface.

From the above considerations it follows that an approach
through the simplified procedure by calculating the actual ad
ded mass coefficients for the large bodies and then applying
the Morison equation with a non-linear wave theory, is fully
justified.
Rather different is the case when the platform is in floating
condition during towing or installation. In this situation a
large part of the storage/stabilizing cylinders and bases is

exposed directly to the surface wave and their interaction ef
fect becomes important. In addition the whole triangular connecting structure is included in the much more perturbated
area.
As for the interaction among the cylinder-base bodies, the ty
pical headings shown in Fig.4 and following clearly demonstra
te that for a tripod-type structure like that presented here
this effect is actually important.
The following table presents the main results obtained for
the whole structure in towing conditions taking into account
the large body mutual interaction (Computation "A"); they are
compared with the corresponding total load produced by adding
the single body load according to the appropriate phases and
thus disregarding the above mentioned effect (Computation "B").
Three different wave approaches are considered and the acting
loads are expressed in a non-dimensional form for a ka value
of 0.5.

TABLE 1

	Computation "A"		Computation "B"	
	$F/\rho g \pi a^2 \frac{H}{2}$	Phase (°)	$F/\rho g \pi a^2 \frac{H}{2}$	Phase (°)
HEAD SEA in line component	1.39	150.7	1.82	- 17.3
FOLLOWING SEA in line component	1.81	-126.6	1.82	-137.2
BOW QUARTERING SEA in line component transverse compon.	1.07 0.52	95.6 140.5	0.94 --	- 77.2 --

The above results definitely confirm that the interaction bet
ween the large bodies is strongly effective on the structure
global loads. For instance a significant difference between
the head and the following sea computation of the entire struc
ture load may be observed. Furthermore it can be noticed that
the total loads for the following sea conditions are rather si
milar, while a different situation occurs for the head sea con
ditions.
These unlike results closely agree with the field modification
observed in Fig.4 and following.

Another important aspect to be emphasized is that, for the
bow quartering sea, relevant to a wave heading along the line
connecting the fore cylinder to an aft one, a transverse load
component arises. In fact, in this case, the interaction effect induces on each body a perturbation asymmetrical with re
spect to the wave approach direction.

As for the modifications induced on the tubular element total
tension two principal aspects are to be taken into account:
the value of the tension caused by the undisturbed wave kinematics and its variation due to the field perturbation. Then
the necessity for the designers to consider the modified field
effect is actually related to the significance of both the pre
vious aspects together.
In the present case, according to the high perturbation of the
hydrodynamic field presented,the calculations performed have
shown variations of the tubular element tension up to 100 per
cent with respect to that induced by the unmodified wave.
However, even in towing condition, the latter tension is demonstrated to be a minor part of the total which is mainly
dictated by the large body loads and by the deck payload during a possible safe damaged condition.
As a general conclusion, it may be pointed out that, in the
real case presented here, both the basic procedures to perform the wave loading analysis must be carried out. The simplified one for the resting-on-bottom platform according to
the possibility of disregarding any mutual influence effect.
The fully integrated one for the platform during towing as a
result of the necessity to take into account the large structure component mutual interaction rather than their influence
on the framed structure itself.

CONCLUSIONS

An integrated computer procedure for a reliable wave
loading analysis of a tripod-type gravity platform has been
dealt with.

The major features of such a platform type have been illustrat
ed together with its principal characteristics which required
the newly established procedure. Among these the presence of
three large storage/stabilizing cylinders and bases which mo-
dify the hydrodynamic field so as to induce interaction effects on each other as well as on their framed connecting
structure.

It has been demonstrated that, due to the triangular configuration of the platform presented, the interaction effects are basically a function of the wave heading considered.

Finally the salient results produced for a real case now under design for the North Sea have been illustrated: they actually demonstrate the necessity to take into account the mutual interaction between large bodies rather than the field's modifi cation influence on the small cylindrical member, and definitely prove the reliability of the especially developed computing methods.

NOMENCLATURE

a	typical body dimension
CM	added mass coefficients
F	amplitude of the force
g	gravitational constant
H	wave height
$k = \dfrac{2\pi}{\lambda}$	wave number
V_o	undisturbed wave velocity amplitude
V_L	diffracted wave velocity amplitude in line with wave approach
V_T	diffracted wave velocity amplitude transverse the wave approach
λ	wave length
ρ	fluid density

REFERENCES

1. Morison, J.R., O'Brien, M.P., Johnson, J.W. and Schaff,S.A. (1950) "The force exerted by surface waves on piles" Petro leum Trans., 189, TP2846, 149-154

2. McCamy, R.C. and Fuchs R.A. (1954) "Wave forces on a pile: A diffraction theory", Tech. Memo. 69, U.S.Army Corps of Engineers Beach Erosion Board, Washington, D.C.

3. Skjelbreia, L. and Hendricksen, J. (1960) "Fifth-order gra vity wave theory", Proc. Coastal Engr. Conf., p. 184-196

4. Wehausen, J.V. and Laitone, E.V. "Surface Waves", Encyclopedia of Physics, Vol.9, Springer-Verlag, Berlin, p.446-778

5. Monacella, V.J. (1966) "The disturbance due to a slender ship oscillating in waves in a fluid of finite depth",

Journal of Ship Research, 10, No.4, p. 242-252

6. Faltinsen, O.M. and Michelsen, F.C. (1974) "Motion of large structures in waves at zero Froude number", The Dynamics of Marine Vehicles and Structures in Waves, Paper no.11, The Institution of Mechanical Engineers

7. Garrison, C.J., Rao, V.S. and Snider,R.H. (1970) "Wave interaction with large submerged objects", Proc. Offshore Technology Conference, Paper OTC1278

8. Garrison, C.J., and Rao, V.S. (1971) "Interaction of waves with submerged objects", J. Waterways, Harbors & Coastal Engr. Div. Proc., ASCE 97, p. 259-277, No. WW2

9. Garrison, C.J. (Jan.1974) "Hydrodynamics of large objects in the sea - Part I: Hydrodynamic analysis", Journal of Hydronautics, AIAA, Vol.8, No.1, p. 5-12

10. Garret, C.J.R. "Wave forces on a circular dock", Journal of Fluid Mechanics, Vol.46, Pt.1, p. 129-139

11. Løken, A.E. and Olsen, O.A. (1976) "Diffraction theory and statistical methods to predict wave induced motions and loads for large structures", Paper OTC no.2502

12. Raman, H. and Venkalanarasaiah, P. (1976) "Forces due to nonlinear waves on vertical cylinders", Journal of the Waterways, Harbors and Coastal Engineering Division, Proc. ASCE, Vol. 102, No.WW3

13. Garrison, C.J. (1976) "Consistent second-order diffraction theory", presented at the Fifteenth Coastal Engineering Conference, Honolulu, Hawaii

14. Lee, C.M. (1968) "The second-order theory of heaving cylinders in a free surface", Journal of Ship Research, 313-327

15. Potash, R.L. (1970) "Second-order theory of oscillatory cylinders", Dissertation, University of California, Berkeley Ca. 157

16. Apelt, C.J. and Macknight, A. (1976) "Wave action on large offshore structures", Proceedings Fifteenth Coastal Engineering Conference, Honolulu, Hawaii

17. Garrison, C.J., Field, J.B. and May, M.D. (1976) "Drag and inertia coefficients in oscillatory flow about cylinders", in Press, Journal of Waterways, Port and Coastal and Ocean Division, ASCE, 103, WW2

18. Hess, J.L. and Smith, O.M.A. (1962) "Calculation of non-lifting potential flow about arbitrary three-dimensional bodies", Rept. No.E.S.40622 (Douglas Aircraft Division, Long Beach, Ca.) also Journal of Ship Research, 1964, 8

19. Garrison, C.J., Tørum, A., Iversen, C., Leivseth, S. and Ebbesmeyer, C.C. (1974) "Wave forces on large volume structures - a comparison between theory and model tests", Paper OTC 2137, Offshore Technology Conference, Houston, Texas

20. Berta, M., Blandino, A. and Paruzzolo, A. (1979) "An integrated procedure to compute wave loads on hybrid gravity platforms", Conference on 'Environmental Forces on Engineering Structures', London July 2-6

One of the Loango platforms
during towing

ANALYSIS OF AN OFFSHORE GRAVITY PLATFORM USING BOUNDARY
ELEMENTS

C. Brebbia & R. Nakaguma

Southampton University

1.   INTRODUCTION

In the present paper a concrete offshore gravity platform of
the type used in the UBARANA field (Rio Grande do Norte,
Brazil) is analysed using boundary elements. This recently
developed method has some of the advantages of finite elements
as well as the high accuracy associated with integral equation
solutions. The method is based on the division of the external
surface of a body into a series of elements, which can be of
different types. Unknowns are defined at nodes taken over the
elements and the relationship between them is obtained using a
series of Green's type influence functions. These functions
are well suited for problems having boundaries at infinity,
such as soil problems. Because of this, boundary elements
were chosen to model the platform-soil interaction problem,
with special reference to the interface between structure and
soil where the state of stress is critical. The results
presented in this paper confirm the validity of using boundary
elements for these problems and the economy of the solution.
Had the same problem been analysed using finite elements,
a large number of three dimensional elements would have been
required to model the soil.

2.   GOVERNING EQUATIONS

Consider a domain Ω, bounded by an external boundary Γ. The
boundary Γ can be divided into 2 regions; Γ_1 where displacements are prescribed and Γ_2 where forces are prescribed. ($\Gamma =
\Gamma_1 + \Gamma_2$). Let us define two systems,

    System 1 is defined by the actual displacements u_k and
stress components σ_{ij} with surface forces or tractions
$p_k = n_j \sigma_j k$ (n_j is the direction cosines of the normal with
respect to x_j).

System 2 corresponds to the u_k^*, σ_{ij}^*, and $p_k^* = n_j \sigma_{jk}^*$ components of the fundamental solution (in this case Kelvin or Mindlin solutions) such that

$$\sigma_{jk,j}^* + \Delta_\ell^i = 0$$

where Δ_ℓ^i is the Dirac delta function and it represents a unit point load at 'i' in the 'ℓ' direction.

Following reference [1] we obtain for each 'ℓ' direction the following equation,

$$u_\ell^i + \int_{\Gamma_1} \bar{u}_k p_k^* \, d\Gamma + \int_{\Gamma_2} u_k p_k^* \, d\Gamma =$$

$$= \int_\Omega b_k \, u_k^* \, d\Omega + \int_{\Gamma_1} P_k \, u_k^* \, d\Gamma + \int_{\Gamma_2} \bar{P}_k \, u_k^* \, d\Gamma \tag{1}$$

u_ℓ^i represents the displacement at 'i' in the 'ℓ' direction, and b_k are the body force components.

In general we can write for the point 'i' before any boundary conditions are imposed,

$$u_\ell^i + \int_\Gamma u_k \, P_k^* \, d\Gamma = \int_\Gamma P_k \, u_k^* \, d\Gamma + \int_\Omega b_k \, u_k^* \, d\Omega \tag{2}$$

where $\Gamma = \Gamma_1 + \Gamma_2$.

Note that u_k^* and p_k^* are the fundamental solutions, i.e. the displacements and tractions due to a unit concentrated load at the point 'i' in the 'ℓ' direction. If we consider unit forces acting in the three directions, equation (2) can be written as,

$$u_\ell^i + \int_\Gamma u_k \, P_{\ell k}^* \, d\Gamma = \int_\Gamma P_k \, u_{\ell k}^* \, d\Gamma + \int_\Omega b_k \, u_{\ell k}^* \, d\Omega \tag{3}$$

where $p_{\ell k}^*$ and $u_{\ell k}^*$ represent the tractions and displacements in the k direction due to unit forces acting in the ℓ direction. Equation (3) is valid for the particular point 'i' where these forces are applied.

Fundamental Solutions

Two fundamental solutions for linearly elastic three dimensional isotropic solids are used in this paper, the first is the

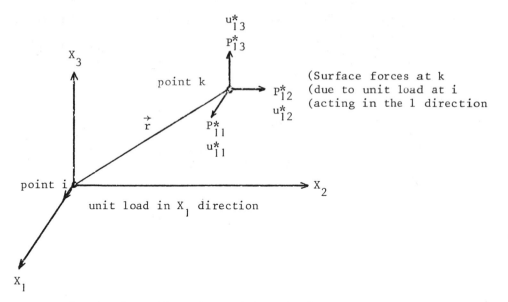

Fig. 1   Three dimension Kelvin Solution

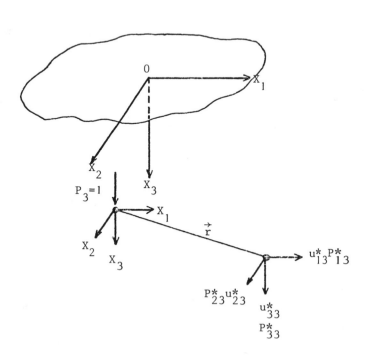

Fig. 2   Three dimensional Mindlin Solution

Kelvin solution [2] and the second a special case of it called the Mindlin solution [3].

The Kelvin solution represents the effect of a point load applied at any point of an infinite space on other points in the same space. It is represented in figure 1. The resultant $u^*_{\ell k}$ and $p^*_{\ell k}$ values are given by well known formulae, see for example reference [1].

The Mindlin solution instead (figure 2) represents the same effects but for a semi-infinite space. It can be obtained from Kelvin solution but applying images. Its mathematical expression is somewhat more complex but equally well defined, (see reference [3]).

Boundary Point

When equation (3) is specialised for the boundary a singularity will occur in the integrals of the type $\int_{\Gamma_2} u_k \, p^*_{\ell k} \, d\Gamma$ or $\int_{\Gamma_1} u_k \, p^*_{\ell k} \, d\Gamma$. These singularities can be studied and integrated analytically and they produce an expression of the type,

$$c^i_{\ell k} \, u^i_k + \int_{\Gamma} u_k \, p^*_{\ell k} \, d\Gamma = \int_{\Gamma} p_k \, u^*_{\ell k} \, d\Gamma + \int_{\Omega} b_k \, u^*_{\ell k} \, d\Omega \qquad (4)$$

The coefficient c^i is $\frac{1}{2}$ for smooth boundaries and Kelvin solution and equal to 1 for the Mindlin solution.

Matrix Formulation

It is now more convenient to work with matrices than to carry on with indicial notation. We can define the following

$$\underset{\sim}{u}^i = \begin{Bmatrix} u_1 \\ u_2 \\ u_3 \end{Bmatrix} \quad : \text{displacement vector at point 'i' with components } x_1 \; x_2 \; x_3 \text{ directions}$$

$\underset{\sim}{u}$ = displacement vector at any point on boundary Γ.

$$\underset{\sim}{p} = \begin{Bmatrix} p_1 \\ p_2 \\ p_3 \end{Bmatrix} \quad : \text{tractions at any point on boundary } \Gamma. \qquad (5)$$

$$\underset{\sim}{b} = \begin{Bmatrix} b_1 \\ b_2 \\ b_3 \end{Bmatrix} = \text{body forces at any point on domain } \Omega$$

$$\underset{\sim}{p^*} = \begin{bmatrix} p^*_{11} & p^*_{12} & p^*_{13} \\ p^*_{21} & p^*_{22} & p^*_{23} \\ p^*_{31} & p^*_{32} & p^*_{33} \end{bmatrix} \quad : \text{matrix whose coefficients, } p^*_{\ell k} \text{ are the forces in k direction due to a unit force at 'i' acting in the 'ℓ' direction}$$

$$\underset{\sim}{u^*} = \begin{bmatrix} u^*_{11} & u^*_{12} & u^*_{13} \\ u^*_{21} & u^*_{22} & u^*_{23} \\ u^*_{31} & u^*_{32} & u^*_{33} \end{bmatrix} \quad : \text{matrix whose coefficients } u^*_{\ell k} \text{ are the displacements in the 'k' direction due to a unit force at 'i' acting in the 'ℓ' direction.}$$

Equation (4) can now be expressed in matrix form as follows,

$$\underset{\sim}{c}^i \underset{\sim}{u}^i + \int_{\Gamma} \underset{\sim}{p^*} \underset{\sim}{u} \, d\Gamma = \int_{\Gamma} \underset{\sim}{u^*} \underset{\sim}{p} \, d\Gamma + \int_{\Omega} \underset{\sim}{u^*} \underset{\sim}{b} \, d\Omega \qquad (6)$$

We can assume that the boundary Γ is divided into elements and that the u and p functions can be approximated on each element using the following interpolation functions,

$$\underset{\sim}{u} = \underset{\sim}{\phi}^T \underset{\sim}{u}^n = \begin{bmatrix} \underset{\sim}{\phi}^T & \cdot & \cdot \\ \cdot & \underset{\sim}{\phi}^T & \cdot \\ \cdot & \cdot & \underset{\sim}{\phi}^T \end{bmatrix} \underset{\sim}{u}^n$$

$$\underset{\sim}{p} = \underset{\sim}{\psi}^T \underset{\sim}{p}^n = \begin{bmatrix} \underset{\sim}{\psi}^T & \cdot & \cdot \\ \cdot & \underset{\sim}{\psi}^T & \cdot \\ \cdot & \cdot & \underset{\sim}{\psi}^T \end{bmatrix} \underset{\sim}{p}^n \qquad (7)$$

The interpolation functions can be considered as the standard two dimensional finite element type functions. (See reference [1]). u^n and p^n are the nodal displacements and tractions.

We can now substitute those functions into (6) to obtain for a particular nodal point,

$$c^i \, \underset{\sim}{u}^i + \sum_{j=1}^{n} \left\{ \int_{\Gamma_j} \underset{\sim}{p}^* \, \underset{\sim}{\phi}^T \, d\Gamma \right\} \underset{\sim}{u}^n = \sum_{n=1}^{n} \left\{ \int_{\Gamma_j} \underset{\sim}{u}^* \, \underset{\sim}{\psi}^T \, d\Gamma \right\} \underset{\sim}{p}^n$$

$$+ \sum_{s=1}^{m} \left\{ \int_{\Omega_s} \underset{\sim}{u}^* \, \underset{\sim}{b} \, d\Omega \right\} \tag{8}$$

$\sum$ j=1 to n indicates summation over the n elements of the surface

Γ_j is the surface of 'j' element.

Note that we have also considered that the volume was divided into m internal cells or elements over which integrals
corresponding to the body forces have to be computed. These
are not finite elements but simply regions where the integration (usually numerical) is carried out. Once this is done
the problem is reduced to a boundary problem.

The integrals are generally solved numerically and the
functions ϕ and ψ expressed in some homogeneous system of
coordinates such as the ξ_i system of figure 3. The coordinates
need to be transformed from the ξ_i system to the global x_i
system.

Equation (8) corresponds to a particular node 'i'. The
terms in p* and u* relate the 'i' node with the element 'j'
over which the integral is carried out. We call these inte-
grals $\hat{\underset{\sim}{H}}_{ij}$ and $\underset{\sim}{G}_{ij}$. Hence one has,

$$c^i \, \underset{\sim}{u}^i + \sum_{j=1}^{n} \hat{\underset{\sim}{H}}_{ij} \, \underset{\sim}{u}_j = \sum_{j=1}^{n} \underset{\sim}{G}_{ij} \, \underset{\sim}{p}_j + \underset{\sim}{b}^i \tag{9}$$

This equation relates the value of u at node 'i' with the
values of $\underset{\sim}{u}$'s and $\underset{\sim}{p}$'s at all the nodes on theboundary, including 'i'.

One can write equation (9) for each 'i' node obtaining
$3 \times n$ equations where n is the total number of nodes. Let us
now call

$$\begin{aligned}
\underset{\sim}{H}_{ij} &= \hat{\underset{\sim}{H}}_{ij} && \text{when } i \neq j \\
\underset{\sim}{H}_{ij} &= \hat{\underset{\sim}{H}}_{ij} + c^i && \text{when } i = j
\end{aligned} \tag{10}$$

In general we can write for the node 'i'

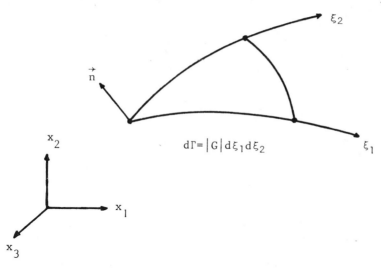

Fig. 3 Coordinate system for a boundary element

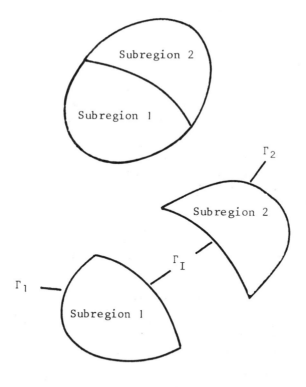

Fig. 4   Two Subregion Body

$$\sum_{j=1}^{n} \underset{\sim}{H}_{ij} \underset{\sim}{u}_j = \sum_{j=1}^{n} \underset{\sim}{G}_{ij} \underset{\sim}{P}_j + \underset{\sim}{b}^i \qquad (11)$$

System of equations

Numerical evaluation of the governing equations will produce a system of equations for the node under consideration. Repeating for all the nodes gives a final system of equations that can be written as,

$$\underset{\sim}{H}\,\underset{\sim}{U} = \underset{\sim}{G}\,\underset{\sim}{P} + \underset{\sim}{B} \qquad (12)$$

where $\underset{\sim}{U}$ are the displacements and $\underset{\sim}{P}$ the values that the distributed tractions take at all the boundary nodes. $\underset{\sim}{B}$ contains the body forces.

The diagonal coefficients in the H matrix can be obtained by applying rigid body conditions. ~ Note that n_1 values of displacements and n_2 values of tractions are known, hence one has a set of n unknowns in the above equation. Reordering the equations i.e. with the unknowns on the left hand side vector $\underset{\sim}{X}$, we obtain,

$$\underset{\sim}{A}\,\underset{\sim}{X} = \underset{\sim}{F} + \underset{\sim}{B} \qquad (13)$$

where $\underset{\sim}{X}$ contains the unknown displacements and tractions.

Once the boundary values are known we can compute the internal values of displacements and stresses.

Non-homogeneous body

If the body is non-homogeneous one can divide it into a series of subregions with different properties and then joint these subregions together by applying continuities of tractions, equilibrium, and equalizing the displacements at the interfaces.

Consider for simplicity a body consisting of only two regions as shown in figure 4. The interface surface will be called Γ_I and one can define on subregion 1 the following functions

$\underset{\sim}{P}^1$: Tractions on external surface of region 1.

$\underset{\sim}{P}^1_I$: Tractions on interface Γ_I (considering it belongs to region 1)

$\underset{\sim}{U}^1$: Displacements on external surface of region 1.

$\underset{\sim}{U}^1_I$: Displacements on interface Γ_I (considering it belongs to region 1)

Similarly for Part 2 we have,

P^2 : Tractions on external surface of region 2.

P^2_I : Tractions on interface Γ_I (considering it belongs to region 2).

U^2 : Displacements on external surface of region 2.

U^2_I : Displacements on interface Γ_I (considering that it belongs to region 2).

The equation corresponding to region 1 can be written (without body forces for simplicity),

$$
\begin{bmatrix} G^1 & G^1_I \end{bmatrix}
\begin{Bmatrix} P^1 \\ P^1_I \end{Bmatrix}
=
\begin{bmatrix} H^1 & H^1_I \end{bmatrix}
\begin{Bmatrix} U^1 \\ U^1_I \end{Bmatrix}
\tag{14}
$$

and similarly for region 2, i.e.

$$
\begin{bmatrix} G^2 & G^2_I \end{bmatrix}
\begin{Bmatrix} P^2 \\ P^2_I \end{Bmatrix}
=
\begin{bmatrix} H^2 & H^2_I \end{bmatrix}
\begin{Bmatrix} U^2 \\ U^2_I \end{Bmatrix}
\tag{15}
$$

Let P_I and U_I indicate the tractions and displacements at the interface Γ_I, where the following conditions apply,

i) Compatibility $\qquad U^1_I = U^2_I = U_I$

ii) Equilibrium $\qquad P^1_I = -P^2_I = P_I$ $\qquad\qquad$ (16)

Hence equations (14) and (15) can be written in function of U_I and P_I as follows,

$$
\begin{bmatrix}
G^1 & G^1_I & -H^1_I & 0 \\
0 & -G^2_I & -H^2_I & G^2
\end{bmatrix}
\begin{Bmatrix} P^1 \\ P_I \\ U_I \\ P^2 \end{Bmatrix}
=
\begin{bmatrix}
H^1 & 0 \\
0 & H^2
\end{bmatrix}
\begin{Bmatrix} U^1 \\ U^2 \end{Bmatrix}
\tag{17}
$$

$$
\underbrace{}_{\substack{\text{Sub-}\\\text{region}\\1}} \quad \underbrace{}_{\substack{\text{inter-}\\\text{face}}} \quad \underbrace{}_{\substack{\text{Sub-}\\\text{region}\\2}}
$$

This system needs to be reordered to take into consideration the boundary conditions.

For the case of the body divided into 2 subregions the final system matrix A, is shown below.

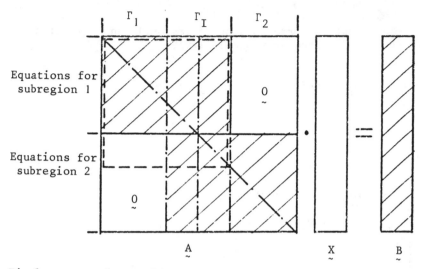

Final system of equations considering two subregions

where $\underset{\sim}{X}$ contains the unknown displacements or tractions on Γ_1 and Γ_2 and the unknown displacements and tractions on the interface Γ_I. If the subregion 2 is a semi-infinite space, like a foundation, and the Mindlin fundamental solution is being used for this subregion, the part of the matrix $\underset{\sim}{A}$ correspondent to the unknowns Γ_2 does not exist because there are no elements on the ground surface apart from those at the interface. Thus, the size of the matrix $\underset{\sim}{A}$ is reduced as shown by the dotted lines.

3. THE OFFSHORE PLATFORM

The method was applied to study the response of a concrete gravity platform in shallow waters of the type used in the UBARANA field, Brazil due to wave forces acting.

The structure has the shape of a parallelepiped 46m × 53m

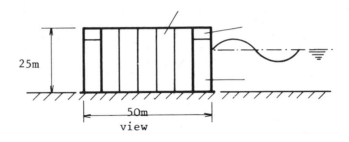

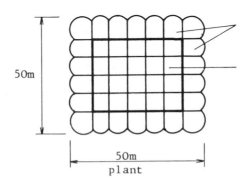

25m

50m
view

50m

50m
plant

Fig. 5 Dimensions of the Platform

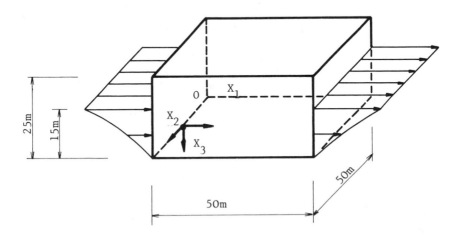

Fig. 6 Geometry and Loads of the Equivalent
Structure

in plant, with a height of 27.50m (see figure 5). It is essentially composed of a foundation slab of 0.60m thickness in the
central part and 0.80m towards the outside, and a series of
vertical walls, plus a 0.25m thick slab at the top. Hence the
platform is basically a box type structure. The vertical walls
(thickness of inside walls: 0.27m, outer walls: 0.40m) divide
the volume into a series of 42 different cells. The 20 central
cells are used for oil storage and the 22 on the outside area
are divided in two parts: their bottom part is used as ballast
tanks and the top to house equipment.

The following constants were used to define the properties
of soil and concrete

$$E_{concrete}: 250000*10^5 \text{ N/m}^2 \qquad E_{soil}: 15000*10^5 \text{ N/m}^2$$

$$\nu_{concrete}: 0.133 \qquad \nu_{soil}: 0.4$$

The platform was modelled using boundary elements (see
figure 6) as a 50m × 50m × 25m solid, with an equivalent modulus
of elasticity. The equivalence was found by considering the
shear and bending behaviour of the box type structure. It gave
an average modulus of elasticity of $30000.*10^5$ N/m^2.

The vertical loads due to the selfweight of the platform
plus the equipment and ballast was 600000 KN. This load was
applied as a body force of 9600 N/m^3 acting in the vertical
direction.

The design wave acting on the structure has a height of
H = 11m and a period of T = 10.4s. This gives a wave length
of 114m (wave number K = 0.055). The dimensions of the structure will then appreciably change the incident wave field, producing wave diffraction and a different force regime than the
one acting on slender members. These forces can be computed
by considering an equivalent cylinder with the same area as
the prismatic structure which gives a radius R = $\sqrt{\text{Area}}/2\pi$ = 56m
and applying diffraction theory. The wave forces produce a
horizontal component H and a moment M (figure 6). The forces
F^D can be given in terms of the Morinson's forces F^M (i.e.,
the forces which would occur if the dimensions of the structure
did not alter the waves) as

$$F^D = \frac{2}{K^2 R^2 \pi} \frac{1}{H_1^{(2)'}(KR)} F^M$$

where $H_1^{(2)'}$ is the derivative of a Hankel function of the
second type and order 1.

In our case

$$F^D = 0.41 \ F^M$$

We can now compute the horizontal component

$$H_D = \int_o^d F^D \, dZ \simeq 74100 \text{ KN}$$

$$M^D = \int M^D \, Z \, dZ \simeq 741000 \text{ KN} \times \text{m}$$

Two fundamental solutions were used to analyse the problem, the Kelvin solution for the gravity platform and the one due to Mindlin for the soil. Using the latter the soil is modelled as a semi-infinite domain which gives more accurate results than those obtained using solutions such as finite elements. Furthermore the Mindlin solution only requires discretizing the interface between structure and foundation, in addition to the external surface of the structure (see figures 7 and 8). For the present analysis 160 constant elements (32 of them on the interface) were used.

Results for horizontal and vertical displacements at the interface due to the wave loading only are shown in figures 9 and 11 - Figures 10 and 12 present the shearing and normal stresses also at the interface due to the wave loading. Notice that the average value of shearing stresses obtained by dividing the total horizontal force H by the foundation area is 0.35×10^5 N/m^2 which agrees well with the results shown in figure 10.

The results obtained by considering the weight of the platform only are shown in figures 13 to 15 (the horizontal displacements were not plotted as they are very small).

Equilibrium in the three directions was checked and the relative percentual errors between applied and calculated loads was less than 1.5%. The problem was also run with a finer mesh of 220 elements and practically the same results were obtained.

REFERENCES

1. Brebbia, C.A. "The Boundary Element Method for Engineers". Pentech Press, London, Halsted Press, New York, 1978.

2. Love, A.E. "A Treatise on the Mathematical Theory of Elasticity", Dover, 1944.

3. Mindlin, R.D. "Force at a point in the Interior of a Semi-Infinite Solid", J. Physics, Vol.7, May 1936.

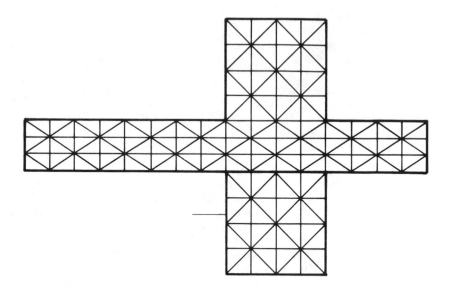

Fig. 7 Developed Surface of the Structure

Subregion 1

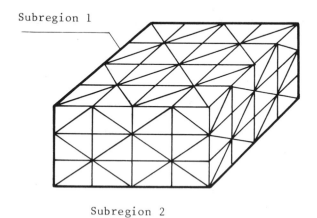

Subregion 2

Fig. 8 Discretization of the Surface
of the Structure

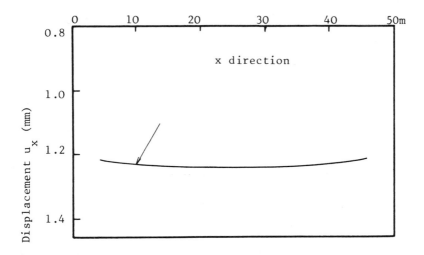

Fig. 9 Displacements of the interface structure-soil
in the x direction (wave loads)

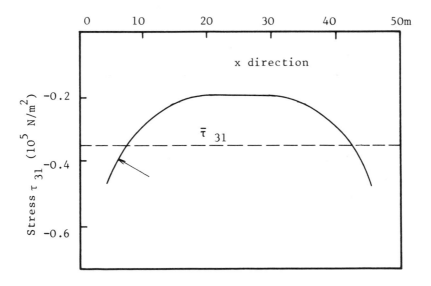

Fig. 10 Shearing stresses at the interface
structure -soil (wave loads)

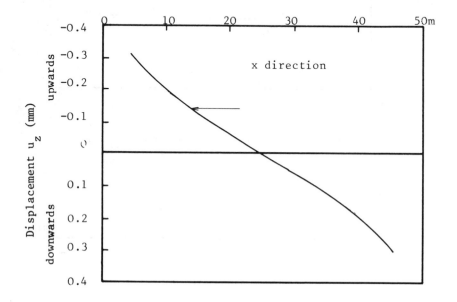

Fig. 11   Displacements of the interface structure-soil
in the Z direction (wave loads)

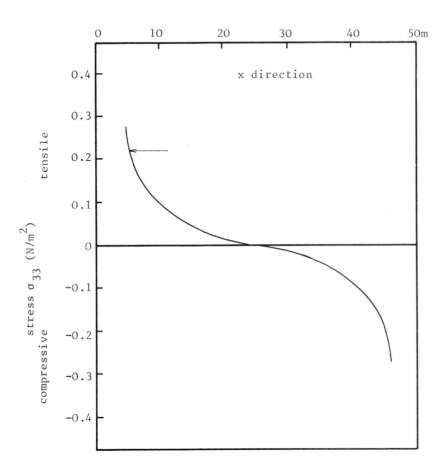

Fig. 12 Normal stresses at the interface structure-
soil (wave loads)

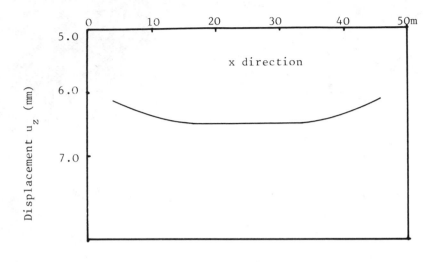

Fig. 13   Displacement of the interface structure –soil
          in the x direction (vertical loads: 9600 N/m^3)

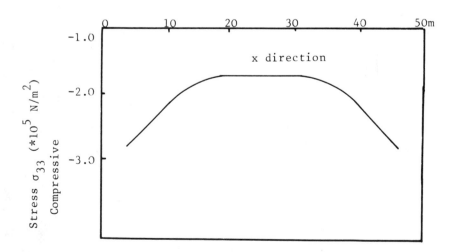

Fig. 14   Normal stresses at the interface structure-soil
          (vertical loads: 9600 N/m^3)

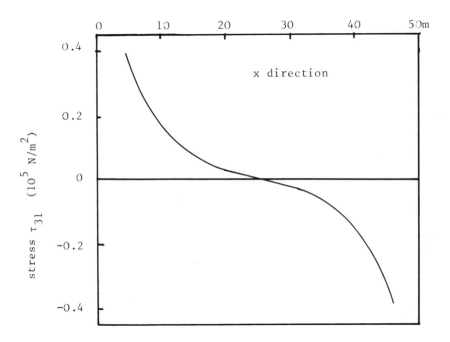

Fig. 15 Shearing stresses at the interface structure-
soil (vertical loads: 9600 N/m^3)

NONLINEAR FINITE ELEMENT ANALYSIS OF PLANE REINFORCED
CONCRETE STRUCTURES WITH SPECIAL ATTENTION TO SHEAR FAILURE

Svein I. Sørensen

Division of Concrete Structures, The University of Trondheim
The Norwegian Institute of Technology, Norway

INTRODUCTION

A commonly used approach in analytical models for determination of the capacity of a reinforced concrete member
subjected to a combination of bending moment and shear and
axial forces, is to consider bending and shear actions
separately. The influence of the axial force may be accounted for in several ways according to different design code
regulations.

The present paper describes a finite element approach for
analysis of plane reinforced concrete members. Effects of
inelastic behaviour and cracking of concrete, and yielding
and hardening of reinforcement steel are included. The
capabilities of a computer program which is developed are
demonstrated by several comparisons to experimental results.

The finite element approach is used to obtain information
about the deformations in critical sections of members
which fail in a shear type failure mode. These results are
used to explain some assumptions in an analytical model
proposed by Lenschow and Reinertsen (1979). This analytical
model gives the capacity of a reinforced concrete member
when the effects of bending moment and shear and axial force
are considered at the same time.

MATHEMATICAL MODELS AND NUMERICAL APPROXIMATIONS

Modelling of behaviour and strength of materials

Concrete   The stress-strain behaviour in compression is
approximated by an elastic-strain hardening plastic approach,
se Fig. 1a. The stress-strain response is assumed to be
linearly elastic below the stability limit, while linear
strain-hardening is assumed after the initial yielding.

Since only plane states of stress are considered, the biaxial
compressive strength is approximated by a failure envelope
according to von Mises, see Fig. 1b. This is a very simple
approach, and no increase of strength for equal compression
in two directions is achieved. Compression failure
(crushing) is assumed to occur when the compressive strength,
corresponding to an ultimate uniaxial compressive strain
value.

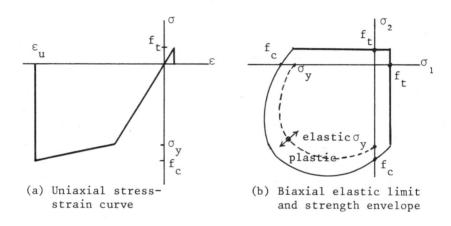

(a) Uniaxial stress-   (b) Biaxial elastic limit
    strain curve   and strength envelope

Fig. 1 Assumed concrete behaviour in one-
         and two-dimensional states of stress

The tension cracking process in this model is governed by
the state of stress. Cracks are assumed to open perpendicular to the highest principal tensile stress direction when
the failure envelope in Fig. 1b is reached. The material
is taken to behave linearly in tension up to the onset of
cracking. At this point there are of course no shear stresses to be transferred across the crack. By further straining
however, shear strains may occur parallel to the crack.
This raises the question of whether aggregate interlocking
is capable of transferring shear stress over the crack.
Shear transfer is taken into account by assuming that a
"cracked" shear modulus is retained through a factor
$0 \leq \alpha \leq 1$ times the elastic shear modulus. This factor   is
made dependent upon average crack widths computed in the
program, see Fig. 2. Secondary cracks are allowed to form
when the other principal stress component exceeds the
failure criterion.

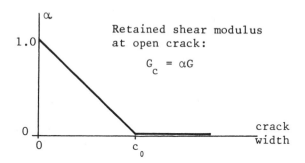

Fig. 2   Shear retention factor

Reinforcement   The behaviour of reinforcement steel is
approximated by a uniaxial stress-strain relationship. A
plasticity formulation is used, assuming linear, isotropic
strain hardening after initial yielding. The stress-strain
curve is assumed to be the same in tension and compression.

Finite element approximations

The concrete is modelled by quadrilateral, isoparametric
finite elements, based on the assumption of linear interpolation functions in terms of displacements. This quadrilateral has four corner nodes with two translational degrees
of freedom each. It is well known that this element is far
too stiff in in-plane bending modes due to spurious shear
strains. It was suggested by Doherty et al. (1969) that the
in-plane bending performance can be improved by selective
integration: the strain energy associated with stretching
is computed using regular 2x2 Gaussian integration, whereas
the shear strain energy is obtained from a one point integration using the centroid. There are no spurious shear
strains at the centroid. The same concept is used here for
the nonlinear concrete element, the shear strain is sampled
at the centroid, but used in accumulation of strain history
at the four Gaussian points.

The reinforcement bars are modelled by simple two-noded bar
elements with linear displacement interpolation. Compatibility between concrete and reinforcement bars is assured
at common nodal points.

Numerical solution technique

The elasto-plastic material model and the finite element discretization are used with the principle of virtual work in
order to establish the total equilibrium equations and the
incremental equilibrium equations. The solution of these
nonlinear equations is based on a standard Euler-Cauchy in-
crementation combined with Newton-Raphson iteration. After
a load increment has been applied, the internal forces are
not in equilibrium with the external applied loads, due to
cracking or crushing of concrete or yielding of concrete or
steel. Unbalanced forces are computed, and applied as a
load correction, and this process is repeated iteratively.
The incremental (tangential) stiffness matrix serves as
gradient for the iteration process, and considerable saving
is obtained by keeping the same gradient for several iteration cycles ("Quasi-Newton"). The iteration is terminated
when the displacement corrections become sufficiently small,
measured in terms of a modified displacement norm, see
Bergan and Clough (1972), or when a prescribed minimum
number of cycles has been reached.

APPLICATIONS

Behaviour and strength of member with diagonal tension failure

A beam tested by Bresler and Scordelis (1964) is analyzed
by the computer program. Figure 3a, b shows the test specimen and the finite element idealization. With reference to
Fig. 1, the concrete stress-strain curve is defined by
$\sigma_y = 20.5$ N/mm^2, $f_c = 24.15$ N/mm^2, $f_t = 3.6$ N/mm^2,
$E_c = 2.3 \cdot 10^4$ N/mm^2 and $\varepsilon_u = 0.0035$. The crack width where
the shear stiffness parallel to an open crack is lost
(C_0 of Fig. 2) is assumed to be 0.3 mm. Reinforcement steel
is modelled with $E_s = 1.914 \cdot 10^5$ N/mm^2 and yield stress
$\sigma_{ys} = 1000$ N/mm^2.

The test specimen failed by a rapid diagonal tension failure
mechanism, as could be expected for the actual percentage
of reinforcement and shear span, $a/d = 4$. The observed
ultimate load was 258.1 kN. Figure 4a shows experimental
and calculated midspan load-deflection curves. The computed ultimate load is approximately 92 percent of the
experimental value.
Crack patterns just prior to failure load are shown in
Fig. 4.b.

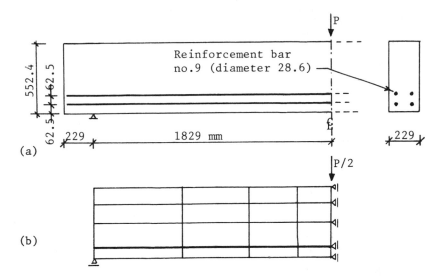

(a)

(b)

Fig. 3   Beam tested by Bresler and Scordelis

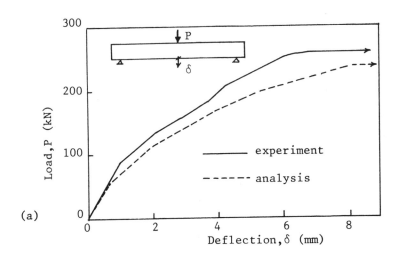

(a)

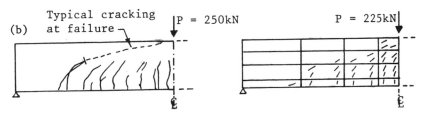

(b)

Fig. 4   Midspan load-deflection curves and crack
patterns of Bresler-Scordelis beam

Members with different modes of failure

A comprehensive experimental investigation on shear strength
of reinforced concrete members was carried out by Morrow and
Viest (1957). A series of 38 beams was tested. The beams
had a reinforced column stub at midspan, and were simply
supported and loaded at midspan through the top of the column
stub. Nine different shear spans in the range $1.0 \leq a/d \leq 7.8$
were considered, in order to study different modes of failure.

It was observed that the distribution of axial normal strain
across the beam depth was nonlinear in the case of shear
failure (shear compression or diagonal tension). A similar
strain distribution can be found from the computed results
for the Bresler-Scordelis beam, see Fig. 5. The reinforcement strain is considerably smaller than it could be expected
from a linear strain distribution (dashed line). The somewhat
irregular shape between the neutral axis and the reinforcement layer is due to the strain is taken as a mean value for
one element of length 250 mm, hence, crack widths are included
in the strains.

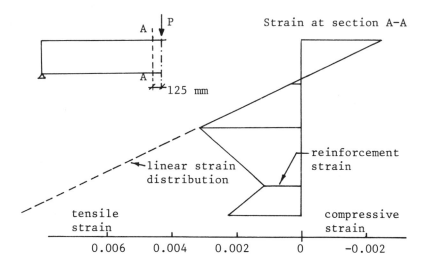

Fig. 5   Strain distribution in critical
section of Bresler-Scordelis beam

In order to study the effect of different shear spans, a
selection of five beams from Morrow and Viest (1957) are
analyzed by the computer program; these are the beams termed
B21B4, B40B4, B56B4, B84B4 and B113B4R, with a = 533, 1016,
1422, 2134 and 2870 mm, respectively. Figure 6 shows the
finite element idealization of beam B21B4; the same mesh
fineness is used for the other beams.

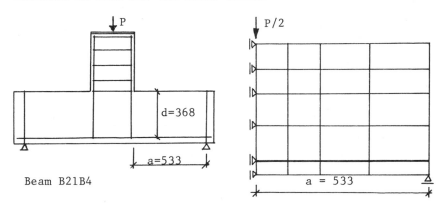

Beam B21B4

Fig. 6 Finite element idealization of
Morrow-Viest beams

With reference to Fig. 1, Table 1 shows the input values
that are used to describe the stress-strain curves for the
materials.

Specimen	Concrete					Steel	
	f_c	σ_y	E_c	ε_u	f_t	f_y	E_s
B21B4	27.1	20.3	24600	.0035	4.0	423	$2 \cdot 10^5$
B40B4	34.8	26.1	27900	.0035	4.5	378	$2 \cdot 10^5$
B56B4	27.1	20.3	24600	.0035	4.0	423	$2 \cdot 10^5$
B84B4	27.1	20.3	24600	.0035	4.0	465	$2 \cdot 10^5$
B113B4R	28.7	21.5	25400	.0100	4.0	345	$2 \cdot 10^5$

Stresses and moduli in N/mm^2

Table 1 Material parameters for concrete and
steel, Morrow-Viest beams

Computed midspan load-deflection curves are shown in Fig. 7.
The ultimate load levels are indicated by arrows. Points of
experimental observed ultimate loads at corresponding deflections are also indicated in the figure.

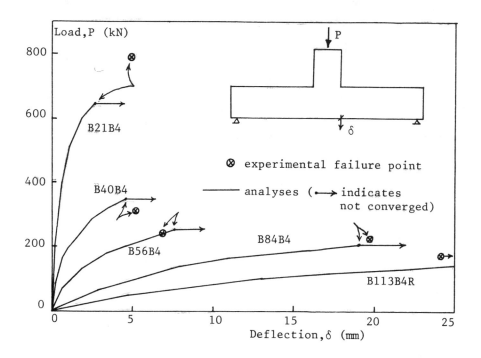

Fig. 7 Computed midspan load-deflection curves
of Morrow-Viest beams

In Fig. 8a the shear force at failure (V) is plotted versus
the a/d-ratio. Figure 8b shows the moment at failure (V·a)
versus the a/d-ratio. It can be seen that the computed
results agree fairly well with the experiments, except for
the shortest beam B21B4. This beam failed in a shear
compression failure mode, and the computed ultimate load is
approximately 80 per cent of the experimental value. The
discrepancy between experiment and analysis can probably be
explained by the assumed failure criterion in biaxial compression, see Fig. 1. The computed stress-state in the
compression zone just prior to failure indicates approximately equal biaxial compression. Experiments indicate increase

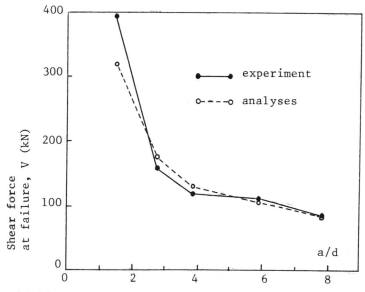

(a) Shear force at failure vs. a/d-ratio

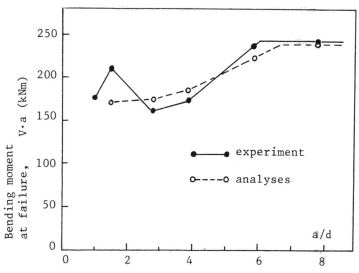

(b) Bending moment at failure vs. a/d-ratio

Fig. 8   Plots of shear force and bending moment at
failure versus a/d-ratio

in strength of approximately 20 per cent compared to uniaxial
compression. Since the computed failure occurs as diagonal
crushing in this zone, it is reasonable to assume that a
better approximation of the real failure envelope in biaxial
compression would have improved the results considerably.

Beams B40B4, B56B4 and B84B4 failed in a diagonal tension
failure mechanism, which was also indicated by the computed
crack patterns. Beam B113B4R failed in a flexural failure
mode by yielding of the reinforcement; the same failure mode
was found by the analysis.

The afore mentioned nonlinear distribution of axial normal
strains across the beam depth at the critical section is
found from the analyses of all beams, as shown in Table 2.
For comparison the measured strains are included in the table.

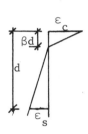

Specimen	$\varepsilon_c \cdot 10^3$		$\varepsilon_s \cdot 10^3$		β
	exp.	calc.	exp.	calc.	
B21B4	2.37	2.89	1.5	1.05	0.20
B40B4	1.96	2.08	1.11	1.06	0.19
B56B4	2.03	2.22	1.21	1.09	0.24
B84B4	3.11	3.03	1.81	1.41	0.27
B113B4R	3.95	4.10	2.83	1.93	0.33

Table 2   Strain distribution in Morrow-Viest beams

It should be noted that the computed strains are found at
the last increment before failure load, while the measured
strains reported by Morrow and Viest (1957) are extrapolated
values from the last measured values before failure. Hence,
the experimental and numerical values are not necessarily
directly comparable.

Analytical model   An analytical model for calculation of
the capacity of a reinforced concrete cross section subjected
to bending moment and shear and axial forces is proposed by
Lenschow and Reinertsen (1979). This model is based on a
failure criterion as a relationship between shear stresses at
failure as functions of the normal stress level, according to
test results by Kupfer (1969). Stress resultants at a
critical cross section are obtained by assuming a nonlinear

strain distribution similar to the results in Fig. 5 and Table 2. Static equilibrium between external applied loads and the stress resultants at the critical cross section is established by iteration. The model is capable of predicting realistic capacities for different shear spans, as demonstrated by Lenschow and Reinertsen (1979).

CONCLUSIONS

Based on the presented results the following conclusions may be drawn:

1. Load-deflection behaviour and ultimate loads of reinforced concrete members which fail in different failure modes can be fairly good approximated by the finite element computer program.

2. The model cannot express discrete cracks, otherwise the calculated crack patterns agree fairly well with experiments.

3. Members with a diagonal tension failure mode exhibit a nonlinear strain distribution across the depth at critical sections.

ACKNOWLEDGEMENT

The author would like to thank Professor R. Lenschow and Dr.ing. E. Reinertsen for useful discussions.

REFERENCES

Bergan, P.G. and Clough, R.W.(1972)"Convergence Criteria for Iterative Processes" AIAA Journal, 10, 8:1107-1108

Bresler, B. and Scordelis, A.C (1964) "Shear Strength of Reinforced Concrete Beams - Series II", SESM Report No.64-2, University of California, Berkeley

Doherty, P.W., Wilson, E.L. and Taylor, R.L. (1969) "Stress Analysis of Axi-Symmetric Solids Using Higher Order Quadrilateral Finite Elements", SESM Report No. 69-3, University of California, Berkeley

Kupfer, H.(1969) "Das Verhalten des Betons unter zwei-
achsiger Beanspruchung", Bericht Nr.78, Lehrstuhl für
Massivbau, Technische Hochschule München

Lenschow, R. and Reinertsen,E. (1979)"An analytical model
for determination of the carrying capacity of a member
subjected to moment, shear-and axial forces", Int.Symp.
Offshore Structures, "Brasil Offshore '79".

Morrow, J. and Viest, I.M. (1957) "Shear Strength of
Reinforced Concrete Frame Members without Web Reinforcement"
ACI Journal, 53, 9:833-869

CALCULATION OF STRESS CONCENTRATION FACTOR (SCF) IN SOME
TYPICAL TUBULAR JOINTS IN OFFSHORE PLATFORM STRUCTURES BY USE
OF FINITE ELEMENT METHOD

Alfredo Coaracy Brazil Gandolfo
Célio Taniguchi
Miguel Angel Buelta Martinez
Edson Couto

Escola Politécnica da USP

ABSTRACT

This paper introduce a method to analyse tubular joints of the
type used in the jacket structure of offshore platforms.
Initially, a computer program was developed to define the joint
geometry by means of node coordinates. As a second step the
generated mesh is checked by the use of pre-processors and then
the entire structure is analysed by SAP IV computer program. In
this study, shell elements were used to perform the analysis.
The results obtained were then compared to some figures found in
the literature.

INTRODUCTION

The "oil crisis" has already caused many economical troubles,
mainly to those countries which depend directly of the import of
that energy source. In Brazil, the crisis has led the government
to search for new oil resources to at least balance the constant
ly increasing oil demand.
One of the advantages of this government policy was the construc
tion for the first time in Brazil, of offshore platforms for the
exploration of already known oil fields. However, the design and
construction of such platforms require the knowledge of new type
of technologies which must be learned from more experienced
countries, and, for this purpose, an efficient program of research and development should be established under the government
supervision.
In order to help the nucleation of a technological background in
this subject, a group in the Department of Naval Architecture and
Marine Engineering of Escola Politécnica of University of São Pau

lo, is at present working in a research project, involving the
design and construction aspects of stationary offshore platforms.
This project work is described in detail in another paper submit
ted to this Congress and is sponsored by Financiadora de Estudos
e Projetos, FINEP.

STUDY OF TUBULAR JOINTS

One of the critical points in the platform structure refers to
the design and construction of structural joints, since they
have to withstand complex load configurations which can lead to
highly stressed areas in the mentioned joints.
The type of joint treated in this paper is the tubular joint. In
spite of looking very simple structural components, they are
actually fundamental parts of an offshore platform since they
promote the connexion between jacket elements, jacket and deck
structures, etc. imparting the total structural system the
strength and rigidity required for its operation.
A simple failure in one of such a joint can at least cause *Catastrophic failure*
serious damages to the section to which it belongs, and depending on the conditions it can extend to other points of the struc
tural system. Actually, statistics shows that tubular joints
have been responsible for numerous structural failures, consisting in a major cause of damages in stationary offshore platforms.
Investigations on the subject have shown that failures in those
tubular joints were not always caused by a poor structural
design, which can lead to undersizing of the whole joint, but
they resulted from more complex mechanisms, such as brittle
fracture, fatigue, stress corrosion cracking and problems within
the base material or the welded joints.
On the other hand, it is now well recognized that all those
material problems are closely related to the existance of critical stress states within the material, which can either start or
continue a given failure process. Those stress states can be
brought about by,for instance, a lamination problem, residual
stresses induced by welding or fabrication processes, or by a
physical or metallurgical notches, all of them having the tenden
cy to cause stress concentrations in critical zones of the joint
structure.
The type of stress concentration treated in this paper refers to
those caused by the so called "geometrical notches", such as
abrupt changes in the sectional areas of structural members,sharp
bends, and equivalent geometries. Stress concentration problems
can adequately be modeled and solved by computer programs and so
this paper will describe the steps involved in the development of
the solutions.

TYPES OF TUBULAR JOINTS

A typical tubular joint is shown in Figure 1 and it consists
basically of three parts, i.e., chord, branch and plugs. They are
differentiated with respect to the type of reinforcements as well
as their geometries.

Type of reinforcement
Tubular joints can be subdivided in three categories:
- Ordinary tubular joint, as shown in Figure 1, consists in a joint without any structural reinforcement. The stresses acting on these joints are mainly influenced by the value of bending moments.
- Tubular joint with local reinforcement, as shown in Figure 3, has the reinforcements located in the joint area, since this is the weakest point of the structure. In this case, bending moments effects are more severe in the reinforced zone.
- Totally reinforced tubular joint, as shown in Figure 4, in which the stresses are mainly transmitted by membrane action and the bending moment effects are of secundary importance, although they are included in the calculation of Stress Concentration Factor (SCF).

Type of geometry
Figure 2 shows 7 basic types of tubular joints: - Fig. (2a)- Tee joint, (T), Fig. (2e)
Double Tee joint (DT); Fig. (2c) - K joint (K); Fig. (2f)
Double K joint (DK); Fig. (2d) - TK joint (TK); Fig. (2g)
Double TK joint (DTK) and Fig. (2b) - Y joint (Y)
Much information is available for ordinary tubular joints[1][2][3]
In reference (1) for instance, parametric study on stress concentration factors (SCF)[1] was carried out resulting in a series of equations to estimate them, based on the following variables:

$$D = \text{chord diameter}$$
$$T = \text{chord wall thickness}$$
$$d = \text{branch diameter}$$
$$t = \text{branch wall thickness}$$
$$L = \text{distance between chord supporting points}$$
$$\theta = \text{angle between chord and branch axis}$$

The results of parametric or experimental studies were always compared to ones obtained by analytical means, by using finite element methods (FEM). For instance TKJOINT and SATE programs were based on shell elements proposed by Johnson and Clough as shown in Figure 5.
In this study concerned only to ordinary joints, SAP IV program[5] was employed, by using a plate element as shown in Figure 6. This figure shows a quadrilateral element composed by 4 compatible triangles. The properties of such an element are presented in reference (6). The element itself has 17 degrees of freedom internally, which are reduced only to 5 degrees per node when its stiffness matrix is assembled: 2 degrees of freedom refers to the plane stress behaviour and the other 3 correspond to the plate behaviour of the element.
The element used by Johnson and Clough considers the surface curvature, what does not happen in SAP IV program. This difference however is overcome by taking a finer mesh when using SAP IV computer program.

COMPUTER SUB-ROUTINES FOR THE JOINT GEOMETRY

Even the simpler tubular joint has such a geometry, so that it
becomes quite cumbersome to supply the node coordinates to the
computer. Therefore, for that purpose it was necessary to devel
op two computer routines in order to be incorporated to the
main program.
One of them establishes the node coordinates of all elements
which belong to the intersection between the chord and a branch,
while the second one establishes the coordinates of nodes for
all elements belonging to a branch outside the intersection area
For the chord. SAP IV has itself the capacity to transform polar
into orthogonal coordinates, so that no special problem is
involved in this operation.
Figure 7 shows the coordinate systems adapted in this study.There
are two orthogonal coordinate systems, namely a global x, y, z
system in which the y axis coincides with the chord axis; and a
local x̄,ȳ,z̄ system, in which the ȳ axis coincides with the
branch axis.
In the same Figure 7 are presented the geometrical relationship
between the two coordinate systems.

APPLICATION EXAMPLE

For the application of the developed computer program an ordinary T joint (T) was studied. Figure 9 shows the joint under
consideration and this is the same case study conducted by a
group at Southwest Research Institute (SWRI) in San Antonio.,
Texas. This T joint was selected since stress values along its
chord as well as circunferential stresses were all measured and
the respective SCF calculated.

Mesh generation
The following procedure was adopted for the mesh generation:
- The sharpest stress gradient occurs in the neighborhood of the
  intersection between the chord and the branch, so that a finer
  mesh was utilized in that area.
- Chose to the ends of both chord and branch, rougher meshes will
  be utilized, since stress values at those points are smaller.
  However, the mesh size will be such to keep the curvature of
  the structure.
- The nodes were numbered in such a way to minimize the incidence
  of elements and so trying to reduce the size of the global
  stiffness matrix.
- Triangular meshes were also avoided, since they cause some
  discrepancies in bending moment values.
Due to the double sinmetry of the tubular joint, only a quarter
of structure was analysed, according to Figure 11. This resulted
in utilizing a total of 265 shell elements and 241 nodes. The
total load was then equivalently subdivided, and applied in its
respective node.

Use of pre-processors

Due to the geometrical complexity of the mesh it will be very
hard to an analyst to check the correctness of all input data.
Therefore some pre-processor already developed in the Department of Naval Architecture was utilized to check the generation
of the mesh. Figures 12 and 13 shown the discretized structure
by means of the mentioned pre-processors. In figure 12 some input errors were detected, and they were corrected in Figure 13.
The total computer time spent in the analysis was about 30
minutes.

RESULTS OF ANALYSIS

Figures 14 and 15 show results of the analysis and a comparison
between the outputs of TKJOINT[1] and SAP IV program, as well as
the experimental results obtained in SWRI.
In figure 14, normal stresses along the external surface of
chord top sections are plotted against the distance from one of
joint ends. The plotted stress values take into account the
flexural as well as membrane behaviour of the plate elements.
It is noticed in Figure 14 that there is a very good agreement
between the results, although in TKJOINT program a finer mesh
than that used for SAP IV has been employed. There is a little
divergence at the ends of the chord, but this is mainly caused
by the effects of the vertical supports on the chord boundaries.
In Figure 15, normal stresses along the external surface of
circumferential sections are plotted against the distances from
the intersection between joint chord and joint branch. From the
results, one can also notice the chose agreement between the
compared results.
Since the maximum stress value occurs at the exact point lying
on the intersecting line between the chord and branch, its values
was obtained by extrapolation in Figure 15, for the plotted
values are supposed to occur at the middle of each element, as
shown in Figure 16. The extrapolated value was 190 Kpsi. The
nominal stress value σ_o, acting on that point would be:

$$\sigma_o = \frac{4 \times P}{\pi (D^2 - d^2)} = 21,83 \ Kp/in^2 \qquad (1)$$

So that the SCF will result in

$$SCF = \frac{190,00}{21,83} = 8,70 , \qquad (2)$$

very close to that obtained in reference (1) which is equal to
9,10.

FINAL COMMENTS

Just as a final comment, one can say that the method developed
by the project group to analyse tubular joints by FEM technique,

presents good results when compared to other existing either computacional or experimental methods. The analysis carried out has only considered a very simple ordinary T joint, however, this study was further advanced in order to expand the capacity to other type of more sophisticated joints. The intention of this effort is to find shortly a reliable method to analyse reinforced joints since a parametric study for those types becomes much more complex.

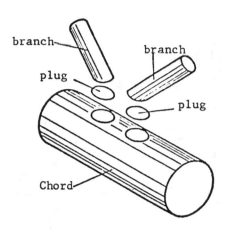

Fig.1 - Components of a tubular joint

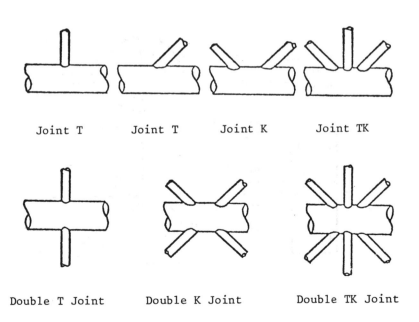

Joint T   Joint T   Joint K   Joint TK

Double T Joint   Double K Joint   Double TK Joint

Fig.2 - Ordinary Tubular Joints

2.142

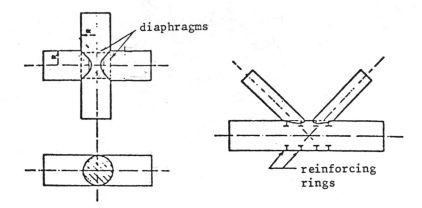

Fig.3 - Locally reinforced tubular joint

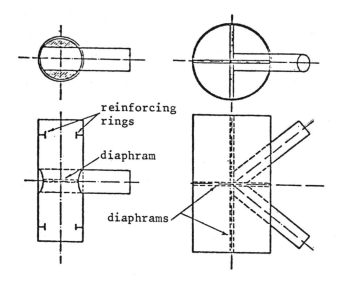

Fig.4 - Completely reinforced tubular joint

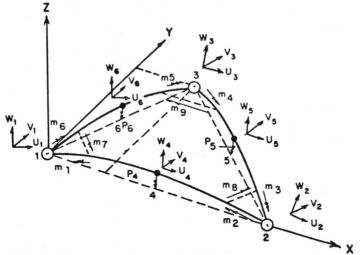

U,V - displacement in XOY plane
W   - displacement normal to XOY plane
m   - moments
XOY - reference plane for the shell

Fig.5 - A shell triangular element (Johnson and Clough)

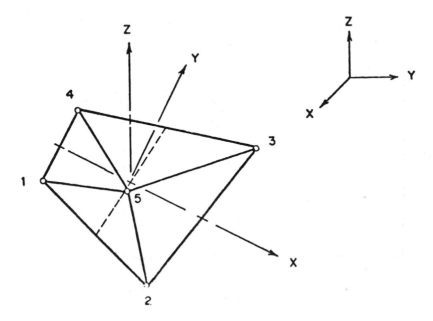

Fig.6 - A shell triangular element (Fillipa and Clough)

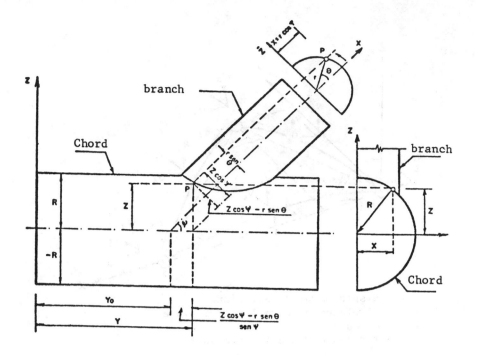

Fig.7 – Coordinates belonging to a point on the intersection

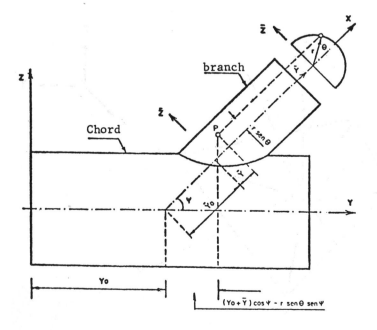

Fig.8 – Coordinates of a point outside the intersection

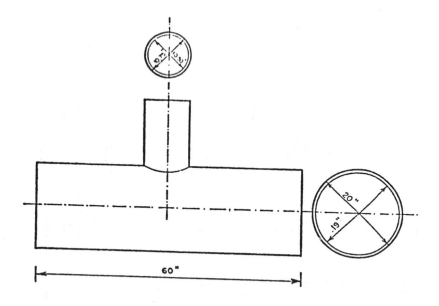

Fig.9 - T Joint model studied at SWRI

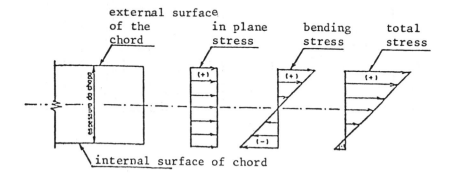

Fig.10 - Stress component in the plate

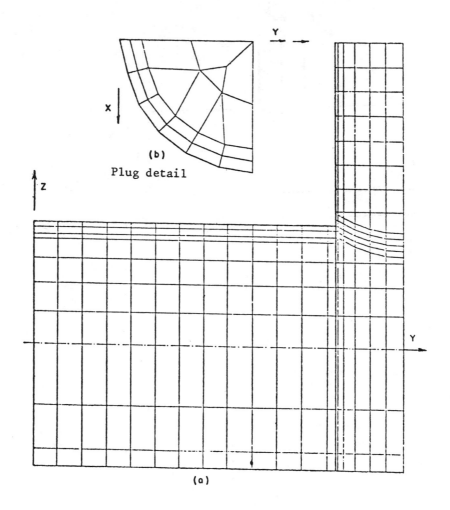

(b)

Plug detail

(a)

Fig.11 - Modeled structure

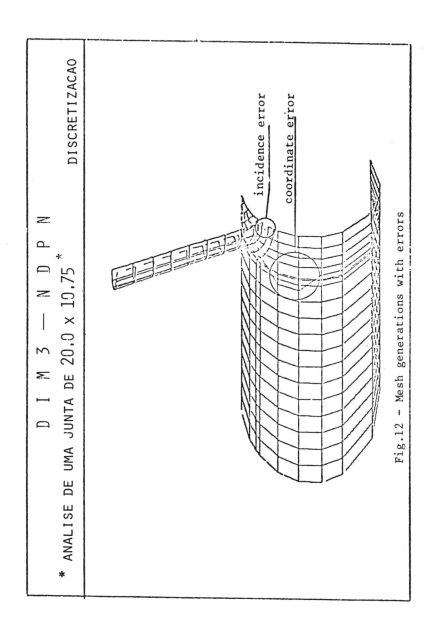

* ANALISE DE UMA JUNTA DE 20.0 × 10.75 *

D I M 3 — N D P N   DISCRETIZACAO

incidence error
coordinate error

Fig.12 - Mesh generations with errors

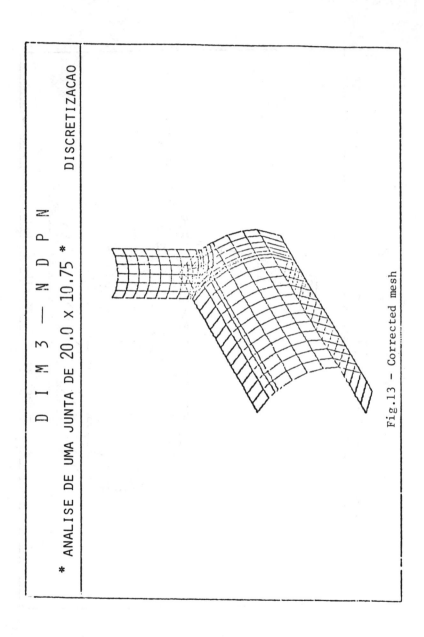

D I M 3 — N D P N

* ANALISE DE UMA JUNTA DE 20.0 x 10.75 *

DISCRETIZACAO

Fig.13 - Corrected mesh

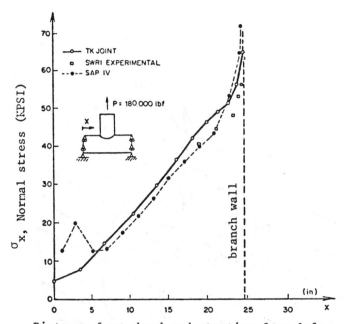

Distance from chord end starting from left

Fig.14 – σ_x stress on external surface of chord top

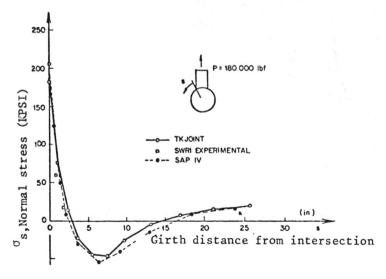

Girth distance from intersection

Fig.15 – σ_s stress on external surface of chord structure

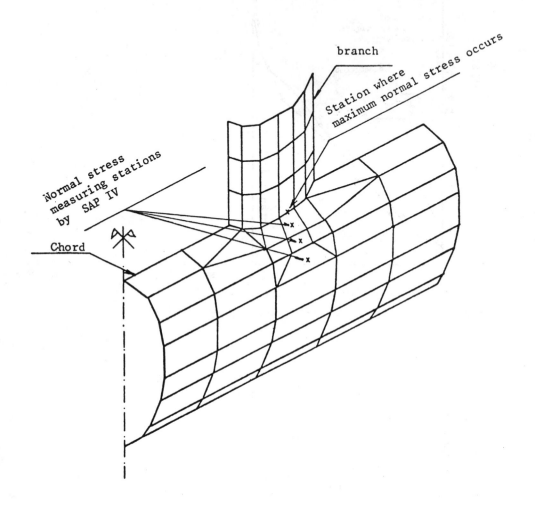

Fig.16 – Location of normal stress measuring stations

MOTION RESPONSE OF FLOATING STRUCTURES TO REGULAR WAVES

B.J. Natvig and J.W. Pendered

Ph. D., Aker Engineering A/S
Ph. D., Partner of Pell Frischman Offshore

SUMMARY

Linearized and non-linear methods for analysing motion response of floating structures to regular waves are discussed in this paper.

The linearized method is based upon a traditional frequency domain approach, whereas the non-linear method is based upon the time integration method as proposed by Newmark.

In addition, a new approximate method is proposed. This method, which employs a Newton-Raphson solution of the equations of motion, is an extension of the linearized method and is therefore valid for near linear systems.

These methods are applied to a taut line moored structure; the Aker Tethered Production Platform and to a conventional semisubmersible, the Aker H3.

INTRODUCTION

Spectral methods for the analysis of motion response and structural strength of floating structures, have been widely used in recent years. (e.g. ref. 2). However, spectral methods assume that the motion response can be adequately represented by linearized equations. It is common practise to assume that conventional semisubmersibles behave in a linear manner, but it is not apparent that this assumption can also be applied to a taut line moored structure.

During the development of the Aker Tethered Floating Production Platform, it was found necessary to develop a computer based analysis of linearized and non-linear motion response so that the assumptions of linearity could be tested before entering into a spectral analysis. Spectral

analysis, for the calculation of short and long term extremes
of rigid body motion response and mooring line forces are
easily performed due to the few (6) degrees of freedom
required. Structural strength analysis by the use of spectral
methods are, however, impractical for ordinary design work
due to the high costs and should hence only be used as a
final check on the structural integrity. This approach was
previously adopted for the semisubmersible Aker H3 as
described in ref. 2.

A practical and popular method of strength analysis is the
design wave method. This has obvious application to fixed
structures, but can also be applied to floating structures
if motion induced forces are included in the analysis. It
was found that this method could be made more realistic by
using non-linear motion response when calculating the
structure motion forces and by including wave non-
linearities when calculating the wave forces before these
forces are applied to a structural space frame analysis.

By using "the non-linear design wave method" during the
design phase and by running a final check on the structural
strength by a linearized spectral method, it is possible to
perform two independent checks on structural integrity by
two methods of which the shortcommings and features are to
some extent complimentary.

These ideas were developed during a three year research
project at Aker Engineering, in collaboration with the
Departement of Mechanical Engineering, University College
London.

Whilst the work on the tethered production platform provided
the initial motivation for this project, the resulting
computer program will also handle semisubmersibles in a
similar manner. The computer program named SEARESPONS
was used for all dynamic analysis of the Aker TPP. This
included; motion response, mooring line design, loads for
the structural analysis and offsets for marine riser design.

LINEARIZED ANALYSIS

Linear Forces
The first order (Airy) wave theory is implicit in linear
analysis for the calculation of fluid particle accelerations
and velocities and dynamic pressures. The corresponding wave
forces are calculated by the well known Morison equation
(see refs. 1,2,3) which is assumed to be valid as long as
the cross-sectional dimensions are less than one fifth of
the wave length. This corresponds to wave periods down to 5-
6 seconds for most current floating structures.

The relative velocity between fluid and structure is a second power term in the Morison equation. An explicit and linear solution to the equations of motion is therefore only possible if the structure velocity and the wave particle velocity are separated and linearized. This is usually achieved by the substitution $u/u/ = (8/3\pi) u_a u$, where u is either the wave particle velocity or structure velocity, u_a is the velocity amplitude and $8/3\Pi$ is the linearization constant which makes the energy absorbed during one wave period equal for both assumed forms in the above aquation.

Equations of Motion

The simplified equations of motion (see refs. 2 and 3) result from equating the external forces on the structure (assumed to be prevented from moving) to the reactive motion forces acting on the structure (which is assumed to be moving in a calm fluid). This results in a second order differential equation which may be expressed in matrix form as

$$(\underset{\sim}{M}+\underset{\sim}{A_1})\ddot{\psi} + \underset{\sim}{B}\frac{8}{3\pi}\dot{\psi}_a\dot{\psi} + (\underset{\sim}{C_1} + \underset{\sim}{C_2})\psi = F\exp(i\omega t) \qquad (1)$$

Where:

$\underset{\sim}{M}$ - is the structure mass matrix

$\underset{\sim}{A_1}$ - is the added mass matrix

$\underset{\sim}{B}$ - is the damping matrix

$\underset{\sim}{C_1}$ - is the hydrostatic restoring matrix.

$\underset{\sim}{C_2}$ - is the anchor restoring matrix

$\ddot{\psi}, \dot{\psi}, \psi,$ - are the complex vectors of structure acceleration, velocity and displacement.

$\dot{\psi}_a$ - is the real velocity amplitude vector

F   - is the complex forcing vector

All the matrices are symmetrical except for the damping matrix which is unsymmetrical due to the way in which the velocity amplitude must be included.

A special anchor restoring matrix for taut line situations has been developed by the writers. This restoring matrix assumes straight mooring lines and includes the restoring effect due to the change in direction of the pretension force during motion as well as that due to the material stiffness of the mooring lines.

In order to reduce the above second order differential equations to a set of linear equations it is necessary to assume harmonic motion. Thus, the velocities and accelerations are expressed in terms of the complex displacement amplitude:

$$\psi = \Psi\exp(i\omega t)$$
$$\dot\psi = i\omega\Psi\exp(i\omega t)$$
$$\ddot\psi = -\omega^2\Psi\exp(i\omega t) \tag{2}$$

the equation of motion can hence be solved for the complex response Ψ.

Since the damping forces are linearized as dependent on the velocity amplitude, an iterative solution technique is required. The solution using this iterative technique is also only valid for a given wave height and is hence again not strictly a linear solution. In practice, however, the motion damping force is only significant at resonance and the wave induced drag force is only significant at the period of cancellation of vertical added mass and dynamic pressure forces; leaving the response basically linear wrt. wave height outside these regions.

NON-LINEAR ANALYSIS

Non-linear forces
Apart from linearization of the viscous drag force, several other non-linear effects have to be omitted in the linearized analysis in order to achieve an explicit solution to the equations of motion. In a non-linear analysis, however, it is possible to include any non-linear force as long as it is possible to formulate this force. In the present study, the following non-linearities were assumed to be important enough to be included in the force calculations:

a) Wave forces are calculated at the displaced and rotated structure position and not at the mean position as for the linearized analysis.

b) The drag force is calculated using the true relative velocity between fluid and structure (including the current velocity) before squaring.

c) All fluid forces are calculated up to the wave surface and not to the still water level as for the linearized analysis.

d) Non-linear mooring forces are included.

By a suitable choice of the added mass and drag coefficients, the linear wave theory can be made to yield wave forces close to those obtained using the more complex higher order wave theories. Thus first order theory is retained here.

This first order wave theory is inconsistent in the splash area when applied to finite waves. This inconsistency was overcome by assuming the wave surface as the datum for the wave forces instead of the still water level which is usually done. This assumption makes the sum of the hydrostatic and dynamic pressure at the surface equal to zero and also makes the wave particle velocity and acceleration have a depth attenuation of unity at the surface.

Non-Linear Equations of Motion

The non-linear components of the forces are, in general, not of simple forms capable of concise mathematical description. Hence, every position of interest in a wave must be examined separately and a numerical evaluation and summation of all the various force contributions acting on all submerged parts of the structure must be carried out.

The non-linear equations of motion can be written:

$$\Sigma A_2 \ddot{\eta} - (M+A_1)\ddot{\psi} + \Sigma B (\dot{\eta}+C_u - \dot{\psi}) |\dot{\eta}+C_u - \dot{\psi}|$$

$$- \Sigma C_1 (\psi ; \eta) - \Sigma C_2 (\psi) + W + F_w = 0 \qquad (3)$$

where:

$\Sigma A_2 \ddot{\eta}$	- is the sum of all wave inertia forces
M	- is the structure mass matrix
A_1	- is the instantaneous added mass matrix
$\Sigma B(\dot{\eta}...$	- is the sum of all drag forces due to the relative fluid velocity.
$\Sigma C_1 (\psi ...$	- is the sum of all buoyancy and dynamic pressure forces.
$\Sigma C_2 (\psi ...$	- is the sum of all mooring line and pretension forces.
W	- structure weight
F_w	- wind forces and moments

$\dot{\eta}, \ddot{\eta}, \eta$ - fluid particle displacements,
velocities and accelerations

C_u - current velocity

Time series solution

The most obvious approach to the solution of nonlinear equations of motion is through an integration of the acceleration and velocity curves in the time domain. The well known Newmark method (ref. 4) is widely used. In the offshore context, this method has been applied to fixed jacket type structures by Burke and Tighe (ref. 4), but no reference is found on the application of this method to floating structures.

The Newmark method describes the kinematic relationship in the form:

$$\dot{\psi}(t_{n+1}) = \dot{\psi}(t_n) + (1 - \gamma)\ \ddot{\psi}(t_n)\Delta t + \gamma\ddot{\psi}(t_{n+1})\Delta t$$

$$\psi(t_{n+1}) = \psi(t_n) + \dot{\psi}(t_n)\Delta t$$

$$+ (\tfrac{1}{2} - \beta)\ \ddot{\psi}(t_n)\Delta t^2 + \beta\ddot{\psi}(t_{n+1})\Delta t^2 \tag{4}$$

Where $\psi(t_n)$ denotes, the responses at time t, and $\psi(t_{n+1})$ denotes the responses at a small time interval ahead of t_n. The value of γ is usually set to 1/2 from damping considerations and the value of the coefficient β is chosen in the range 1/4, 1/6 or 1/8 to give good convergence properties.

Substituting for the vector of velocities and displacements at time t_{n+1} into the equations of motion(3), the vector of accelerations at time t_{n+1} are found thus:

$$\ddot{\psi} = (\underset{\sim}{M} + \underset{\sim}{A})^{-1} \cdot (\Sigma A_2\ddot{\eta} + \Sigma B(\dot{\eta} + C_u - \dot{\psi}) \mid \dot{\eta} + C_u - \dot{\psi}\mid$$

$$- \Sigma C_1 (\psi; \eta) - \Sigma C_2 (\psi) + F_w + W) \tag{5}$$

If this is repeated for a sufficient number of time steps using sufficiently small time increments Δt, a convergent solution for the displacements, velocities and accelerations will be obtained.

The time step method is often started from zero response. This will result in an initial transient solution which will be damped out after a few cyles. The method to be presented in the next section, however, will produce a good estimate of the start values for the responses and considerable saving in computer costs is therefore possible.

Time series solution methods are also well suited for
calculating the mean offset. This is simply the area under
the displacement curve over one response cycle divided by
the wave period.

A Newton-Raphson technique

Several authors eg. ref. (3) have shown that linearized
methods will give good correspondence with results obtained
from model tests or full scale measurements. The writers aim
was therefore to develop a cheap and simple method for
solving the non-linear equations of motion assuming firstly
that the motion is near linear and secondly that the
linearized solution is known.

A feature of this method is that the response is found for a
specified position in a wave, whilst time integration
methods will find the solution over the complete wave cycle.
This method is mainly intended to be used with a non-linear
design wave strength analysis and the response is therefore
only required for a single position.

It was shown in ref. 8, that the linearized solution to the
velocities corresponded well with those calculated by the
Newmark method, whilst the linearized accelerations and
displacements gave less good agreements. This is of course
due to the fact that the degree of non-linearity increases
with the displacement. For a near linear system, the
displacements are small at large velocities which explains
why the linerarized solution is more accurate for velocities
than for displacements and accelerations.

Therefore, another assumption made in this method is that
the linearized velocity can be retained so that the non-
linear equations of motion need only be solved wrt. the
displacements and accelerations.

Before the kinematic relationship between displacements and
accelerations is discussed, it is necessary to split the
displacements into a mean and a dynamic part:

$$\psi = \psi_{dyn} + \psi_{mean} \tag{6}$$

The mean response ψ_{mean}, which must be calculated for all
degrees of freedom, is due to wind, current and wave drift
forces. An approximate, but simple method to calculate ψ_{mean}
was found :

a) The linearized solution to the displacements, velocities
and accelerations are substituted into the non-linear
equations of motion for a number of positions along the
wave length. (8 positions was found to be adequate.)

c) Since the mooring line stiffness and the hydrostatic stiffness are non-linear, the mean response vectors ψ_{mean} for all degrees of freedom are therefore found by the Newton-Raphson method. The gradient matrix to yield zero residual force is the sum of the tangent mooring line stiffness and the tangent hydrostatic stiffnesses. The Newton-Raphson method, which is also used to solve the equations of motion, will be discussed later.

Since this method for solving the non-linear equations of motion is restricted to near linear systems, it can be assumed that the kinematic relationship for simple harmonic motion remains valid.

$$\psi_{dyn} = \psi \cos (\Theta - \omega t)$$

$$\ddot{\psi} = -\omega^2 \psi \cos(\Theta - \omega t) \tag{7}$$

Where:
ψ - is the response amplitude
Θ - is the phase angle
found from the linearized analysis.

The acceleration can hence be written in terms of the dynamic part of the displacments.

$$\ddot{\psi} = -\omega^2 \psi_{dyn} \tag{8}$$

Choosing a position in a wave at which the response is required and substituting for the assumed values of ψ_{dyn} and the linarized velocity $\dot{\psi}_{1in}$ into the non-linear equations of motion yields.

$$\Delta(\psi_{dyn}) = \Sigma A_2 \ddot{\eta} + (\underset{\sim}{M} + \underset{\sim 1}{A}) \; \omega^2 \psi_{dyn}$$

$$+ \Sigma B(\dot{\eta} + C_u - \dot{\psi}_{1in}) \; |\dot{\eta} + C_u - \dot{\psi}_{1in}|$$
$$+ \Sigma C_1(\psi_{dyn} + \psi_{mean} \; ; \; \eta)$$
$$- \Sigma C_2(\psi_{dyn} + \psi_{mean}) + W + F_w \tag{9}$$

$\Delta (\psi_{dyn})$ is the unbalanced force vector due to an inaccurate displacement ψ_{dyn}. Starting with the linearized solution, the vector ψ_{dyn} can be modified so as to reduce the unbalanced force $\Delta(\psi_{dyn})$ below a specified minimum. Once the true ψ_{dyn} is found, accelerations can be derived from the expression 8 above.

The iterative process for the response ψ is of the form:

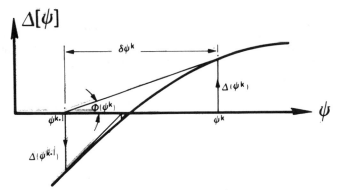

Fig. 1 - Newton - Raph'son iterations.

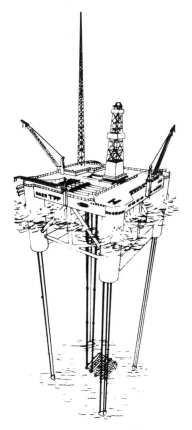

Fig. 2 - Aker - TPP.

$$\psi^{k+1} = \psi^k - \underset{\sim}{\Phi}(\psi^k)^{-1} \cdot \Delta(\psi^K) \tag{10}$$

where k denotes the iteration cycle number, and $\underset{\sim}{\Phi}$ (ψ) is the gradient matrix required to zero the balanced force. The iterative solution is illustrated in fig. 1 for one degree of freedom.

The gradient matrix is a 6 x 6 matrix of partial derivatives, defined as:

$$\Phi(\psi) = \frac{\partial \Delta(\psi)}{\partial \psi} = (\underset{\sim}{M} + \underset{\sim}{A_1})\omega^2 + \underset{\sim}{C_1} + \underset{\sim}{C_2} \tag{11}$$

where the matrices $\underset{\sim}{M}$, $\underset{\sim}{A_1}$, $\underset{\sim}{C_1}$ and $\underset{\sim}{C_2}$ are the tangent matrices, ie. the matrices are calculated for the displaced position of the floating structure.

It is possible that the initial start value, taken from the linearized solution, could be too far from the final solution to produce a convergent iterative process. This might be the case for extreme wave heights since the linearized solution is based on small wave heights. The non-linearites are, however, increasing with the wave heigh. To overcome this, an otherwise non-convergent solution is made convergent by first finding the solution for a smaller wave height and by using this solution as the start value for a larger wave height. This is repeated until the required wave height is reached.

COMPARISON OF METHODS

Introduction

The objectives in developing the Newton-Raphson method presented in the previous section were that it would be cheaper and simpler to use than the Newmark method and that it would give a better solution than the linearized method. In this section the usefulness of this method will be tested against each of these more generally accepted alternatives.

Due to the different motion characteristics of taut and slack moored structures, results are presented here for both types of structures. The configuration of such structures vary considerably, but the Aker-TPP and the Aker-H3 may be considered representative of many existing structures or later generation proposed designs.

The response methods have been tested for several headings
and wave conditions, but in the interest of brevity a few
sets of heave and surge curves are presented here. These
are, however, for a typical sea condition and the results
presented are representative of all the tested conditions.

Aker TPP Fig. 2 shows a version of the Aker Tethered
Production Platform for which the analysis is discussed
below. The parallel mooring lines are kept taut by
sufficient excess buoyancy to avoid snatching. This mooring
line configuration and the necessary pretension result in
heave, roll and pitch natural periods of the order of 2-4
seconds and surge, sway and yaw natural periods of about 60
seconds.

The first analysis presented below is for a water depth of
180 m, a wave height of 20 m, a head sea (parallel to
pontoons) with a wave length of 200 m which corresponds to a
period of 11.3 seconds.

Fig. 3 shows the surge response (horizontal motion) in terms
of the displacement, velocity and acceleration curves for
each of the linearized method, the Newmark method and the
Newton-Raphson method.

The surge displacement curves for the Newton-Raphson and the
Newmark methods are reasonably close to each other. The
linearized method, however, only gives good correspondence
when the drift offset is added (since this is not calculated
by the linearized method). This part of fig. 3 also shows
that the drift offsets from the two methods are reasonably
close.

The linearized and the Newmark method also give virtually
identical results for the surge velocity. It was noted
earlier that the linearized velocity solution is used in the
Newton-Raphson technique, due to the good agreement with the
non-linear solution.

The surge acceleration curves for the Newmark and the
Newton-Raphson solutions are again almost identical but
differ significantly from the solution given by the
linearized method. It is interesting that the Newton-Raphson
and the Newmark method should give good correspondence for
this case since the acceleration dependent forces are the
predominant forces for surge motion.

The heave response curves are shown in fig. 4 and it should
be noted that this degree of freedom is highly stiffness
dominated since the excitation period is much higher than

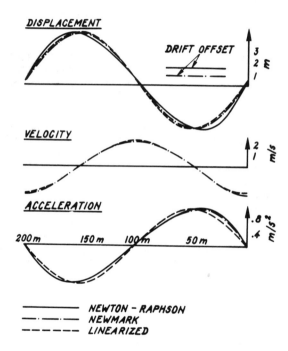

DISPLACEMENT

DRIFT OFFSET

VELOCITY

ACCELERATION

200 m   150 m   100 m   50 m

—————— NEWTON – RAPHSON
—·—·—·— NEWMARK
– – – – – LINEARIZED

FIG. 3 AKER-TPP SURGE RESPONSE

WAVE HEIGHT 20m   WAVE PERIOD 11.3 sec.   NO WIND AND CURENT
WAVE LENGTH 200m   WATER DEPTH 180 m

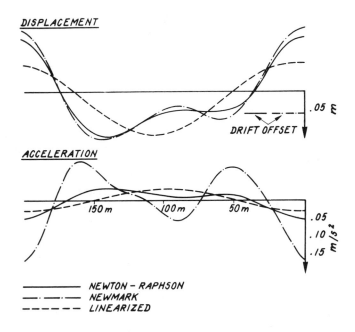

DISPLACEMENT

.05 m

DRIFT OFFSET

ACCELERATION

150 m   100 m   50 m

.05
.10 m/s²
.15

———————— NEWTON – RAPHSON
—·—·—·— NEWMARK
— — — — LINEARIZED

FIG. 4   AKER – TPP HEAVE RESPONSE

WAVE HEIGHT   20 m   WAVE PERIOD   11.3 sec.   NO WIND AND CURRENT
WAVE LENGTH   200 m   WATER DEPTH   180 m

the heave natural period. The heave displacement curves show this motion to be highly non-linear and thus one should exercise caution in applying the assumption of near linearity in the Newton-Raphson method.

Despite this, the Newton-Raphson method is seen to correspond well with the Newmark method. It should be noted, however, that whilst the heave motion is highly non-linear the displacements are small. It is interesting to note the presence of the two downward humps on the non-linear heave curves. These humps occur at the positions of maximum horizontal displacements and are due to the inverted pendulum type motion of the structure. It is also interesting to note that the non-linear solution gives a much higher upward displacement at the wave crest than the linearized solution. This is due to the wave-structure intersection effects which the linearized method cannot handle.

The heave velocity curves (not shown) are widely different. But again these velocities are small and hence will have little influence on the motion of the structure.

The Newton-Raphson heave acceleration curve is quite different in magnitude from that of the Newmark method, but the general shape is the same.

The second condition presented represents the 100 year storm condition which corresponds to a wave height of 30 metres. The wave period is 16.06 seconds, the current is set to 1.40 m/sec. and the one minute sustained wind velocity is 56 m/sec. The water depth is 180 meters.

For this condition, the surge response curves, which are not shown, gave even better correspondence with the three methods than for the 200 m wave length case.

The heave displacement and acceleration curves are shown in fig. 5. This solution will be even closer to a static solution than for the previous condition due to the difference between the wave period and the natural heave period. Despite the high non-linearities, the heave displacements from the Newmark and Newton-Raphson methods are again almost identical whilst the linearized method gives a completely different result. It is interesting to notice how the wind and the current affects the heave displacement curve. The maximum horizontal displacement occurs at the 200 metres wave position resulting in a large down-pull of the structure. At one half wavelength ahead in the wave, the horizontal dynamic displacement is counteracted by the mean offset and there is hence no downpull for this position. It is also interesting to note that the only

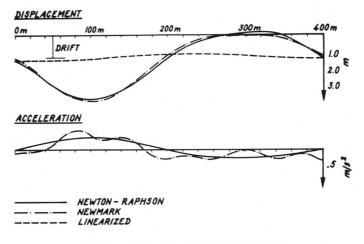

DISPLACEMENT

ACCELERATION

——————— NEWTON - RAPHSON
—·—·— NEWMARK
- - - - - LINEARIZED

FIG.5 AKER-TPP HEAVE RESPONSE

WAVE HEIGHT	30 m	WAVE PERIOD 16.06 sec.	CURRENT 1.40 m/sec.
WAVE LENGTH	400 m	WATER DEPTH 180 m	WIND 56 m/sec.

position where the linearized and non-linear solutions correspond is at the wave crest and wave trough.

The damping and inertia heave forces are small compared to the dominating stiffness force. It is still, however, of interest to study the acceleration curves since they illustrate how the Newmark method is converging. The Newmark and the Newton-Raphson heave acceleration curves are shown at the bottom of fig. 5. The Newton-Raphson solution gives a smooth curve whilst the Newmark solution oscillates about some mean near to the Newton-Raphson solution. Ie. there is a time lag before an inaccurate acceleration is detected and this will make the acceleration oscillate about the correct solution rather than to converge towards it. By reducing the time increments this effect will reduce in magnitude, but such improvement in the acceleration curve does not appear to alter the corresponding displacement curve. It is also the experience that this oscillation is more apparent for a stiff than for a soft dynamic system.

The mooring line forces due to the motion in the 400 meter wave case are shown in fig. 6 and fig. 7. Fig. 6 represents the anchor force in a mooring line on the windward side of the structure and both the linearized and Newton-Raphson solutions are shown. It is noticed that whilst the Newton-Raphson curve is sinusoidal in shape, its amplitude is about twice that of the linearized curve. It was not unexpected to find a discrepancy between linearized and non-linear analysis for this mooring line. Model tests of a similar structure showed the same kind of discrepancy between the tests and linearized calculations.

Fig. 7 shows the analysis carried out for a mooring line on the lee side of the structure. Considering the highly non-linear heave response for this condition, it is surprising to find such a good correlation between linearized and non-linear mooring forces. Yet, good correlation was again in confirmation of model tests which also gave good correlation with linearized calculations for this mooring line.

Aker H3 The Aker H3 (see fig. 8) is a semisubmersible oil drilling rig with conventional mooring. 28 rigs of this design are built. The heave natural period for this design is about 22 seconds, the roll and pitch of the order of 35 seconds and the natural periods for the remaining degrees of freedom are higher than 60 seconds.

The surge linearized response curves for the Aker-H3 were even closer to the non-linear curves than for the Aker-TPP and they are therefore not shown here.

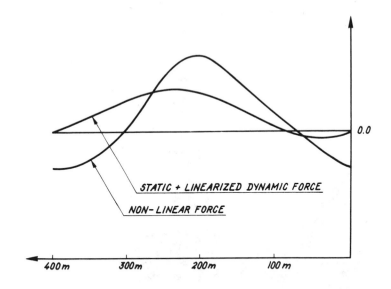

FIG. 6 ANCHOR FORCE OF LEG ON WINDWARD SIDE OF STRUCTURE

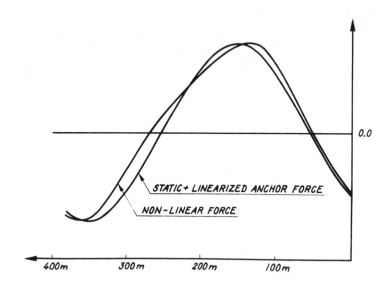

FIG. 7 ANCHOR FORCE OF LEG ON LEE SIDE OF STRUCTURE

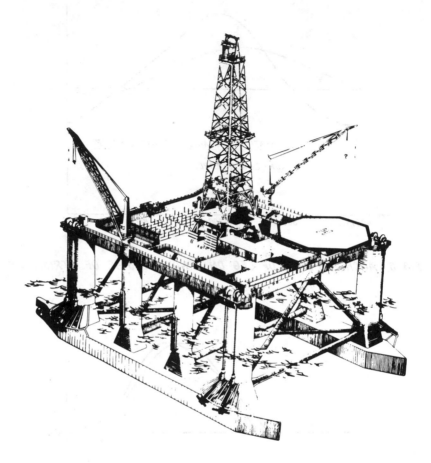

FIG 8 AKER H3

Heave response in the case of semisubmersible rigs has proved to be difficult to analyse using the Newmark method. Considerable effort has been made to optimize the values of the coefficient β and the step length, and the calculations have been carried out for up to 6 cycles starting from both the linearized and the Newton-Raphson solution. But despite this, a truly repeating solution to the heave motion response has not been obtained. The general trend is that the solution almost repeats itself every two cycles and the results from two consequtive cycles would lie on either side of the Newton-Raphson solution. This is illustrated in fig. 9 where the Newmark heave acceleration curves are almost repeating whilst the heave displacement curves are much further apart. Similar difficulties were experienced with the pitch and roll curves, but to a lesser extent than for the heave curves.

In the writers opinion, these difficulties are due to the implicit formulation of the response parameters in the Newmark method whereby an inaccurate extrapolation of velocities and displacements at one time instant will be corrected by means of a derived acceleration at the next time instant. If the stiffness forces are small, which is usually the case for a semisubmersible, a considerable error in the displacemet curve can build up before this is detected by the acceleration. For a floating structure, this formulation is made even more implicit by the fact that the underwater geometry and hence the exciting forces are dependent on the combined heave, roll and pitch displacements. (Note that the horizontal motion (surge) does give a repeating solution). Runs in which the heave and pitch stiffnesses were increased artificially showed this oscillatory effect to a much lesser degree.

CONCLUSIONS

A linearized and two non-linear methods for finding motion response for taut or slack moored floating structures have been presented. The results for the three methods have been compared and are presented for typical sea conditions and for a taut and a slack moored structure. Based upon the experience of applying these methods to date the following conclusions are drawn:

1. In general, linearized methods give good results particularly when proper account is taken of the mean offset. The velocity was found to be the most accurate of the three response parameters. The linearized method does not give good results for heave motion for taut mooring, but in this case the displacements are small anyway.

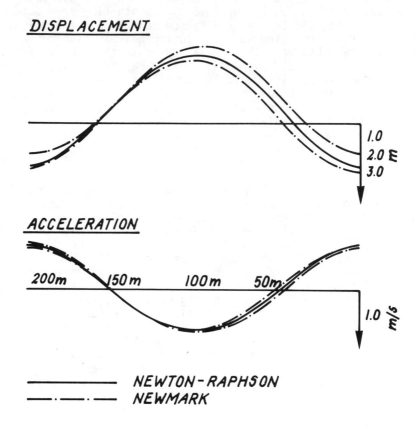

DISPLACEMENT

ACCELERATION

200m   150 m   100 m   50m

——————— NEWTON-RAPHSON
—— · —— · —— NEWMARK

FIG. 9   AKER H-3   HEAVE RESPONSE

The main advantages of a linearized analysis is that it is cheap on computer time, the complete motion for a wave cycle is described by an amplitude and a phase angle and it is readily incorporated whitin spectral methods.

2. The time integration method - the Newmark method - was intended to be the standard against which the other two methods could be compared. This method worked well for most cases except for heave, roll and pitch for the slack moored system. Whilst the Newmark method is a general method, it was found to be expensive on computer time even when started from an approximate solution. This method will find the response for a whole wave cycle which is an advantage if the whole motion is required, but is a positive disadvantage if results are only required at descrete time instants.

3. It may be noted that the Newmark method was initiated from the Newton-Raphson solution which again was initiated from the linearized solution. This is an obvious and simple procedure when all the three methods are included in the same computer program. As a result, in most cases, only a few wave cycles were required before a repeating solution was obtained. In order to check the efficiency of this procedure, this method was also started by setting the accelerations, the velocities and the displacements to zero. When this process was terminated after 300 time steps (which corresponded to 3 wave cycles) the solution was still far from its stable solution. This is shown in fig. 10.

4. A new approximate method has been presented here in which the response can be found directly at a given position in a wave. This method uses the linearized result for displacements and accelerations as the start value for a Newton-Raphson type iteration, whilst the linearized solution for velocity is retained throughout. The Newton-Raphson approach was found to be cheap on computer time, to have good convergence properties (it would find a solution to heave motion of slack moored systems) and in general the results would compare well with those of the Newmark method. This method in its present form can not, however, be used at resonance.

It is seen that all the three methods for finding motion response enjoy certain merits whilst also suffering from several limitations. The methods share several common links and features in such matters as start values and by the fact that the same wave force and structure motion force subroutins can be used for both the Newmark and Newton-Raphson methods. It is thus natural to include all methods in the same computer program as was done in the program SEARESPONS. This makes it possible to chose the method which

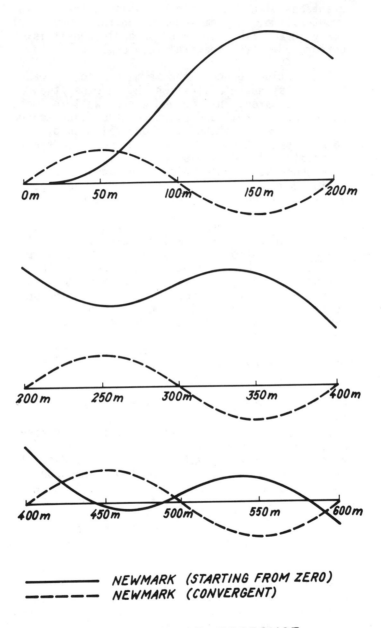

FIG. 10 SURGE RESPONSE

is most appropriate to the type of structure, the type of analysis and the degree of accuracy required.

REFERENCES

1. Fluid Loading on Offshore Structures, a State of the
    Art Appraisal: Wave Loads
    N. Hogben
    Royal Institution of Naval Architects 1974

2. Calculation of Long Term Values for
    Motions and Structural Response of
    Mobile Drilling Rigs
    Pedersen et. al.
    OTC 1881
    Offshore Technolgy Conference 1973

3. Hydrodynamic Aspects of Semi-Submersible Platforms
    J. P. Hooft
    Wageningen 1972

4. A Method for Computation for
    Structural Dynamics
    N.M. Newmark
    Proceedings for ASCE Mech. Eng. Div.
    July 1959.

5. A Time series Model for Dynamic
    Behaviour of Offshore Structures
    B.J. Burke and J.T. Tighe
    OTC 1403 Offshore Technology Conference 1971.

6. A Comparative Study of Different
    Numerical Solution Techniques as
    applied to a Non-linear Structural
    Problem
    P.G. Bergan and T. Søreide
    Computer Methods in Applied Mech
    and Eng.
    North-Holland Pbl. Co. 1973.

7. Numerical Methods for the Solution
    of Non-linear Problems in Structural
    Analysis
    J.R. Tillerson, J.A. Stricklin and
    W.E. Haisler
    ASME nov. 1973

8. Non-linear Motion Response of Floating
    Structures to Wave Excitation
    B.J. Natvig and J.W. Pendered
    OTC 2796. Offshore Technology Conference 1977.

STATIC AND DYNAMIC ANALYSIS OF OFFSHORE STRUCTURES
SUPPORTED ON PILE FOUNDATIONS

N.F.Ebecken, E.C.P.de Lima, A.J. Ferrante and E.D.C.Valenzuela

COPPE-UFRJ and Petrobras S.A., Brazil.

INTRODUCTION

The fixed steel offshore platforms are generally
composed of a deck of one or more levels, resting
atop of a steel jacket. This is fixed to the
seabed by a set of piles, which generally pass
through the legs of the jacket, and then penetrate
in the soil.

The external actions applied on such structures
include loads due to the dead weight, buoyancy,
currents, waves, winds, operations, drilling,
earthquakes, etc. Several of those loads have a
dynamic nature. Of fundamental importance, among
these are the wave loads. Although for structures
of small and medium size a quasi static
representation of the wave loads may suffice, in
order to determine the structural behaviour with
reasonable accuracy, a full dynamic analysis is
mandatory for larger structures. This is particularly
true when the fundamental period of the structure
exceeds 2.5 seconds.

The dynamic analysis for wave load actions can be
deterministic or stochastic. In the first case the
forces exerted on the structural members are applied
as known functions of time.Those forces are computed
for a given design wave,and considering a particular
wave theory. The stochastic analysis is based on a
wave spectra, selected to represent the sea states
which the structure might have to resist during its
useful life.

This paper is concerned with the computer analysis,
both static and dynamic, of piled steel offshore

structures under wave loads, and discusses two
integrated procedures implemented by the authors.

The static analysis procedure considers an analysis
model consisting of three parts. These are the
structural assemblage located above seabed, the
portion of the piles below seabed, and the soil. The
first part is considered as a conventional space
frame, and it is condensed at the seabed, using substructure analysis techniques. The piles are modelled
by a sequence of space frame segments, which can
have either geometrically linear or non linear
behaviour. The soil is represented by a set of
lumped springs, whose stiffness vary non linearly
according to P-Y and P-δ curves. The global non
linear analysis procedure used follows the
incremental Newton-Raphson method. This procedure
was added to the ICES STRUDL II language, as a part
of a joint development project established between
Petrobras S.A. and the Federal University of Rio de
Janeiro (UFRJ).

The procedures for dynamic analysis use a similar
analysis model but, of course, including inertia and
damping characteristics as well. These procedures
are based on the modal superposition and the direct
integration methods. Both of them include an
iterative algorithm providing for equilibrium checking at each time step. Currently they are available as
a part of the LORANE DINA language, developed at
COPPE-UFRJ.

The following sections present the formulations used
for the analysis models, and numerical examples
corresponding to real offshore structures analyzed
for different types of behaviour and parameters.

THE STATIC ANALYSIS SCHEME

The capability for static analysis of foundation-
structure interaction problems was implemented as an
integrated computational procedure, and was added to
the ICES STRUDL II Language [1]. That procedure
considers a three component system, including the
deck and the portion of the piles above seabed as a
first component, the portion of the piles below
seabed as a second component, and the soil as a third
component [2].

The first component is defined as a space frame,
possesing linear behaviour, and is condensed at the
level of the connection nodes, using convenient

substructure commands. The piles, which form the
second component, are modelled as sequences of space
frame segments, which can have either linear or
geometrically non linear behaviour. The numerical
model adopted for the soil consists of a series of
discrete springs, connected to the piles at the nodal
points joinning together each pair of consecutive
segments [3] . Three springs are considered at each
nodal point. Two of them are normal to the pile,and
their stiffness coefficients are evaluated using the
soil P-Y curves, as defined by API-RP-2 code. The
third spring acts in the direction of the pile
baricenter and simulates the effect of skin friction.
Springs simulating tip resistance are also included.
All the soil springs exhibit non linear behaviour,
corresponding to the piece-wise linear representation
adopted for the soil curves [4,5,6] .

As mentioned before the first component is condensed
using substructure analysis techniques, so that it is
represented by compact stiffness matrix and load
vector, relative to the nodes located at the seabed
level. The equations corresponding to each pile,and
the springs representing the soil surrounding it,are
also reduced with regard to its top node. Thus at
the end of the reduction process the complete
structural system is represented by a system of
equations of very small order, relative to the
connection nodes between the first and the second
component. The order at that system, in nodes, is
equal to the number of piles.

After solution of the compact system of equations the
displacements of the connection nodes are known, and
all displacements and forces, for both the first
component and the piles, can be evaluated.

The general solution scheme corresponds to a non
linear analysis procedure, based on incremental
Newton-Raphson scheme. The first component being
linear, it can be condensed at the start of the
process, and is mantained without changes during the
increments and interactions. Only the equations
relative to the piles and the soil are successively
reduced and backsubstituted,until the total loads
are applied and convergence is achieved. Then the
evaluation of the secondary results, such as forces
acting on the elements of the first component, is
performed, if requested.

The procedure described above was implemented in the
form of several new user-oriented commands added to

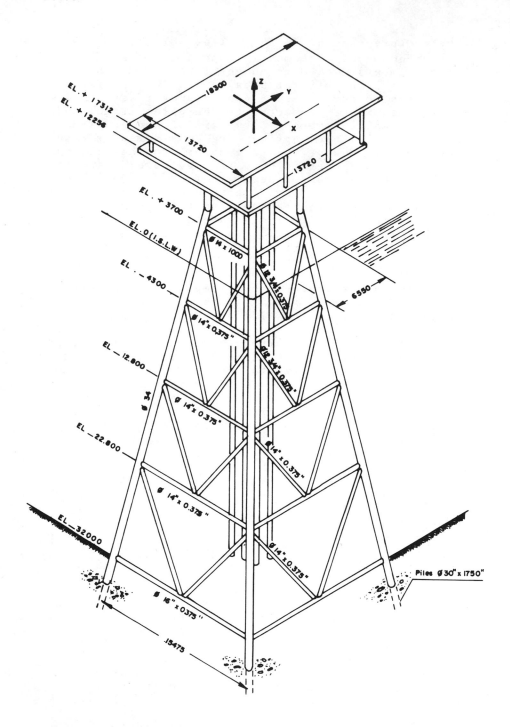

FIGURE I . THE PETROBRAS PDO-2 PLATFORM.

the ICES STRUDL II language. These new commands
include, among others, the following

- Automatic evaluation of dead weight, buoyancy and
  wave loads
- Generalized constraints
- Condensation and de-condensation of substructures
- Definition of soil characteristics
- Analysis of foundation-structure interaction
  problems
- Evaluation of baricenter and list of materials
- Definition of new property types
- Code checking
- New finite element types

The analysis of the six well Petrobras PDO-2 platform will be considered to illustrate the application
of some of the capabilities discussed above. The
platform is located in the Dourado field, with UTM
coordinates X = 721950 and Y = 8770850 and a batimetric
depth of 30 mts, southeast of the city of Aracajú,
in the state of Sergipe, Brazil.

The structure has four legs of 34" diameter and four
piles of 30" diameter, passing through the legs. The
pile penetration is 65 mts. The total height of the
structure is 50.69 mts. and its approximate weight is
700 tons. Figure 1 gives a view of this platform.

The STRUDL commands required to perform the
foundation-structure interaction studies on an
analysis model having 88 nodes and 177 elements for
a given wave load case, are shown in the next page.

The first part of the listing includes conventional
STRUDL commands to define title, units, joint
coordinates and member incidences. The MEMBER
PROPERTIES command shows the direct specification of
the properties of a tube member, which is a new
option.

The GENERALIZED CONSTRAINTS command is used to
represent the case of the piles passing through the
legs of the structure. In such cases, it is
specified that each pile joint node and its
corresponding leg joint must have the same lateral
displacements (U1 and U2). This allows for
differential longitudinal displacements and rotations.

The WAVE LOAD command is used to generate the loads due
to waves. In this case a design wave with a period
of 10.5 seconds and a height of 12.57 mts. was
considered. Other data given in the command include

```
STRUDL 'PDO' 'PLATFORM'
TYPE SPACE FRAME
UNITS METERS MTON DEGREES
JOINT COORDINATES
1   7.6125   7.6125   -1.000
    .          .          .
    .          .          .
    .          .          .
MEMBER INCIDENCES
 1      1      2
    .      .      .
    .      .      .
    .      .      .
MEMBER PROPERTIES
1 TO 20 TUBE '34X1.000' DIAMETER 0.864 THICKNESS 0.025
    .                .
    .                .
    .                .
GENERALIZED CONSTRAINTS
59   12   U1   U1   U2   U2
    .     .     .
    .     .     .
    .     .     .
LOADING
WAVE LOAD PERIOD 10.5 HEIGHT 12.527 SWL 32.78 -
ANGW 0. SURFC 1.37 BOTTC 0.305 MARG 4 -
MEMBERS 1 TO 114 301 TO 322 401 TO 406
0.    15.
0.05 22.0
0.075 28.0
0.05 32.0
RETRIEVE STIFFNESS ELEMENT 'CONVES' FILE 'MATRIX' 'CM-20X20'
ELEMENT INCIDENCES
'CONVES' 203 204 201 202
SUBSTRUCTURE
'PDO2' ELEM 1 TO 114 151 TO 154 .... 'CONVES' -
BOUNDARY NODES 97 98 94 91
SOIL CHARACTERISTICS LAYERS 1
1 SAND MEDIUM DEPTH 65. WEIGHT 0.8 ANGLE 30.
PILE ANALYSIS WITH LAT FRICTION SEGM 2. PILES 4 SUBST 'PDO2'
1 NODE 97 X  15.61 X  15.61 Z -65 ED .762 THIC .044 E 21000000
2 NODE 98 X  15.61 X -15.61 Z -65 ED .762 THIC .044 E 21000000
3 NODE 94 X -15.61 X  15.61 Z -65 ED .762 THIC .044 E 21000000
4 NODE 91 X -15.61 X -15.61 Z -65 ED .762 THIC .044 E 21000000
SUBSTRUCTURE ANALYSIS 'PDO2'
LIST DISPLACEMENTS FORCES ALL
FINISH
```

the still water level(32.78 mts.), the wave attack
(0º), the surface and bottom currents (1.37 and
0.305 m/s respectively)the number of marine growths
zones (4), and the members for which loads must be
computed. The end of each marine growths zone
(0., 0.05, 0.075 and 0.05) is given indicating its
distance from seabed.

With the data specified the command first selects the
best applicable wave theory (considering the Airy
Stokes fifth order, c-noidal and solitary wave
theories). Then, if an offset was given, the command
computes the member forces for the position of the
wave corresponding to that offset, and stores it in
the STRUDL data structure for later use. If the offset is not given, as is in the case in the present
example, the forces will be computed for several
different positions of the wave, but keeping only
those corresponding to the critical wave, i.e. the
one which produces the maximum base shear force.

The command RETRIEVE is used to retrieve the compact
stiffness matrix corresponding to the decks,
assigning to it the name 'CONVES'. These decks were
defined in an earlier run as a substructure, and its
stiffness matrix was saved on secondary memory. The
element incidences given indicate to which nodes that
stiffness matrix relates.

The next command, SUBSTRUCTURE, is used to condensate
the first component at the seabed level, corresponding
to nodes 97, 98, 94 and 91. Since it is possible to
use substructures within substructures, the PD02
substructure element list can include the substructure CONVES, as shown. After this command, the
structure and part of the piles above seabed are
represented by compact stiffness matrix and load
vectors corresponding to nodes 97, 98, 94 and 91,
only.

The soil CHARACTERISTICS command is used to specify
the properties of the soil, by layers. Although in
this case there is only one layer of 65 mts.,composed
of medium sand having a specific weight of 0.8 T/m^3
and a friction angle of 30º, in general any number
of layers, of different types of sands or clays, can
be used.

The PILE ANALYSIS command is used to perform the
foundation-structure interaction analysis. According
to the command given lateral friction springs, and
also tip resistance spring, must be considered. The
piles are to be divided in segments of 2. mts. each

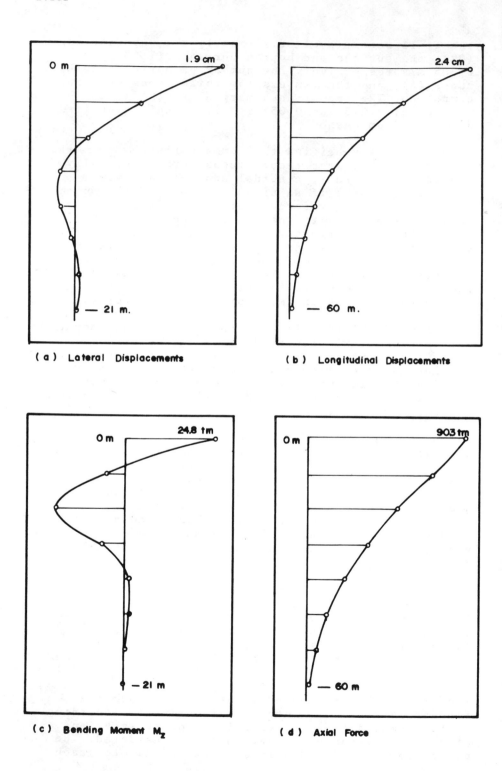

FIGURE 2 . SOME RESULTS FOR PILE — STATIC ANALYSIS

There are 4 piles, and the first component will be
represented by substructure PD02. Then there is a
line for each pile, defining its upper node, its
end coordinates, external diameter, thickness, and
modules of elasticity.

This command performs a non linear analysis based on
the Newton-Raphson method for the system substructure-
piles-soil. After the analysis is finished the
behaviour of the piles and the soil has been
determined, and the displacements for nodes 97, 98,
94 and 91, are known. It is possible then, based on
those displacements, to perform the analysis of the
substructure PD02, to compute the results
corresponding to its elements and internal joints.
The request for the output of the results is issued,
and the processing is ended.

Some of the results obtained, for the piles, are
shown in Figure 2.

THE DYNAMIC ANALYSIS SCHEME

Programs for non linear dynamic structural analysis
are generally based on time stepping algorithms,
such that the effective stiffness matrix has to be
evaluated at each time step. Since the nodal displacements are the unknowns, the evaluation of the
stiffness matrix for step $t+\Delta t$ is made using the
already known displacements for step t. As a
consequence, the system for step $t+\Delta t$ is not in
dynamic equilibrium, and it is necessary to introduce
a correction. This is normally done using an iterative
process.

The scheme described above is very expensive in
terms of computer time, because although the
stiffness matrix is not changed during the iterations,
it has to be updated for each time step. For problems
where the non linearities derive from scalar
elements having physical non linear behaviour, it is
possible to formulate more efficient procedures,
which do not require the actualization of the
stiffness matrix for each time step. This can be
done as suggested recently by Hofmeister [7], by
grouping all the non linear terms in a pseudo force
vector. This vector is normally estimated using
extrapolation techniques. The algorithm proposed by
Hofmeister, which combines the Newmark operator and
linear extrapolation of the pseudo-forces, has
produced good results for the analysis of the pipe
whip problem, in which the pipe has linear behaviour
but non linear springs are used to simulate the

support gaps.

In the analysis of foundation-structure interaction problems relative to offshore structures, when linear behaviour is assumed for the structure and the piles, the only non linear component is the soil. Since the soil is represented by springs and dampers, i.e. scalar elements, the use of a procedure based on a pseudo force vector would seem appropriated. Those systems, however, normally involve a large quantity of unknowns.

In addition, a large number of time steps are required in the time integration, in order to reach the steady-state response. Two new procedures, based on the modal superposition and the direct integration techniques respectively, specially tailored for offshore structure foundation-structure interaction problems, are being implemented.

The algorithm based on the modal superposition technique uses a precise integrator in order to improve the time response calculation. As the number of modal components considered decreases, the iterative process becomes more efficient [8].

The dynamic equilibrium equations, for time step $t+t\Delta t$, assume the form

$$\underset{\sim}{K} \, U_{t+\Delta t} + \underset{\sim}{B} \, \dot{U}_{\sim t+\Delta t} + \underset{\sim}{M} \, \ddot{U}_{\sim t+\Delta t} = \underset{\sim}{F}_{t+\Delta t} + \underset{\sim}{N}(U_{t+\Delta t}) \quad (1)$$

where K, B and M are the stiffness, damping and mass matrices, respectively, $\dot{U}_{t+\Delta t}$, $\ddot{U}_{t+\Delta t}$ and $U_{t+\Delta t}$ are the displacement, velocity and acceleration vectors, $\underset{\sim}{F}_{t+\Delta t}$ and $\underset{\sim}{N}(U_{t+\Delta t})$ are the applied load and pseudo-force vectors. Notice that the only non linear term corresponds to the pseudo force N.

The system defined by expression (1) is then reduced to the modal coordinates of the associated eigenvalue problem, such that

$$\underset{\sim}{k} \, \zeta_{t+\Delta t} + \underset{\sim}{b} \, \dot{\zeta}_{t+\Delta t} + \underset{\sim}{m} \, \ddot{\zeta}_{t+\Delta t} = \underset{\sim}{\phi}^{t} \, \underset{\sim}{F}_{t+\Delta t} + \underset{\sim}{\phi}^{t} \, \underset{\sim}{N}(U_{\sim t+\Delta t}) \quad (2)$$

where $\underset{\sim}{\phi}$ is the modal matrix, and

$$\underset{\sim}{k} = \underset{\sim}{\phi}^{t} \, \underset{\sim}{K} \, \underset{\sim}{\phi}$$

$$\underset{\sim}{b} = \underset{\sim}{\phi}^{t} \, \underset{\sim}{B} \, \underset{\sim}{\phi} \quad (3)$$

$$\underset{\sim}{m} = \underset{\sim}{\phi}^t \ \underset{\sim}{M} \ \underset{\sim}{\phi}$$

Equation (2) is integrated using the precise Duhamel integrator operator [9] at each time step, and the vector of pseudo-force is successively updated. The initial conditions required in order to start the iterative process corresponding to each time step, derived using linear extrapolation, are given by

$$\underset{\sim}{N}(\underset{\sim}{U}_{t+\Delta t}) = 2\underset{\sim}{N}(\underset{\sim}{U}_t) - \underset{\sim}{N}(\underset{\sim}{U}_{t-\Delta t}) \tag{4}$$

Hofmeister [7] developed a criteria which can be used to determine the time step required to achieve convergence, when using the class of algorithms being discussed. In practice however, the determination of the time-step using such criteria is too complex. Usually, starting with a reasonable estimate, the time-step is systematically reduced, until convergence is achieved.

In the implementation of the proposed algorithm the use of a variable time-step is allowed. The convergence test adopted is the following

$$\frac{\| \underset{\sim}{U} \|^i - \| \underset{\sim}{U} \|^{i-1}}{\| \underset{\sim}{U} \|^{i-1}} \leq \text{ tolerance} \tag{5}$$

where i indicates the iteration number

The algorithm based on the direct integration technique uses the Newmark's operator integrator. As all direct integration methods it assumes that the unknown accelerations, velocities, and displacements, at some time $t+\Delta t$, can be approximated by using the corresponding quantities known at some previous time points t, $t+\Delta t$... etc. This assumption, when used in the solution procedure of linear problems with non linear springs, leads to a recurssive relationship of the form

$$\left[(\underset{\sim}{K}_o + \underset{\sim}{K}_s \ (\underset{\sim}{U}_{t+\Delta t}) \right] \ \underset{\sim}{U}_{t+\Delta t} = \underset{\sim}{F}_{t+\Delta t} \tag{6}$$

where $\underset{\sim}{K}_o$, the effective stiffness matrix, and $\underset{\sim}{F}_{t+\Delta t}$, the load vector, are in several functions of mass, damping, and stiffness, as well as of the time-step Δt. The spring stiffnesses are contained in the matrix $\underset{\sim}{K}_s (\underset{\sim}{U}_{t+\Delta t})$. Since these stiffnesses are functions of the unknown displacements, equation (6) is non-

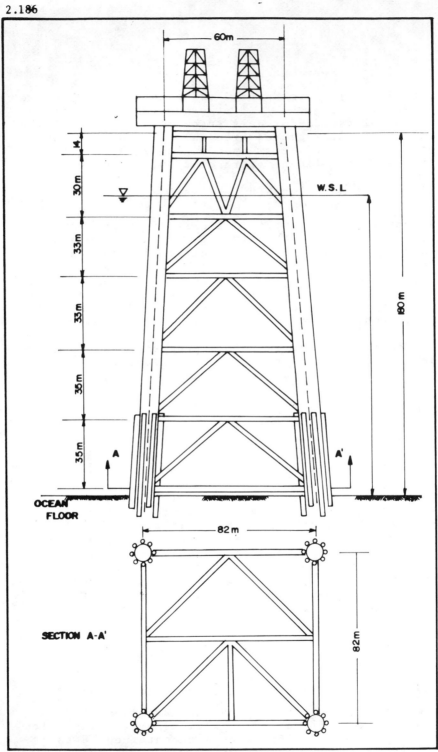

FIGURE 3 - EXAMPLE OFFSHORE STRUCTURE

linear. Following reference [7] the nonlinear
terms are placed on the right-hand side of equation
(6). The displacements are computed using the
expression

$$\underset{\sim o}{K} \ \underset{\sim t+\Delta t}{U} = \underset{\sim t+\Delta t}{F} + \underset{\sim}{N}(\underset{\sim t+\Delta t}{U}) \qquad\qquad (7)$$

where $\underset{\sim}{N}(\underset{\sim t+\Delta t}{U})$ is the pseudo-force vector.

The vector of pseudo-forces is successively updated.
The initial conditions, required in order to start
the iterative process, and the convergence test
adopted for equilibrium checking, are the same
described in equations (4) and (5).

A DYNAMIC ANALYSIS EXAMPLE

The case of the offshore structure shown in Figure 3
will be considered in order to illustrate the
application of the algorithms described above. This
example offshore structure [10] is a steel structure
consisting   of   four main vertical legs with cross-
bracing members connected at seven different levels.
The height from the seabed to the upmost bracing
level is 180 meters. The width from centerline of
the main legs at the upmost bracing level is 60
meters. The member   sizes are indicated in Figure
4, which shows the mathematical model selected. Four
piles, penetrating 80 meters, are attached to each
leg, having a total area of 24.904 m^2 and a total
moment of inertia of 27.364 m^4.

The soil is divided in two layers. The first layer,
from the seabed up to a penetration of 10 meters is
a medium sand having a specific weight of 0.9 T/m^3
and a friction angle of 30º. The second layer,
extending up to a penetration of 80 meters, is a
clay having a specific weight of 0.9 T/m^3 and a
cohesion factor of 3 T/m^2.

This structure was analyzed for a wave load with a
period of 13 seconds and a height of 20 meters. The
still water level corresponds to 150 meters.

Figure 5 shows the maximum horizontal displacements
for the nodes corresponding to one of the legs, for three
different cases, including the structure hinged at
the seabed, the soil represented by linear springs,
and the soil represented by non linear springs. The
stiffnesses of the springs were obtained from the P-Y
curves corresponding to the soil. In the second
case, linear soil behaviour, the spring stiffnesses

2.188

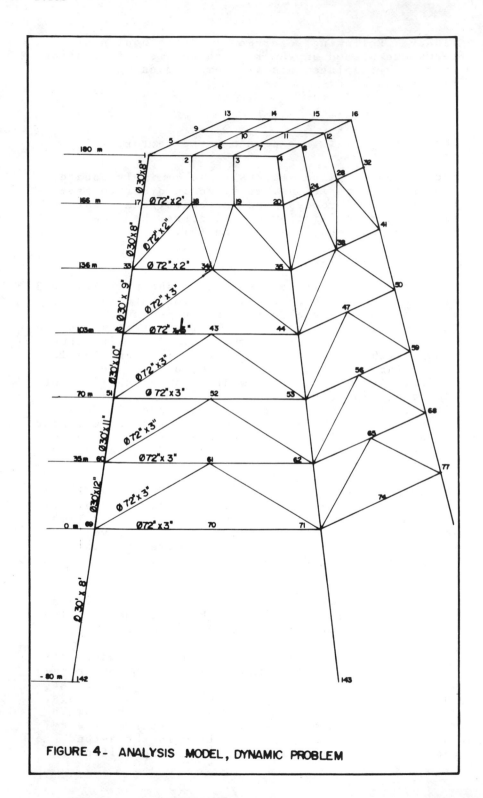

FIGURE 4- ANALYSIS MODEL, DYNAMIC PROBLEM

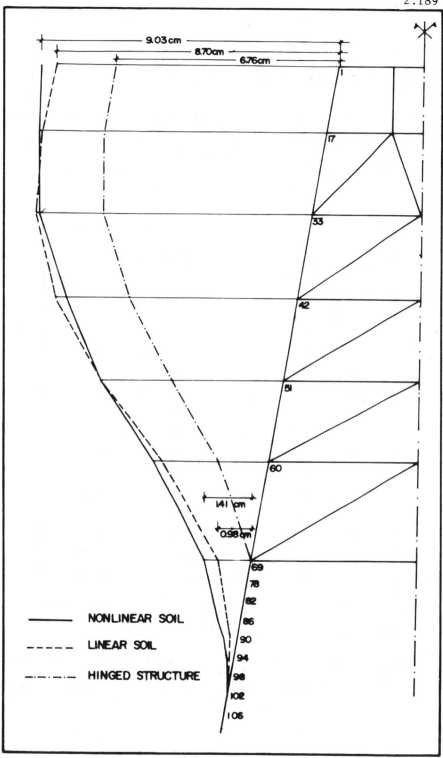

FIGURE 5 - MAXIMUM HORIZONTAL DISPLACEMENT, DIRECT INTEGRATION.

correspond to the first tangent to the P-Y curves.
Figure 6 shows the maximum axial force in the same
leg, for the linear and non linear soil behaviour
cases.

The problem was also analyzed using the modal superposition technique. Table 1 shows the maximum
horizontal displacements obtained with the direct
integration algorithm, and with the modal superposition algorithm taking into account 18 and 36
modes. Some of those displacements are also shown

NODE	DIRECT (CM.)	MODAL (CM.)	
		18 MODES	36 MODES
1	9.03	8.56	8.80
17	8.83	8.54	8.78
33	8.28	8.19	8.44
42	7.01	7.08	7.34
51	5.49	5.31	5.53
60	3.55	3.15	3.27
69	1.41	0.93	1.05
78	1.19	0.74	0.87
82	0.96	0.57	0.71
86	0.67	0.36	0.51
90	0.41	0.20	0.34
94	0.20	0.08	0.20
98	0.06	0.07	0.10
102	0.00	0.00	0.00

TABLE 1 - MAXIMUM HORIZONTAL DISPLACEMENTS

in Figure 7. The variation in time of the horizonta.
displacement for node 1 is shown in Figure 8, both
for the direct and the modal superposition algorithms.

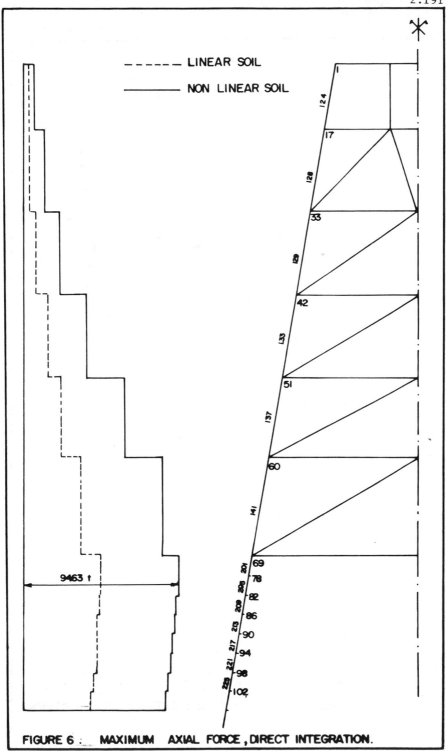

FIGURE 6 :   MAXIMUM   AXIAL   FORCE , DIRECT   INTEGRATION.

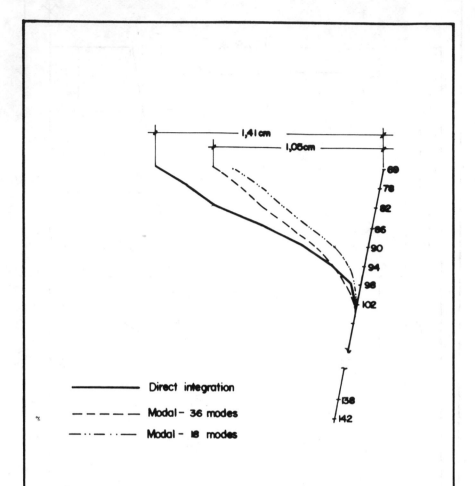

FIGURE 7 - MAXIMUM HORIZONTAL DISPLACENT FOR PILE , DIRECT
INTEGRATION AND MODAL SUPERPOSITION ALGORITHMS

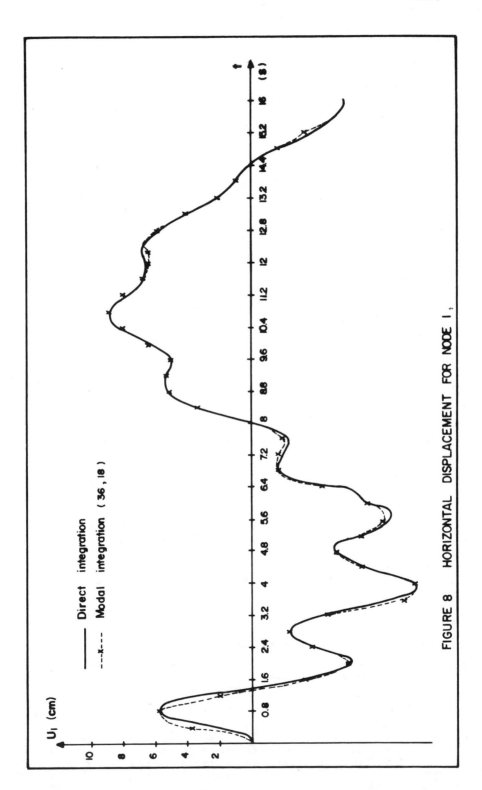

FIGURE 8   HORIZONTAL DISPLACEMENT FOR NODE 1,

CONCLUSIONS

The integrated procedure for static analysis of the foundation-structure interaction problem has been already in use, by the engineers of Petrobrás S.A., for nearly one year, showing to be an adequate computational tool for the solution of the practical problems encountered.

Regarding the algorithms proposed for the dynamic analysis of offshore structures, including soil non linearities, the results obtained for the example of the previous section seem to indicate the adequacy of both the direct integration and modal super-position schemes.

For linear problems, the modal superposition analysis is a highly efficient technique. The same seems to be true in general for non linear problems. However, study of different types of problems, considering variable numbers of modes, indicated that the method is very sensitive to localize non linearities. This is because of the difficulty in representing a localized loading with a reduced number of modes. In such cases the modal superposition method may become more inefficient than the direct integration method, due to the large number of modes required to obtain an adequate representation. Thus, in general, it is convenient to be able to use either technique, according to the case.

The consideration of non-linearities as pseudo-forces requires the use of a procedure for equilibrium checking. A precise solution of the equilibrium equations in each step is much more important in the dynamic analysis than in the static analysis. Errors introduced in dynamic stepping solutions are cumulative and cannot be compensated later, as in the analysis of some static non linear problems.

REFERENCES

1. - R.D. Logcher et all, "ICES STRUDL II - Engineering User's Manual", Vol. 1, Report R68-91, and Vol. 2, Report R70-71, Massachusetts Institute of Technology, Cambridge, Mass., USA.

2. - A.J. Ferrante, E.C. Valenzuela, and G.B. Ellwanger, "A Computational Approach for the Analysis of Fixed Offshore Structures including Piling", Proceedings of the International Conference on Environmental Forces on Engineering Structures

Imperial College, London, July of 1979.

3. - A.J. Ferrante, N.F. Ebecken, E.C. Prates de Lima and E.C. Valenzuela, "Influence of the Soil Characteristics in the Behaviour of a Fixed Steel Platform", Offshore Structures Engineering, F.L.L.B. Carneiro, A.J. Ferrante and C.A. Brebbia (Editors), Pentech Press, London, 1979.

4. - H. Matlock, 'Correlations for Design of Laterally Loaded Piles in Soft Clay', Paper OTC 1204, Proceedings, Second Annual Offshore Technology Conference, Houston, Texas, 1970.

5. - R.C. Reese, W.R. Cox, F.D. Koop, 'Analysis of Laterally Loaded Piles in Sand', Paper OTC 2080, Proceedings, Sixth Annual Offshore Technology Conference, Houston, Texas, Vol.2, pp 473-483.

6. - American Petroleum Institute, API-RP-2 Code, Planning, Designing and Constructing Fixed Offshore Platforms, Seventh Edition, January 1976.

7. - Ofmeister L.D.,"Dynamic Analysis of Structures Containing Non Linear Springs", Computers and Structures, Vol.8, pp. 609-614, 1978.

8. - Nickell R.E., "Non Linear Dynamics by Mode Superposition", Computer Methods in Applied Mechanics and Engineering, Vol. 7, pp.107-129, 1976.

9. - "The NASTRAN Theoretical Manual", NASA SP-221, September, 1970.

10.- Liou D. and Penzien J., "Seismic Analysis of an Offshore Structure Supported on Pile Foundations", Report Nº UCB/EERC-77/25, Univ. of California at Berkeley, November, 1979.

OFFSHORE PIPELINING - PARAMETERIZATION AND DYNAMIC
ANALYSIS

G.Clauss and R.Schmitz

Technical University Berlin

1. INTRODUCTION

With the increase of offshore oil discoveries deep
water pipelining has become a vital branch in offshore technology. With a new generation of semisub-
merged laying barges the industry now is even capable
of bridging the mediterranean sea with water depths
up to 600 m. As the tension capacity of barge and
thus the weight of the pipeline are limited the pipe
diameter is restricted at great water depths.
Nevertheless 36"-pipelines in the Northern North
Sea have been laid without major problems. In such
operations, for example, about 500 m of the pipe
are freely suspended at a water depth of 150 m.
Nearly 90 % of its weight of approximately 10 KN/m
are compensated by the buoyancy of the pipe, while
its virtual mass is the double of the actual pipe
mass, according to the hydrodynamic portion which
is equal to the displaced water mass. This paper
deals with some aspects of the pipe behaviour
during laying with emphasis to the theoretical
analysis of pipe geometry, stresses and forces. This
investigations are backed up by an experimental program dealing with pipe dynamics in the seaway.

2. DIFFERENTIAL EQUATIONS AND CHARACTERISTIC
   COEFFICIENTS

During laying operations the pipeline is welded
aboard the laying vessel, passes a tensioner and
slides over the stinger or ramp with constant curvature. From the lift-off point on the stinger the
suspended pipeline lowers gently to the touch-down
point at the sea floor (Fig. 1). The equilibrium

of forces (V, H) and moments (M) of an element of
the suspended pipe (Fig. 2) yields the differential equation

$$\frac{d^2 M}{dx^2} + \frac{W}{\cos \vartheta} - H \frac{d^2 z}{dx^2} = 0 \qquad (1a)$$

with w being the pipe unit length weight.

Introducing

$$M = EI \frac{\dfrac{d^2 z}{dx^2}}{\left[1 + \left(\dfrac{dz}{dx}\right)^2\right]^{3/2}} \qquad (2a)$$

from beam theory with EI being the pipe stiffness
it follows

$$EI \frac{d^2}{dx^2} \left\{ \frac{\dfrac{d^2 z}{dx^2}}{\left[1 + \left(\dfrac{dz}{dx}\right)^2\right]^{3/2}} \right\} + \frac{W}{\cos \vartheta} - H \frac{d^2 z}{dx^2} = 0 \qquad (3a)$$

Relating all geometric parameters to the water
depth d, i.e.

$$\bar{x} = \frac{x}{d} \quad ; \quad \bar{z} = \frac{z}{d}$$

this yields

$$\frac{EI}{wd^3} \frac{d^2}{d\bar{x}^2} \left\{ \frac{\dfrac{d^2 \bar{z}}{d\bar{x}^2}}{\left[1 + \left(\dfrac{d\bar{z}}{d\bar{x}}\right)^2\right]^{3/2}} \right\} + \frac{1}{\cos \vartheta} + \frac{H}{wd} \frac{d^2 \bar{z}}{d\bar{x}^2} = 0 \qquad (3b)$$

This differential equation proves that all solutions can be presented non dimensional, the results
depending only on the normalized pipe stiffness

$$s^* = \frac{EI}{wd^3} \qquad (4a)$$

and the normalized horizontal force

$$H^* = \frac{H}{wd} \qquad (4b)$$

Solutions of the differential equation have been found by numerical procedures and model tests, the latter being the proof of all static calculations as well as the key to pipe dynamics.

3. NUMERICAL PROCEDURES

For computations the above differential equations (1a) and (2a) are written as finite difference equations (Fig. 3).

$$\frac{M_{i+1} - 2M_i + M_{i-1}}{\Delta x^2} + \frac{W}{\cos \vartheta_i} - H \frac{tg\, \vartheta_{i-1} - tg\, \vartheta_i}{\Delta x} = 0 \qquad (1b)$$

$$M_{i+1} = EI\,(\,tg\, \vartheta_i - tg\, \vartheta_{i+1})\,\cos^3 \vartheta_i \qquad (2b)$$

From Eq. (1b) the moment is calculated, from Eq. (2b) follows the associated slope angle. Changing back to Eq. (1b), the succeeding moment is determined and so forth.

For a pipe of given weight and stiffness the boundary conditions at a fixed water depth include

- the maximum yield stress at the stinger lift-off point and
- the slope of the pipe at the sea floor where the bending stress decreases to zero.

If stinger length and curvature as well as the barge tension force Z are known, the calculation starts with an approximate value of the horizontal force

$$H = Z - wd \qquad (5a)$$

and a chosen value of the lift-off angle ϑ_o. The calculation continues extending the pipeline down

to the sea floor where the pipe slope and the accompanying moment both should arrive at zero. To obtain
this solution the stinger lift-off point has to be
varied. In general the boundary conditions at the
sea floor can only be satisfied if the original horizontal force is modified.

Thus the relationship of the horizontal force and the
barge pulling force has to be rewritten more accurately by introducing a correcting coefficient α

$$H = Z - \alpha wd \tag{5b}$$

where α reaches 1 for a catenary and decreases with
increasing pipe stiffness. It was noticed that the
final solution requires ultimate accuracy of all input data which have been iterated over several runs.

Our first set of data gives a general view of pipeline characteristics using a non dimensional presentation. All pipelines were calculated from the inflection point near the tip of the stinger down to
the sea floor, the parameters being the normalized
pipe stiffness and horizontal force. For all realistic combinations of these parameters the Figs.
4-9 show pipe geometry and bending stresses. Here
the dimensionless stress is defined by

$$\sigma^* = \frac{d}{D} \frac{\sigma}{E}$$

where D is the pipe diameter and E the module of
elasticity. Low stiffness S^* combined with high horizontal forces H^* yield catenary-type pipe geometries and stresses (e.g. Fig. 4). Similarly
beam-type solutions are observed at high stiffness
values and dimensionless low tension forces (e.g.
Fig. 9). Both parameters define the maximum bending stress σ_o^* of the pipe which is shown in Fig.
10.

Pipe stiffness and horizontal force both extend the
relative horizontal pipe dimension and yield an overall decrease of the bending stress. Thus the bending stress is roughly determined by this parameter
as can be noticed from Fig. 11. Here the limiting
dotted curve refers to a catenary. The next diagrams in Fig. 12 and 13 show the bottom reaction

force of the pipeline and its departure angle. As
can be seen, the bottom force is high for the
"beam-type" pipeline and decreases to zero for a
catenary.

After these general remarks a detailed analysis
of a specific laying problem is given. Here we refer to a certain pipeline (diameter D, weight w,
stiffness EI) which shall connect an oilfield with
the shore, the water depth depending on the route.
At selected depths and tensioner forces Z the Figs.
14-16 show pipe geometry and bending stresses. The
following diagrams Fig. 17 and 18 deal with the
forces at the stinger lift-off point. As can be
seen in the insert of Fig. 17 the total force K
does not act in the direction of the pipe axis. Its
longitudinal component Z' is the slightly reduced
tensioner force $Z_0 = Z - w(d-d_0)$, while Q is a
transverse force which depends largely on pipe
stiffness and the immediate decrease of the curvature behind the stinger lift-off point. Of course,
also near the tensioner a sudden change of pipe
curvature occurs resulting in an analogous force.

As constant curvature along the stinger results in
constant moment and bending stress distribution no
transverse force is obtained in the middle section
of the stinger. In practice, however, the large forces on the stinger edges will deformate the construction and radiate to neighbouring sections.
Thus it is advisable to design a smoothly changing
curvature at the upper and lower stinger ends.

Discussing the influence of the input parameters it
was observed that all forces grow with increasing
water depth and tensioner force, the merit of the
latter being a lower bending stress in the suspended pipe and a shorter stinger length. In this context it is surprising that the transverse force
remains nearly constant at all water depths.

4. DYNAMICS

As the computer program is very flexible, any change
of the configuration can be evaluated accordingly.
This includes the influence of transverse currents
varying in depth and time which requires a distinct
barge yaw and offset related to the pipe direction.
It is also possible to evaluate dynamic reactions
as long as quasi-stationary conditions are applicable. This assumption is valid if a critical fre-

quency is not exceeded where the hydrodynamic pipe
mass and damping characteristics determine pipe dynamics. These phenomena are analysed experimentally.

Up to this critical frequency, the quasi-stationary
pipe motions as well as stress and force variations
can be calculated directly. Discussing the relevant
degrees of freedom - surge, heave, pitch and roll -
it is obvious that pitch motions of the barge can
be described in terms of horizontal and vertical
motions of the center of curvature of the stinger
as its rotation affects only the stinger length.
In this context surge, heave and pitch motions of
the laying barge, i.e. its transfer functions, have
to be converted to the center of the stinger curvature with special regard to the phase differences.

4.1 Experimental analysis
Pipe dynamics have its main source in barge motions.
Model tests are feasible if inertia forces are reduced adequately to all other forces acting on the
system. As has been derived in [1], complete geometric similarity of model and full scale pipe is not
possible. Based on Eq. (3b) and the resulting non
dimensional coefficients S^* and H^* a model with
partial geometric similarity was proposed (Fig. 19).
Here the air-filled steel pipe with concrete coa-
ting is substituted by a model pipe with one or
several internal rods and a liquid filling. The non
dimensional coefficients describe the relation of
forces, i.e.

$$S^* = \frac{EI}{wd^3} = \frac{EI/d^2}{wd} = \frac{\text{elastic force}}{\text{weight force}}$$

$$H^* = \frac{H}{wd} = \frac{\text{external force}}{\text{weight force}}$$

These forces, i.e.

- the external forces H, V, Q
- the weight force $\quad w = \gamma \ell^3$ and
- the elastic force $\quad e = \frac{EI}{\ell^2}$ as well as
- the inertia force $\quad m \frac{\ell}{t^2} = \varrho \frac{\ell^4}{t^2}$,

with ℓ being an arbitrary length, must be scaled
equally. The mass force hereby includes the hydro-

dynamic mass which, for transverse motions of a cylindrical pipe, is equal to the displaced water mass.

Equating these forces yields the

- model scale $\lambda = \dfrac{\ell}{\ell''} = \sqrt[5]{\dfrac{EI/E'I'}{\gamma/\gamma'}}$ and the

- time scaling factor $\tau = \dfrac{t}{t'} = \sqrt{\dfrac{\varrho/\varrho'}{\gamma/\gamma'}}\,\lambda = \sqrt{\dfrac{\varrho/\varrho'}{EI/E'I'}}\,\lambda^3$

It requires some skill to select a suitable model as
the scale has to satisfy the self-evident condition

$$\lambda = \frac{D}{D'}$$

to model the hydrodynamic inertia forces appropria-
tely. As model scale is determined by these strict
physical requirements it is very difficult to investigate a model pipe in connection with a laying
barge. Therefore stinger and hull motions of laying vessels (Fig. 20) are determined separately and
their results are transfered to any other pipe model scale.

The main purpose of the experimental program, however, was the evaluation of the basic dynamic behaviour of the pipe itself during laying operations.
For this a water tank, 12 m long and 5 m deep was
installed with windows on one side for pipe observation. On top of this tank a planar motion mechanism is installed (Fig. 21) which simulates the
stinger motions within the following limits

- heave	$\pm$ 0,15 m
- surge (or sway)	$\mp$ 0,15 m
- pitch	$\mp$ 15°
- roll	$\mp$ 15°

All phase differences can be set arbitrarely in
steps of 15 degrees. The period is continuously
variable between

$$0,75 \text{ sec} < T < 7,5 \text{ sec}$$

Only the lift-off section of the stinger is used in
experiments as the remaining upper part is not relevant for pipe motions. The horizontal and vertical
force as well as the pipe moment at the lift-off
point are measured at the stinger support.

At the opposite end of the water tank a horizontal
frame can be shifted up and down. Its supports a
long and narrow container filled with mercury. Thus
the lower end of the pipe slides into this heavy
fluid and floats there horizontally. The floating
end of the pipe is tied to a strain gauge where the
horizontal force H can be measured directly. Every
60 centimeters a pair of strain gauges is fixed to
the model pipe indicating the bending stresses respectively. As for the determination of the static
stress distribution the pipeline is rotated by 180°
degrees about its axis, the difference of the strain
gauge outputs being the double of the relevant
stress. Finally the lower end of the pipeline is
equipped with a series of sealed metal rings which
are part of an electrical circuit. If a ring dives
into the mercury the circuit with a signal lamp is
closed indicating the temporary touch-down point.

4.2 Investigations
For investigations of pipe dynamics a 40" x 1,25"
pipe was selected. Due to the steady-state analysis Fig. 22 shows motions and stress variations in
a water depth of 200 m if horizontal and vertical
motions are applied. Note that these motions which
refer to the barge and the pipe inflection point
near the stinger lift-off point result from surge,
heave and pitch motions of the laying vessel. Detailed results have been compiled in Fig. 23
where the combined action of horizontal and vertical motions are presented.

To illustrate dynamic phenomena Fig. 24 shows stress
amplification in surge and heave motions in a certain pipe section while the excitation frequency
is increased. The model test proofed that laying
barge motions alterate the basic stress distribution considerably (Fig. 25). Resonance phenomena
and standing waves were observed as the dynamic
motion is reflected at the sea floor. Compared
with steady state calculations the dynamic effects
show considerable magnification (Fig. 26). In conclusion it was not possible to file all phenomena
in a systematic and handy manual to predict the dynamic behaviour of pipes during laying. From our
results, however, it follows that a steady-state
analysis is not sufficient and dynamic model tests
are strongly recommended if pipes have to be laid
under adverse weather conditions.

5. CONCLUSIONS

This paper presents an extensive study of offshore
pipelining including a parametric display of all
relevant pipe geometries and stresses. The results
are based on a non dimensional analysis and include
forces at the stinger lift-off point and the touch-
-down point at the sea floor. Pipe dynamics are investigated by numerical calculations and model
tests. It was noted that steady-state analysis is
not sufficient if pipes have to be laid under adverse weather conditions. In this case dynamic model tests are strongly recommended.

6. ACKNOWLEDGEMENTS

The authors wish to express their gratitude to the
staff of the "Institut für Schiffstechnik", in particular to Mr. T. Lejeune, who helped with the experiments and to Mrs. Weber and Mrs. Erdenberger,
who typed and touched up the manuscript.

7. REFERENCES

1 Clauss, G. and Kruppa, C. (1974) Model Testing
   Techniques in Offshore Pipelining. OTC 1937,
   Houston.

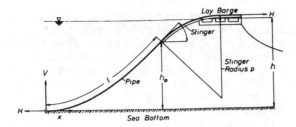

Fig. 1   Pipe geometry

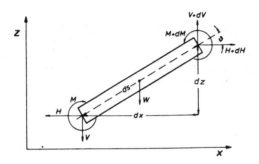

Fig. 2   Pipe element

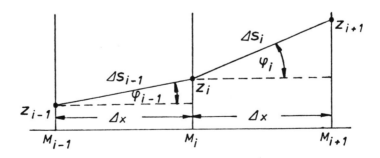

Fig. 3   Finite element analysis

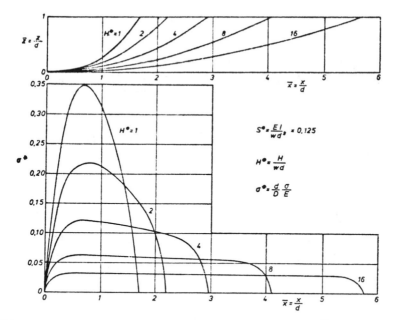

Fig. 4   Pipe geometry and stresses - $S^* = 0.125$

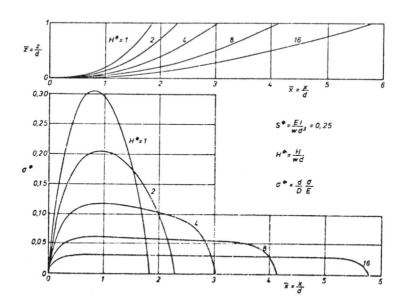

Fig. 5   Pipe geometry and stresses - $S^* = 0.25$

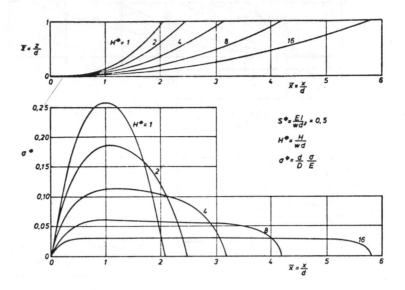

Fig. 6   Pipe geometry and stresses - $S^* = 0.5$

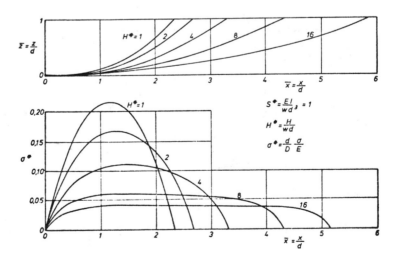

Fig. 7   Pipe geometry and stresses - $S^* = 1.0$

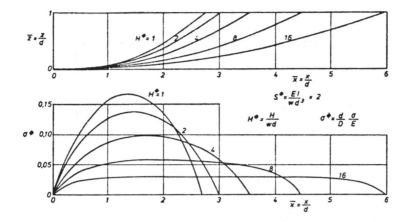

Fig. 8   Pipe geometry and stresses - $S^* = 2.0$

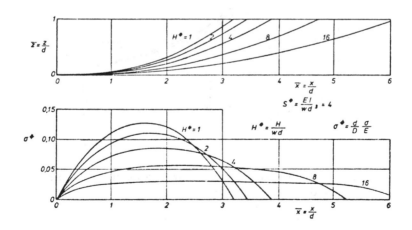

Fig. 9   Pipe geometry and stresses - $S^* = 4.0$

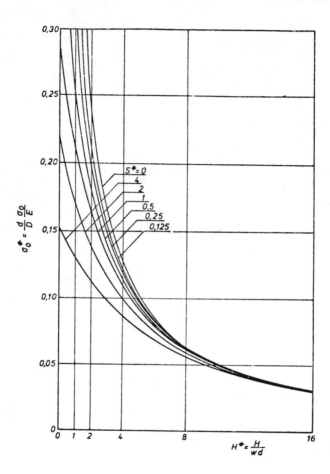

Fig. 10   Maximum normalized bending stress
during laying

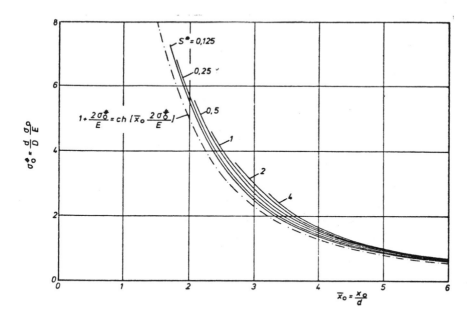

Fig. 11   Maximum normalized bending stress versus
           relative pipe length

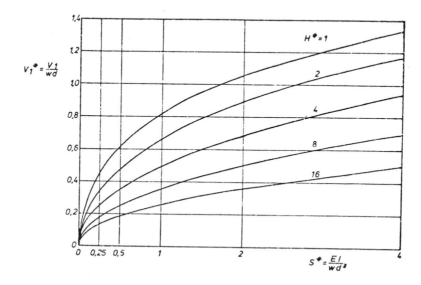

Fig. 12   Normalized bottom reaction force of the
           suspended pipe

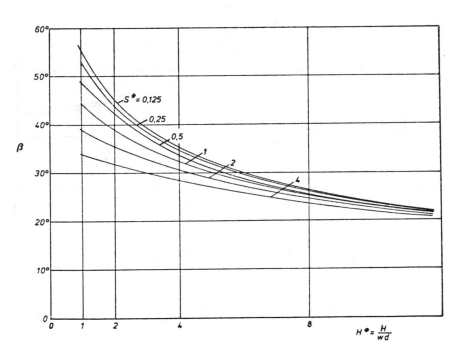

Fig. 13   Departure angle at inflection point

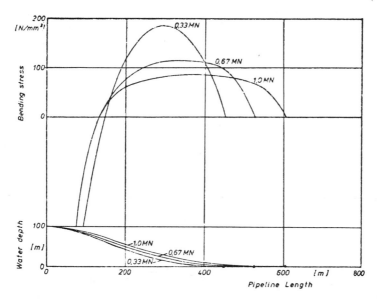

Fig. 14   Laying of a 40" x 1.25" pipeline in 100 m
           water depth - geometry and stresses -

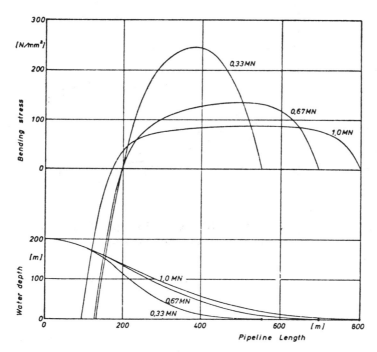

Fig. 15   Laying of a 40" x 1.25" pipeline in 200 m
           water depth - geometry and stresses -

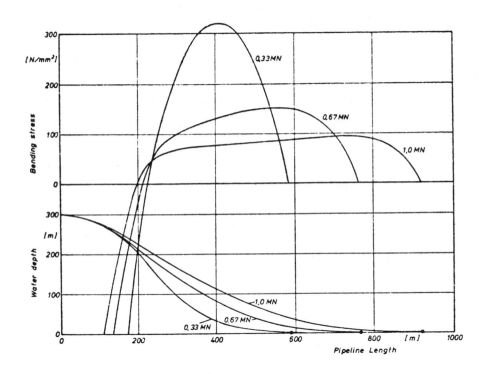

Fig. 16   Laying of a 40" x 1.25" pipeline in 300 m
           water depth - geometry and stresses -

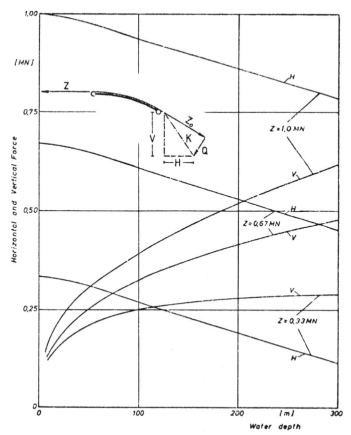

Fig. 17   Laying of a 40" x 1.25" pipeline - Horizontal and vertical forces at the stinger
lift-off point -

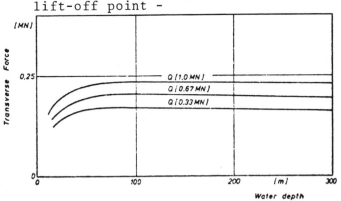

Fig. 18   -Transverse force at the stinger lift-off
point -.

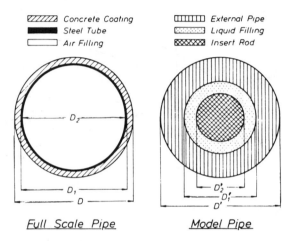

Full Scale Pipe   Model Pipe

Fig. 19   Model pipe geometry

Fig. 20 Laying vessels – model scale 1:100

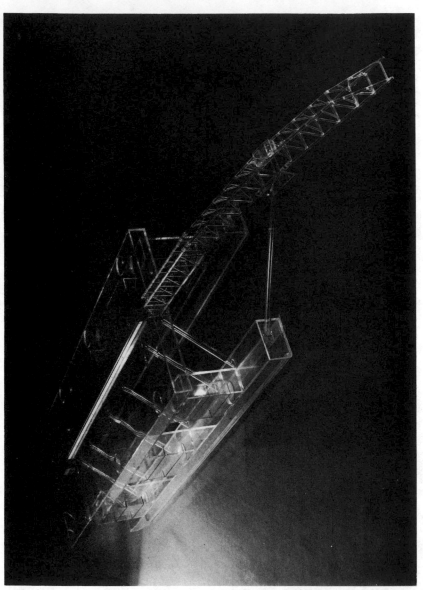

Fig. 20 (contd.)

Fig. 21   Planar motion mechanismus for simulation
          of barge motions - double exposure

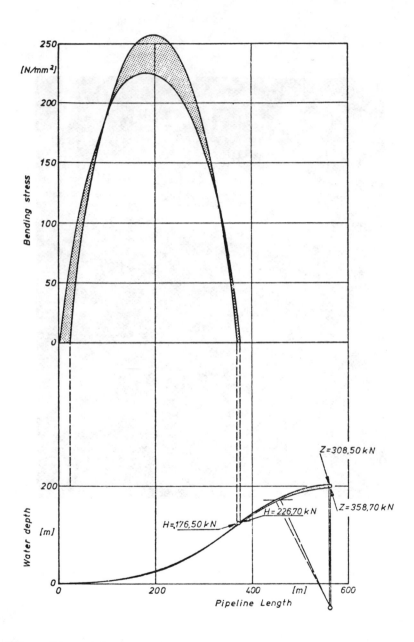

Fig. 22   Pipe motions and related stress variation of a 40" x 1.25" pipe

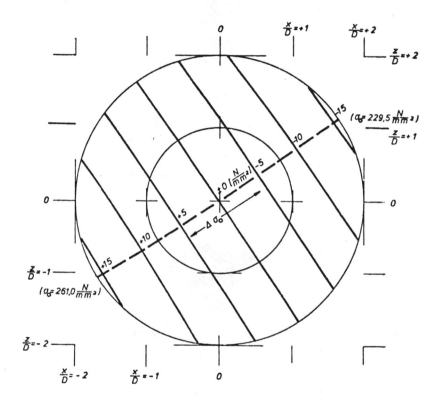

Fig. 23   Stress variations related to arbitrary
           motions of the inflection point of a
           40" x 1.25" pipe

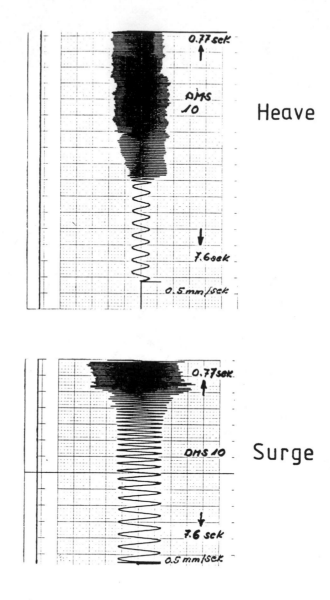

Fig.24 Dynamic magnification of bending stress

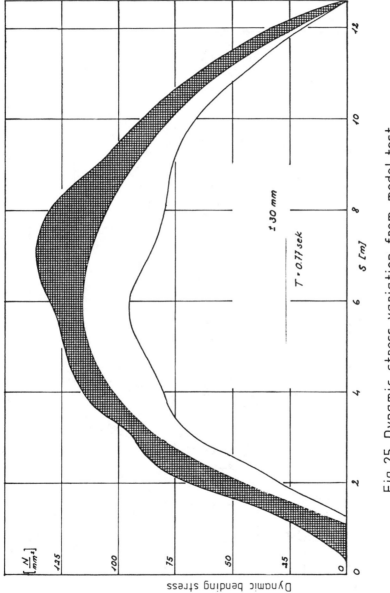

Fig. 25 Dynamic stress variation from model test
– heave and surge ±30 mm

2.224

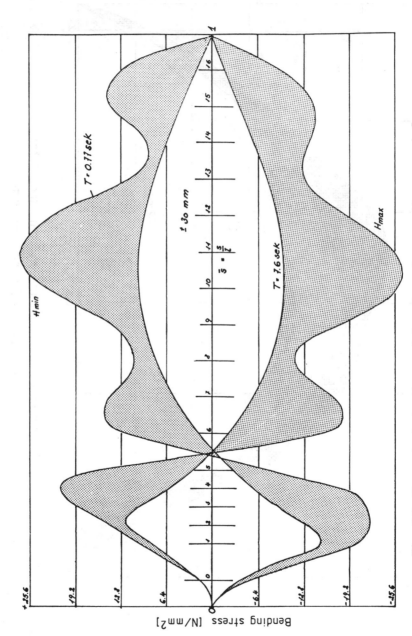

Fig.26 Dynamic behaviour of bending stress – Heave and Surge

STUDY OF A STRUCTURAL DESIGN METHOD FOR A CONCRETE BARGE

Hirohiko Emi   Riichi Kobayashi and Kenichi Noguchi

Nippon Kaiji Kyokai   Taisei Corporation

INTRODUCTION

The barge described here is a barge-type floating offshore
structure made from concrete, and differs from an ordinary barge
or boat, in that it has a large water plane area and a shallow
draught compared with an ordinary ship. Moreover, it is
expected to be used mostly under moored conditions. The barge
is a floating offshore structure developed to provide marine
capacity, as a new-type usage, on which it is possible to house
various kinds of plants: refinery, desalination and power, and
various kinds of facilities: hotel, storage, medical and
educational.

Design criteria of various standards organisations exist which
give recommendations on design methods for concrete barges, most
of which, however, provisionally apply conventional design-rules
for ships subjected to wave loads, and those for coastal
structures and land structures to determine the material strength.

This paper, for the purpose of establishing a design method for
concrete barges, describes the result of investigations on the
wave forces of a barge-type floating structure and the
applicability of reinforced concrete as a barge construction
material.

ON DESIGN WAVE LOADS

Evaluation of wave loads
Up to 1960, the design of boats and ships was based on the
Froude-Kriloff hypothesis in which sinusoidal or trochoidal
surface waves act on a body without any disturbance. Later,
statistical prediction of a wave-induced load is introduced for
designing ships' hull structures, and these prediction methods
are based on a response function using a strip theory, etc. in
regular wave and wave statistics of the North Atlantic. A part
of these methods is introduced into "Provisional Rules for

Pre-stressed Concrete Barges" of the Nippon Kaiji Kyokai.

It will be limited to apply to a strip method for a dynamic response of the barge, because it is a flat shaped barge with a shallow draught. Moreover, it is expected to be used mostly in moored conditions in a gulf of inshore waters. Therefore, it is necessary to evaluate wave loads in conformity with the shape of the barge and the wave condition of its surrounding sea area.

Experiments for the modified barge in a basin

For the above mentioned problems, experiments were carried out on the fundamental characteristics of the motion and hydrodynamic pressures on the barge, to determine the suitability to apply a strip method to the analysis of the barge movement and the longitudinal distribution of wave bending moments and shear forces.

A model of the barge is shown in Fig. 1. The experiments were made under two conditions: the semi-anchoring condition which was similar to the mooring one, and the towing condition. The latter was carried out involving a travelling crane. The experiments were made with variables of wave length, wave height, wave direction, draught and towing speed.

Hydrodynamic pressures on the bottom of the barge

Hydrodynamic pressures were measured with pressure transducers. Longitudinal distributions of the maximum hydrodynamic pressures on the bottom in the semi-anchoring and the towing conditions are shown in Figs. 2 and 3.

In the semi-anchoring condition, each distribution is different by draught and wave length at the bow and stern, but not different at any other position. The distribution modes are mostly similar, so that hydrodynamic pressure decreases drastically from the bow to midship. There is little difference in the hydrodynamic pressure at the bow whether the vertical part of the bow is under the water surface (d=7.25, 9.0cm) or above it (d=5.0cm).

In the towing condition, hydrodynamic pressure on the bow increases as the towing speed increases and the draught is deeper. When the towing speed is 0.6 m/s, they become about 1.5 times compared with the cases of the same waves in the semi-anchoring condition.

The calculated values, by an ordinary strip method (O.S.M.) are similar to the measured values except the values at the bow for shallow draught (d=5.0cm). There is a tendency for the calculated values to be larger than the measured values at midships.

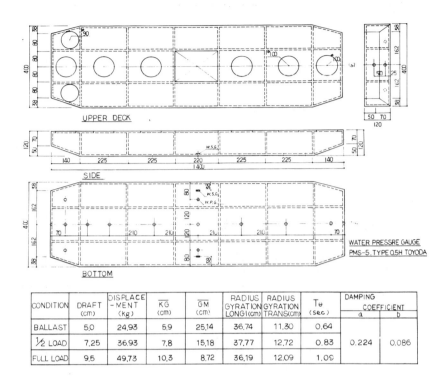

UPPER DECK

SIDE

BOTTOM

WATER PRESSRE GAUGE
PMS-5. TYPE 0.5H TOYODA

CONDITION	DRAFT (cm)	DISPLACE-MENT (kg)	$\overline{KG}$ (cm)	$\overline{GM}$ (cm)	RADIUS GYRATION LONGI (cm)	RADIUS GYRATION TRANS(cm)	Tθ (sec)	DAMPING COEFFICIENT a	b
BALLAST	5.0	24.93	5.9	25.14	36.74	11.30	0.64		
½ LOAD	7.25	36.93	7.8	15.18	37.77	12.72	0.83	0.224	0.086
FULL LOAD	9.5	49.73	10.3	8.72	36.19	12.09	1.09		

Fig. 1 Test model of a barge-type floating structure

Fig. 4 shows the distributions of the hydrodynamic pressure on
the transverse section at midships.

In the case of a 90° encounter angle (γ), hydrodynamic pressure
decreases drastically from the incident side to the centre of
the bottom. At the transmissive side it increases as the
draught is shallower and the wave length is longer. But their
values are under a third of the values at the incident side.
The calculated values by O.S.M. are roughly the same as the
measured values of the experiments.

In the case of γ = 135°, hydrodynamic pressure on the incident
side increases as the wave length increases until it is three
times that of the barge breadth.

The calculated values of motions are also similar to the
measured ones. There is a tendency for the values calculated
by O.S.M. using theoretical values for the rolling period and
damping coefficient to be at variance with the measured values.
Therefore, the values of motion and hydrodynamic pressures
were calculated using the experimental values. A flat rectangular section is transformed to the Lewis' form with a kind of
conformal representation. The transformed section is
dissimilar to the original section. But O.S.M. is shown to be

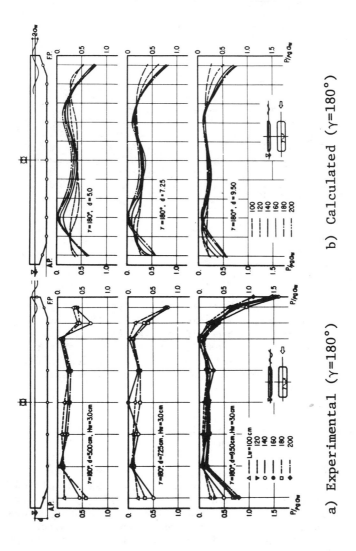

a) Experimental (γ=180°)   b) Calculated (γ=180°)

Fig.2   Longitudinal distributions of hydrodynamic pressures
         (semi-anchoring condition)

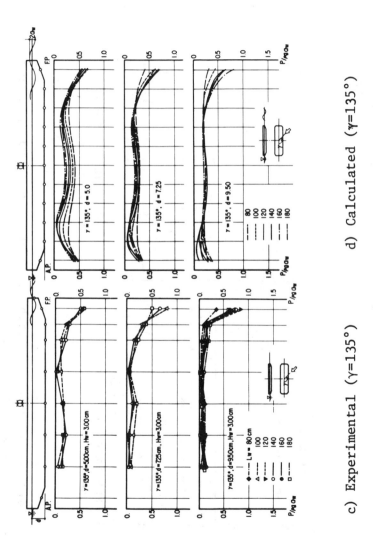

c) Experimental (γ=135°) d) Calculated (γ=135°)

Fig.2 (contd.)

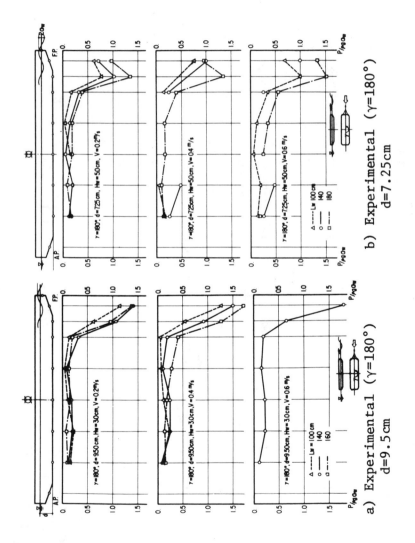

a) Experimental (γ=180°)
d=9.5cm

b) Experimental (γ=180°)
d=7.25cm

Fig.3   Longitudinal distributions of hydrodynamic pressures
(towing condition)

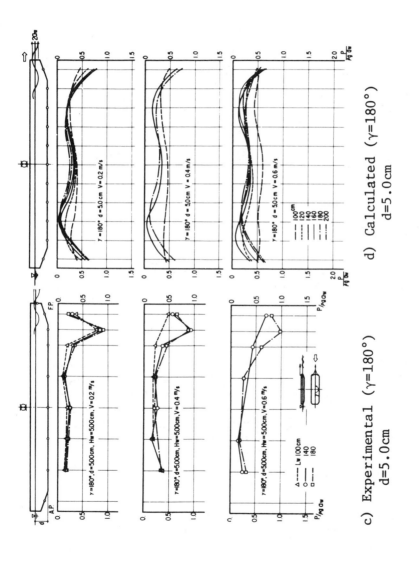

c) Experimental (γ=180°)
   d=5.0cm

d) Calculated (γ=180°)
   d=5.0cm

Fig.3 (contd.)

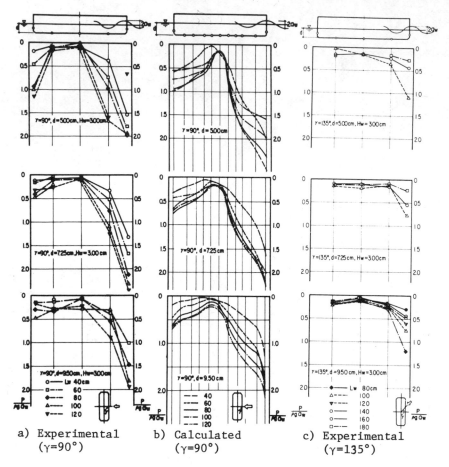

| a) Experimental (γ=90°) | b) Calculated (γ=90°) | c) Experimental (γ=135°) |

Fig.4 Transverse distributions of hydrodynamic pressures

a practical analysis method, because the calculated values of hydrodynamic pressure are mostly similar to the measured values as well as the values of motions calculated macroscopically.

Longitudinal bending moments and shear forces in wave
The values of ME1, vertical bending moments of the midship calculated with the strain amplitude measured by wire strain gauges are shown in Fig. 5 and the value of ME2, calculated with the hydrodynamic pressures on the bottom, are shown in Fig. 6.

Fig. 5 shows clearly that the moments in the semi-anchoring condition are similar to those in the towing condition.

When the ratio of wave length (Lw) to length of barge (L) is less than 1, both ME1 and ME2 increase as the wave length increases. When the ratio is greater than 1, ME1 is nearly

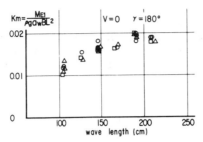

a) Semi-anchoring condition

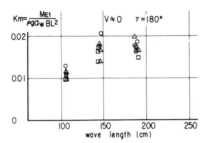

b) Towing condition

Fig.5　Vertical bending moments
　　　　(calculated　by the strain)

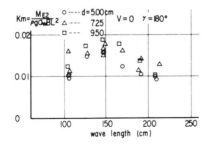

Fig.6　Vertical bending moments
(calculated　by the pressures)

constant and ME2 decreases as the wave length increases. This
effect is considered in the calculation method ignoring the
accelerations of the ship motions. But the maximum values of
ME1 and ME2 are for the most part the same, so that this method
of calculation will be satisfied in design.

Compared with the vertical bending moments of the midship
calculated by a hypothesis that sinusoidal or trocoidal surface
waves act on a floating body without any disturbances, ME2 is
from 0.3 to 0.4 times the value.

Using the distributions of hydrodynamic pressures, longitudinal
bending moment and shear force diagrams were drawn for each wave
length. Then their envelope was drawn so that the longitudinal
distributions of the maximum bending moments and shear forces
were obtained. Their modified distribution are shown in Fig. 8
compared with those prescribed by the rules of other classification organisations.

Maximum values of the longitudinal bending moment and shear
force can be expressed as

$$M = \pm 0.02 \ aw \ L^2 B$$
$$Q = \pm 0.06 \ aw \ L \ B$$

where aw, L and B are amplitude of wave, barge length and barge
breadth respectively.

The reduction of wave loads according to working sea-area
The criteria of the Nippon Kaiji Kyodai (NK-rules) estimate the
reduction of design loads (wave+static) according to working
sea-area. For example, the design loads in coastal areas may be
reduced to about 0.9 times that in ocean going areas, and in
smooth water areas by about 0.8. These values have been
experimentally specified and are not based on theoretical
predicting methods. So using North-Atlantic wave statistics in
winter as standard data, and Tokyo Bay wave statistics as data
for a smooth water area, the maximum expectation values of wave
loads in the long term were calculated by the direct method.
The model barge is 37m in length, 9m in breadth and 2.5m in
draught. The results are shown in Table 1.

The values of longitudinal loads using Tokyo Bay wave
statistics are $1/4 \sim 1/5.6$ of those using North Atlantic wave
statistics, so that the reduction according to sea-area may be
recognised as far larger than the prescribed reduction. We do
not have enough data in coastal areas, and must research from
now on. It is considered that the wave loads in smooth water
areas may be reduced to one third of those in ocean going areas
and two thirds in the coastal area. Hydrodynamic pressures on
the transverse section of the midship using Tokyo Bay wave
statistics are a quarter to a fifth of those using North

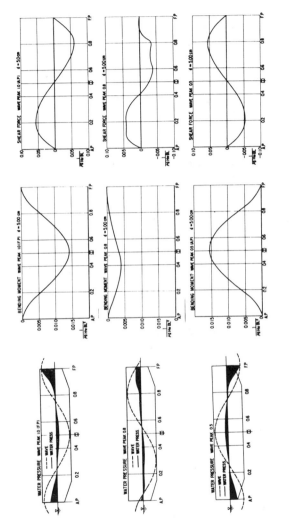

Fig.7 Transition of hydrodynamic pressures and induced wave
loads

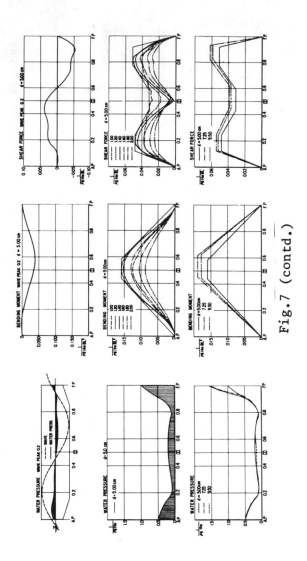

Fig.7 (contd.)

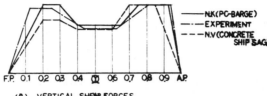

(a) VERTICAL SHEAR FORCES.

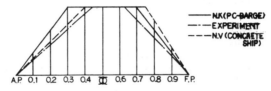

(b) VERTICAL BENDING MOMENTS

Fig.8 Modified distributions of bending moments and shear forces

Table 1. Comparison of wave loads according to sea-area

	Longitudinal loads		Transverse induced water pressure	
	Maximum bending moment	Maximum shear force	Bottom: H_s	Side: H_L
Direct calculation Wave: TokyoBay	299.6^{tm} (1)	27.1^t (1)	$2.1^{t/m^2}$ (1)	$3.6^{t/m^2}$ (1)
Direct calcation Wave: NorthAtlantic	1492.0 (5.0)	135.6 (5.0)	8.3 (4.0)	14.0 (3.9)
NK—Rules (ocean area)	870.0 (2.9)	150.9 (5.6)	1.0 (0.48)	3.3 (0.92)
(Smooth water area)	870.0×0.5 (1.7)	150.9×0.6 (3.3)	0.8 (0.38)	3.3×0.8 (0.73)
Load distribution	(AP ‒ FP trapezoidal diagram)	(AP ‒ FP diagram)	(H_L, H_s pressure diagram)	

North Atlantic wave statistics, so that the transverse loads may
be reduced as may the longitudinal loads. The values of the
NK-rules are less than these predicted values, and are not
applicable to a barge of these dimensions. The rules for
hydrodynamic pressures on small-sized barges should be
investigated in future.

The calculation of longitudinal bending moment M and shear force
Q of the barge by the wave load is basically done by the direct-
calculation method using the observed wave data for the sea area
concerned. If the direct-calculation method cannot be applied,
their maximum values are given by the following formulae in
smooth water areas. In coastal areas twice the value of those
in smooth water should be taken

$$M = \frac{1}{3} \left[0.14 Km \ L^2.B.Cb \ (1+0.04\frac{L}{B}) \right]$$

$$Q = \frac{1}{3} Ks.L.B$$

where
    L: Length of barge in meters
    B: Width of barge in meters
    Cb: Block coefficient of barge

$$Km = \sqrt{1 - (\frac{300-L}{300})^2}$$

$$Ks = (Cb+0.5L/B-0.46) \cdot (0.35Cb+0.55)$$

ON THE APPLICABILITY OF CONCRETE MEMBERS TO THE BARGE

Covering depth to reinforcements
Concrete is generally taken to have superior durability in the
severe marine environment and rarely shows great deterioration
due to erosion in the sea even if it is of poor quality. It is
widely known that C_3A included in cement reacts on sulphate
in sea water in the process of hydration, leading to cubical
expansion, even the occurrence of cracks. In the latest
investigation, dense concrete deposition is found to be more

important for sea water resistance of concrete and rust-prevention of the reinforcement than using anti-sulphuric acid cement in concrete.

If concrete is deposited densely enough, sea water will permeate only into the surface of the concrete. Surface expansion will cause destruction of the surface if it is left as it is, but may be helped by chemical prestress or by the restraint effect of reinforcing bars near the under-surface. Chemical prestress may prove to be very effective in considering the longterm usage of ferro-cement boats.

Fig. 9 shows the variation of the expansion coefficients of the concrete specimens steeped in a magnesium sulphate solution. So far as the expansion coefficient is concerned, the concrete including 5% of CSA is clearly different from that without it. Expansion increases as water-cement ratio (W/C) increases. These facts show that the covering depth of reinforcing bars in concrete shall be the minimum value that can be structurally achieved, and the dense concrete shall be deposited carefully.

The best effect on anti-permeability and cracking resistance is obtained if the concrete is densely deposited with the water-cement ratio as small as possible. We suggest that concrete should be graded depending on the water-cement ratio and the method of depositing the concrete, and the concrete depth to bar should be selected in accordance with the concrete grading. The suggested values are shown in Table 2 compared with the values given elsewhere.

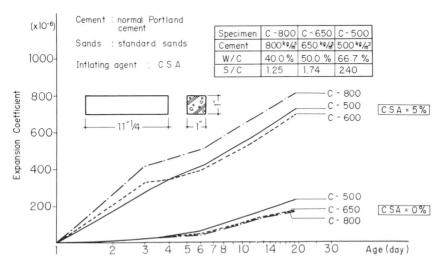

Fig.9 Expansion coefficients of concrete in a magnesium sul-fate solution

Table 2. Minimum covering depth of concrete to reinforcement (mm)

	NK P.C.Barge	USSR Register	ABS	FIP	JSCE Marine concrete	AIJ RC Rule		JSCE PC Rule	Proposal			
outer hull surface	70 (100)	15	21	30 (1.25d)(1.5)	70	normal light-weight ∘slab		slab beam column	w∕c	40% 50 44 45 & under		
						20 20 (30)(30)		① 10 15 20	30 30 13 (1.0d)			
inner hull surface	40 (45)	10	18	20 (1.0d)(1.0)	50	∘wall column and beam inner 30 30 (30)(40)		② 20 25 30	25 18 9 (1.5d)			
others	40 (45)	5	18 outer deck surface	10 (1.0d)(1.0)	50	outer 30 40 (40)(40) (40)(50)		③ 30 35 40	30 15 9 (1.5d)			
working floor of deck	40	20	–	–	–	∘foundation (60)(70)						
remarks	( )is in the case of P.C.steels.	w∕c<4.3%		d:diameter of bar ( )is ratio to aggregate diameter	in the concrete standard speci-fication	( )is in the case of no finish ( )is in the case of on or under the ground.		①be exposed to the weather ②be important or large size ③be in severe environment				

Allowable crack width

The contraction of concrete, the external loads and the chemical erosion by sea water all cause concrete to crack. As soon as cracks appear on the concrete surface, neutralization of the concrete is promoted and rust is produced on the reinforcement.

According to the latest investigations, a crack width which is under 0.2mm on a concrete surface in sea water is considered to have no effect on the corrosion of the reinforcement, because autogenous healing is produced by the hydration of non-reacting cement in concrete. Table 3 shows the comparison of allowable crack widths prescribed by the various criteria. Mostly, it allows a crack width of about 0.1mm on the surface in sea water.

Table 3 Comparison of allowable crack widths   (mm)

Environments	JSCE	USSR Register	FIP	NV	ACI	CEB-FIP	NK	ABS	PCI
Indoor or applied correspondingly to indoor		0.20 (0.15)			0.40	(0.20)			
Open-air or humid air		0.15		0.15	0.30				
Alternating dry and wet with sea water or sea water spray	0.15	0.08 (0.07)	RC:0.30 PC: class1...... not allow tensile stress	not allow tensile stress	0.15	0.20 (0.10)	∘longitudinal :not allow tensile stress ∘transverse:	0.125	0.10
Watertight structure or continuously in the sea	0.20	0.10 (0.08)	class2...... 0.04 class3...... 0.10		0.10	0.20 (0.10)	not allow harmful crack		
remarks		( )is in the case of no co-mpessive zone in the sect-ion.					( )is to the con-tinuous load		

With regard to the cracking by external loads we suggest that the crack width by bending stress is under 0.08mm on the surface in sea water, otherwise under 0.1mm, that the tensile crack and shearing crack through a section is not allowed and cracking stress should be more than 1.15 to 1.3 times the member's stress.

Member strength

It is regarded in the design of a ship that wave loads are continuous phenomena, the latgest load which may happen only once in the life of a ship must be taken in the special design for ultimate strength and continuous wave loads must be taken in designing for complete security. When the above mentioned method is applied to reinforced concrete and pre-stressed concrete, concrete members with the required ultimate strength, fatigue strength and cracking strength must be evaluated with a proper safety coefficient.

From here on high strength concrete with an artificial light-weight aggregate is used for the purpose of light-weight hull construction. First the characteristics of the strength of a thin concrete plate were confirmed by experiments. The specimens taken represented the bottom plating or the side plating and were made with its concrete and the various kinds of bar arrangement. Experiments aimed at ultimate flexural strength, cracking characteristic and fatigue strength were carried out.

The results of the experiments are shown in Figs. 10 and 11. In the flexural bearing experiment, Type-B is superior in ultimate strength, ductility and cracking characteristic. When the load is one half of the ultimate strength, the maximum crack width of Type-B is about 0.06mm. When the stress-ratio to ultimate stress is 33.3% and 37% in the fatigue experiments of Type-B, the members can endure a cyclic load of two million times, without being affected by the cyclic load in the flexural bearing experiments after the fatigue experiments. The cracking characteristic in impact test is superior in the plate of Type-C. Synthetically the plate of Type-B is the most appropriate of the three types of plate members.

Next the strength characteristic of prestressed concrete beams used for the main longitudinal members was confirmed by experiments. Representing the hull construction by a prefabrication method, were monolithic beams and beams jointed in the center. Fatigue experiments by alternating load were carried out and confirmed the fatigue strength. The ultimate bending strength of a jointed beam is reduced 10% to that of a monolithic beam. If the stress ratio is 30%, the influence of fatigue is not confirmed. These members proved therefore to be appropriate enough as structural members for constructing a concrete barge.

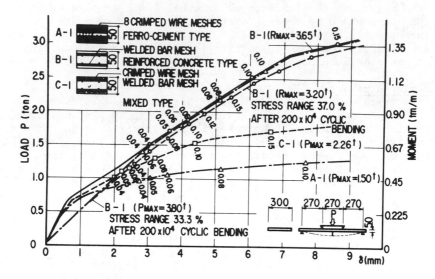

Fig.10　Load-deflection curves of concrete plates

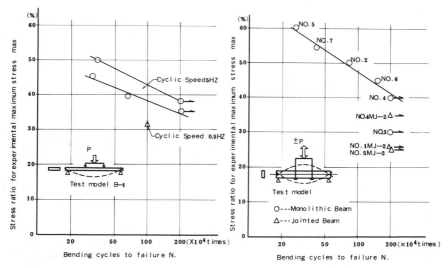

Fig.11　S-N curve of rein-　Fig.12　S-N curves of pre-
forced concrete plates　　　　stressed concrete beams

DESIGN AND CONSTRUCTION OF THE ACTUAL BARGE

Specifications

In order to prove that the design method mentioned above might
be appropriate, a prototype concrete barge was constructed by
way of a trial. The specifications of the barge are given in
Table 4. The dimensions and capacities were chosen as a trial
construction for research and development, not a particular
usage. The working area, purpose of usage and capacity of this
barge deviated a little from the limits of "Provisional Rules
for Prestressed Concrete Barges" by Nippon Kaiji Kyokai.

Design loads

The longitudinal bending moment and shear force diagrams in still
water in ballast and full load condition are shown in Fig.14.
For the full load condition it was assumed that all stowage was
uniformly distributed throughout the holds.

Using the wave statistics of Tokyo Bay near Kisarazu, the values
of long-term response evaluation of the wave loads were calculated. The values at a probability level $Q=10^{-5}$ were fixed as the
design wave loads.

Design of structural members' sections of the hull

Of the principal members, the sections were designed after making sure of cracking characteristic and ultimate strength by
full scale experiments, mentioned above.

Arranging thin and strong members with reinforced concrete, for
example a plate of thickness 60mm, and prestressing in the longitudinal direction, a superior light-weight hull was designed.
The prestressed part is the only standard section of the hull.
The longitudinal structural members were fully prestressed for
all combined stress of every load condition.

The sections of transverse and local members were designed so
that the maximum crack width should be less than 0.08mm on the
outer surfaces of the hull, and less than 0.1mm on the inner
surface. The safety coefficients of ultimate strength to design
load should be 1.5 to 2.5 according to position, a sort of stress
or a loading condition.

Construction and launching

The customary concreting in site makes quality and execution
control for the dense concrete depositing difficult. In consideration of the problems of these controls and applicability to
the construction technique to vast offshore structures, the
barge was constructed by a prefabrication method. The midship
hull of standard section was divided into forty parts.

An outline of the construction process is shown in Fig.17. The
precast concrete blocks were produced in a prefabrication plant,
carried to the shipway of a shipyard and constructed on it.

2.244

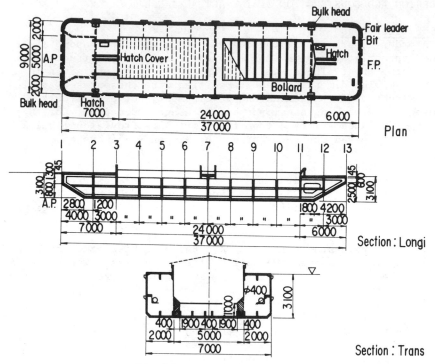

Fig.13 General arrangement

Table 4 Specifications

Principal dimensions	Length over all 37.000 m Breadth 9.000 m Depth 3.100 m Designed load water-line 2.600 m
Cargo capacities	Dry bulk cargo Dead weight 500 tons
Working	Working area: Smooth water area Designed towing speed : 6 knots
Main structure	Longitudinal : Prestressed concrete Transverse : Reinforced concrete Material : Light-weight concrete (specific gravity: 1.81, compressive strength: 500 Kgw/cm^2
Fittings	Equipment for towing and mooring
Classification	Nippon Kaiji Kyokai NS*(Smooth Water Service),(P.C. Barge)

Fig.16 The values of long-term response evaluation of hydro-dynamic pressures on the transverse section of midship

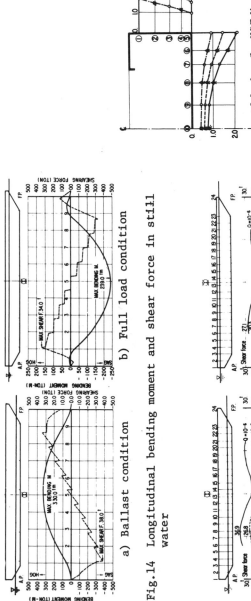

a) Ballast condition   b) Full load condition

Fig.14 Longitudinal bending moment and shear force in still water

a) Ballast condition   b) Full load condition

Fig.15 The values of long-term response evaluation of wave loads

After construction, the barge was loaded onto two launching trucks, moved to a launching slope, and launched.

Various kinds of experiments on the actual barge

After launching, an inclining experiment and oscillation experiment were carried out to determine the stability of the barge. The result showed the weight and the center of gravity of the barge to be similar to the calculated values, proving the barge was accurately constructed.

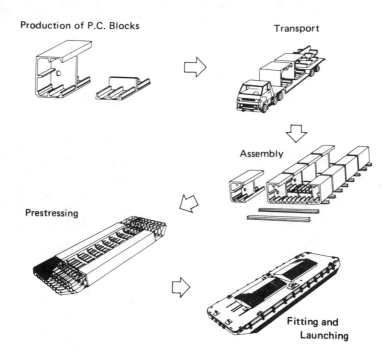

Production of P.C. Blocks

Transport

Assembly

Prestressing

Fitting and Launching

Fig. 17 Construction process

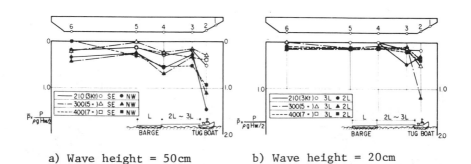

a) Wave height = 50 cm   b) Wave height = 20 cm

Fig.18 Longitudinal distributions of hydrodynamic pressures in the actual experiment

Continuous towing experiments were carried out to measure motion, hydrodynamic pressure and so on. The distribution of hydrodynamic pressure was similar to the result for the model experiment.

The barge was given a classification certificate by the Nippon Kaiji Kyokai, assuring that the barge has no problem regarding safety of the structure due to the thorough investigation of basic matters, such as the applied design method, construction procedures and tests of the actual barge on the open sea. The authors hope the contents described herein have made some con-tribution to the design method of concrete floating structures.

REFERENCES

Nippon Kaiji Kyokai (1975)"Provisional Rules for Prestressed Concrete Barges", Tokyo

Nippon Kaiji Kyokai (1976)"Rules for the Survey and Construction of Steel Ships", Tokyo

R.J.Ferguson (1963)"U.S.S.R. Register, Rules for the Construct-ion of Sea-going Reinforced Concrete Ships and Floating Docks", Publishing House (Transport), Leningrad

H.R.Hansen and K.Waagaard (Det Norske Veritas) (1975)"Some Recommendations for Design Loads and Design Criteria for Concrete Vessels", University of California Extension, Berkeley

American Bureau of Shipping "Classification of Concrete Vessels"

2.248

Photo.1 Model test in
        basin

Photo. 2 Flexural bearing test
         of RC Plate

Photo.3 Production of
        precast blocks

Photo.4 Stockyard of the blocks

Photo.5 Construction on
        shipway

Photo.6 Launching

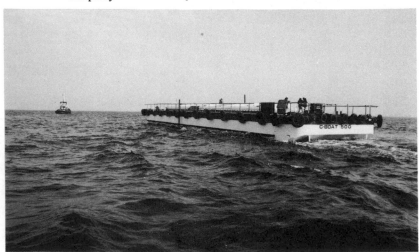

Photo.7 Actual experiment of towing on the sea

PART 3 CONSTRUCTION AND REPAIR OF OFFSHORE
STRUCTURES

SERVICEABILITY STATE OF MARINE STRUCTURES
WITH EMPHASIS ON CRACKING

Rolf Lenschow, Professor
Division of Concrete Structures, The Norwegian Institute
of Technology, The University of Trondheim,   Norway

INTRODUCTION

The use of serviceability limit state

The limit states of ultimate load or failure, of fatigue and
of progressive failure take care of the safety of the structures.
Provided the structure is considered to be safe, the users are
concerned about how the structure behaves. The serviceability
limit state shall ensure that the users can make full use of the
structure during its fixed lifetime without hinderance or in-
convenience due to load and time effect.

Loads

Loads considered in the serviceability limit state are the
same as considered in the ultimate limit state and the fatigue
limit state. However, accidental loads or misuse are not taken
into account in the serviceability limit state.

The load factor γ_f in this limit state is set 1,0 connected to
permanent load, p, live load, ℓ, imposed deformations, D, environmental loads, E. For environmental loads, E, it is usual to
take 50% of the characteristic value, but it has to be checked
that the effect of loads including the full characteristic
environmental load does not exceed certain limits. These limits
are wider than the ordinary requirements but still restricted.
For instance is yielding of steel not acceptable under full
characteristic environmental load and the allowable stress is
in some rules limited to 0.8 f_{sy}.

The force introduced by prestressing is also connected to
$\gamma_f = 1,0$.

The reduced probability that various loading effects will all be simultaneously at their characteristic value, is not taken into account in rules or regulations dealing with off-shore structures at serviceability limit. It is up to the designer to check that the possible load combinations are considered. However, it is of great importance that unrealistic load combinations are not taken into account because this can substantially add to the cost of the structure.

Controlling the serviceability limit state

Checking of the serviceability of a marine concrete structure covers:
- permeability
- durability
- dynamic response
- deformations
- cracking of concrete

The three first items are covered by Moxnes /3/ and Bell /4/. Cracking and to some extent deformation are treated in the following paragraphs.

CRACKS AND CRACKWIDTHS

Introduction

Cracks in reinforced concrete members have been dealt with in numerous reports and articles. There are also numerous proposals for calculating the crack widths. None of the proposals predicts the widths of the cracks as accurately as the other significant properties can be calculated.

Although the calculations of crack widths are inaccurate, they definitely reduce the risk for harmfull cracks in the construction. However, this may not be true in cases where the reinforcement crosses the cracks at an angle $\neq 90^{\circ}$. Although both theory and tests show that such inclined reinforcement may be far less effective in reducing the crack width, such a case is not taken care of in ordinary official codes.

There are numerous cases where the direction of the main reinforcement does not cross the cracks perpendicularly. Fig. 2.1
shows a few examples, and the examples could be continued with
rectangular slabs, kew bridges etc.

<u>Recent requirements for reinforcement to limit crack width</u>
The requirements given in approved codes are for instance:
Norwegian Standard 3473 requires generally only "an adequate
distribution of tensile reinforcement". For watertightness
and good corrosion protection, the tensile force shall be taken
by reinforcement distributed according to the stress-distribu-
tion in the structure. For prestressed concrete the NS 3473 is
more specific and limits the steel stresses to:

    200 MPa for structures in dry environments
    120 MPa for structures in humid environments
     60 MPa for structures in aggressive environments

The German DIN 1045 gives a detailed prescription for amount
of reinforcement, steelstress and bar-dimension in order to
limit the crack widths.

The ACI Code 318-71 does not treat exposure to sea water.
Minimum reinforcement is required.

The CEB-model code of April 1978 /5/ has a more detailed
approach. Firstly the requirements are related to the category
of the exposure to which the structure or the element under
consideration is subjected and then the sensitivity of the
reinforcement to corrosion. The exposures are "mild", "moderate"
and "severe". Seawater belongs to the last category.

The sensitivity of the reinforcement to corrosion is "slight"
or "high". Highly sensitive to corrosion are

    - steels of all types when diameter does not exceed 4 mm
    - treated steel of any diameter
    - cold-walsed steel subjected to permanent tension
      exceeding 400 MPa (prestressing in particular)

Slight sensitivety is attributed to all other types of
reinforcement.

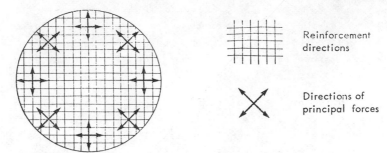

Reinforcement
directions

Directions of
principal forces

Disk or dome uniformly loaded.

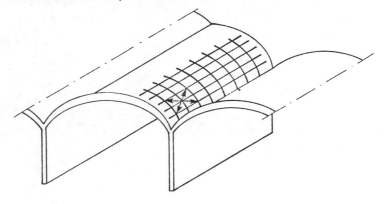

Cylindrical barrel roof uniformly loaded.

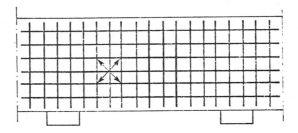

Wall or deep beam.

Fig. 2.1 Sketch of directions of reinforcement and
principal forces in some locations

For marine environments Table 2.1 refers the CEB-recommendations

Combinations of actions	Sensitivity of reinforcement to corrosion			
	Highly sensitive		Slightly sensitive	
	Limit state	W_k	Limit state	W_k
rare	Cracking or formation of cracks	$\leq W_1$	Cracking	$\leq W_2$
frequent	Decom-pression	(no crack)	Cracking	W_1

TABLE 2.1 Durability requirements

The recommended crackwidths, W_k-values, are: $W_1 = 0,1$ mm and
$W_2 = 0,2$ mm. The given values for W_k are connected to the minimum
cover as given by the CEB-model code which would be at "highly"
aggressive exposure $\approx$ 35 mm, + 10 mm for reinforcement susceptible to
corrosion, - 5 mm for of concrete quality C40 or higher. That makes
min. cover = 40 mm. For a concrete cover, c, thicker than the
minimum cover c_{min}, the values of W_k in Table 2.1 may be increased
by a factor

$$\frac{c}{c_{min}} \not> 1,5$$

The CEB-model code gives a computed conventional crackwidth.
There is no certainty that some crack widths in the structure will
not occasionally exceed this value. The crack width, W_k, corresponds
to the width measured at the concrete surface, in the zone containing the reinforcing bars in the "effective embedment section",
see Fig. 2.2. Outside this zone the crack-widths can be larger, but
such crack openings can be allowed only if no appearance requirements
are present or if no frost damage to the concrete surface is to be
expected.

The FIP-recommendation /6/ considers the cracking in the case of
normal environmental conditions with maximum imposed loads. Imposed
loads are defined as equipment, vehicles, ship-impact etc. The
assessed surface widths of cracks at points nearest the main reinforcement should not, in general, exceed 0,004 times the nominal
cover to the main reinforcement. It is realized that some cracks

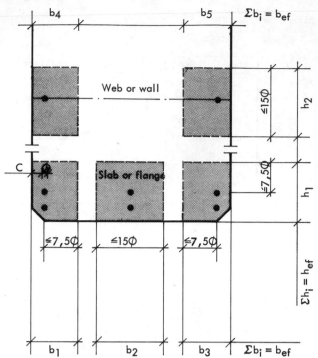

Fig. 2.2 Illustration of the "effective embedment section,
$$A_{c,ef} = b_{ef} \times h_{ef},$$ according to CEB-model code

may be larger because of the scatter and also under extreme environmental loads in short periods.   Under extreme conditions the
steel stresses should not exceed 0,8 f_y or the level at which the
designer considers the reinforcement will suffer no permanent strain.

    Det norske Veritas, DnV /7/, in its rules for the design of
offshore structures does not specify crack width but limit the steel
stresses. Ordinary bonded reinforcement steel stresses are limited
to 160 MPa at ordinary load condition (environmental loads taken as
50% of the characteristic value for design).

A possible treshold-value of crack widths for corrosion protection

    It is realized that the reinforcement in a marine concrete
structure is most exposed to corrosion at sea level or in the tidal
zone and splash zone. Salt, air and moisture are abundently
present.

Many investigations have been undertaken to study corrosion of
reinforcement in uncracked concrete at or in sea water, but very
few investigations have included cracked concrete in the tidal zone.
A comprehensive study is carried out by Schiessl /8/. He placed
small beams 150x250x1800 mm at the sea where the air contained
considerable amount of salt. The beams were subjected to moment
until the crack widths measured on the surface were 0,10-0,40 mm
wide. The corrosion observed after 4 and 10 years is illustrated
in Figs. 2.3 - 2.6.

Considering the corrosion in Figs. 2.3-2.6 from the point of
view that there may be a limit of the crack width below which the
corrosion is not significantly more severe than at uncracked
concrete. Identical tests were aldo performed in industrial area
(Ruhr) and in a town (Munich). The same tendencies were observed
in these places as to a threshold value for corrosion. The
corrosion was more severe in these places and most in the town.

An ordinary approach to determine corrolation between corrosion
and crackwidth has been used by evaluating mean- and standard
deviation of the amount of corrosion as a function of crackwidth. In Schliessl's tests (8) covering widths from 0 to 0,4 -
0,5 mm, no significant trend was found by this approach.

Another approach is to consider number of cases where the bars
have significant corrosion and relate this to the crackwidths.
This approach is applied at Schiessl's tests (8) and Fig. 2.7
indicates a significant trend after 4 years of exposure.
Steelbars in a cracked zone with crackwidths greater than 0,3 mm
are more exposed to corrosion than bars in uncracked zones and
than bars in zones where the crackwidths are smaller than 0.2 mm.
The same indications are present after 10 years, see Fig. 2.8.

If we define serious corrosion as the one causing more than 4%
reduction of cross-section, Fig. 2.9 indicates an increasing
probability for serious corrosion for steelbars in zones where
the crackwidths approach 0.5 mm.

Thus, the confusion about the relation between corrosion and
crackwidth may be due to the expectations that it should be
a relation so that 0.2 mm cracks should result in more corrosion
than 0.1 mm cracks and this again should be more unfavourable
than no crack at all. The limit for unfavourable effect of
crackwidths is much wider than most experts anticipated and the
scope of test series may have been too narrow to realize this.

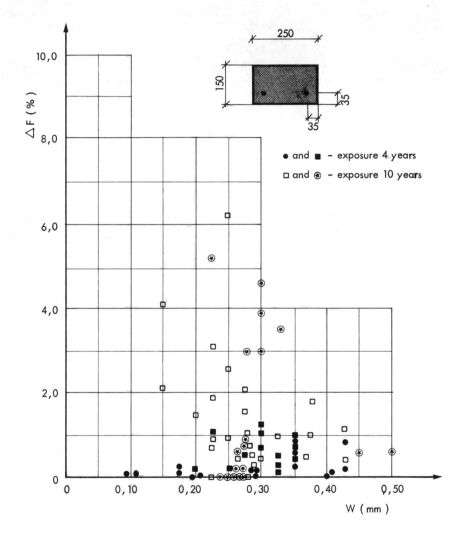

Fig. 2.3 Cross-section reduction ΔF of the longitudinal reinforcement
related to the crack widths, W, in sea air, 35 mm cover
(Source: Schiessl /8/)

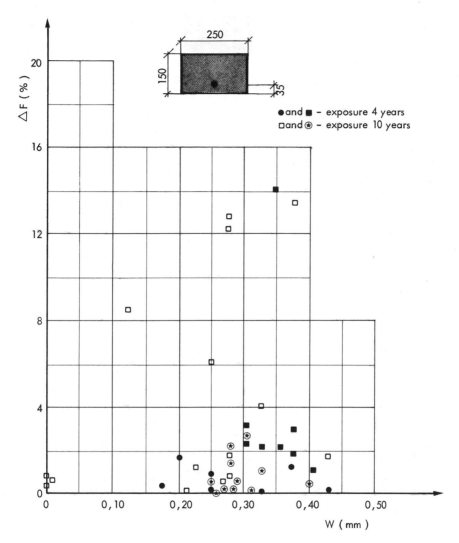

Fig. 2.4 Cross-section reduction F of the longitudinal reinforcement
related to the crack widths, W, in sea air, 35 mm cover
(Source: Schiessl /8/)

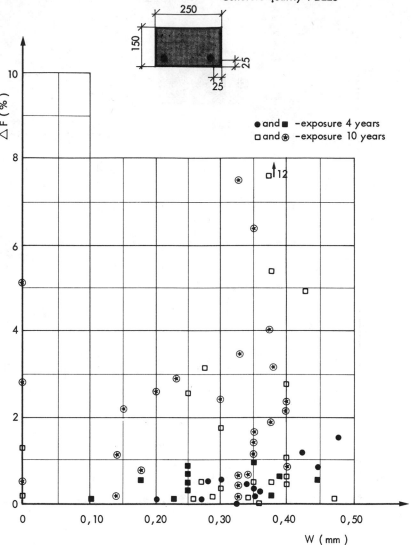

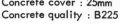

Reinforcement bars : Rippentorstahl 8mm
Concrete cover : 25mm
Concrete quality : B225

Fig. 2.5 Cross-section reduction ∆F of the longitudinal reinforcement
related to the crack widths, W, in sea iar, 25 mm cover
(Source: Schiessl /8/)

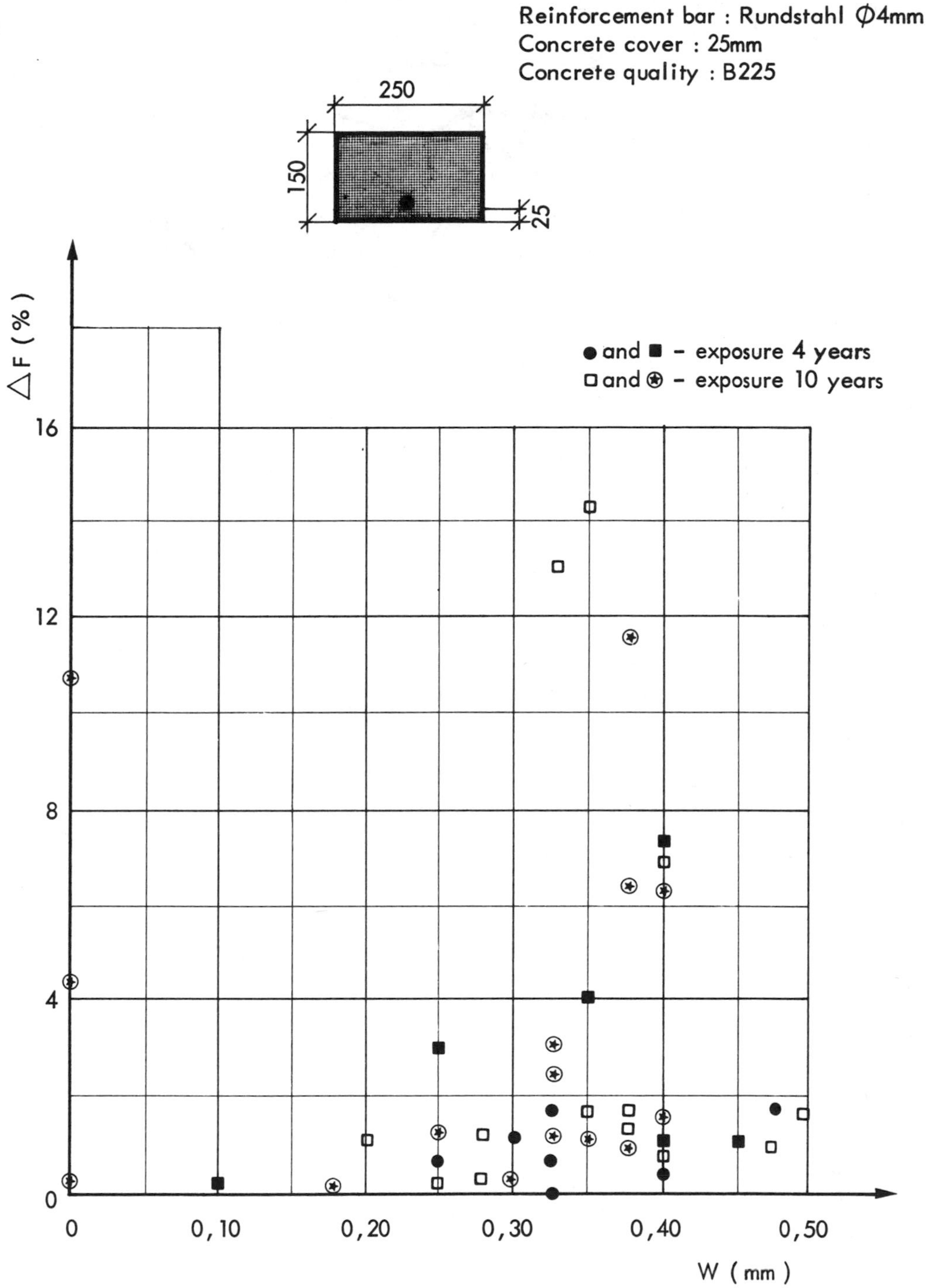

Fig. 2.6 Cross-section reduction ΔF of the longitudinal reinforcement
related to the crack widths, W, in sea air, 25 mm cover
(Source: Schiessl /8/)

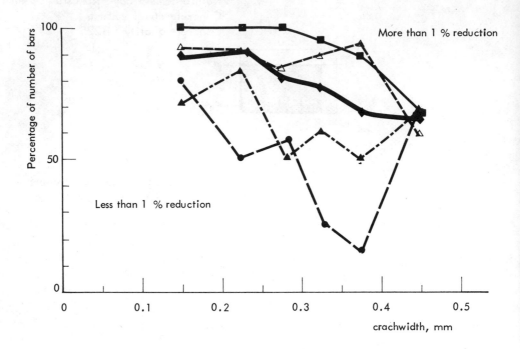

Fig. 2.7 Percentage of bars with less corrosion than 1% reduction
of cross-section in relation to crackwidths;
after 4 years.

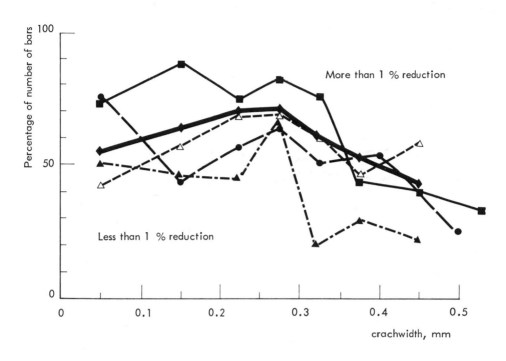

Fig. 2.8 Percentage of bars with less corrosion than 1% reduction of cross-section in relation to crackwidths; after 10 years.

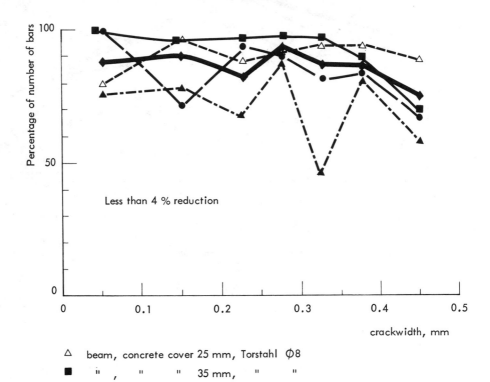

△	beam, concrete cover 25 mm, Torstahl $\phi 8$
■	" , " " 35 mm, " "
▲	slab , " " 25 mm, Rundstahl $\phi 4$
●	" , " " 35 mm, " "
◆	sum of all specimens

Fig. 2.9 Percentage of bars with less corrosion than 4%
reduction of cross-section in relation to crackwidths;
after 10 years.

Effects of cracks on steel corrosion in submerged concrete
structures are also investigated, but not so systematically,
as yet. In the sea water a galvanic cell is established where
the exposed steel in the concrete crack becomes the anode and
the embedded steel the cathode. The current in the galvanic
cell and the rust-process is controlled by the availability
of oxygen at the cathode and the resistance of the electrical
path through the concrete between the cathode and the anode.
Hence, the crack itself does not radically increase the corrosion process. In a real structure, however, there is a large
system of reinforcing bars which is part of the galvanic
coupling. Serious steel corrosion has been observed in cracks,
but also in this case there seems to be a threshold value.
Healing of small cracks may take place after a while as well
as formation of corrosion products may clog a small crack.
The threshold value seems to be somewhat larger than for concrete
in aggressive air environment. However, because of the present
lack of conclusive experimental results in sea water and more
so for crack widths variable with time for instance at structures
exposed to wave loads, the limit of crack widths are chosen to
be the same in sea water and in aggressive air environment.
Recalling that CEB-model code recommends the characteristic
crack width, W_k, to be 0.1 mm and 0.2 mm for reinforcement
slightly sensitive to corrosion, this magnitude seem to be well
on the conservative side.

Corrosion of reinforcement in concrete in seawater has been
studied for some years at the Cement and Concrete Research
Institute in Norway. C.J. Bernhard (19, 20, 21, 22) carried
out a testprogram on 232 concrete prisms exposed to sea water
in natural tide-water rhythm over 600 mm of the middle of the
prism height. The test specimens used were concrete columns
150x150x1000 mm, each reinforced with 4 longitudinal deformed
bars of diameter 16 mm and 5 round-bar stirrups of diameter
6 mm. After exposure times ranging from 30 to 88 months the
specimens were split and the reinforcement inspected for corrosion.

The effects of several variables were tested: w/c ratio = 0.50,
0.67 and 1.00; concrete cover = 15, 30 and 45 mm; with and
without air entraining agent; temperature; remaining forms;
epoxy surface; galvanizing etc.

12 specimens with w/c = 0.50 and concrete cover = 15, 30 and
45 mm were after approximately 800 days placed in a testrig.
In the rig the specimen was supported 100 mm from either end
and loaded in the middle of the span until cracking.

In Fig. 2.10 and 2.11 specimens no. 67 and no. 63 are both
cracked and have w/c = 0.50 but with and without air entraining
agent. The crackpattern and typical crackwidths are shown.
These cracked specimens can directly be compared with the uncracked specimens no. 70 and no. 65. The two prisms were 806
days at cracking and afterwards the tidal seawater treatment
was continued for 135 days before all 4 specimens were split
and inspected. It can be observed from Fig. 2.10 and Fig. 2.11
that the cracks are wide, maximum 1.0-3.0 mm. The corroded area
is significantly greater in the cracked specimens than the
uncracked ones. The heavy lines indicate the corroded area of
the stirrups, while the shadowed areas indicate the corroded
area of the longitudinal reinforcement. 6 more of the cracked
specimens were continuously subjected to tidal sea water 452
days after being cracked, after 806 days, and 426 days after
being gracked after 832 days respectively. The results are
seen in Figs. 2.12-2.16.

The crackwidths are much smaller in this case. It can be seen
in the figures that where the crackwidths are not greater than
0.5 mm there is not a significant difference in the corroded
area in a cracked and uncracked specimen. This limit does not
seem to be dependent on the magnitude of the concrete cover
which is varied in Figs. 2.12 - 2.16. Tests on Treat Island,
U.S.A. indicate also a threshold around 0.5 mm crackwidth.
However, the statistical data are too few to conclude that the
 threshold value for the crackwidth is 0.5 mm for concrete in
the tidewater zone. On the other side these tests indicate
 there is a higher threshold value in the tide-water zone than
expected and probably higher than in air only. An explanation
may be that cracks under water is easier healed than in air.

In Figs. 2.10 - 2.16 the electrical potential between the naked
steel on top of the column specimen and the surface of the
concrete. The potential increase from 50 - 100 mV to 300 -

- 600 mV when corrosion of the reinforcement starts. Measuring
the potential is therefore a very good non-destructuve method
to detect corrosion attack on embedded steel. It is, however,
no base for determining the magnitude of the corrosion from
reading the magnitude of the potential.

In this test series 4 more test specimens were cracked by force
after approximately 800 days. These specimens together with
accompanying uncracked reference specimens were thereafter
inspected regularly. Only one of the test specimens had cracks
greater than 0.5 mm. At an age og 1815 days the specimen with
crackwidths in the order of 1.0 mm, had visible rustspots on
the surface, while the other specimens had not changed.

It is claimed that cracks along the steelbar have a much more
severe effect than cracks across bars. Therefore it is not
logical to investigate only the longitudinal reinforcement with
perpendicular cracks.

In Fig. 2.10 - 2.16 the stirrups are parallel to the crack
direction. The tendency to corrode are approximately the
same for longitudinal reinforcement and the stirrups, indicating
that there is no drastic difference because of the crack-
direction.

During the test program it was observed that cracks were filled
with a material. Analysing this material a typical result was
after the water was evaporated: $CaO-55,4\%$, $Mg-6,8\%$, $CO_2-36,2\%$.
Other $-1,6\%$.

W/c =0,50

Without Air Entr. Agent

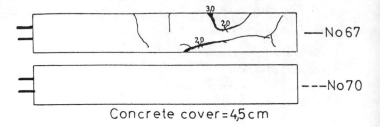

—No 67

---No 70

Concrete cover = 4,5 cm

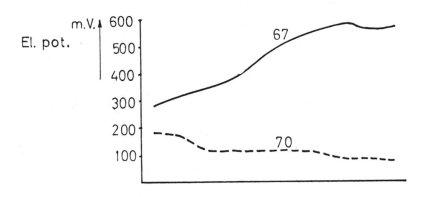

El. pot.

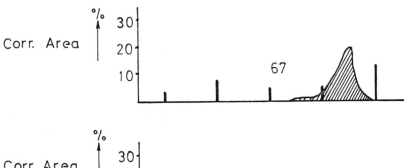

Corr. Area

Corr. Area

Fig. 2.10

W/c = 0,50
With Air Entr Agent.

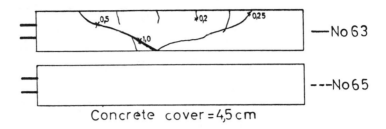

—No 63

--- No 65

Concrete cover = 4,5 cm

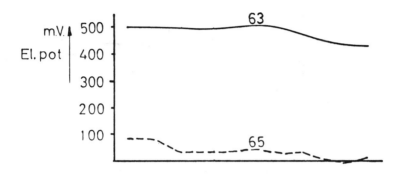

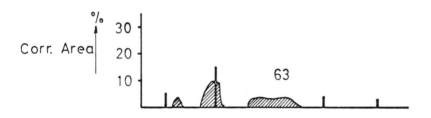

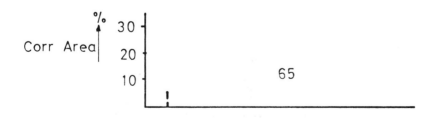

Fig. 2.11

w/c=0,50

Without Air Entr. Agent

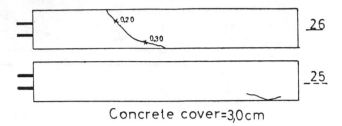

26

25

Concrete cover=3,0cm

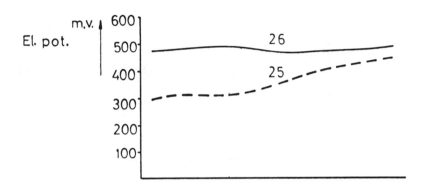

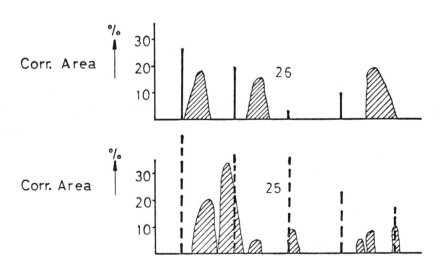

Fig. 2.12

w/c=0,50

Without Air Entr. Agent

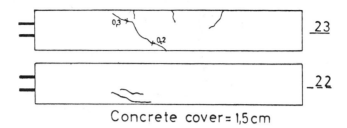

Concrete cover=1,5cm

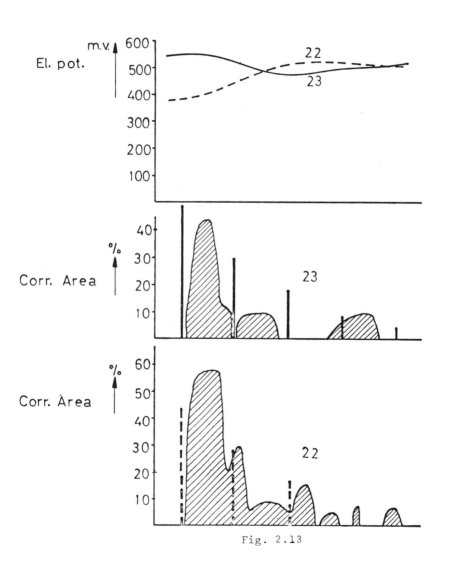

Fig. 2.13

w/c = 0,50
With Air Entr. Agent

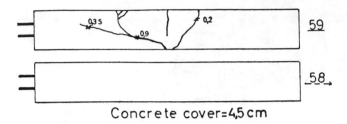

Concrete cover = 4,5 cm

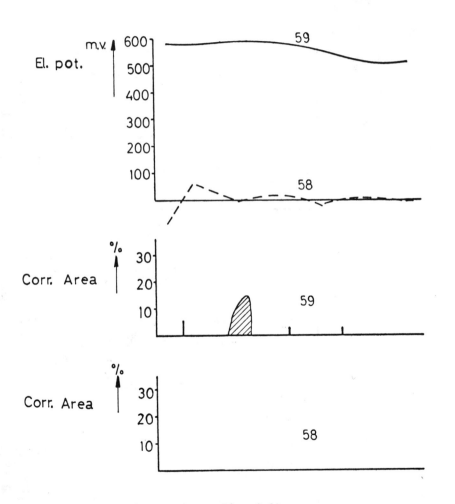

Fig. 2.14

w/c=0,50

With Air Entr. Agent

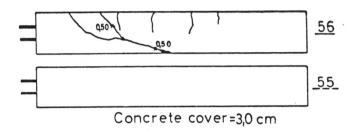

56

55

Concrete cover=3,0 cm

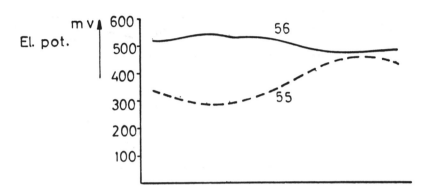

El. pot.

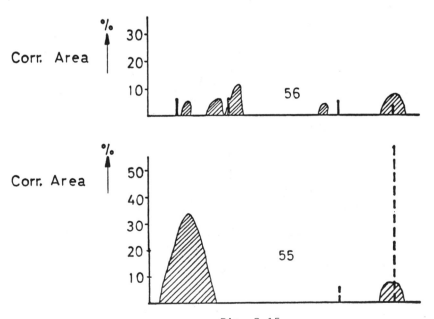

Corr. Area

Corr. Area

Fig. 2.15

w/c=0,50

With Air Entr. Agent

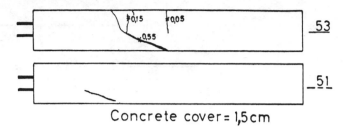

53

51

Concrete cover= 1,5cm

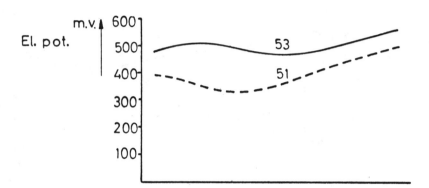

El. pot.

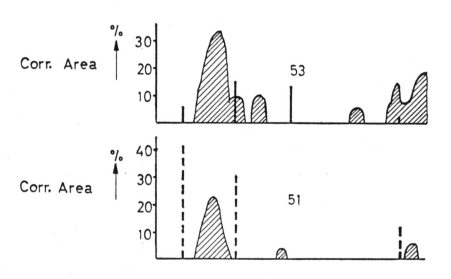

Corr. Area

Corr. Area

Fig. 2.16

Crackwidth of the reinforcing bar

The crackwidths discussed above refer to widths at the surface of the concrete. Dealing with corrosion the crackwidths at the surface of the reinforcement are of major importance. There are some observations of the crackwidths at the reinforcement. In Fig. 2.7 observations by Hussein and Ferguson /17/ and Schiessl /8/ are plotted. Based on these observations the relation between the crackwidth at the concrete surface, W_c, and the crackwidth at the reinforcement, W_s, can be set:

$$\frac{W_s}{W_c - W_s} = \frac{20}{c}$$

This formula is based on a limited number of observations with great scatter, and is given here only to give an idea about the crackwidth-formation.

Referring to the tests by Schiessl /8/ the difference of cover, from 25 mm to 35 mm, should not change the crackwidth at the reinforcement with more than approximately 20%, if the crackwidths at the concrete surface are equal. Referring to Figs. 2.3 - 2.6 the difference in concrete cover does not result in a clear difference in a threshold value for the concrete surface crackwidth. The scatter of the observations excludes the possibility to see a difference in the threshold value when the crackwidths at the reinforcement differ only about 20%.

Concrete Cover

The parts of a marine structure most susceptible to the corrosion of embedded steel are those exposed to intermittent wetting and drying, especially by salt water. There are, nevertheless, a large number of structures which have been in service under these conditions for a long time without problems having arisen due to corrosion of the reinforcement. This is because the steel has been surrounded by high-quality, well-compacted, homogeneous concrete, free from honeycombing or other surface defects. The protection of reinforcement depends much more upon the quality of the concrete, its compaction and impermeability as upon the amount of cover.

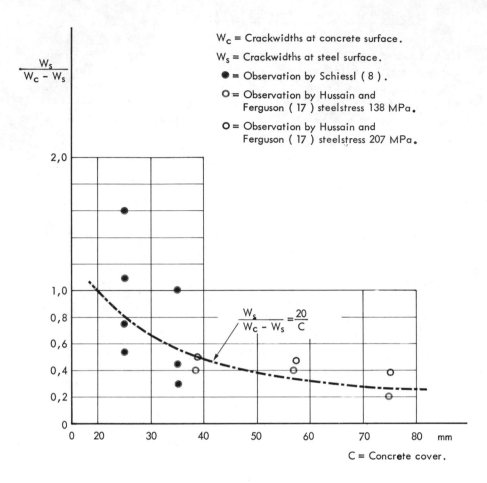

Fig. 2.17 Relations between the crackwidt, W_c, at the concrete surface
and the crackwidth, W_s, at the surface of the reinforcement
for deformed bars and variable concrete cover, c.

There has been a great uncertainty with regard to a proper amount of concrete cover of embedded steel.

Harbour-constructions cast in situ under water have usually had cover 70 mm for beams and columns and 50 mm for wall and shell-structures. For concrete structures cast in air the cover is set 50 mm and 40 mm, respectively /18/. These are the covers from which we have considerable experience, mentioned above.

For offshore structures FIP /6/, 1976, has recommended 75 mm and 100 mm cover for normal reinforcing steel and prestressing tendors respectively in the splash zone. The cover is reduced to 60 mm and 75 mm in the submerged zone.

DnV /7/, 1977, represents the trend back to the previous requirements for cover:

> For normal reinforcement the concrete cover is not to be less than

>> 40 mm in the atmospheric zone, not subject to severe splashing

>> 50 mm for all other parts of the structure

> In addition, the cover is not to be less than 1,5 times the nominal maximum size of aggregate.

> For prestressing tendons the cover is not to be less than twice the values given above.

THE EFFECT OF INCLINED REINFORCEMENT ON THE CRACK WIDTH

The inclination of the reinforcement in relation to the crack
direction will have an effect on the crackwidth, W_m, if
it changes the crack spacing or the mean strain of the
reinforcement, or both.

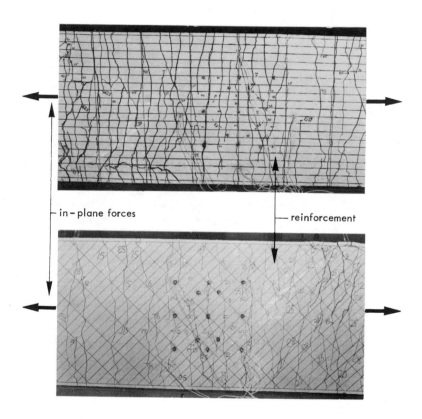

in-plane forces   reinforcement

Fig. 3.1 Crack pattern in plates where the reinforcement
          is rotated in relation to the in-plane forces /7/

Crack spacing

As far as the writer knows no specific testseries has been
carried out to study relations between crack spacing and
inclination of reinforcement. From tests carried out in order
to study inclined reinforcement's effect on flexibility it may
be concluded that the crack spacing is not significantly changed
if the reinforcement is rotated in relation to the crack
direction. Photos in Fig. 3.1 and Fig. 3.2 show no significant
difference in the crack spacing when the orientation of the
reinforcement is rotated with respect to the crack orientation.

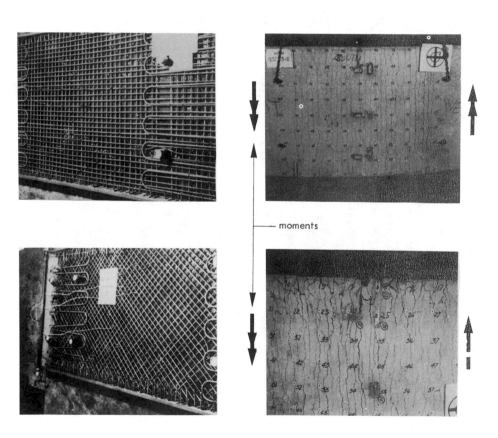

moments

Fig. 3.2 Crack pattern in slabs subjected to moments /8/

Mean Elongation of Plates subjected to In-Plane Forces

In Fig. 3.3 an arbitrary system of co-ordinates n-t is chosen, and the reinforcing bar has the direction x. List of symbols is found at the end of this paper.

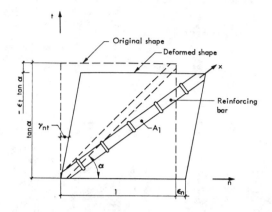

Fig. 3.3 Deformation of element with
reinforcing bar

We have the following relation between the strains

$$\varepsilon_{sx} = \varepsilon_n \cos^2\alpha + \varepsilon_t \sin^2\alpha + \gamma_{nt} \sin\alpha\cos\alpha \qquad (3.1)$$

This can be converted to

$$\varepsilon_n = \varepsilon_{sx} \sec^2\alpha - \varepsilon_t \tan^2\alpha - \gamma_{nt} \tan\alpha \qquad (3.2)$$

The force in the n-direction, per unit length

$$N_{nx}^{'} = A_1 E_s \varepsilon_{sx} \frac{\cos\alpha}{\tan\alpha} \qquad (3.3)$$

Reinforcement, per unit length measured perpendicular to the direction of the bars

$$A_{sx} = \frac{A_1}{\sin\alpha} \qquad (3.4)$$

By combining the last two equations

$$N_{nx} = A_{sx} E_s \varepsilon_{sx} \cos^2\alpha \qquad (3.5)$$

In the same way for the reinforcement in y-direction

$$\varepsilon_{sy} = \varepsilon_n \sin^2\alpha + \varepsilon_t \cos^2\alpha - \gamma_{nt} \sin\alpha\cos\alpha \qquad (3.6)$$

$$\varepsilon_n = \varepsilon_{sy} \csc^2\alpha - \varepsilon_t \cotan^2\alpha + \gamma_{nt} \cotan\alpha \qquad (3.7)$$

Force in n-direction

$$N_{ny} = A_{sy} E_s \varepsilon_{sy} \sin^2\alpha \qquad (3.8)$$

Total force in n-direction, $N_n = N_{nx} + N_{ny}$, substituting the expressions in (3.1) and (3.6) for ε_{sx} and ε_{sy}

$$N_n = \varepsilon_n E_s (A_{sx} \cos^4\alpha + A_{sy} \sin^4\alpha) + \varepsilon_t E_s \sin^2\alpha\cos^2\alpha (A_{sx} + A_{sy})$$

$$+ E_s \gamma_{nt} \sin\alpha\cos\alpha (A_{sx} \cos^2\alpha - A_{sy} \sin^2\alpha) \qquad (3.9)$$

If the n-direction coincides with the direction of the principal tensile stress, the crack direction will be approximately perpendicular to the n-direction. As soon as the crack is formed, the forces in the reinforcement will produce a shear force, N_{nt}, alon the crack, Fig. 3.4.

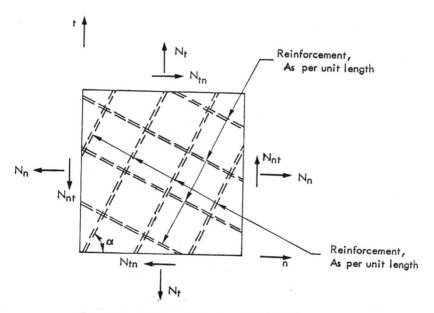

Fig. 3.4 Reinforcement in unit element

$$N_{nt} = (A_{sx} \epsilon_{sx} - A_{sy} \epsilon_{sy}) E_s \sin\alpha \, \cos\alpha \qquad (3.10)$$

Substituting the expressions in (3.1) and (3.6) for ϵ_{sx} and ϵ_{sy}

$$N_{nt} = \{\epsilon_n (A_{sx} \cos^2\alpha - A_{sy} \sin^2\alpha) + \epsilon_t (A_{sx} \sin^2\alpha - A_{sy} \cos^2\alpha)$$

$$+ \gamma_{nt} \sin\alpha \, \cos\alpha (A_{sx} + A_{sy}) \} E_s \sin\alpha \, \cos\alpha \qquad (3.11)$$

The relation between N_n and N_{nt} is obtained from (3.9) and (3.11) for $\alpha \neq 0$ and $\alpha \neq \frac{\pi}{2}$.

$$N_n = N_{nt} \frac{A_{sx} \cos^2\alpha - A_{sy} \sin^2\alpha}{A_s \sin\alpha \, \cos\alpha} + \epsilon_n E_s \{ A_{sx} \cos^4\alpha (1 - \frac{A_{sx}}{A_s})$$

$$+ A_{sy} \sin^4\alpha (1 - \frac{A_{sy}}{A_s}) + \frac{2 A_{sx} A_{sy}}{A_s} \cos^2\alpha \, \sin^2\alpha \}$$

$$+ \epsilon_t E_s \frac{A_{sx} A_{sy}}{A_s} \qquad (3.12)$$

where $A_s = A_{sx} + A_{sy}$

If no relative movement (sliding) takes place in the crack, γ_{nt} will be very small, and the force N_{nt} will prevent this sliding. With this assumption, Fig. 3.5 shows how the strain, ϵ_n, varies with constant force, N_n, when the reinforcement changes direction and the amount of reinforcement is the same in the two directions, $A_{sx} = A_{sy}$. Fig. 3.6 shows the same conditions for $A_{sy} = \frac{1}{4} A_{sx}$.

If relative movement (sliding can take place freely in the crack, then $N_{nt} = 0$, and the sliding can be expressed as a function of γ_{nt}. With this assumption the values of ϵ_n in Fig. 8 will be larger for α between 0^0 and 45^0 than in the case of prevented sliding. The equation (3.12) is not immediately valid for small values of α, as second order effects will have influence for α below 10^0.

Usually the sliding is prevented by the unevenness along the crack. Increase in crack width will reduce the prevention of sliding as well as N_{nt}. The test results in Fig. 3.5 illustrates this relation. Higher load steps means larger crack width and therefore smaller shear force, N_{nt}. The test results

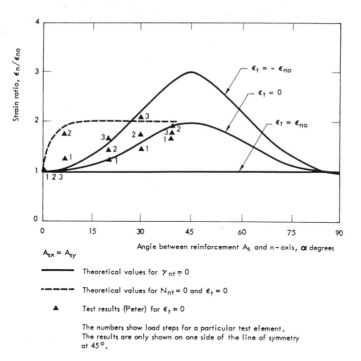

Fig. 3.5 Relative crack width in relation to
         direction of reinforcement

for the lowest load step after crack formation are therefore
expected to be near the curve for $\gamma_{nt} = 0$, while the test results
for the highest load steps will draw near the values corresponding
to $N_{nt} = 0$. The test results in Fig. 3.5 show this tendency.

A limited series of tests was carried out in the autumn 1976
at Norges tekniske høgskole /15/. A total of 7 discs with the
dimensions 2600 × 900 × 60 mm was tested. The discs were subjected
to tension in the longitudinal direction. The reinforcement
deviated $\alpha = 0^{\circ}$, $22,5^{\circ}$ and 45° from the longitudinal direction
in the various discs. The amount of reinforcement was 0,5%, 1%,
1,5% or 2,9%. The ratio between the reinforcement in the two
directions, A_{sy}/A_{sx} was 1,0, 0,33 or 0,17.

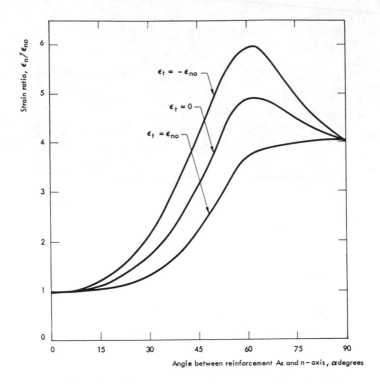

Fig. 3.6 Relative crack width in relation to direction
of reinforcement

Fig. 3.7 shows results for discs with 2,9% reinforcement in
x-direction and 1,0% reinforcement in y-direction. The deviation of the reinforcement from the longitudinal direction was
α = 0°, $22,5^\circ$ and 45°. The longitudinal deformations were measured
by extensometers with gauge length 200 mm.

Each test result shown is the mean of measurements at 4 different
places in the central part of the disc. At the test results
marked "1" in Fig. 3.7 the crack pattern was only partly developed.
At the test results marked "2" the crack pattern was fully developed
but displacement or fracture had not occurred.

The cracks were distributed rather evenly in all the test
elements with a distance of about 70 mm between the cracks.

The test results are shown in more detail in Fig. 3.8. The
control test element with reinforcement in the longitudinal
direction shows that the contribution from the concrete stresses
between the cracks is so small that it can be neglected. Moreover,

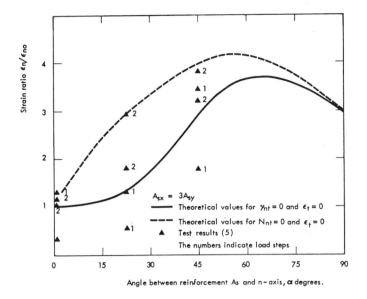

Fig. 3.7 Relative crack width in relation to direction
of reinforcement

the test results display a considerable scattering. There are
various reasons for that: uneven crack formation, sliding along a
crack or new crack directions influencing the conditions at other
cracks, loosening of gauge points during cracking, the precision
of the extensometer depending highly on practice and competence.

The trend of the observations supports the calculations in
such a way that change is observed, from a state with shear force
transmission through the cracks to another state with sliding in
the cracks or with new crac- direction, at a considerable increase
in the relative deformations. In this test series the change
appeared at a crack width of the order 0,1 mm.

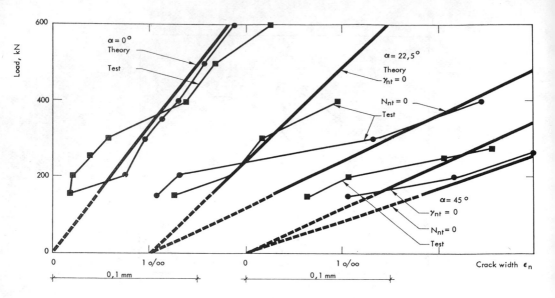

Fig. 3.8 Deformations and crack widths in relation to
load and direction of reinforcement

3.3 Mean Elongation of Tensile Zone of Slabs

The orientation of reinforcement in the tension zone of a slab
has approximately the same effect as the reinforcement in a plate
subjected to in-plane forces. There are, however, two factors
which are specific for slabs:

- The compression zone will - in addition to interlock forces
  in the cracks - try to prevent sliding at the crack so
  that the factor γ_{nt} can be considered small at large
  deformation.

- A variation of the orientation of the reinforcement results
  in change of the flexibility of the tension zone which again
  affects the height of the compression zone so that the
  flexibility of the slab will increase less than the
  flexibility of the tension zone of the slab, although this
  effect is diminutive at small percentage of reinforcement.

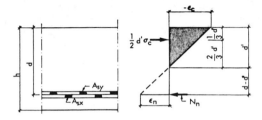

Fig. 3.9 Stresses and strains perpendicular
to the n-direction

Figur 3.9 shows that height of compression zone, curvature
etc. can be calculated in the same way for inclined reinforcement
as for reinforcement perpendicular to the cross-section considered.
As long as no sliding takes place along the crack the effect of inclined reinforcement compared to perpendicular reinforcement is the
same as a reduced amount of perpendicular reinforcement or a
perpendicular reinforcement with a ficticious lower modulus of
elasticity.

A slab subjected to torsional moments is more complicated.
If the reinforcement directions are significantly deviating from
the principal moment directions the reinforcement in both directions
and both the bottom-layers and the top-layers are in tension in
the same cross-section as shown in Fig. 3.10.

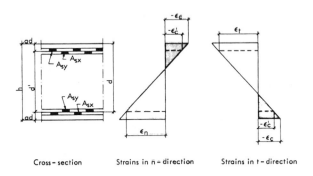

Cross-section   Strains in n-direction   Strains in t-direction

Fig. 3.10 Strains in slab subjected to torsion

In this case the effect of "inclined" reinforcement is still greater than at an uniaxial moment-load. This can be shown experimentally as well as analyticaly.

Experimentally results in Fig. 3.11 show the variation of the curvature in relation to variation of directions of reinforcement and moment combinations. The relations between the crackwidths are approximately the same as those between the curvatures in the cracked state of the concrete tension zone.

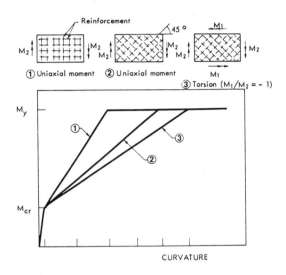

Fig. 3.11 Experimental results

Test results compare well with calculations based on the principles above. The calculated values referred to in Fig. 3.12 are based on no sliding along the cracks, $\gamma_{nt} = 0$, assuming that interlock in the cracks or the compression zone prevent the sliding. The test results indicate that this assumption does not lead to inacceptable errors, see Fig. 3.12.

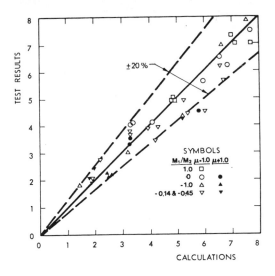

Fig. 3.12 Observed and calculated bending stiffness

4. CONCLUSION

The calculations of crackwidths can only give the order of magnitude. To estimate characteristic crackwidths the CEB-model code proposes to multiply the calculated mean crackwidth by a factor 1,7. This high value underlines the uncertainty of the calculated crack widths.

If the reinforcement crosses the cracks at an angle different from 90°, the relative direction of reinforcement in relation to the crack direction may effect the crack width so significantly that a calculated crackwidth is of no use, unless a proper consideration of the reinforcement direction is included in the calculations.

This paper presents a fairly simple analytical procedure to calculate the influence of inclined reinforcement. Comparisons with test results indicate that the calculated influence of inclined reinforcement agrees significantly better with observations than calculations of crackwidths in general. Therefore the calculations of crack widths for cracks with inclined reinforcement can be carried out with approximately the same accuracy as for the ordinary case with reinforcement crossing the cracks at an angle of 90°.

LIST OF SYMBOLS

A_1 =sectional area of one reinforcing bar

A_{sx} =area of reinforcement in X-direction per unit length

A_{sy} =area of reinforcement in y-direction per unit length

A_s =steel area in $A_{c,ef}$ or = A_{sx} + A_{sy}

$A_{c,ef}$ =effective embedment zone which is within 7,5 Ø in horisontal and vertical direction from the bar center

N_{nx} =force in n-direction per unit length from reinforcement in x-direction

N_{ny} =force in n-direction per unit length from reinforcement in y-direction

N_n =N_{nx} + N_{ny}

N_{nt} =shear force (in the crack)

S_{rm} =average distance between cracks

c =concrete cover

c_{min} =minimum concrete cover

f_y =steel yield stress

f_{sy} =steel yield stress

k_1 =coefficient which characterises the bond properties of the bars

k_1= 0,4 for high bond bars

k_1± 0,8 for plain bars

k_2 =coefficient depending on the form of th stressdiagram

k_2= 0,125 - 0,250

s =spacing of bars

$\emptyset$ = bar diameter

W   = crach width

W_k = calculated concential crach width

α = angle between n- and x-direction

β_1 = bond property: 1,0 for high bond bar and 0,5 for plain bar

β_2 = coefficient depending on the loads

      β_2 = 1 for static load

      β_2 = 0,5 for repeated loads

γ_f = load factor

γ_{nt} = shear strain in relation to n-t-axes

ε_n = strain in n-direction

ε_t = strain in t-direction

ε_{sm} = mean elongation of reinforcement

ε_{sx} = strain of reinforcement in x-direction

ε_{sy} = strain of reinforcement in y-direction

σ_s = steel stress in state 2 (cracked section)

σ_{sr} = calculated steelstress at cracking assuming state 2

REFERENCES

|1| Hafskjold, Sigvart: "WEGEMT Jan. 1979",
NTH, Trondheim

|2| Olsen, Olav: "Wegemt Jan. 1979", NTH, Trondheim

|3| Moxnes, Jan: "

|4| Bell, Kolbein: "

|5| CEB-model code, Avril 1978

|6| FIP-Recommendations for the design and Construc-
tion of Concrete Sea Structures. Draft Third
Edition for Comment, October 1976.

|7| Rules for the Design Construction and Inspection
of Offshore Structures, 1977, Det norske Veritas

|8| Schiessl, Peter: "Zur Frage den zuhissigen Riss-
breite und der erfordenlichen Betondeckung im
Stahlbetonbau..", Deutscher Ausschuss für Stahlbeton, Heft 255, Berlin 1976

|9| DIN 1045 - Beton- und Stahlbeton, Januar 1972

|10| NS 3473 - Prosjektering av betongkonstruksjoner,
February 1977

|11| ACI Standard, 318-71, Building Code, Requirements
for Reinforced Concrete, January 1972

|12| CEB-FIP Model Code, April 1978

|13| Peter Jørg: "Zur Bewehrung von Scheiben und Schalen
für Hauptspannungen Schiefwinklig zur Bewehrungs-
richtung", Technische Hochschule Stuttgart 1964

|14| Lenschow, Rolf: "Betongkonstruksjoner, Dimensjonering,
Deformasjonsberegning. Videregående betraktninger
av armeringens virkning", Tapir 1977

|15| Astad, Unni, Heyerdahl, Knut: "Spesielle skjær-
problemer på skiver". Institutt for betongkon-
struksjoner, NTH, 1976

|16| Lenschow, Rolf, Sozen, M.: "Yield Criterion for
Reinforced Concrete under Biaxial Moments and
Forces", University of Illinois, July 1966

|17| Husain, S.I. and Ferguson, P.H.:
"Flexural Crack widths at the bars in rein-
forced concrete beams", Research Report
No. 102-1F, senter for Highway Research,
University of Texas, Austin, USA

|18| Norwegian Standard 472A, 1962

|19| Bernhardt, C.J., Waldum, A.: "Sak 65. Korrosjon
av armering i betong". Rapport 15.7.1966, FCB,
Rapport 23.1.1967, FCB, Trondheim, Norway

|20| Bernhardt, C.J. and Søpler, B.: "Sak 65. Korrosjon
av armering i betong", Rapport 14.6.67, FCB,
Trondheim, Norway

|21| Bernhardt, C.J.: "An Experimental Study of
Corrosion of Reinforcement in Concrete in Sea
water Environment", Betongtekniske Publikasjoner,
nr. 10, Oct. 1968

|22| Bernhardt, C.J. and Søpler, B.: "An Experimental
Study at the Corrosion of Steel in Reinforced
Concrete in Marine Environment", Nordisk Betong,
nr. 2, 1974

THE USE OF RISK ANALYSIS TO EVALUATE THE SEAWORTHINESS OF OFFSHORE STRUCTURES

C. Östergaard and T.E. Schellin

Germanischer Lloyd, Germany

ABSTRACT

The evaluation of "risk" is based on long term cumulative distributions of such design parameters which influence the seaworthiness of offshore structures. It is shown how risk distribution functions can be derived from cumulative distribution functions and how safe design values are defined with regard to specified risk levels.

The examples given include two most modern designs which have already obtained a quality assurance at Germanischer Lloyd: a semi-submersible LNG-liquefaction platform with a built-in concrete LNG-tank and a semi-submersible drilling platform. Special attention is given to the question of reasonable platform clearance above still water level as specified by the Classification Societies, as well as to the definition of safe design values of loads which occur independently but have to be combined in a structural analysis.

Finally, safety factors are critically examined in light of risk analysis and a basic design principle is suggested.

INTRODUCTION

The term risk, as we use it, is the probability of any unwanted event which restricts the capabilities of an offshore structure to certain limiting conditions. In this paper we concentrate on events which are in one way or another related to sea conditions expected to occur during the offshore operating time of a structure. This means that probabilities of occurrence of any such events considered here have - through different kinds of filtering processes - some relationship to the probabilities of waves. The variety of possible filtering processes of different structures is usually referred to as seakeeping characteristics. It is normally an elaborous and sometimes difficult task to determine these relationships between output- and input-(wave)-signals, e.g. the cumulative response functions. Nevertheless, we consider such seakeeping characteristics of a structure as already determined, and we proceed further to determine - on this basis - what is generally called the seaworthyness of offshore structures. We shall describe how cumulative distributions of wave and/or response amplitudes can be used to determine measures for a safe design on the basis of specified risk levels. Practical applications shall illustrate the advantages of the procedure.

DEFINITIONS

We begin by referring to the well-known cumulative distribution functions. Normally they are obtained through spectral analysis of input (i) or output (o) signals of a system (Θ). A schematic representation of such cumulative distribution functions (ogives) is given in Figure 1.

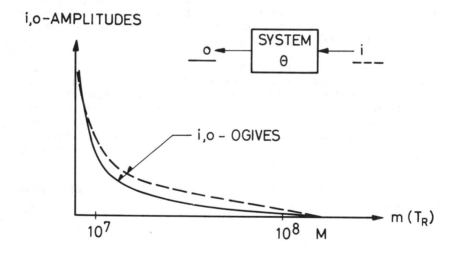

Figure 1   Schematic representation of cumulative
                distribution functions (ogives)

It should be realized that "safe" design values of o- and i-amplitudes will be exceeded with frequencies (m) of the order of 1 or less. Therefore, these frequencies are preferably represented on a log-scale as given in Figure 2, and thus we define our basic relationships with respect to the latter type of a representation of the ogives.

The calculation formula on top of Figure 2 is given here only for the sake of completeness and ready applicability. Further details are given by Östergaard and Payer (1973) and by Germanischer Lloyd (1976). The explanation of the symbols used can be found at the end of the paper.

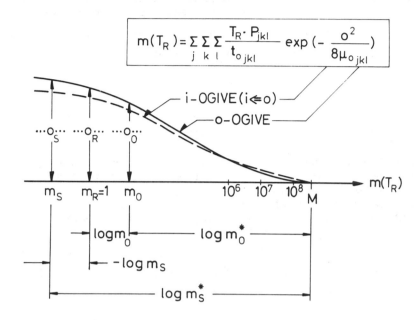

$$m(T_R) = \sum_j \sum_k \sum_l \frac{T_R \cdot P_{jkl}}{t_{o\,jkl}} \exp\left(-\frac{o^2}{8\mu_{o\,jkl}}\right)$$

Figure 2   Log plot of cumulative distribution functions

It can be seen that a calculation of $m(T_R)$ has to be based on a "reference time interval" (T_R), most commonly - but not necessarily - taken to be 50 or 100 years as specified by safety regulations of today. We define the "reference value" (o_R) which is exceeded with the frequency $m_R = 1$ in T_R, "safe design values" (o_S) which are exceeded with frequencies $m_S < 1$ within T_R, and "operating values" (o_O) which are exceeded with a frequency $m_O > 1$ within T_R. The same definitons hold for the input values, i.e. the i-ogive for the wave climate, and we identify the i_R-value at $m_R = 1$ as the so called 50-year- or 100-year-wave amplitude if T_R is assumed to be 50 or 100 years, respectively. Of course, it must still be specified which of the frequencies $m_S < 1$ yields a design value that is regarded as safe enough. We shall deal with this subject during the course of the paper.

Note, it is not specified in Figure 2 that "safety time intervals" (T_S) and "operating time intervals" (T_O) can be regarded as time intervals within which the respective values of $(i, o)_S$ or $(i, o)_O$ are expected to be exceeded just once.

Östergaard and Röhl (1978) have given a detailed derivation of the probability of all amplitudes (i, o) occurring within T_O which are greater than the safety values (i_S, o_S). Here we recall their result, i.e. the risk (R_{SO}) of exceedence of (o_S, i_S) within T_O is given by

$$R_{SO} = 1 - \exp(- m_O^* / m_S^*) \tag{1}$$

or

$$R_{SO} = 1 - \exp(- m_S / m_O) \tag{2}$$

These Equations represent the exponential distribution which implies rather general and well-known relationships between risk values and stochastic events of many kinds. For our purposes, i.e. the evaluation of the seaworthyness of offshore structures, we keep concentrating on events which are specified as the response of structures to the actions of the sea. In this respect it is practical to evaluate R_{SO} from Equation (2) for m_O as a parameter held fixed, while reading values of $o(m_S)$ or $i(m_S)$ from the respective ogives given in Figure 2. Then we obtain risk distribution functions of the kind schematically plotted in Figure 3.

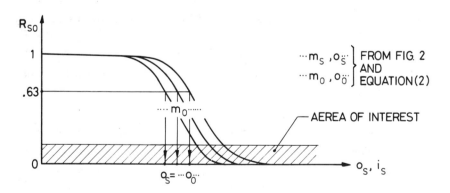

Figure 3   Schematic representation of risk
              distribution functions

In practice we are interested in values of $(o, i)_S$ for relatively small values of R_{SO}. Therefore, we shall plot R_{SO} on a log-normal scale when applying this type of risk distribution function to determine the seaworthyness of offshore structures.

APPLICATIONS

In applying the above definitions to offshore structures, we shall investigate the influence of the filtering process of two systems (θ_1, θ_2) with respect to input signals of two different wave climates (i_1, i_2). Hence, we shall demonstrate how safe design values can be obtained through risk analysis. The systems under consideration are presented schematically in Figure 4.

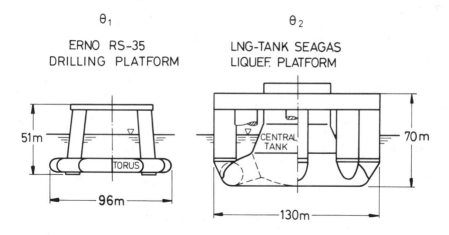

Figure 4   Examples of systems analyzed

On the left hand side of Figure 4 is shown the ERNO RS-35 semi-submersible drilling platform. Östergaard and Schellin (1977) have verified the seakeeping characteristics of this rather unconventional design by extensive calculations with the FMTHT computer program for hydrodynamically transparent structures of Germanischer Lloyd, and Clauss (1978) has conducted model tests at the Technical University Berlin. Model test results and calculations were found to be in very good agreement.

On the right hand side of Figure 4 is shown the MARINE SERVICE SEAGAS semi-submersible LNG-liquefaction platform with built-in LNG storage tank. This again is an unconventional design with favourable seakeeping characteristics, although the motion behavior was found to be quite different from most conventional semi-submersibles. Öster-gaard et al. (1979) have done extensive calculations with the FMTKST computer program for hydrodynamically compact structurs of Germani-scher Lloyd, and Blume and Hattendorff (1978) have conducted model tests at the Hamburgische Schiffbau-Versuchsanstalt. Again, model test results and calculations were found to be in very good agreement.

We can thus conclude that the filtering process of both systems is well known. Therefore, uncertainties, if any, in the calculated i-ogives (wave amplitudes ζ) or o-ogives (relative motions r) can only be due to the long-term spectral analysis and/or the available statistics of the sea. For the wave climate of the North Sea we used statistical data as given by Pflugbeil et al. (1971) (AREA 3), and for the sea area East of Malaysia we used statistical data as given by Hogben and Lumb (1967) (AREA 31). The spectral analysis is based on the Pierson-Moskowitz spectrum of the sea and a Rayleigh distribution of the wave amplitudes. Applying the formula on top of Figure 2, we obtained the ogives as given in Figure 5.

It is interesting to observe the difference in the motion behavior of the semi-submersible θ_1 - this system more or less follows the wave contour - and the unconventional system θ_2 - this system, to a certain degree, moves against the surface elevation. Realizing this situation, it seems natural to ask for a meaningful definition of the platform clearance such that safe design values are verified for both systems with respect to the same risk level. To answer this question, we shall make use of risk distribution curves pertaining to the relative motions. They can be derived form Figure 5 in the same manner as outlined in DEFINITIONS when deriving Figure 3 from Figure 2. Thus we obtained Figures 6 and 7. They show the risk values R_{SO} plotted on a log-normal scale.

In Figure 6 we present the risk distribution functions of relative motion of the two systems operating in the same wave climate, i.e. the North Sea. It is shown that the influence of different operating time intervals T_O is of relatively minor importance in these cases. However, if we consider very short time intervals T_O (in the order of weeks, e.g. change of location), the influence of the operating time interval on the definition of safe design values should then be taken into account. For present purposes we shall concentrate on T_O = 20 year operating time and define the required platform clearance on this basis.

The demand, i.e. the tolerated risk level, is implicitly specified by Classification Societies. They define a minimum of the so called wave clearance between the 100-year-wave crest and any fixed platform deck to be 1.20 [m]. The 100-year-wave crest is exceeded at a frequency m $(T_R = 100$ years) $= 1$ and can be read from Figure 5 to be 11.27 [m]. This yields the minimum clearance above the highest still water level of any fixed platform to be 12.47 [m]. Figure 6 shows that this results in a risk of exceedence of 12.47 [m] by all wave amplitudes occurring within 20 years of operation of $R_{S20} \approx 0.009 = 0.9\%$. In order to define a

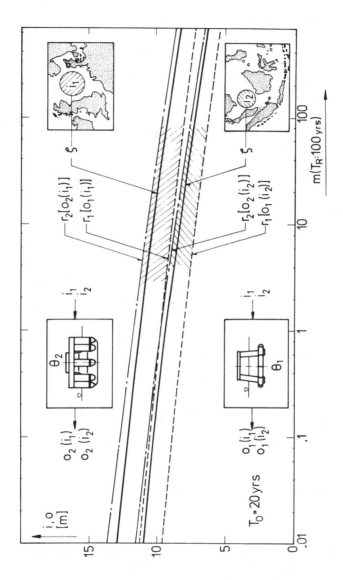

Figure 5   Cumulative frequency of exceedence of wave
amplitudes and relative motion amplitudes

demand for our floating systems we refer to the respective Classification Societies' requirement which states that a "reasonable" clearance

between the wave crest and the platform deck is to be provided. It is deemed "reasonable" to apply the same risk level to fixed as well as to floating platforms. Hence, we obtain the safe platform clearance above

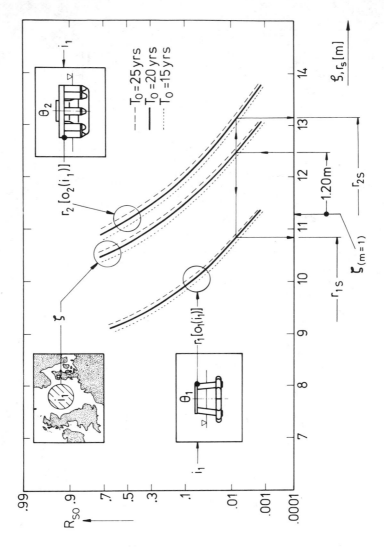

Figure 6   Risk distributions of relative motion ampli-
             tudes of two systems operating in the same
             wave climate

still water level for the specified North Sea area to be $r_{1S} = 10.86$ [m] for the ERNO RS-35 system θ_1 and $r_{2S} = 13.14$ [m] for the SEAGAS system θ_2 (see Figure 6). It should be noted that the relatively high risk level of nearly 1 % is tolerable with due regard to the fact that wave or relative motion amplitudes higher than specified do not necessarily preclude a destruction or demolition of the platform as a whole, but have only limited consequences with respect to the structure's safety.

Realizing the great differences of the obtained safe design values r_S for the platform clearance of the two systems under consideration, it might now be interesting to also observe the influence of different wave climates (i_1, i_2) on a system. For this purpose we have calculated risk distribution functions of the relative motion of the ERNO RS-35 semi-submersible system θ_1 in two wave climates. The results are plotted in Figure 7.

Applying the same reasoning as before, we obtained the safe platform clearance above still water level to be $r_{1S} = 9.20$ [m] in the wave climate East of Malaysia i_2. This latter platform clearance is found to be 1.66 [m] below the required value for the previously considered North Sea wave climate i_1. Here we also note that the required risk level changed somewhat. This already indicates a fundamental distinction that has to be observed when considering risk levels on the one hand and safety factors or - as in this example - safety margins on the other hand. We state here that constant safety factors in general mean variable risk levels under different conditons and vice versa. Moreover, we will show in the following that the application of safety factors alone may be too limiting if, for example, combined loads have to be considered in the evaluation of the strength of a structural member.

To be more specific, we calculated the risk distribution curves of the bending moment (B) and the axial force (N) acting as internal loads in the upper part of the legs of the system θ_1 in a wave climate i_1, i.e. the ERNO RS-35 operating for 20 years in the North Sea area. The risk distribution functions of B (θ_1, i_1) and N (θ_1, i_1) are plotted in Figure 8. They have been derived from the respective ogives as given by Östergaard (1975).

At first we assume a tolerable risk level for simultaniously ("parallel") acting B- and N-values to be specified. A basic probability law for independently occurring events yields this combined risk level to be

$$R_{SO(BN)} = R_{SO(B)} \cdot R_{SO(N)} \tag{3}$$

Thus we conclude that there are many, in fact an infinite number, of possible combinations of B- and N-values which satisfy the condition as stated in Equation (3). The inserted graph in Figure 8 shows these combinations at several specified risk levels. The parameteric curves in this graph have been constructured by assuming $R_{SO(BN)}$ and N as

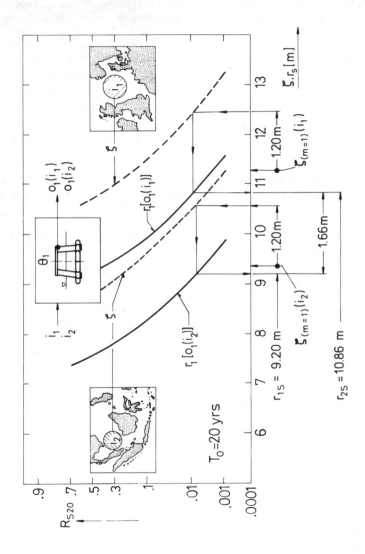

Figure 7   Risk distributions of relative motion ampli-tudes of a system operating in two different wave climates

given; hence by specifying $R_{SO(N)}$ from Figure 8 and $R_{SO(B)}$ from Equation (3), we finally obtained B also from Figure 8. For the sake of simplicity we assumed the bending moment acting in only one direction (2-dimensional analysis). The procedure may easily be extended to two

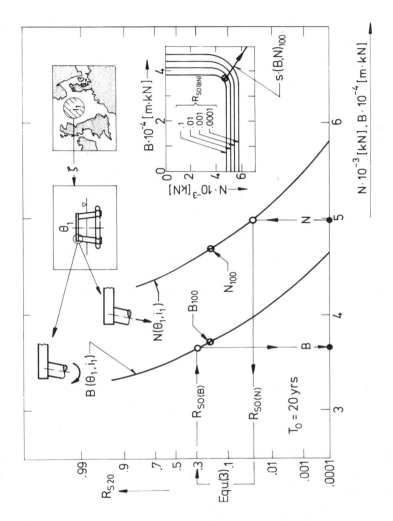

Figure 8   Risk distributions of bending moment amplitudes and axial force amplitudes in two different wave climates

bending moments with the aid of

$$R_{SO(B_1, B_2, N)} = R_{SO(B_1)} \cdot R_{SO(B_2)} \cdot R_{SO(N)} \qquad (4)$$

and would then yield a 3-dimensional graph with an additional B-axis.

If, on the other hand, we use the so called 100-year-values of B and N, i.e. B_{100} = 37200 [m $\cdot$ kN] and N_{100} = 4710 [kN], and if we apply safety factors for design purposes, the resulting design combinations of B and N will be found on the straight line (s $\cdot$ (B, N)$_{100}$) in the small graph of Figure 8. Such a procedure also yields a design based on a certain risk level. However, this procedure disregards all other possible combinations of B and N at the same risk level. Only with risk analysis can all possible combinations of B and N at a given risk level be identified. With due regard to the load capacity of the structural member under consideration, it is then possible to decide which combination of B and N has to be selected for a safe design at a given risk level.

Eventually, we should like to extend this reasoning to a more general case if a design is governed by stresses. At Germanischer Lloyd we then usually do not analyse the loads, but the resulting stresses. In fact, we calculate response amplitude operators for normal (σ) and shear (τ) stresses with FE-methods and apply spectral analysis to both of these stress components. The risk analysis as outlined above then yields risk distribution functions for σ and τ similar to those given in Figure 8 for B and N. Evaluating these curves in the same manner as described above, it is possible to specify combinations of σ- and τ-values which may be expected to act simultaneously at a given risk level. For each of these combinations it is then meaningful to define equivalent stresses and to compare the maximum of these stresses with the allowable stresses of the material in the usual way. The available space of this paper does not permit any further examples to be given, but we hope the basic principle has been illustated.

A DESIGN ASPECT

We have described how the risk distribution function of any output signal (o) is influenced by the shape of the related cumulative distribution of the response, i.e. its o-ogive. We can now conclude the following, "the steeper the o-ogive, the higher the required safe design value (o_s) at a given risk level". Further, it can be shown that the steepness of the o-ogive is influenced by the average steepness of the transfer function. (The transfer function is the relation of the response of the structure due to the action of waves of different lengths.) The transfer function is a design characteristic of the system under consideration. Thus, if the system is to be designed with safe design values as low as possible at a given risk level, we suggest the following as a desirable design principle, "the longer the waves, the lower the response should be".

Again, space does not permit us to illustrate this principle with an example and we must leave this to the reader's own experience with risk analysis. Nevertheless, we hope that this paper has outlined some advantages of risk analysis and that it may encourage designers to use it as a powerful method to build efficient and safe offshore structures. At Germanischer Lloyd this method is well established in the course of quality assurance and classification of modern designs.

REFERENCES

Blume, P. and Hattendorff, H.G. (1978) Seekeeping Model Tests of the SEAGAS Semi-Submersible (in German). HSVA. Hamburg, S. 126/78.

Clauss, G.F. (1978) Multi-Scale Model Tests with a Ring-Shaped Semi-Submersible. Offshore Technology Conference, Houston, OTC 3297.

Germanischer Lloyd (1976) Rules for the Construction and Inspection of Offshore Installations. Hamburg.

Hogben, N. and Lumb, F.E. (1967) Ocean Wave Statistics. National Physical Laboratory. Her Majesty's Stationery Office, London.

Östergaard, C. (1975) ERNO Project 618, Calculation of Motions, Hydrodynamic Forces and Internal Loads of a Semi-Submersible in a Seaway (Part 2, in German). Germanischer Lloyd, Hamburg.

Östergaard, C. and Payer, H.G. (1973) Rational Evaluation of the Strength of Semi-Submersibles (in German). Transactions, Schiffbautechnische Gesellschaft, Hamburg.

Östergaard, C. and Röhl, O. (1978) Reliability of Offshore Structures: Rules and Risks (in German). Transactions, Schiffbautechnische Gesellschaft, Hamburg.

Östergaard, C. and Schellin, T.E. (1977) On the Treatment of Viscous Effects in the Analysis of Ocean Platforms, Part 1: Wave Loads and Motions. Schiff und Hafen (4), Hamburg.

Östergaard, C., Schellin, T.E. and Sükan, M. (1979) Safety of Marine Structures: Hydrodynamic Calculations for Compact Structures (in German). Schiff und Hafen (1), Hamburg.

Pflugbeil, C., Schäfer, P. and Walden, H. (1971) Wave Observations by Ship-Borne German Weather Stations in the North Sea 1957-1966 (in German). Deutscher Wetterdienst, Seewetteramt, No. 75.

ABBREVIATIONS

List of Symbols

B   bending moment (internal)
i   input signal (wave amplitude)
m   frequency of exceedence
N   axial force (internal)
o   output signal (amplitude)
P   probability of significant (observed) waves
r   relative motion (amplitude) between a fixed point in the system's waterline and the local sea surface, platform clearance
R   risk of exceedence
s   safety factor (s> 1)
S   wave or wave effect energy distribution function

t	characteristic period of waves or wave effects $(2\pi\mu/\mu_1)$
T	time interval
ζ	wave amplitude
Θ	system (offshore structure)

$$\mu = \int_0^\infty S(\omega)\,d\omega/4$$

$$\mu_1 = \int_0^\infty \omega S(\omega)\,d\omega/4$$

σ	normal stress
τ	shear stress
ω	circular frequency

List of Subscripts

B	bending moment (internal)
j, k, l	refers to observed: principle wave directions (j)
	wave heights (k)
	wave periods (l)
N	axial force (internal)
o	output signal (amplitudes)
O	operating
R	reference
S	safe
1 or 2	system 1 or 2, sea climate 1 or 2, input-output 1 or 2
20	20 years
100	100 years

A REVIEW OF ACI COMMITTEE 357 REPORT: GUIDE FOR THE DESIGN AND CONSTRUCTION OF FIXED OFFSHORE CONCRETE STRUCTURES

Karl H. Runge
Member, ACI Committee 357 - Offshore Concrete Structures

Exxon Production Research Company, Houston, Texas.

SUMMARY

This paper presents a review of the safety and serviceability requirements of ACI Committee 357 Report: Guide for the Design and Construction of Fixed Offshore Concrete Structures, which was recently published in the Journal of the American Concrete Institute (ACI, 1978).

The most interesting aspect of the committee report is the endorsement of two alternative methods to calculate the "design strength" of concrete members. In one method, which is based on the limit-state philosophy, material factors and stress-strain diagrams for the constituent materials have been specified, while an alternative method endorses the selection of strength reduction factors from the American Building Code Requirements for Reinforced Concrete (ACI 318-77). For both methods, the "required strength" of members is determined from identical combinations of "characteristic" loads multiplied by recommended load multipliers. These multipliers were chosen on the basis of a review of the FIP Recommendations for the Design and Construction of Concrete Sea Structures (FIP, 1977). Since only the design strength representation by the use of material factors is recommended by the FIP design practices, this raises the question as to the level of safety of a design achieved through the alternative "hybrid" approach, i.e., the use of ACI building code strength reduction factors combined with limit-state load multipliers.

This paper has explored the implications of both design methods in terms of their relative structural safety. Specific recommendations for load combinations and structural resistances, given in ACI Committee 357 Report, have also been compared to those of the FIP recommendations and DnV rules.

This study concluded that the use of ACI-recommended partial factors of safety, based on the limit-state philosophy, led to structural design solutions consistent with those of the FIP and DnV documents. It was further concluded that the hybrid approach could lead to lower levels of safety than the first alternative but that for the range of anticipated environmental loads for concrete gravity structures the resulting safety was still higher than that of the DnV rules.

INTRODUCTION

The frontier areas of the U.S. Outer Continental Shelf (OCS) have recently received increased attention because they are believed to contain significant natural resources, including oil and gas fields. Such regions as the Gulf of Alaska and the Bering Sea are characterized by harsh environmental conditions and extreme remoteness.

Concrete gravity structures may be realistic candidates for production platforms in those regions of relevant water depth and adequate foundation conditions because of their large deck weight and oil storage capacities. Such structures can be built at convenient industrial sites, completely outfitted with deck and production modules, and then towed to the designated offshore site for quick installation.

Until recently, the technology required to design and construct offshore concrete structures has been largely generated in Europe where twelve concrete gravity structures have been built for use in North Sea oil and gas fields. Significant progress has been made in the preparation of design and construction recommendations for these concepts. Most notable has been the effort of the FIP (Federation International de la Precontrainte) with its Recommendations for the Design and Construction of Concrete Sea Structures (FIP, 1977). This document provides guidance for the design engineer on matters of structural design to achieve minimum requirements for safety. The FIP recommendations endorse the use of any "relevant" national building code to model concrete strength characteristics to be used in conjunction with FIP recommended partial safety factors for loads and materials.

A need to develop design recommendations, that could rely on domestic concrete building code practices for the design of OCS offshore structures, was recognized by ACI Committee 357 - Offshore Concrete Structures. In their endeavor to prepare a committee report on this subject, they discovered that the application of the ACI 318-77 Building Code by itself was inadequate to deal with the design of offshore concrete structures because of lack of guidance relevant to the marine environment. Therefore, when defining specific requirements of structural performance for safety and serviceability, the committee report incorporated substantial aspects of the limit-state design concept. Only in the area of design strength representation did the report permit a departure from the limit-state approach by allowing the use of ACI building code strength reduction factors as an alternative to the use of limit-state material factors.

The purpose of this paper is to summarize the design principles recommended by the committee, relating to the strength and serviceability aspects of structural design, and to compare the suggested levels of safety with those of the FIP recommendations and DnV rules.

REVIEW OF CONCRETE DESIGN PHILOSOPHIES

The trend in concrete design philosophies, as reflected by international model codes and several national building codes, has been toward the acceptance of probabilistic design methods in which structures are designed to a specific level of reliability for a given environment. In such methods, load effects and structural resistances are taken as random variables, which conform to measured statistical distributions. Since such distributions can only be defined by a sufficiently large number of statistical measurements, it is often found that available data are insufficient to justify the application of probabilistic design methods. This is particularly true for novel structures such as concrete gravity structures.

In lieu of truly probabilistic design methods, the model codes have allowed for substitution with semiprobabilistic methods, where the need for statistical data of load effects and structural resistance has been partially replaced by experience and judgment factors that are designed to achieve specific levels of structural safety when combined with "characteristic" values for prevailing loads and material strength. The characteristic values, however, require evaluation by probabilistic processes.

FIP Limit-State Philosophy
The FIP limit-state design method is an example of one semiprobabilistic method. The basic design assumptions remain the same as for the probabilistic method, namely, that the main parameters controlling the design are random variables. It is understood, however, that uncertainties associated with their assessment can be adequately accounted for by partial load and material safety factors. These factors are then applied together with characteristic values for load effects and structural resistances, to achieve desired levels of safety.

The emphasis of the FIP design method lies in the definition of specific limit states and their respective performance requirements.

A limit state, as defined by FIP, is a condition of structural usefulness that must be assured with an acceptable probability when the structure or individual structural components are subjected to the characteristic loads of that limit state.

For the design of offshore concrete structures, several limit states require verification to assure safety and serviceability. These limit states and their specific requirements are:

Strength Limit State The structure or any of its components must be able to resist the maximum design loads without sustaining permanent damage.

Serviceability Limit State Durability, structural integrity and serviceability have to be maintained for loads frequently occurring in nature. Limitations on excessive deformations, corrosion resistance, and cracking are generally specified.

Fatigue Limit State The structure must be able to maintain structural integrity during its entire service life when subjected to cyclic or repeated loads.

Progressive Collapse Limit State Proof of alternate load paths to prevent catastrophic collapse is necessary, should the structure be subjected to certain extraordinary loads, e.g. explosions, severe earthquakes, or ship collisions.

Individual limit states are identified in terms of characteristic loads and material strength, and associated partial load and material factors.

Characteristic loads are normally determined from the mean load and their coefficients of variation and correspond to a certain probability of exceedance. Design load effects for specific limit states are then obtained by multiplying these characteristic loads with appropriate partial load factors.

The partial load factors, γ_L account for:

1. uncertainties in characteristic values of the loads
2. inaccuracy in the method of analysis for load determination
3. deviation from the structure's nominal geometric dimensions as they would influence the determination of load effects
4. excessive loads
5. unfavorable effects due to reduced probability of simultaneous occurrence of assumed load combinations.

The characteristic material strength, as defined by the FIP design method, means that not more than 5% of the test results from the constituent materials will be below this characteristic

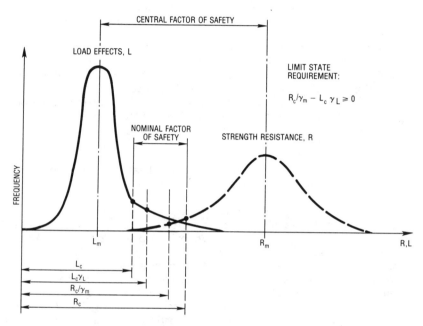

Figure 1. Semi-Probabilistic Approach to Design

value. To obtain the structural resistance of a member, the
characteristic member strength is divided by the appropriate
partial material factor for the limit state under consideration.

The partial material factors, γ_m account for:
1. deviation from the characteristic value of material
   behavior
2. material imperfections
3. geometric imperfections as they affect the structure's
   strength
4. consequences of assumed failure modes
5. inaccurate assessment of structural resistance.

Characteristic load effects, L_c, and structure resistance, R_c,
are shown in Figure 1. These values suggest specific
probabilities of exceedance for the shown distribution
functions. For a particular limit state to be satisfied, the
resistance of a structure or any of its structural components
must equal or exceed the design load effects, i.e.

$$R_c/\gamma_m \geq L_c \, \gamma_L$$

From Figure 1, it may be observed that the "nominal" safety
factor for a limit state has been defined as R_c/L_c.

American Concrete Building Code Philosophy
A Load and Resistance Factor (LRF) format, similar to the FIP
design method, has also been adopted by the American
Building Code ACI 318-77. It recognizes that the actual
resistance of a member and the load effects acting on it, are
variable quantities which differ randomly from their nominal
values. The possibility, that the actual resistance (design
strength) may be less than its nominal strength, R_n, and the
actual load effects (required strength, U) may be larger than
its nominal value, L_n, are recognized separately by strength
reduction factors, $\phi < 1$, and overload factors, $\gamma > 1$. The
desired safety margin is then provided by the condition,

$$\phi R_n \geq U[\gamma L_n]$$

Strength reduction factors are assigned with appropriate
consideration given to the following:
- o past performance experience with the particular
  structural component
- o engineering judgment
- o rational method of design approach.

The individual elements of design strength of a member are
defined as

$$P_u = \phi \, P_n, \quad M_u = \phi \, M_n, \quad V_u = \phi \, V_n,$$

where P_n, M_n, and V_n are nominal axial, bending and shear capacities of the member, based on idealized strength and geometric properties and ϕ is the assigned strength reduction factor. ACI 318-77 allows for the idealized stress-strain relationship of concrete in the form of rectangular, trapezoidal, or parabolic stress blocks. The simplest, but perhaps most often used form for building design application is the rectangular stress block. When representing the capacity by rectangular stress blocks, only the relationship of stress at maximum strain is needed. No information is generally available to define the stress-strain relationship at intermediate stress states. Therefore, for serviceability verification, deflections and stresses under service loads are frequently checked by assuming linear behavior of the concrete section.

Loads are defined in terms of service loads, their selection is normally based on deterministic procedures. Therefore, the nominal load, L_n should not be construed as being the same as L_c, the characteristic load, as used in the FIP limit-state method.

While the current ACI Building Code is not a limit-state code, it is obvious that the LRF-format is the basis for such a procedure.

DISCUSSION OF RELEVANT DESIGN TOPICS FROM ACI COMMITTEE 357 REPORT

In an attempt to extend the applicability of ACI building code design practices to bottom-founded offshore concrete structures, the committee found that the influence of the marine environment would play a dominant part in successful structural design. The need for information about this environment was categorized as:

1. environmental loading unique to the marine environment (e.g. waves, currents, hydrostatic pressures)
2. concrete durability in the ocean (e.g. corrosion, durability and fatigue resistance)
3. design methodology to insure safety and serviceability in the marine environment.

In accumulating this information, significant guidance was found in already available documents addressing such topics. The FIP recommendations and DnV rules were particularly useful.

With emphasis on the marine environment, the final ACI 357 report addresses such diverse topics as concrete material behavior and durability, load classifications, design and analysis, foundations, construction and installation, and inspection and repair. Two appendices present state-of-the-art information on environmental loads and design against earthquakes.

In the remainder of this presentation, the chapters on Load Classifications and Design and Analysis will be discussed. This will be followed by some example calculations that demonstrate that reasonable consistency exists between the ACI 357 recommendations and the FIP and DnV practices in terms of safety and serviceability.

Load Classifications
Loads to be considered in the offshore environment appear to be more complex than those in building design. A thorough review of construction, towing and installation sequences is required to identify the prevailing loading conditions. Loads may be classified as follows:

- dead loads, D
- deformation loads, T
- live loads, L
- environmental loads, E
- accidental loads, A

While this classification agrees with building code practices, the nature of the loads to be considered in each class and the determination of their magnitudes, are uniquely defined by the character of the structure and its site-dependent environment, i.e. the ocean.

Dead Loads   These are static loads that are constant in magnitude and fixed in position. Examples are

- weight of the structure
- permanent ballast
- dry weight of equipment and machinery that is stationary
- hydrostatic pressure, based on a fixed datum such as the mean water level (MWL).

Comments In determining structural weights, the relative position of a component with respect to the surface of the ocean is important to make a proper decision whether to use the air or buoyed weight. Where members are subjected to hydrostatic pressure, i.e. submerged in the ocean, the rate of water absorption of concrete must be considered in assessing the structure's proper weight for floating stability calculations. Changes in weight due to the varying position of the free water surface may be accounted for under live loads or environmental loads.

Confidence in determining the actual dead weight of the structure should be relatively high, because the unique method of construction in the floating mode allows for verification of assumptions in weight calculations at various stages of construction.

Deformation Loads   Loads to be considered in this category are:

- differential settlements of the foundation
- prestressing loads
-- temperature loads
- creep and shrinkage

Comments   Concrete gravity structures in the past have been installed without substantial preparation of the sea bed foundation. Although installation sites are selected on the basis of an extensive survey for levelness and uniformity of soil deposits, a structure should be designed to tolerate a reasonable amount of differential settlement. However, such settlement is difficult to express in terms of applied loads to satisfy design strength requirements.

Differential settlement and temperature loads are ideally treated as prescribed boundary conditions, especially if the applied structural analysis consists of a major computational undertaking, using numerical methods such as Finite Elements.

Prestressing loads lend themselves to applied load expressions, but may also be incorporated as initial strains into the structural analysis process.

Creep due to applied stress or temperatures, and shrinkage may best be described in terms of modified material parameters, e.g. a reduced modulus of elasticity, when creep is expected to be uniform throughout the entire structure.

Live Loads   These loads are variable in magnitude and position, and may be either static or dynamic in nature. Among them are:

- movable equipment load (e.g. drilling rig, helicopters)
- consumable liquids stored on deck (fuel, water)
- dynamic loads induced by machinery
- mooring and breasting loads

Comments When live loads are dynamic in nature, their magnitudes may initially best be expressed in terms of equivalent static loads, so that they can be considered in the structure's design strength requirements. A distinction should also be made between maximum and minimum live loads to allow for the special activities that take place on petroleum production platforms. Maximum live loads should be expected early in the life of a platform during drilling activities, while the effects of minimum loads would have to be investigated once the drilling rig and necessary accessories have been removed, and the platform is engaged in normal production activities.

Environmental Loads   Loads associated with the offshore environment are the result of natural phenomena.   Dominant among these are:

- waves, wind, currents
- earthquake
- tsunamis
- ice

Comments   Due to the origin of these loads, a higher degree of uncertainty to predict their load effects is associated with them.   This uncertainty has been accounted for by the choice of larger load multipliers.

The shape of the structure has a profound effect in influencing the environmental forces. For wave loading, diffraction, which is caused by the presence of the generally massive structure in the path of a propagating wave, should be accounted for.

Diffraction also influences the "added masses" of a structure when excited by earthquake ground shaking. The concept of added masses is a conceptual simplification to incorporate the net hydrodynamic forces due to the formation of nonuniform pressure distributions when a relatively rigid structure is accelerated through the water.

Ice forces appear to be particularly difficult to predict. Historical data on ice coverage, thickness, ridges, etc., and physical property data on sea ice are required to predict forces acting on offshore structures. Because of the recent interest in ice infested offshore regions such data are now being collected.

Accidental Loads   Accidental loads are defined as loads resulting from misuse or accidents, but loads resulting from rare environmental events (e.g. severe earthquakes, iceberg collisions) are often placed into this category as well. This load category is generally characterized by the low probability with which these loads will actually occur.

Accidental loads, as defined in the ACI 357 report, are not considered to be part of the design strength load combinations, but instead should be checked separately under the progressive collapse mode analysis. No guidance has been provided for the selection of accidental loads to be considered for a specific design situation.

Design and Analysis

The Design and Analysis chapter of the ACI 357 report discusses the use of the limit-state approach as an optional design method. This is significant to the designer because ACI building code practices do not address specific requirements of safety and serviceability that may be applicable to offshore concrete structures.

The introduction of the limit state design approach provides for design flexibility so that specific performance objectives can be met. These objectives have been specified for strength, serviceability, fatigue and survival. The ACI 357 report gives specific recommendations for only two limit states, i.e. the strength and serviceability limit states, and provides some general guidance on fatigue and survival.

Strength Limit State The performance criteria for adequate strength is intended to prevent the following:

1. loss of overall equilibrium
2. structural failure of individual components
3. structural instability
4. excessive long-term deformations.

The design strength of the structure and each member should be equal or greater than the maximum required strength, U, calculated by one of the following:

$$U = 1.2 (D + T) + 1.6 L_{max} + 1.0 E_o \qquad (1)$$
$$or = 1.2 (D + T) + 1.2 L_{max} + \gamma_L E_{max} \qquad (2)$$
$$or = 0.9 (D + T) + 0.9 L_{min} + \gamma_L E_{max} \qquad (3)$$

In Equations (1) to (3) the symbols introduced, have the following meaning:

L_{max}, L_{min} ≡ maximum, minimum characteristics live loads

E_o ≡ frequently occurring characteristic environmental load (e.g. monthly wave load)

E_{max} ≡ extreme characteristic environmental load (e.g. 100 year wave load)

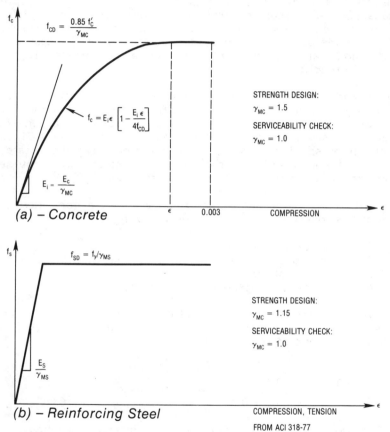

$$f_{CD} = \frac{0.85\,f_c'}{\gamma_{MC}}$$

$$f_c = E_i\epsilon\left[1 - \frac{E_i\,\epsilon}{4f_{CD}}\right]$$

$$E_i = \frac{E_c}{\gamma_{MC}}$$

STRENGTH DESIGN:

$\gamma_{MC} = 1.5$

SERVICEABILITY CHECK:

$\gamma_{MC} = 1.0$

(a) – Concrete ϵ 0.003   COMPRESSION ϵ

$$f_{SD} = f_y/\gamma_{MS}$$

$$\frac{E_S}{\gamma_{MS}}$$

STRENGTH DESIGN:

$\gamma_{MC} = 1.15$

SERVICEABILITY CHECK:

$\gamma_{MC} = 1.0$

(b) – Reinforcing Steel   COMPRESSION, TENSION ϵ

FROM ACI 318-77

Figure 2. ACI 357 Recommended Stress-Strain Diagrams

In Figure 1, the required strength U is represented by $L_c \gamma_L$, while the design strength is shown as R_c / γ_m.

The choice of γ_L values reflects on the experience with the environmental event under consideration. For wave loads, a recommended value of 1.3 appears to be consistent with the state of the art of calculating design wave forces. For ice loading, the committee chose not to make a recommendation, while for the selection of γ_L for earthquake forces Appendix B gives some guidance in this regard.

Generally it is expected that for major structural component design, Equation (2) will govern the selection of a member's cross section and reinforcing steel, while Equation (3) will primarily affect the selection of the amount of prestressing steel. It is anticipated that Equation (1) will only be of importance when the live load is a dominant factor.

Load combinations other than those stated may govern certain aspects of platform design, particularly during construction and towing phases. The anticipated environmental events at the construction site, during tow-out and installation at the offshore site require careful review of available oceanographic and meteorologic data for the particular season in which such operations are planned.

Concrete Strength Model   The use of strength reduction factors, ϕ, to determine the design strength of structural members while calculating the required strength by the use of limit state partial load factors was recommended as one design option. It has been referred to in this paper as the hybrid approach. Strength reduction factors are selected from the ACI 318-77 Building Code. For shell panels which are common structural components for offshore gravity structures, a ϕ-factor of 0.7 has been recommended.

Alternatively, the strength of a structural member may also be defined in terms of appropriate stress-strain diagrams of the constituent materials (Figure 2). Appropriate selections of material factors will depend on the limit state under investigation.

While the recommendations do not specifically address possible increases in the design strength of concrete due to aging, the strength characteristics of concrete as a function of age may be taken advantage of, if sufficient evidence exists to warrant such consideration for a given concrete mix design.

Special Design Requirements   A characteristic feature of offshore concrete structures is the arrangement of cylindrical, square, or sometimes lobated enclosures of the submerged storage caisson.   These enclosures provide buoyancy during

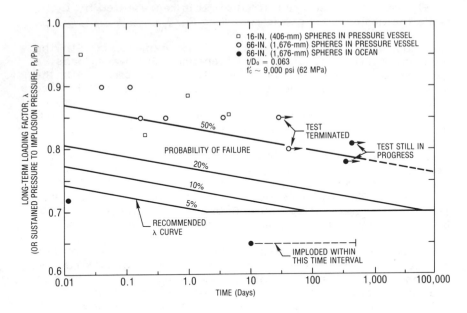

Figure 3. Long-term Loading Behavior of Concrete Spherical Structures Under Hydrostatic Loading. (Haynes, 1976)

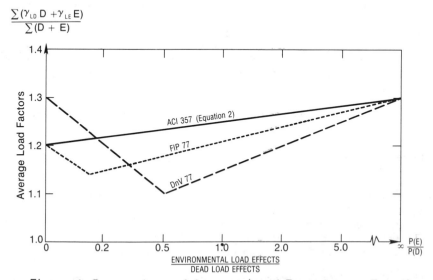

Figure 4. Comparison of Average Load Factors as a Function of Environmental to Dead Load Effects Ratios

construction, tow and installation and serve as storage cells, either filled with sea water or crude oil when in operation.

The design of the enclosures is of extreme importance and requires special considerations to assure the platform's safety during critical transit phases.

Implosion   Implosion is a catastrophic failure due to collapse under excessive hydrostatic pressure. Danger of implosion primarily exists during periods of submergence for deck and production module installation. The structure then normally attains its maximum draft with extensive volume of the storage cells at ambient air pressure. Deck to structure mating activities may require the structure to be maintained at such draft for several days.

The structural stability of the individual cells requires a realistic estimate of buckling capacity by an appropriate non-linear concrete strength model (Runge, 1978). Unintentional construction out-of-roundnesses may reduce implosion resistance, particularly for relatively thin shell structures. Another factor to be accounted for is the effect of prolonged pressure exposure. There is some experimental evidence (Haynes, 1976) of long-term strength reduction as shown in Figure 3, even when the exposure is limited to 2 or 3 days. Use of compressed air to counteract the external hydrostatic pressure may be useful in cases where the existing implosion strength is found to be marginal. Actual field experiences with at least four gravity structures have demonstrated air pressurization to be an effective way to increase the margin of safety during critical construction maneuvers.

Caisson Effect   Because of the constraints imposed by the interconnected walls in the arrangement of individual enclosures within a caisson, resulting tensile and shear stresses require careful identification. Proper detailing of reinforcing steel should prevent cracking of the cell walls to avoid leakage. The complex global behavior of the caisson when subjected to hydrostatic loading necessitates the use of sophisticated numerical analysis tools to identify critical stress conditions.

Design Against Shear   Adequate shear strength is an essential element of satisfactory structural performance. Shear in gravity structures has been a serious concern because complex stress states exist within the structure, for which shear capacities are not well known. In regions of structural restraints and geometric discontinuities, e.g. dome-cylinder junctions of the storage cells, three-dimensional stress states are present, that are characterized by high axial compression, high bending stresses, and significant through-thickness shear stresses, all occurring simultaneously. Another region

Table 1 – Allowable Tensile Stresses For Prestress and Reinforcing Steel for Serviceability Limit State

STAGE	LOADING	ALLOWABLE STRESS, ksi	
		Δ_{ps}	f_s
Construction: Where cracking during construction would be detrimental to the completed structure	All loads on the structure during construction	18.5 (130 MPa)	23.0 (160 MPa)
Construction: Where cracking during construction is not detrimental to the completed structure	All loads on the structure during construction	18.5 (130 MPa)	30 (210 MPa) or $0.6\,f_y$ whichever is less
Construction	All loads on the structure during transportation and installation	18.5 (130 MPa)	23.0 (160 MPa)
At offshore site	Dead and live loads plus monthly recurring environmental loads	11.0 (75 MPa)	17.0 (120 MPa)
At offshore site	Dead and live loads plus extreme environmental loads		$0.8\,f_y$

Table 2 – Concrete Strength Definitions

DESIGN PRACTICE	STRENGTH TEST	DESIGN STRENGTH f_c	MATERIAL FACTOR γ_{mc}	CHARACTERISTIC STRENGTH (f_c') / DESIGN STRENGTH (f_c)
ACI 357	Cylinder	$0.85\,f_c'/\gamma_{mc}$	1.5	1.76
ACI 357 "Hybrid"	Cylinder	$0.85\,f_c' \times \phi$	$1.43\left(\frac{1}{\phi}\right)$	1.68
DnV 77	Cylinder	$0.85\,f_c'/\gamma_{mc}$	1.5	1.76
FIP 77	Cube	$0.67\,f_{cu}/\gamma_{mc}$	1.5	1.79

NOTE: Assumed ϕ – value = 0.7

of concern is the support tower-caisson interconnection where large in-plane shear stresses are induced as a result of the environmental load transfer into the base. In-plane shear stresses also exist in the vertical walls of box-type cell arrangements. These stresses in most cases can be controlled by adequate prestressing. Because the behavior of shell panels in shear is presently not well understood, larger factors of safety may be warranted when designing against shear. This concern is evident in the choice of a recommended ϕ-value equal to 0.7.

Shear capacity equations defined in national building codes, including ACI 318-77, have presently not been adequately verified to judge whether they are applicable under these circumstances, since their empirical derivations are based on traditional building components, such as beams or beam columns.

Accidental Loads   The load combinations suggested in Equations (1) to (3) do not directly call for the inclusion of accidental loads. No guidance has been given in the committee report with respect to load combinations involving accidental loads, except that it has been suggested to make allowances for alternative load paths. From North Sea experiences, it has been found that accidental loads, such as impact loads from dropped objects, can no longer be assumed to have significantly lower probabilities than those events for which the structures were designed. It therefore appears to be desirable to reclassify accidents by the relative frequency of their occurrence. Work boat collisions and dropped objects may justifiably be superimposed on normal operating conditions. Equation (1) would then be applicable to check if strength capacities are exceeded and to make appropriate design changes, if necessary. Other accidents, such as explosions, could continue to be treated as low probability events, for which adequate ductility and structural redundancy should be provided.

Serviceability   The primary objective to be met in the serviceability limit state is to insure structural integrity and concrete durability. To achieve this, the control of cracking is considered essential. The committee felt that this could best be achieved by limiting the allowable stresses in reinforcing and prestressing steel. Recommended reinforcing steel stresses under various site-prevailing environmental conditions have been presented in Table 1. Their selection was influenced by a recently initiated fatigue study (Waagard, 1977) where it was observed that the penetration of sea water into opened cracks may have caused hydraulic spalling during repeated load reversals, thereby severely exposing the reinforcing bars. Only during periods of temporary load exposure, such as during construction, are reinforcing steel stresses allowed to exceed maximum values specified.

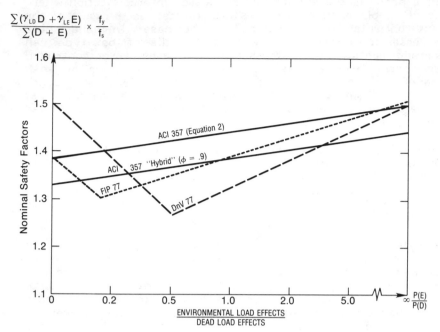

$$\frac{\sum(\gamma_{LD}D + \gamma_{LE}E)}{\sum(D + E)} \times \frac{f_y}{f_s}$$

Figure 5. Comparison of Nominal Safety Factors
against Yielding of Steel

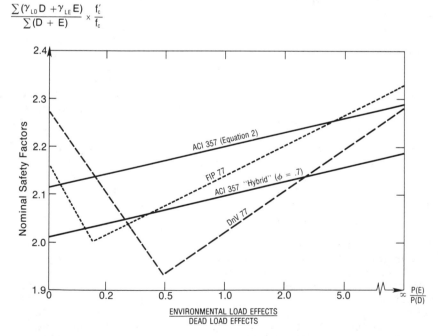

$$\frac{\sum(\gamma_{LD}D + \gamma_{LE}E)}{\sum(D + E)} \times \frac{f_c'}{f_c}$$

Figure 6. Comparison of Nominal Safety Factors
against Crushing of Concrete

The serviceability criterion is checked for the stated load combinations of Equations (1) to (3), except that all loads remain unfactored. To calculate the structural behavior, material factors for concrete and steel are set to unity if the consistent limit state approach is followed.

Special serviceability requirements have been specified for thin-walled, hollow cross sections where cracks could easily propagate through the entire thickness of the wall. For such members, the maximum permissible tensile membrane strain across the wall at any part of the circular cross section has been limited to prevent cracking.

Fatigue Considerations The fatigue limit state requires that stress ranges be limited in the constituent materials, i.e. in the concrete, reinforcing steel and prestressing steel. Specified stress limitations were selected to prevent the concrete from cracking. Under those conditions, it is generally assumed that the fatigue life of concrete is unlimited. While this requirement may impose considerable constraints under certain design conditions, an endorsement of recently proposed fatigue models, based on the concept of cumulative fatigue damage, would seem to be premature.

Comparisons of Safety Aspects of Relevant Recommendations
The main parameters that define structural safety as recommended by the ACI 357 report will now be compared with those of DnV recommendations and FIP rules. Several graphs have been prepared to highlight these comparisons:

1. Comparison of "average" load factors as a function of the ratio of environmental to dead load effects. (Figure 4)
2. Comparison of "nominal" safety factors against yielding of reinforcing steel as a function of the ratio of environmental to dead load effects. (Figure 5)
3. Comparison of "nominal" safety factors against crushing of concrete as a function of the ratio of environmental to dead load effects. (Figure 6)

The definition of the "nominal" safety factor, as presented in Figures 5 and 6, and previously introduced in Figure 1, was adopted from the European concrete literature (Leonhardt, 1973). It represents the ratio of the characteristic structural resistance to the characteristic load effects. In Figures 5 and 6, which show the strength limit state, the ordinate values represent the products of the average load factors from Figure 4, multiplied by the ratio of the characteristic to the design strength of the constituent materials. These values have been plotted against R_{LE}, the ratio of the environmental load effects to the dead load effects.

Comparisons of Average Load Factors (Figure 4)

In presenting average load factors for the three design recommendations under discussion, the critical load combination for each recommendation was first identified. These have been presented below:

ACI 357 $U = 1.2 D + 1.3 E_{max}$ $0 \leq R_{LE} \leq \infty$

DNV 77 $U = 1.3 D + 0.7 E_{max}$ $0 \leq R_{LE} \leq 0.5$

          $U = 1.0 D + 1.3 E_{max}$ $0.5 \leq R_{LE} \leq \infty$

FIP 77 $U = 1.2 D + 1.4 E_{o}$ $0 \leq R_{LE} \leq 0.15$

          $U = 1.1 D + 1.3 E_{max}$ $0.15 \leq R_{LE} \leq \infty$

All individual load components imply characteristic values. Because the influence of live loads on structural design of individual members is generally only important for top-side supports, they have been neglected in this presentation.

While for the ACI 357 representation, a single equation governed for the entire range of R_{LE}, DnV 77 rules and FIP 77 recommendations, each were controlled by critical segments of two equations. In presenting the first FIP 77 equation, it was assumed that for frequently occurring environmental loads, $E_o = 0.5 E_{max}$. This assumption was required to be able to plot the equation, but its validity is limited to northern North Sea wave loadings, where the monthly wave load is often assumed to be one half of the design wave load, i.e. the 100 year wave load.

From Figure 4, it is apparent that the ACI 357 average load factor curve is consistently above FIP and DnV equivalents, except in the range of $R_{LE} \leq 0.15$, where DnV achieves higher average load factors.

Comparison of Nominal Safety Factors Against Yielding of Steel (Figure 5)

Nominal safety factors against the tensile yielding of reinforcing steel have been presented in Figure 5 as a function of the ratio of the environmental to dead load effects. The ordinate component, f_y/f_s, is the ratio of the yield strength to the design strength of steel, which for the design procedures under discussion, is recommended as 1.15. However, one exception should be noted:

> For the ACI 357 hybrid method, the curve shown in Figure 5 was derived by presenting the strength reduction factor ϕ as $1/\gamma_{ms}$. A ϕ-value of 0.9, which is typical for structural members whose dominant mode of failure is yielding of reinforcing steel, was plotted as $\gamma_{ms} = 1.11$.

In reviewing Figure 5, it should be pointed out, that the average load factors contained in the ordinate values, were taken from Figure 4, which was identified as being representative of the critical load combination for each of the design procedures. However, other load combinations than those presented in Figure 4, may govern maximum tensile stresses. Since the precise determination of critical stress states can only be made for specific design conditions, the conclusions that can be drawn from Figure 5 should be considered valid only to establish relative safety among the design practices. In general, it may be concluded that the nominal safety factors for both ACI 357 representations are larger than those of the FIP 77 recommendations and the DnV 77 rules in the range of environmental loads typical for concrete offshore structures.

Comparison of Nominal Safety Factors Against the Crushing of Concrete (Figure 6)

Nominal safety factors against the crushing of concrete have been presented in Figure 6 as a function of environmental to dead load effects ratios. Similar to Figure 5, the ordinate values consist of the average load factors for load combinations of Figure 4, multiplied by the ratio of the characteristic strength to the design strength of concrete, f'_c/f_c. Specific data on concrete strength have been tabulated in Table 2. The ACI 357 hybrid design alternative has been presented by a ϕ-value of 0.7, which is representative of members, whose mode of failure is controlled by the crushing strength of concrete.

In comparing the nominal safety factors for the three design procedures, it may be observed that the trend established in Figures 4 and 5, is also evident in Figure 6, with ACI 357 (Equation 2) providing the largest safety factors over a wide range of the environmental to dead load effects ratios. There are, however, distinguishable differences between the two ACI 357 design alternatives.

Discussion of Serviceability Requirements

While it is expected that the strength limit state will govern most aspects of structural design, the serviceability limit state may have some impact on the amount of prestressing steel required for the individual structural components.

The serviceability limit state is checked by letting the loads and material strength remain unfactored, i.e. $\gamma_L = \gamma_m = 1.0$. In addition, each of the design procedures under discussion specifies limitations on steel stresses under various environmental exposures. An example of this has already been presented in Table 1.

To determine the consequences imposed by the requirements of the serviceability limit state by each of the three design procedures, the amounts of reinforcing and prestressing steel were calculated in a separate study (Runge, 1977) for a typical support tower of a North Sea gravity structure. The tower design was governed by the requirement for thin-walled, hollow sections, which limits the concrete membrane tensile strains. This requirement was common to all three documents, and led to substantially identical design solutions. In applying the ACI 357 procedure, only the limit-state material representation was used.

CONCLUSIONS

Based on the presented comparisons of suggested design recommendations of the ACI 357 committee report, the FIP recommendations, and the DnV rules, no outstanding differences in nominal safety could be identified.

In comparing the alternative design methods permitted by the ACI 357 recommendations, it was found that the application of the hybrid method led to lower nominal safety factors (Figures 5 and 6) than through the use of the alternative method. The reason for these differences can be found in a review of safety and serviceability provisions of the ACI 318-77 Building Code (Winter, 1979). Here, it has been suggested, that large load multipliers are used together with the suggested ϕ-values to obtain the desired levels of safety.

In applying the ACI 357 design recommendations, the designer should therefore be aware of these differences. Where the designer wants to achieve an extra margin of safety, e.g. for unconventional critical platform members, he may want to follow the ACI 357 limit-state procedure.

REFERENCES

American Concrete Institute, ACI Standard Building Code Requirements for Reinforced Concrete (ACI 318-77), Detroit, Michigan, 1977.

American Concrete Institute, Guide for the Design and Construction of Fixed Offshore Concrete Structures, Reported by ACI Committee 357, Journal of the American Concrete Institute, December 1978, Detroit, Michigan.

Det norske Veritas, Rules for the Design, Construction and Inspection of Offshore Structures, Oslo 1977.

FIP Commission on Concrete Sea Structures, Recommendations for the Design and Construction of Concrete Sea Structures, third edition, July 1977, London.

Haynes, H., Collapse Behavior of Pressurized Concrete Shells, Boss '76, Vol. 1, pg. 720-743, International Conference on the Behavior of Off-Shore Structures, NIT, Trondheim, 1976.

Leonhardt, F., Vorlesungen ueber Massivbau, Erster Teil, pg. 92, Springer-Verlag, Berlin, 1973.

Runge, K., Comparison of Design and Serviceability Requirements for DnV, FIP, and Proposed ACI Recommended Practices, Report to ACI Committee 357 - Offshore Concrete Structures, 1977.

Runge, K. and Haynes, H., Experimental Implosion Study of Concrete Structures, Proceedings of the Eighth Congress of the Federation International de la Precontrainte, Part 1, pg. 19-31, London, May 1978.

Waagard, K., Fatigue of Offshore Concrete Structures - Design and Experimental Investigations, Offshore Technology Conference, OTC 3009, pg. 341-350, Vol. IV, Houston, Texas, May 1977.

Winter, G., Safety and Serviceability Provisions in the ACI Building Code, ACI-CEB-FIP-PCI Symposium, ACI Special Publication, 1979.

COMMENTS ON CODES FOR DESIGN AND CONSTRUCTION OF FIXED STEEL AND CONCRETE OFFSHORE STRUCTURES

Fernando L.L.B. Carneiro and Sergio H. Sphaier
COPPE-UFRJ - Brazil.

INTRODUCTION

1. -The methods for loading effects, i. e. displacement and stress analysis of offshore structures have already a high degree of sophistication, and further improvements are reported frequently.That would be meaningless, however, if at some time the criteria for determination of loads and safety factors, i.e. the design criteria, were not established on solid bases.

A good indication of the diversity still subsisting in this domain, particularly with reference to safety factors, is given by the comparison of the load factors explicitly or implicitly adopted by several commonly used codes.

In the limit state design method, based on a semi-probabilistic approach, the strength of the materials are divided by partial safety factors, namely the "material factors" γ_m (γ_s for steel and γ_c for concrete) and the loads are multiplied by others partial safety factors, namely the "load factors" γ_f as known. The strength and the loads are established, whenever possible, on statistical bases, and are called "characteristic strength" and "characteristic loads".

For the "extreme loading conditions" the load factors recommended by seven codes do vary between the following values:

G - permanent loads (dead loads): 1.00 to 1.30
Q_o - variable loads (live loads): 1.00 to 1.30
Q_{Emax}- environmental extreme loads : 1.09 to 1.30

TABLE 1 ULTIMATE LIMIT STATE γ_f PARTIAL SAFETY FACTORS

CODES, RULES, GUIDES	Dead loads		Live loads	Environmental loads	
	fav. G	unf. G	Q_o	ordinary Q_{Eo}	extreme Q_{Emax}
Det Norske Veritas 74, steel; Bureau Veritas 75 steel; A.P.I. 76, steel (suposing $\gamma_s=1,15$)	1.45 1.09	1.45 1.09	1.45 1.09	– –	– 1.09
Det Norske Veritas 74, concrete	1.40 1.10	1.40 0.90	1.60 1.30	– –	– 1.30
FIP 74 concrete	1.20 1.20	1.20 0.90	1.60 1.20	1.40 –	– 1.20
Bureau Veritas 75, concrete	1.40 1.20 1.20	0.90 1.20 0.90	1.60 1.60 1.20	– 1.40 –	– – 1.20
Det Norske Veritas 77, steel and concrete	1.30 1.00	1.00 1.00	1.30 1.00	– –	0.70 1.30
ACI 78, concrete	1.20 1.20	1.00 0.90	1.60 1.20	1.00 –	– 1.30
Suggestion of this paper, based on CEB-FIP S.I.R.T.U.S. Vol.1	1.30 1.30	1.00 1.00	1.50 1.20	1.30 –	– 1.30

For the "ordinary (frequently ocurring) loading conditions" these values are:

G - permanent loads (dead loads): 1.20 to 1.45
Q_o - variable loads (live loads): 1.30 to 1.60
Q_{E_o} - environmental frequent loads: 0.00 to 1.40

Table I shows the partial safety factors applied to loads ("load factors") recommended by the several codes. To allow for comparison of safety criteria, partial safety factors applied to the strength of the materials were assumed to be $\gamma_s = 1.15$ (steel structures) for all codes based on the allowable stress method.

2. - In what follows, the design criteria are discussed on the basis of the principles adopted in Volume 1 of the International System of Unified Standard Codes of Practice for Structures ("Système International de Règlementation Technique Unifiée des Structures - S.I.R.T.U.S."), for structural safety and serviceability.

This volume 1 - "Common Unified Rules for Different Types of Construction and Materials" was prepared by a"Joint Committee on Structural Safety",sponsored by six international associations, including CEB and FIP.

In a previous paper (ref.1), presented to the International Conference on Offshore Structures Engineering, Rio de Janeiro, September 1977, by the first author, an analysis of the codes commonly used at that time was included, and several suggestions were made.

Afterwards the 1977 version of the "Rules for the Design, Construction and Inspection of Offshore Structures", from Det Norske Veritas, was published, extending the principles of the limit states design method and the semi-probabilistic approach, to the steel structures, on the basis of the "Common Unified Rules" of the S.I.R.T.U.S.

A new code, the "Guide for the Design and Construction of Fixed Offshore Structures", was published in 1978 by the American Concrete Institute. This"Guide" is also consistent, in many points, with the Common Unified Rules" from the S.I.R.T.U.S.

A special mention must be made of the code "Limit

States Design Steel Manual",. published in 1977 by the
Canadian Institute of Steel Construction, where the
same principles adopted by the "Common Unified Rules"
are applied to steel structures, in general.

Some important steps taken by those three codes, Det
Norske Veritas'77, ACI'78, and the Canadian Steel
Manual, in order to place the analysis methods for
structural safety on a level of sophistication
consistent with that of analysis methods for loading
effects, will be commented in the following sections.

SOME COMMENTS ON LIMIT STATES

1. The "ultimate limit state" corresponds to the
maximum load-carrying capacity of the structure.

In the case of concrete structures, the CEB/FIP
Model Code definition of ultimate limit state
corresponding to the failure (rupture or excessive
deformation) of critical cross sections is accepted,
with slight modifications, by the Det Norske Veritas,
FIP and ACI Codes. The ACI "Guide" prescribes the
adoption of a "strength reduction factor" for the
members, instead of the "material" partial safety
factors γ_s (for reinforcement) and γ_c (for concrete),
but in special cases, it allows the use of these
factors.

For steel structures the ultimate limit state can be
reached, in an elastic analysis, when in some point
of the structure the characteristic yield stress of
the material is attained, or, in cases of bars in
flexure, when the moment of plastification is attained
in some cross section. This does not imply that the
structure is transformed into a mechanism as in the
case of a plastic analysis.

The Det Norske Veritas 77 "Rules" allows, for the
case of an elastic design, that the contribution of
the bending moment to the longitudinal stress be
calculated by the formula

$$\sigma_{bd} = \frac{M_{fd} \cdot y}{1.1 \ I}$$

with M_{fd} being the "design" or "factored"(by the load
factors) bending moment. The ultimate limit state
is reached when the longitudinal stress attains the
"design strength", that is, the characteristic
yielding stress divided by $\gamma_s = 1.15$.

When a plastic analysis can be adopted (structures

composed of members which can develop well defined
plastic resistances) the "material factor" is taken
as γ_s = 1,30.

The Canadian "limit States Design Manual" is more
refined, in this part. It classifies the structural
sections in classes depending on the maximum width-
thickness ratios of their elements subjected to
compression:

- Class 1 sections (plastic design sections) will
  permit attainment of the plastic moment and subsequent redistribution of bending moment;

- Class 2 sections (compact sections) will permit
  attainment of the plastic moment but need not
  allow for subsequent moment redistribution;

- Class 3 sections (non-compact sections) will
  permit attainment of the yielding moment.

The sections which have local buckling as the limit
ultimate state are classified as Class 4 (slender
sections, cold formed steel structural members).

The moment resistance developed by a member subjected
to bending moments, when continuous lateral support
is provided to the compression flange, is taken as
the product of the "design strength" of the steel
times the plastic section modulus" Z, for Class 1
and 2 sections, and by the "elastic section modulus"
S, for the class 3 sections. In the case of class 1
sections, a plastic analysis is allowed if certain
others restrictions are satisfied.

2.2 - In the ultimate limit states reached by
buckling, a special consideration must be made
regarding the effects of initial imperfections. The
partial safety factors γ do not in general cover
those effects, for very slender members.

For the analysis of structural instability of
concrete structures, the CEB-FIP Model Code and
Apendix D of Det Norske Veritas'77 give very
detailed rules, based on simplified methods for
non-linear analysis.

For steel structures, Det Norske Veritas'77
prescribes that the usual "material" factor γ_s=1,15
must be combined with two other factors ψ and k,
in the calculation of the "design buckling
resistance":

$$R_d = \frac{R_k}{\gamma_s} \frac{\psi}{k}$$

with R_k being the "characteristic compressive resistance", given by the buckling formulae.

Coefficient k depends of the slenderness ratio for the member, and coefficient ψ reflects the post-buckling behaviour (possibility of redistribution). This is equivalent to multiply the partial safety factor γ_s, in the general case where redistribution is not possible, by 1,11 for low slenderness ratios, and by 1,22 (bars and plates) or 1,44 (shells) for very high slenderness ratios. With these additional coefficients for the calculation of the "design resistance", the limit states method is made consistent with the old practices for the allowable stress method.

2.3 -The "serviceability limit states" correspond to the normal use and durability of the structure.

The "material" and "load" partial factors of safety γ_m and γ_f, are in general taken equal to 1, and in addition, specially in the case of "frequent" combinations, certain of the live loads and the environmental loads can be supposed less than its characteristics values.

The check of the serviceability limit-states is usually to be based on elastic theory (or in elastic theory with cracked sections, concrete structures).

In general, the structure as a whole, and all its parts, shall be designed so that displacements or vibrations will not impair proper operation of equipments or become unconfortable to personnel. In addition, in the case of concrete structures, cracking is to be avoided or limited so that it will not affect the durability of the structure.

Two cases of combinations of loads are considered in the CEB-FIP Model Code, in Det Norske Veritas'77 and in the ACI Guide.

- "infrequent" combinations ("extreme" combinations).
- "frequent" combinations ("ordinary" or "normal" combinations).

In the "infrequent" combinations the environmental loads are taken with their maximum values Q_{Emax} ("characteristic values") defined by a mean period of return of 100 or 50 years. In the frequent combinations, the environmental loads are taken with their frequently occurring value Q_{Eo} defined by a mean period of return of 1 month.

The CEB-FIP Model Code classifies the exposure conditions in the sea environment as "severe". In reinforced concrete structures, whose reinforcement bars present in general a low sensitivity to corrosion, the "cracking limit state" is accepted (crack width limited to 0.1mm with a minimum concrete cover of 35 mm, and to 0.15 mm with a minimum concrete cover of 50 mm). In prestressed concrete structures the prestressing reinforcement (cold worked bars subjected to high permanent tension) is very sensitive to corrosion, and in this case the uncracked limit state is required. For the "frequent combinations" of loads no tensile stress in concrete must occur, and for the "infrequent combinations" limited tensile stress could be accepted, but without cracking. The minimum concrete cover should be 45 mm.

The Det Norske Veritas'77 Rules admit the control of cracking based either on calculation of stress in the reinforcement (or of stress variation in prestressing reinforcement), or in calculation of crack width. Members subjected to a transverse hydrostatic pressure difference are to be designed with a permanent compression zone of not less than 25% of the thickness (or the values given in a table) for frequent combinations of loading. Oil structures with internal pressure larger than external water pressure are to be designed with a minimum membrane compression stress.

The ACI Guide recommends control of cracking based on limiting reinforcing stresses. For thin-walled, hollow structural cross sections the maximum permissible membrane strain across the walls should not cause cracking under any (frequent or infrequent) combination of loads.

There are, therefore, discrepancies in the recommendations of the codes, specially regarding prestressed concrete, where stress corrosion of the reinforcement is to be prevented. The CEB-FIP Model Code for Concrete Structures is more severe than the other codes.

SOME COMMENTS ON LOADS AND LOADING EFFECTS

3.1 - The Common Unified Rules of S.I.R.T.U.S. recommends a pragmatic method for assessment of the characteristic value of the loads, that can be applied to the environmental loads resulting from the action of the waves. The "characteristic loads" are not to be confused with "accidental loads"(like collisions, unexpected earthquakes, huricanes, explosions).

The pragmatic method recommeded by the Common Unified Rules consists in defining the characteristic value of the load by a mean period of return or "design period" equal to 2.4 to 4 times the "reference period". This period is a little less than the planned life of the structure taken, in general, as 50 years. For offshore structures,with a planned life of about 30 years, it seems reasonable to take a "reference period" of 25 years. Thus, the mean period of return, or "design period", for offshore structures, can be taken as 100 to 50 years, as recommended by Det Norske Veritas and by Bureau Veritas, respectively.

In addition, the characteristic load multiplied by $\gamma_f/1,1$, γ_f being the partial load safety factor, should correspond to the mean period of return 20 to 200 times the "reference period".

The choice of the criteria for defining the "characteristic load" corresponding to the wave action is very important, and a special discussion of this problem is justified.

3.2 - The analysis of the action of waves on the structure and of its response ("loading effects")is very complex, due to the randomic characteristics of the sea. Two different approaches are generally used:

- "deterministic approach", based on an extreme condition;

- "stochastic approach", based on the wave power density spectrum.

In the first approach the dynamic response of the structure to a critical wave, whose period and height are defined statisticaly, is obtained by deterministic procedures.

In the second approach it is admitted that the structure has a linear response to wave actions, and the response spectrum is obtained by multiplying the wave spectrum times the squared transfer function.

In both of these approaches the sea is described by the distribution of the occurrence of sea states, characterized by the significant wave height H_s and

by the average zero-crossing period T_z. These
parameters are in generally obtained by analysis
of 20 to 30 minutes recordings, during several years,
or of visual data.

Since for a short period of time the sea states can
be considered as a stationary narrow banded process,
the statistical distribution of peaks and heights
can be described by a Rayleigh distribution.

For each sea state, defined by its parameters H_s and
T_z, it is possible, using adequate formulations like
the Pearson-Moskowitz one, to determine the shape
of its spectrum, and, in consequence, the response
spectrum of the structure. It is also possible to
determine the critical wave in each sea state
according to a probability level.

By the association of this short-term statistics
with the long-term statistics of the sea states, it
is possible to determine the "extreme conditions":

- long term prediction: the "probability level" to
be prescribed is the inverse of the total number of
waves during the "design period", considering all the
sea states occurring during this period;

- short-term prediction: the sea state corresponding
to a critical situation is determined, corresponding
to a mean period of return equal to the "design
period", and the structure is supposed to be sub-
mited to this situation during about 4 hours (1000
wave cycles), corresponding to a probability level
of 10-3. An analysis based on the statistics of
extremals of Gumbel can also be made.

The rules adopted by Det Norske Veritas are an
example of application of these criteria. According
to these rules the structure is to be analyzed as
being under the action of a regular wave whose
probability of occurrence is the inverse of the
number of wave cycles 10^n during the "design period"
of N years:

$$n = 6,7 + \log_{10} N$$

By fitting Weibull distribution to the long-term
statistics of H_s, Nordeström (ref. 2) has obtained
a quite simple formulation to determine the wave
height at a probability level $Q = 10^{-n}$:

$$H_n = \frac{ab_1}{\sqrt{2}} (2,3n)^{k_1}$$

The coefficient b_1 and k_1 are given in a tabular form and depend on a parameter m. This parameter m and the parameter a are defined by fitting a Weibull distribution to the wave statistics.

It may be necessary to investigate the wave loads for a range of wave periods, in order to ensure a sufficiently accurate determination of the maximum response. The following range of wave pariods is recommended:

$$\sqrt{6,5\ H} < T < \sqrt{15\ H}$$

H in meters, and T in seconds.

Another criterion would be obtained by selecting the critical sea-state, and for this, the critical wave height. Since the distribution of the significant wave heights H_s characterizing the sea-states can be described by a two parameter Weibull distribution function, then the probability of exceeding H_s is

$$Q(H_s) = \exp\left[-(\frac{H_s}{a})^m\right]$$

from which

$$H_s = a\left[-\ell_n\ Q(H_s)\right]^{\frac{1}{m}}$$

where a and m are the two parameters of the Weibull distribution.

In each sea state the wave height distribution is described by a Rayleigh distribution and then the probability of exceeding the height H in the sea state is given by

$$Q(H) = \exp\left[-\frac{H^2}{0,5H_s^2}\right]$$

so that the H_{max} for N_c cycles is given by

$$H_{max} = \sqrt{0,5\ell_n N_c}$$

For 1000 cycles this gives

$$H_{max} = 1,86\ H_s$$

or

$$H_{max} = 1.86a \left[- \ell_n \; Q(H_s)\right]^{\frac{1}{m}}$$

The values of the probability of the critical sea
state sometimes used in connection to this criterium,
lead to an underestimation of the height of the
characteristic wave relatively to the Det Norske
Veritas criterium, which is to be preferred.

SOME SUGGESTIONS ON LOAD FACTORS

4.1 - The following suggestions, concerning the
"load partial safety factors" γ_f are based on the
principles of the CEB-FIP.S.I.R.T.U.S." Unified
Rules Common to Different Types of Construction".

The recommended "material partial safety factors"
γ_m, for the ultimate limit state, are γ_c = 1.5 for
concrete, and γ_s = 1.15 for steel. This late factor
is modified by the coefficients ψ and k, prescribed
by Det Norske Veritas'77, for the case of buckling
in steel structures.

For the serviceability limit states $\gamma_c = \gamma_s$ = 1.

4.2 - The partial safety factor applied to the "main
variable load" in the ultimate limit state, is
generally taken as γ_f = 1.5. For sea environmental
loads it seems to be reasonable to reduce this
factor to γ_f = 1.3. In fact according to Det Norske
Veritas, the ratio from the wave height with a mean
period of return of 500 to 5000 years (corresponding
to 20 to 200 times the period reference of 25 years),
to the height of the "100 years" characteristic wave,
can be estimated as 1.10 to 1.20. The pragmatic criterium of CEB-FIP-S.I.R.T.U.S. "Unified Rules"
prescribes that this should not be greater than load
factor γ_f divided by 1.1. This condition is satisfied by taking γ_f = 1.3.

A further reduction of the load factor applied to
environmental loads, from 1.3 to 1.1, could be
accepted in the case of a stochastic dynamic analysis based on spectral techniques, including the
consideration of sea structure and soil-structure
interaction. This reduction of the load factor
would make the design based on the stochastic
approach comparable with the design based on the
deterministic dynamic approach using a load factor
of 1.3.

4.3 The following actions are to be considered. In the notations the subscript k, corresponding to the "characteristic values", is delected for convenience.

G = permanent loads ("dead loads" and hydro-static external pressure)

Q_o = variable "live loads" (weight of supplies, stored products and movable equipment, and loads resulting from occupancy and operation of the platform)

Q_E = environmental loads (wave, wind, currents, "design earthquake")

Q_{Emax} = extreme environmental loads, corresponding to a mean period of return equal to the "design period" of 100 years (waves and wind according to the criteria of Det Norske Veritas, and "design earthquakes")

Q_{Eo} = frequent or "ordinary" waves and wind environmental loads, corresponding to a mean period of return equal to 1 month

Q_ε = effects of prescribed displacements (differential settlement of foundations, uneven sea-bed) or of imposed deformations (prestress) or restrained deformations (effects of tempera ture and shinkrage)

F_{acc} = accidental actions (severe collisions, explosions, effects of fire, "survivability level earthquake" = twice the "design earth-quake")

4.4 - The following load combinations and load factors are suggested (symbolic formulas)

a) Ultimate limit states - Fundamental combinations

a1) Live loads as "main actions" ("ordinary" or "normal" conditions)

$$1.3\ G_{unfavourable} + 1.0\ G_{favourable} + 1.5\ Q_o + 1.3\ Q_{Eo} +$$
$$+ 1.2\ Q_{\varepsilon\ unfavourable} + 0.90\ Q_{\varepsilon\ favourable}$$

a2) Environmental loads as "main actions" ("extreme conditions")

$$1.3\ G_{unfavourable} + 1.0\ G_{favourable} + 1.2\ Q_o +$$
$$+ 1.3\ Q_{Emax} + 1.2\ Q_{\varepsilon\ unfavourable} + 0.9\ Q_{\varepsilon\ favourable}$$

Obs: The factor 1.3 applied to Q_{Emax} can be reduced to 1.1 in the case of a rigorous stochastic dynamic analysis.

b) <u>Ultimate limit states</u> - <u>Accidental combinations</u>
   (Progressive colapse state)

$$F_{acc} + G + 0.8Q_o + Q_\varepsilon$$

Obs: Localized damage may be accepted, but catastrophic collapse should be avoided.

c) <u>Serviceability limit states</u>

c1) Infrequent combinations

$$G + 0.8Q_o + Q_{Emax} + Q_\varepsilon$$

C2) Frequent combinations

$$G + 0.8Q_o + Q_{Eo} + Q_\varepsilon$$

REFERENCES

1. - F.L.L.B. Carneiro - "Codes for Offshore
     Structures. Design Criteria and Safety
     Requirements", Offshore Structures Engineering,
     Pentech Press, London, 1979.

2. - N. Nordeström - "A Method to Predict Long-Term
     Distributions of Waves", Det Norske Veritas,
     Publication nọ 81, 1973.

3. - Systéme International de Réglementation
     Téchnique Unifiée, Vol.I,II, Comité Euro-Inter-
     national du Béton, Bul.124/125, 1978.

4. - Rules for the Design, Construction and Inspect-
     ion of Offshore Structures, Det Norske Veritas,
     1977.

5. - Limit States Design Steel Manual, Canadian Inst.
     of Steel Construction, 1977.

6. - Guide for the Design and Construction of Fixed
     Offshore Concrete Structures, A.C.I., 1978.

PERSPECTIVES ECONOMIQUES DES OUVRAGES EN BETON OFFSHORE

Roger LACROIX

SEA TANK CO

1 - INTRODUCTION

La compétition des deux principaux matériaux de construction
acier et béton, n'est pas un phénomène nouveau. Dans le
domaine des ponts, notamment, le béton s'est taillé une place
de choix, et l'acier n'est guère utilisé aujourd'hui que
lorsque des circonstances exceptionnelles le justifient. Pour
les immeubles élevés, les structures en béton construites à
l'aide de coffrages glissants concurrencent avantageusement
le métal, et les caissons sous pression des réacteurs
nucléaires sont souvent conçus en béton précontraint.

Les constructions offshore n'ont pas échappé à la règle
générale : pendant plusieurs décennies et notamment dans le
Golfe du Mexique, l'acier a obtenu l'exclusivité des plates-
formes marines. Puis le béton est entré dans la compétition,
en Louisiane tout d'abord, pour des installations à faible
profondeur et d'importance relativement faible, puis en Mer
du Nord, où les ouvrages en béton ont connu un développement
très rapide de 1972 à 75, suivi ensuite d'un ralentissement
sensible.

Aujourd'hui, nombreuses sont les mers du globe où les
compagnies pétrolières découvrent des champs exploitables ; le
Brésil et le Mexique en fournissent les exemples les plus
caractéristiques sur le continent américain. Chaque équipement
nouveau exige un choix, effectué lui-même en fonction de
plusieurs critères, dont les trois principaux sont :

. la sécurité,
. l'aptitude au service,
. le coût

Nous vous proposons de passer en revue successivement ces trois critères, afin d'essayer de dégager les caractéristiques des ouvrages les mieux adaptés à la résolution des problèmes difficiles que pose l'exploitation des champs d'hydrocarbures en mer.

2 - SECURITE

La sécurité a toujours constitué une préoccupation essentielle des pétroliers, soucieux au premier chef d'éviter les accidents corporels, soucieux aussi d'assurer la continuité de l'exploitation, et soucieux enfin d'éviter la pollution, qui peut se révéler un fléau redoutable.

L'un des premiers aspects, et le mieux connu est la sécurité structurale ; lors de l'élaboration d'un projet, le bureau d'études doit montrer que la structure présente une très grande probabilité de conserver son intégrité sous l'action des actions les plus sévères susceptibles de s'appliquer. Pour la plupart des types de constructions, des règlements existent qui définissent les contraintes admissibles à respecter, tant pour l'acier que pour le béton. Dans le domaine de l'offshore, aucun texte semblable n'existait et c'est pourquoi, dès 1972, la FIP décidait d'éditer des Recommandations pour le projet des structures marines en béton ; après une première édition en octobre 1973, deux versions nouvelles voyaient le jour, en novembre 1974, puis en juillet 1977, versions qui tenaient compte de l'expérience acquise, en Mer du Nord notamment.

Dans le même temps, les sociétés de classification, traditionnellement compétentes en matière de navires, puis les organismes gouvernementaux éditaient à leur tour des prescriptions sur le calcul et la construction des mêmes ouvrages si bien qu'aujourd'hui l'on ne compte pas moins d'une dizaine de guides, recommandations, codes ou règlements qui donnent chacun leur point de vue sur les actions, la nature des vérifications à effectuer, et les coefficients de sécurité partiels à admettre.

Compte-tenu de la nouveauté des conditions auxquelles étaient soumises les structures-poids, directement posées sur le fond, il était naturel, à l'origine, d'imposer une certaine prudence dans la conception ; c'est ainsi, par exemple, que lorsqu'une structure-poids, en fin d'immersion arrive en contact avec le sol, des surpressions peuvent s'exercer sur le radier en raison de l'irrégularité du sol. Après de longs échanges de vues entre experts de mécanique des sols, il fut admis pour un terrain donné, que le sol pouvait exercer une pression de 1 N/mm2 en une zone quelconque du radier ; les mesures de contraintes effectuées au cours de la mise en

place des structures ont montré que cette estimation était
très prudente, et que les contraintes réelles étaient très
inférieures à celles qui résultaient du calcul. Cette
expérience, ainsi que toutes celles de même nature réalisées
sur des plates-formes en béton, devraient permettre, dans
l'avenir, d'adopter des hypothèses plus réalistes, et d'éviter
la mise en place dans le radier d'une quantité importante
d'armatures inutiles.

De la même façon, les prescriptions relatives aux contraintes
normales paraissent exagérément sévères pour le béton : alors
que pour les vérifications à l'état limite ultime des charpentes en acier, on prévoit en général un coefficient de
sécurité partiel m de 1,10 ou 1,15 suivant les textes, on
adopte pour le béton, dans les mêmes conditions, un coefficient m égal à 1,5/0,85 soit 1,76. S'il est normal d'avoir
un coefficient plus grand pour le béton que pour l'acier
afin de tenir compte en particulier de la plus grande
dispersion des caractères mécaniques de ce matériau, il est
permis de se demander si une telle différence est justifiée.
L'existence du coefficient minorateur de la résistance du
béton, de 0,85, est justifié dans la plupart des codes actuels
par le fait que la résistance du béton est réduite dans le
cas d'une compression appliquée de façon soutenue pendant une
longue durée ; or, ceci n'est évidemment pas le cas des
efforts de houle, dont les valeurs élevées ne sont atteintes
qu'exceptionnellement.

Un autre aspect de la sécurité, très important lui aussi,
concerne le transport et la mise en place de la structure
depuis le site de construction jusqu'à son emplacement
définitif. Dans ce domaine aussi le béton semble être l'objet
d'une rigueur excessive, qui se traduit à la fois par des
prescriptions très sévères, notamment pour la stabilité en
cas d'avarie, et par des taux de primes d'assurance très
élevés, non justifiés par les faits : en effet, pendant leur
remorquage et leur immersion, les structures en béton sont
pourvues d'une stabilité propre qui leur permet de résister
sans dommage à l'action des tempêtes les plus fortes, ce qui
n'est pas le cas des charpentes métalliques remorquées sur
barge, ou auto-flottantes. Quelques exemples récents
d'accidents survenus au cours de la mise en place de "jackets"
en acier montrent la vulnérabilité de ces structures pendant
leur transport et immédiatement après leur immersion, avant
que les pieux qui les ancrent au sol ne soient foncés.

3 - APTITUDE AU SERVICE

L'aptitude au service d'un ouvrage offshore revêt des aspects
très divers qui rendent difficiles une appréciation d'ensemble.

Dans le domaine de l'équipement, l'acier présente un avantage indéniable, grâce à sa souplesse d'emploi, et sa légéreté ; c'est la raison pour laquelle les ponts des plates-formes en béton sont le plus souvent métalliques : la fixation des modules et des différents matériels y est aisée, alors que dans le cas du scellement d'une machine dans une structure en béton, le remplacement de celle-ci par une autre de caractéristiques différentes risquerait de poser des problèmes plus difficiles.

En revanche, il faut citer à l'actif du béton son excellent comportement en milieu marin, confirmé par la longévité de bateaux en béton armé construits pendant la première guerre mondiale, et qui ont assuré leur service pendant plusieurs décennies sans la moindre dépense d'entretien.

Un autre avantage essentiel des structures en béton réside dans la possibilité de stockage qu'elles offrent au prix d'un aménagement simple : la plupart des plates-formes poids peuvent ainsi comporter un réservoir d'une capacité jusqu'à un million de barils dont l'utilisation peut se révéler très précieuse si la plate-forme n'est pas directement raccordée à un oléoduc sous-marin. Cet avantage, important en Mer du Nord au début des années 70, s'est trouvé progressivement réduit en raison du développement d'un réseau de pipe-lines, mais il reprend toute sa valeur dans le cas de l'exploitation d'un nouveau champ.

Avec ou sans stockage, une structure en béton présente une autre caractéristique propre à faciliter l'exploitation : c'est la facilité de ménager une liaison fond-surface au moyen d'une colonne "sèche". En effet, pour la plupart des ouvrages en béton, le pont est supporté par des colonnes d'un diamètre légérement inférieur à une dizaine de mètres. Moyennant un dimensionnement convenable prévu dès l'origine du projet, l'une des colonnes peut être maintenue vide, ce qui permet l'intervention humaine au fond avec un équipement très simple.

Coût

Pour tout investissement industriel, le coût est un facteur essentiel, car c'est lui qui, tout d'abord détermine la décision d'investir, au stage de la prévision qui accompagne un avant-projet. Dans le cas du développement d'un champ offshore, le montant global de l'estimation n'est pas un élément de choix suffisant pour départager deux projets concurrents ; à cet élément, lui-même très important, il faut ajouter :

> les aléas, plus ou moins grands suivant la nature du projet.

. le délai de réalisation, facteur très important, puisqu'il
  entraîne les règlements d'intérêts intercalaires souvent
  très lourds,
. le partage de la dépense totale en devises étrangères et
  en monnaie locale, facteur important lui aussi dans le
  cadre d'une économie nationale.

En ce qui concerne le coût proprement dit, à fonctions
égales, les comparaisons effectuées récemment montrent un
léger avantage en faveur du béton, encore que la différence
ne puisse constituer un argument déterminant pour le choix
de ce matériau. En effet, la décomposition du prix total
d'une des dernières grandes plates-formes construites en
Mer du Nord montre que le prix de la structure en béton
installée sur le site ne représente que 8,5 % environ de la
dépense totale, et 25 % seulement du prix des équipements
installés sur le pont. Il en résulte que les facilités
données par l'utilisation d'un matériau ont plus de poids
dans la comparaison que la valeur du matériau lui-même. En
particulier, la possibilité de remorquer une plate-forme
en béton complètement équipée, à condition d'être prévue dès
l'origine du projet, peut engendrer des économies de main
d'oeuvre sur le site beaucoup plus sensibles que les différences de prix entre l'une ou l'autre structure.

Les aléas, depuis le début du projet jusqu'à la mise en
service de la plate-forme sont difficiles à comparer ;
souvent de nature sociale, ils peuvent affecter la construction quelle que soit sa nature, et le souci de les
éviter amène souvent les compagnies pétrolières à recourir
à des techniques éprouvées, plutôt qu'à faire les frais de
la mise au point d'une conception nouvelle, et c'est la
raison pour laquelle, dans ce dernier cas, de strictes
garanties sont exigées : résultats d'essais en laboratoire,
certificats de qualité des organismes de classification,
etc..

La comparaison des délais de réalisation semble plus facile.
Cependant, on a trop souvent conclu en faveur de l'acier,
en comparant simplement le délai nécessaire pour la construction d'un jacket métallique à celui de la construction
d'une plate-forme en béton, sans tenir compte ni du délai
nécessaire pour l'élaboration du projet détaillé qui exige
au minimum six mois, ni du temps exigé par le remorquage,
la mise en place de la plate-forme métallique, le battage
des pieux, et surtout l'installation du matériel sur le
pont. En fait, une comparaison équitable prenant en compte
le délai global dans les deux cas aboutit à un nombre de
mois équivalent pour les deux solutions, sous réserve que

→

des changements du programme d'équipement initial ne viennent pas perturber la construction.

Reste enfin la question des devises, pour laquelle la comparaison s'établit nettement en faveur du béton : le ciment, les agrégats et les aciers pour armatures sont des matériaux courants, produits dans la plupart des pays, alors que les charpentes métalliques exigent des aciers de haute qualité, qui ne sont élaborés que dans quelques pays seulement, au détriment de l'emploi de la main d'oeuvre locale.

Cependant, cet argument ne peut être retenu que si l'on peut trouver dans le pays même un site de construction convenable pour un ouvrage-poids, c'est-à-dire comportant un plan d'eau en communication directe avec la mer, suffisamment profond et abrité pour permettre la construction en flottaison.

4 - CONCLUSION

Les considérations qui précèdent montrent que le béton constitue un matériau de choix pour la construction des ouvrages en mer pourvu que les deux conditions suivantes soient respectées :

1 - Etablissement dès l'origine du projet d'un programme d'équipement détaillé, auquel ne seront apportées qu'un minimum de modifications.

2 - Existence d'un site abrité présentant un tirant d'eau suffisant pour permettre la construction et l'équipement de la structure.

Dans le cas où cette deuxième condition n'est pas satisfaite, il est encore possible de modifier le projet, de façon à bénéficier partiellement des avantages d'un ouvrage-poids, sans recourir à une innovation hasardeuse : on pourra concevoir un ouvrage mixte, comportant un large caisson en béton, surmonté d'une charpente métallique ; les deux parties de l'ouvrage peuvent être construites simultanément, puis assemblées dans la souille de construction du caisson en béton. La structure ainsi constituée peut ensuite être remorquée, directement sur le champ, où elle sera équipée de la même façon qu'un jacket métallique, à la différence près que le battage des pieux est remplacé par l'injection de la sous-face du radier du caisson beaucoup plus rapide et moins aléatoire.

Cet exemple montre que bien des solutions sont possibles pour permettre de reculer les limites de la rentabilité d'exploitation des champs pétroliers offshore ; les techniques qui

paraissent aujourd'hui éprouvées et classiques étaient presque considérées comme des exercices de science-fiction il
n'y a pas dix ans.

Ces projets futuristes sont devenus réalité grâce à la
conviction de quelques ingénieurs enthousiastes et à la
confiance des compagnies pétrolières. Les recherches menées
aujourd'hui dans de nombreux pays sur le comportement des
ouvrages en béton à la mer montrent que cette confiance était
bien placée. Les années à venir confirmeront ce choix, dans
la mesure où sera poursuivie la coopération étroite entre
les utilisateurs et les constructeurs.

LES PROCEDES THERMIQUES ET MECANIQUES DE DECOUPAGE DES
STRUCTURES EN BETON

Yves MALIER

Laboratoire de Mécanique et Technologie
E.N.S.E.T. - CACHAN-FRANCE

INTRODUCTION

La démolition partielle et la modification locale de grosses
structures en béton (type ouvrages offshore) posent toujours
d'importants problèmes technologiques du fait :
- des dimensions de l'élément, de sa résistance mécanique et
de son comportement hétérogène (béton et acier) sous l'outil
de démolition,
- des conditions strictes de sécurité liées, d'une part à la
stabilité de la structure (risques de fissurations, concentration de contraintes, etc...) et d'autre part à l'environnement
du lieu de l'opération (proximité de canalisations importantes,
etc...).
Hors les techniques mécaniques traditionnelles, nous nous proposons d'effectuer l'analyse de trois procédés pouvant être
envisagés efficacement (découpage thermique à l'oxygène, éclateur hydraulique, sciage et carottage par outils diamantés).
Nous examinons ensuite, sous le double critère des délais et
des coûts, des exemples précis de travaux élémentaires où le
choix de ces techniques peut être recommandé.

LE DECOUPAGE THERMIQUE A L'OXYGENE (1)(4)(5)(7)

Le principe
Il consiste, pour l'ensemble des procédés, à utiliser les chaleurs de combustion des métaux préchauffés dans l'oxygène pour
atteindre localement la température de fusion du matériau à découper et le transformer ainsi en un laitier suffisamment flui-
de pour pouvoir être évacué. En effet un gramme de fer dégage
de 1150 calories (FeO) à 1720 calories (Fe_2O_3); un gramme d'a-
luminium donne 7200 calories.

De façon plus particulière, notre procédé dit "à génération d'eutectiques" permet d'établir, par adjonction de fondants au matériau à découper, des compositions dont les températures de fusion sont proches des points eutectiques. Il en résulte une optimisation de l'usinage en fonction de la nature des corps.

Le procédé

Dans la pratique, les métaux (fer, aluminium, magnésium,...) et les minéraux (dans le procédé à "génération d'eutectiques") sont conditionnés en fils et poudres dans un tube de fer (appelé lance thermique dont la longueur varie de 1 à 4 mètres) alimenté en oxygène (pression : 7 à 12 bars).
Après amorçage, cette lance brûle en forant un trou cylindrique (3 à 4 cm de diamètre). Une coupe "plane" peut être engendrée par juxtaposition de trous tangents (figure 1).

Les performances

Caractéristiques de la coupe : le diamètre du trou (D_t) est déterminé en fonction du diamètre de la lance (D_l) par l'expression : $D_t = 2 D_l + 5$ (en mm).
Dans le cas d'une coupe plane, la précision géométrique est généralement comprise entre 10 et 15 mm.

Vitesse de forage : Ce procédé permet de découper tous les matériaux (métaux, roches, bétons...) jusqu'à plusieurs mètres d'épaisseur. Retenons, à titre d'exemple (figure 2) les vitesses de forages obtenues dans des bétons à granulats siliceux (B1) et dans des bétons à granulats calcaires (B2) dans les deux cas de découpes utilisant les procédés thermiques usuels (courbes a) et le procédé à génération d'eutectiques (courbes b).
Notons que la présence d'armatures (cas des bétons armés) accélère largement la coupe (le fer contribue à l'augmentation des chaleurs de réaction).
Par ailleurs, plutôt qu'une vitesse de forage exprimée,comme sur la figure 2 en mètre par heure, il est plus utile, pour le calcul des temps et des coûts de découpage d'exprimer la vitesse surfacique (en mètres carrés par heure) correspondant à la surface "plane" engendrée par le forage de trous tangents. Dans les conditions d'un chantier organisé elle varie suivant la nature du béton armé de 0,4 m^2/h à 0,9 m^2/h et peut être considérée comme constante durant le temps de l'opération. Cette dernière propriété permet, chose exceptionnelle en matière de démolition, de rationnaliser les calculs de délais et de prix.

Echauffement du béton : Pour le cas de modifications délicates d'ouvrages importants (béton précontraint, coques, voisinage de canalisations,...), les élévations de température dans le béton et dans les armatures au voisinage de la coupe ont fait

Figure 1 : Découpage thermique d'un mur (épaisseur : 0,9 m fortement armé

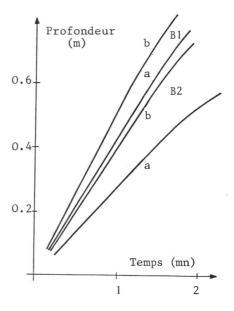

Figure 2 : Vitesse de découpage thermique du béton en fonction de la nature des granulats et du type de procédé

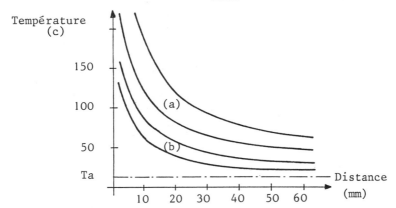

Figure 3 : Fuseaux des températures probables dans le béton en fonction de la distance à la coupe : (a) coupe plane, (b) trou isolé

l'objet d'études précises. A titre d'exemple, nous avons re-
présenté figure 3 les fuseaux probables des températures maximales atteintes dans un voile de béton de granulats silico-
calcaires en fonction de l'éloignement à une coupe plane
(fuseau a) et à un forage cylindrique isolé (fuseau b) réalisés par découpage thermique.
De telles courbes, déterminées dans un grand nombre de cas
différents permettent de prévoir, avec une assez bonne précision, les altérations éventuelles que pourrait entrainer
le découpage thermique sur la partie de l'ouvrage conservée.
Dans la plupart des cas, à l'exception des prescriptions très
précises, ces altérations sont négligeables dès que la distance à la coupe devient supérieure à 5 centimètres. (4)

Nuisances et sécurité : Le découpage thermique utilise l'oxygène comme seul gaz et ne nécessite évidemment à l'inverse
d'autres procédés, ni eau, ni énergie électrique... Après a-
voir remarqué qu'il est une technique totalement silencieuse
et ne créant aucune vibration, il doit être précisé, au plan
de la sécurité, que les dégagements d'étincelles (importants
en début et fin de coupe) nécessitent une simple protection
de l'opérateur. Les fumées, généralement réduites et négligeables en opération extérieure, peuvent devenir plus importantes
dans le cas de découpage de bétons à granulats très calcaires
(ou imprégnés d'huiles); éventuellement, elles peuvent être
captées à la source (aspiration 2500 Watts environ) dans le
cas d'interventions à l'intérieur d'un local opérationnel.

Les domaines d'application
La nature du matériau à découper n'imposant aucune limite
d'utilisation, le découpage thermique trouve un large champ
d'application dans les projets de démolition ou de modifications de grosses structures où les travaux doivent être con-
duits avec rapidité, précision, le minimum de vibrations et
un respect très strict des conditions de sécurité. Sa simpli-
cité, sa faible technicité et le caractère constant de sa pro-
ductivité (délais et consommations sont proportionnels à la
surface découpée) sont le plus souvent des éléments déterminants lors du choix. Enfin, dans le cas de modification de
structure en béton précontraint, il permet un démontage ration-
nel de la précontrainte en respectant, à tous instants, la stabilité de l'ouvrage et la sécurité du voisinage.

LES ECLATEURS HYDRAULIQUES (3)(9)

Le principe
Il consiste à créer et à propager des fissures dans le matériau à partir d'un forage cylindrique de faible diamètre
préalablement réalisé. Les positions géométriques relatives
des forages initiaux pouvant conduire, suivant l'objectif

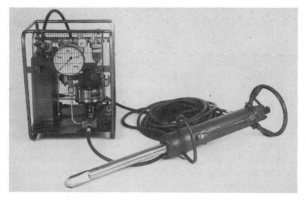

Figure 4 : Eclateur hydraulique (Gullick Dobson)

Figure 5 : Eclatement d'un bloc de béton non armé

Figure 6 : Association découpage thermique – éclateur
hydraulique pour l'ouverture d'une paroi moulée

recherché, à des découpages sensiblement plans (débittage en gros blocs à géométrie régulière) ou, au contraire, sans direction privilégiée (éclatements en petits éléments).

Le procédé

L'éclateur est généralement constitué d'un piston animé par un système hydraulique enfonçant un coin à faible pente entre deux demi-coquilles disposées dans le trou préalablement réalisé dans le matériau (Procédés Gullick Dobson, Darda, Roc Pac, etc...) - figures 4 et 5

Les performances

La force d'éclatement est mesurée par l'effort engendré par l'éclateur sur les deux demi-coquilles disposées entre les plateaux d'une presse.
Cet effort varie entre 600 KN et 3500 KN suivant les appareils.
Afin d'éviter toute perte d'effort, les avants trous - dont les diamètres varient de 30 à 60 millimètres suivant les cas - doivent être calibrés avec précision -tolérance 2 millimètres- et être parfaitement rectilignes.Ils peuvent être réalisés par une perforatrice pneumatique ou une lance thermique montées sur guide.

Les domaines d'application

Destiné initialement à l'abattage des roches, l'éclateur à un rendement équivalent dans les bétons (de 1 à 5 m^3/jour suivant la nature des granulats et les conditions de chantiers). Par contre, l'efficacité se réduit dès que la proportion d'armatures croît (béton armé); encore possible pour des densités d'armatures très faibles (10 kilogrammes d'acier par mètre cube de béton), il devient inefficace pour des densités courantes de l'ordre de 25 à 30 kilogrammes d'acier par mètre cube de béton.
Enfin, remarquons que le système mécanique étant très simple, il peut être utilisé occasionnellement par une main-d'oeuvre non spécialisée (sa fiabilité résulte en fait de celle de son système hydraulique).

LE SCIAGE ET LE CAROTTAGE PAR OUTILS DIAMANTES (10)

La large utilisation de ces procédés rend inutile leur présentation. On rappellera cependant les éléments technologiques suivants :
- la très bonne précision géométrique (tolérance : 1 mm) et l'excellent état de surface obtenus
- la non altération du matériau dans le voisinage de la coupe
- la limite d'utilisation des procédés de sciage : profondeur limitée à 40 centimètres environ
- la nécessité d'une projection d'eau constante dans la zone d'usinage

- la chute du rendement (vitesse réduite, usure des diamants) lors du découpage de matériaux hétérogènes tels que bétons de granulats silico-calcaires et, a fortiori, bétons armés (l'opération reste, techniquement, possible mais devient lente et coûteuse).
- la nécessité d'un guidage (ou d'un support) particulièrement rigide et fixe (risques de rupture des disques ou des couronnes) souvent incompatible avec certaines conditions de chantier.

ETUDES DE CAS

Notre propos est d'examiner une série de problèmes concrets généraux et de déterminer, pour chacun d'eux, la solution optimale en fonction des critères de délais et de prix.

Premier problème
Découpage très précis (tolérance 2 mm) d'une série de trous (1 x 2 m) dans des dalles horizontales et des voiles verticaux constitués d'un béton faiblement armé (15 kg/m^3) d'épaisseur 200 mm.
Solution : sciage par disques diamantés, le bâti de machine étant fixé sur les voiles et dalles par vérins ou par ventouses.

Deuxième problème
Découpage d'une ouverture (3 x 4 m) dans un voile de 1 mètre d'épaisseur constitué de béton de granulats calcaires très peu armé et situé dans un local très sensible aux risques d'incendies et non protégeable.
Solution : Réalisation de la coupe périphérique par carottages tangents (diamètres des couronnes diamantées : 70 à 160 mm), exécution d'une maille de trous (100 environ) sur l'ensemble du bloc, éclatement hydraulique à partir de chacun de ces trous, découpage mécanique des armatures rencontrées et enfin évacuation des blocs (20 kilogrammes environ).

Troisième problème
Découpage d'une ouverture (3 x 4 m) dans un voile d'épaisseur 0.60 m moyennement armé (30 kg d'acier par m^3 de béton) - type paroi moulée - situé à l'air libre en un lieu difficile d'accès (échafaudages). (figure 6)
Solution : Par découpage thermique à l'oxygène, exécution de la coupe périphérique et d'une maille de trous (distants entre eux de 25 cm environ), alésage rapide des trous par perforatrice pneumatique (pour calibrage), réduction du bloc par éclatement hydraulique, découpage des armatures et évacuation.

Quatrième problème
Découpage dans un voile d'épaisseur 1,50 mètre en béton très armé (armatures de gros diamètre et profilés métalliques).

Figure 7 : Découpage d'une structure épaisse très
armée à partir d'un échafaudage léger (conditions
difficiles)

Figure 8 : La coupe thermique obtenue (largeur : 2.70m)

Figure 9 : Découpage thermique d'un élément immergé

Solution : Découpage périphérique puis réduction en éléments (de dimensions compatibles avec les moyens de levage et d'é-vacuation) par découpage thermique uniquement. (fig. 7 et 8)

Cinquième problème
Découpage d'une grande série de poteaux (ou pieux de fondati-ons) en béton très armé de 0,5 m de diamètre.
Solution : (autre que procédés mécaniques traditionnels)
le découpage thermique s'avère une solution extrêmement rapide (mais qui ne permet pas de conserver d'armatures en attente pour une liaison ultérieure avec la structure).

Sixième problème
Forage d'une grande série de trous de petits diamètres dans un ouvrage en béton armé (épaisseur 0,5 m) immergé (profondeur - 12 mètres -). (fig. 9)
Solution : Le découpage thermique à l'oxygène (1)(2)(5)(11)

Septième problème
Découpage partiel d'une structure précontrainte par post ten-sion.
Solution : Les conditions de stabilité de l'ouvrage durant les phases intermédiaires et les conditions de sécurité du chan-tier nécessitent la connaissance de l'évolution de la distri-bution des sollicitations lors de l'opération. La qualité mécanique de l'injection joue alors un rôle fondamental et doit être recherchée. En effet :
- si elle est faible (ou nulle)
le découpage des câbles peut conduire à des projections de tronçons sur le voisinage et à des redistributions brutales et dangereuses des efforts (créations de rotules plastiques, etc...). - figure 10
- si au contraire, la résistance mécanique de l'injection est suffisante, elle va permettre, à une certaine distance de la coupe du câble, un nouvel ancrage et conduire ainsi à la définition d'un nouveau système précontraint... qu'il faudra continuer de réduire - figure 11
Un tel raisonnement, conduit de proche en proche sur la struc-ture, à partir des deux hypothèses extrêmes concernant des qua-lités d'injection susceptibles d'être rencontrées, permet de calculer avec précision les positions géométriques et chronolo-giques des coupes garantissant la sécurité de l'opération.

Ces calculs étant effectués, pour des raisons évidentes (nom-bre de changements de postes de travail, densité d'armatures, sécurité, délais, etc...) l'opération devra, selon nous, être réalisée par découpage thermique.

Figure 10 : Bouclier destiné à éviter les projections
des câbles de précontrainte lors du découpage thermique

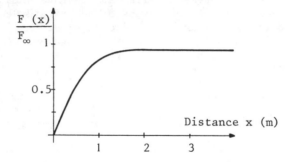

Figure 11 : Exemple d'évolution de l'effort de précontrainte
en fonction de la distance à la coupe thermique dans un
système à post tension (définition d'une longueur d'ancrage 1)

Figure 12 : Suppression de la précontrainte par découpage
thermique dans une poutre console

CONCLUSION

L'importance des investissements que représentent les grandes structures de génie civil, la rigueur des délais d'intervention et des conditions de sécurité rendent nécessaire la connaissance de l'optimisation des technologies actuellement opérationnelles pour localement adapter, modifier ou réparer une partie d'ouvrage.

Nous nous sommes efforcé, à travers les trois méthodes présentées, de contribuer au développement simultané de techniques que nous estimons suffisamment efficaces et performantes tout en relevant de technologies simples et aisément utilisables dans les conditions d'un chantier offshore.

BIBLIOGRAPHIE

(1) ALEXANDER G.H. - Caractéristiques des lances thermiques intéressant leur utilisation pour les opérations de sauvetage sous l'eau - 1è Conf. Technologie Offshore, Houston, 1969 - OTC 1051

(2) GOLDBERG F. - Le coupage des métaux sous l'eau. Sondage et techniques connexes, 1978, France - Sweden, n° 11, 443-455

(3) ITBTP - Les éclateurs. Suppl. Annales (1969) Paris n° 254 (2)

(4) MALIER Y. - La démolition des structures de génie civil par découpage thermique - Thèse Doctorat (1978), Paris

(5) MALIER Y. - Le découpage thermique des bétons armés et précontraints. Annales ITBTP (1977), Paris, n° 353, (9) 93 - 112.

(6) MALIER Y. - Le découpage thermique de la couverture en béton précontraint d'un centre de tri de 11 000 m^2. Construction (1978, Paris).

(7) MALIER Y. - Le découpage thermique des structures de génie civil. Portland Cement Ass. Séminaire "Tech. Avancée du béton" - Sherbrooke - mai 1978

(8) MALIER Y. - Démolition du béton précontraint. Colloque Amer. Conc. Inst. Montréal avril 1978.

(9) MEAD H.T. - Hydraulics bursters demolish tunnel wall
World construction, (1963), G.B., n° 9

(10) SINCLAIR S. - Using the diamond drill for drilling
through reinforced concrete. Civil engineering and publics
works review, G.B., (1963), n° 678 (67-71), n° 679 (227-229)

(11) STALKER A.W. - Vue d'ensemble des techniques de coupage
sous l'eau.
Welding Institute - International Seminar Handbook, 1976

APPLICATION OF HIGH-STRENGTH PREPACKED CONCRETE TO OFFSHORE STRUCTURES

Shigeyoshi Nagataki, Kazumi Kodama and Tadahiko Okumura

Associate Professor, Tokyo Institute of Technology, Director of Research & Development, Nisso Master Builders Co., Ltd. and Research Engineer, Research Laboratory, Shimizu Construction Co., Ltd.

INTRODUCTION

The prepacked concrete method originally was conceived as a means of repairing concrete structures, but its scope of application was widened as the features and economy of the method came to be appreciated, and at present it is used extensively for such work as underwater concrete, underground structures and cast-in-place piles. It is considered an undisputed fact that the application of this method to offshore structures is advantageous, and there are already records of use in large projects such as the Mackinac Bridge ($340,000$ m^3 of pier foundation for main towers and anchors) and Daikoku Ohashi Bridge ($12,000$ m^3 for main tower and 2 piers). The prepacked concrete method is to be adopted also for pier foundation works of the Honshu-Shikoku bridges of Japan now about to go into construction.

If there is to be found a drawback to this superior prepacked concrete method it would be that the design strength to be guaranteed in construction of structures cannot be set at a high level. In essence, with conventional mortar for grouting prepacked concrete, in order to satisfy fluidity requirements there is a limit to the reduction in water-cement ratio which can be made, and the ratio cannot be lowered below a minimum of 0.45, while when filling mortar in the voids of coarse aggregate the quality of mortar deteriorates with increased distance from the grout pipe due to segregation of materials and disturbance between grouted mortar and water, so that the situation is that only a maximum of about 200 kg/cm^2 can be expected as design strength.

The study reported here was carried out with the objectives of improving prepacked concrete with respect to the drawbacks mentioned above applying high-performance water-reducing admixtures developed in recent years to prepacked concrete mortar aiming for reduction in water-cement ratio while improving flowability of the mortar, thereby making it possible to obtain high strength for prepacked concrete and to expand the scope of application of the prepacked concrete method. It has already been pointed out in reports written or co-written by the senior author [1-3] that there are prominent effects in the aspects of improvement of fluidity and strength in case a high-performance water-reducing admixture, or super-plasticizer, is applied to grout mortar for prepacked concrete, while the present report covers measures for improving super-plasticizers for use in mortar for grouting and gives the results of analyses of flow characteristics of mortar and of large-scale model experiments conducted with relation to application of prepacked concrete to offshore structures.

OUTLINE OF EXPERIMENTS

The experiments conducted in connection with this study may be broadly divided into the following three categories: a) experiments regarding fluidity analyses of mortar for grouting prepacked concrete, b) physical property tests of high-strength prepacked concrete, c) grouting properties and strength distribution properties according to large-scale model experiments. The outlines of these are given below.

Experiments Regarding Fluidity Analyses of Grout Mortar
In order to analyze the flow characteristics of grout mortar, rotation viscometers, tubular viscometers and model testing apparatus were used and the flow characteristics of cement paste and cement mortar of various mix proportions were observed. As a result, the rotation viscometer was useful for clarifying behavior when the grout mortar was subject to slip velocity of 0 to 15 sec^{-1}, and the tubular viscometer in case of slip velocity of 10 to 400 sec^{-1}, while the model test apparatus was useful for confirming the plugging properties of grout mortar in voids in coarse aggregate in addition to the above.

Physical Property Tests of High-Strength Prepacked Concrete
Various tests were performed on grout mortar using superplasticizers and on prepacked concrete made with voids in coarse aggregates filled by this mortar. As factors for experimentation, the varieties of water-reducing admixture, the water-binder ratio, use or non-use of fly ash, temperature, etc. were varied, while the items of measurement were bleeding, expansion, setting, and compressive strength for grout mortar, and compressive, flexural and tensile strength properties, bond strength with steel, durability, watertightness, drying shrinkage and others for prepacked concrete. Further, in part of the experiments, the effects of using marine sand and of curing in sea water were also examined.

Tests to Confirm Grouting Properties and Strength Distribution
Properties of Large-Sized Models
Coarse aggregate was placed beforehand in a large-sized form
(inside dimensions: height 3 m, width 5 m, thickness 2 m)
assembled with a transparent acrylic plastic plate at the front,
with the voids between coarse aggregate particles filled with
water, and mortar was grouted from the bottom of the form. In
addition to observing the degree of rise of the mortar with
elapse of time, measurements were made of mortar pressure, heat
of hydration and other items. Further, after the grouted
mortar had hardened and obtained adequate strength, 25-cm diameter specimens were made through core boring, and strength
tests were performed on these specimens.

FLUIDITY ANALYSES OF GROUT MORTAR FOR PREPACKED CONCRETE

It has been indicated in a previous report [4] that grout mortar for prepacked concrete (sand cut at sieve size of 1.2 mm,
sand-cement-ratio 1.0) using superplasticizer does not cause
plugging part way down the flow cone (Corps of Engineers, CRD-
C79-58) even with water-cement ratio lowered close to 0.30 and
measurement values of 60 to 120 sec are obtained, and further,
that when mortar having such flowability is filled in the voids
of coarse aggregate, the voids are filled in a better manner
than with mortar of water-cement ratio of 0.50 using a conventional plasticizer. Therefore, in the work reported in this
chapter, the fluidity of grout mortar was analyzed using
various viscometers and fluidity measurement apparatus to seek
out the fundamental nature of flow of grout mortar using superplasticizer and indicating such special properties.

Firstly, Fig. 1 shows
representative examples of
results of consistency
curve measurements by rotation viscometer at the
initial stages after mixing
of cement pastes and cement
mortars of various combinations of water-cement ratio,
sand-cement ratio, and type
of plasticizer. As seen in
this figure, cement paste
and cement mortar all show
slip velocity fluidized
flow in the slip velocity
range of 0 to 15 sec^{-1}.
However, there are both
thixotropy and antithixo-
tropy indicated by some,
and on summarizing the test
results, it was seen that
mortars containing super-

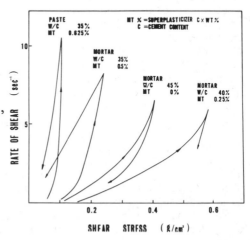

Fig. 1. Consistency curves by
Couette type rotation viscometer.

plasticizer 0.5% or more by weight of cement show thixotropy in
general. According to the report of Ish-Shalom [5] previously
published, in case of cement paste not using plasticizer, antithixotropy is indicated immediately after mixing, with a change
to reversible thixotropy accompanying subsequent elapse of time,
and it is surmised that the reasons lie with physical and chemical changes in cement particles. In case of addition of superplasticizer 0.5% by weight of cement, it has been reported [6]
that cement particles do not form flocs, but are dispersed into
primary particles, and it is surmised that the initial thixotropy behavior after mixing has a relation with the existence
of flocs. Further, it appears that after the elapse of a certain amount of time, the consistency curve appears to be
changed influenced by the chemical reaction of cement.

   Next, Fig. 2 indi-
cates the results of measurements with a tubular
viscometer with the purpose
of obtaining consistency
curves of cement mortar of
high slip velocity. According to this figure, in the
range of 20 to 400 sec^{-1}
which is the scope of the
experiments, mortars with
and without ordinary water-
reducing admixture still
show slip velocity fluid-
ized flow in this range, but
mortar using superplasticizer shows a more or less completely straight line indicating motion close to a
Newtonian fluid. This is
thought to clearly signify
that with the former changes
have occurred in the condition of flocs accompanying

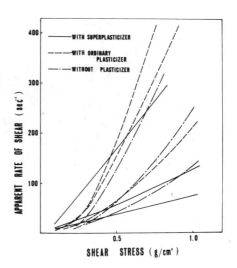

Fig. 2. Consistency curves by
tubular viscometer.

increase in slip velocity, whereas with the latter cement particles are dispersed into primary particles.

   Based on the above, it was thought to be more reasonable
to analyze flow of mortar as slip velocity fluidized flow influenced by flocculation and hydration of cement as previously
described rather than considering it merely as a Bingham plastic. In fact, when the consistency curve determined by rotation viscometer was approximated by the equation $\dot{\gamma} = B\tau^n$ for
slip velocity fluidized flow, fairly good correlations were
obtained between mix proportion factors of cement paste and
mortar, and B and n.

   Fig. 3 next shows slip velocity distributions in the
radial direction inside a rotation viscometer vessel for mortar
using superplasticizer and indicating thixotropy and ordinary

mortar indicating antithixotropy. This property is something which had been recognized in experiments previously reported, but its influence rather had been ignored in past literature [7]. However, as indicated in this figure, it is distinctly shown that slip velocity distributions accompanying increased speed of the rotation vis-

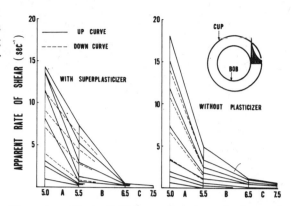

Fig. 3. Distribution of rate of shear in vessel of rotation viscometer.

cometer are of different natures for thixotropy and antithixotropy, "dispersion of strain" being produced with the former and "concentration of strain" with the latter. It appears to be more reasonable for the phenomena to be grasped as the inherent nature of flow of cement mortar rather than to explain them as slipping at wall surfaces.

From the above experimental results analyses were made as follows in this study considering that flow of mortar is governed by two viscosity structures. One is a "primary structure" due to agglomeration of cement particles, where a stable agglomerated condition exists in accordance with slip velocity during flow, and the curve within the scope of this study is that of slip velocity fluidized flow. Relatively large energy is required for breaking up and forming this agglomeration, and because of this, at slip velocity below equilibrium, acceleration of formation due to flow is produced. The other is a "secondary structure" thought to be caused by gelling of components leached from cement, which does not have an equilibrium flow curve and is indicated only by a hysteresis flow curve. Breaking up and formation of this structure occur readily with the breaking up caused by increase in "strain distance" (strain distance is time-integral form of slip velocity, non-dimensional), and appears to be formed again in about several tens of seconds after stop of flow. Because of this the secondary structure is formed ahead of the primary structure when there is a sudden stoppage of flow, and a "memory" phenomenon of prior slip velocity of the primary structure is produced. Since a primary structure does not exist with a mortar to which high-performance water-reducing admixture has been added in large quantity, when the secondary structure is broken by flow, "dispersion of strain" and thixotropy is indicated after which the behavior is that of a Newtonian fluid. With other mortars, both primary and secondary structures exist and it is thought the flow will be extremely complex.

Finally, Fig. 4 indicates the flow characteristics of

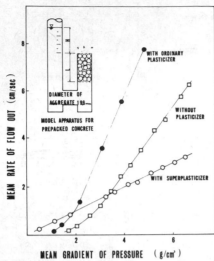

Fig. 4. Consistency curves by model apparatus.

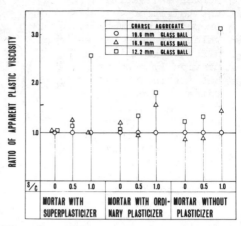

Fig. 5. Effects of size of aggregates on apparent plastic viscosity of cement paste and mortar according to model apparatus.

grout mortar measured to confirm the grouting properties of prepacked concrete using the model apparatus applying the tubular viscometer also indicated in Fig. 4. The trends shown in Fig. 4 and Fig. 3 are fairly similar, and this indicates that it is permissible to an extent to carry out analyses considering aggregate voids as tubes. However, according to experiments varying the maximum size of sand for the particle size of coarse aggregate, it is permissible to consider coarse aggregate voids as tubes up to a certain value of the ratio of

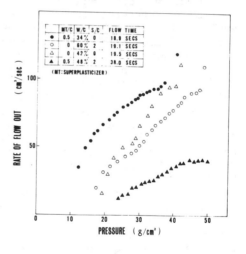

Fig. 6. Relation between pressure and rate of flow from flow cone.

sand size to coarse aggregate size, but it was confirmed by experiments with the model apparatus that when the value becomes large plugging of the coarse aggregate voids by mortar occurs and resistance is increased. Fig. 5 indicates an example of the results where the influence of fine aggregate is checked by the ratio of the apparent coefficient of viscosity of mortar during flow to the apparent coefficient of viscosity obtained when cement paste is made to flow through coarse aggregate voids, and it may be said that the above conclusion is clearly substantiated.

The foregoing results of experiments all indicate the reasonableness of analyzing the flow properties of grout mortar for prepacked concrete not simply as a Bingham plastic as conventionally considered for flow of mortar, but as slip velocity fluidized flow influenced by thixotropy, strain hysteresis and hydration of cement. And in case of grout mortar using a superplasticizer, that the groutability into coarse aggregate voids is good even though the flow time by P-funnel is long is because the flow time by P-funnel is simply time measured for a given quantity of mortar (1725 ml) to flow down from the outlet, while the time-dependent change in discharge related to pressure gradient and flow velocity have not been measured, and in case a superplasticizer has been used it may be explained as something close to a roughly straight line of the relation between pressure gradient and flow velocity passing through the original point; in effect, the mortar is close to a Newtonian fluid (see Fig. 6).

PHYSICAL PROPERTY TESTS OF GROUT MORTAR USING SUPERPLASTICIZER

As previously described, in case a superplasticizer was applied to grout mortar for prepacked concrete, the conclusion obtained was that this is extremely advantageous because of the fluidity, but in application to actual construction, there are many items remaining to be examined such as the variety of superplasticizer, the dosage thereof, quantity of addition of aluminum powder, qualities of cement and fly ash, their quantities used, etc. Examinations are made in this chapter mainly centering on the physical properties of grout mortar with regard to these items.

Consistency
With grout mortar in which a superplasticizer has been used, dispersion of cement particles is extreme and a so-called primary structure does not exist, because of which a phenomenon close to that of a Newtonian fluid is indicated when the secondary structure is broken up by flow, and in case the particle size of fine aggregate is sufficiently small compared with the maximum size of coarse aggregate, it is possible for the coarse aggregate voids of prepacked concrete to be readily filled. Consequently, in experiments conducted on a trial basis, when the coarse aggregate size was made 40 to 80 mm, it was possible to thoroughly fill coarse aggregate voids even with grout mortar of flow value by P-funnel as much as 120 sec. However, if the flow value is too high, it will lead to restrictions on grouting time, while in case the flow value is made around 20 sec as with ordinary grout mortar, segregation will be prominent, and cement paste and sand will be separated extremely readily because of the dispersion action of the superplasti-

cizer. Based on these facts, the flow value was made at least 40 sec in these tests, and further, since high strength was the objective, it was decided for examinations to be made at even less flow of approximately 60 sec as a standard. The relations of cement-water ratio or binder-water ratio determined from compressive strength and specified flow value of grout mortar are shown in Fig. 7, which indicates that considerably high strength is obtained when flow time is made long and cement-water ratio high, and strength values exceeding 600 kg/cm^2

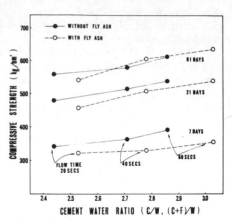

Fig. 7. Relation between compressive strength of grout mortar and cement-water ratio.

have been verified regardless of whether or not fly ash is used.

Varieties of Superplasticizer and Influence of Dosage

Effects were examined for three varieties of superplasticizers, MOD, MD and MG, trial-manufactured with a formalin condensation product of a napthalene sulfonate being manufactured in Japan as a base to which retarding agent, wetting agent, etc. were added. An example of results is given in Fig. 8, where differences in water-reducing effects seen from the fluidities provided by the three varieties of plasticizers cannot be recognized, but with respect to strength gain properties, particularly for the purpose of obtaining high strength, MOD was found to be the most effective. Next, with respect to dosage, a feature of superplasticizers is that when dosage is increased

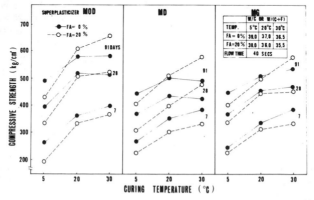

Fig. 8. Effects of superplasticizers on strength of grout mortar under various curing temperatures.

fluidity accordingly is greatly increased. However, there is of course a limit to this effect, and moreover, even though within limits, segregation will become prominent when dosage is high, so that in subsequent experiments the dosage was made 1.0% by weight of cement.

Fig. 8 simultaneously shows the influences on required water-cement ratio and compressive strength of temperature as mixed (curing temperature) when aiming for a given flow value. According to this figure, a feature of using a superplasticizer is that in case of low temperature fluidity is generally decreased but this is not so when the temperature is from 5°C to about 30°C, while in the aspect of compressive strength also, curing at low temperature has an adverse effect on strength gain, and it is thought necessary not to make temperatures as mixed and during curing too low.

Use of Aluminum Powder

In case of prepacked concrete, it is considered indispensable to utilize aluminum powder taking advantage of its foaming and expansive actions because of the necessity of displacing moisture collected at the undersides of aggregate particles by the expansive pressure of grout mortar for tight adherence at the interfaces of aggregate particles and mortar, and consequently, increased strength. Since bleeding is practically zero for grout mortar using a superplasticizer, it may seem at first glance that it would be unnecessary for aluminum powder to be used, but since data have been obtained from past experiments that the use of aluminum powder is nevertheless necessary for strength increase of prepacked concrete, the influences of aluminum powder were investigated. Fig. 9 and Fig. 10 show the results of confirmation of compressive strength of grout mortar and concrete, respectively, by expansion rate of grout mortar.

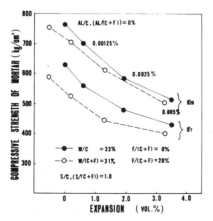

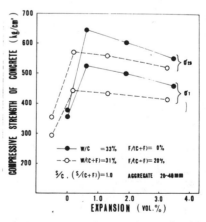

Fig. 9. Relation between compression strength and expansion of grout mortar.

Fig. 10. Effect of expansion of grout mortar on strength of prepacked concrete.

As indicated in Fig. 9, the strength of mortar itself is seen to be lowered in accordance with increased expansion due to action of aluminum powder, and this influence shows a more extreme trend than for conventional grout mortar. With ordinary prepacked concrete 5 to 10% is considered as standard for the expansion rate of grout mortar, but to provide such a high expansion rate is to lose the high strength that trouble has been taken to attain. However, this standard should be set strictly from the relation with the bleeding rate, and it is thought that it would be permissible to set a low expansion rate since the bleeding rate of grout mortar using a superplasticizer is extremely low. In fact, looking at this in connection with the compressive strength of concrete indicated in Fig. 10, the strength is low in this case also when aluminum powder is not used at all, with a maximum indicated at an expansion rate in the range of zero to 1%, and reduction in strength shown again when the expansion rate is made higher than the above, although the degree of reduction is not as prominent as for the case of mortar. And when the optimum expansion rate has been given, values in excess of 500 kg/cm^2 have been measured with 15- x 30-cm cylinder specimens regardless of whether or not fly ash had been used, and it was verified that strength approximately 1.5 times that of conventional prepacked concrete can be obtained. Further, in these experiments the quantity of aluminum powder used for the optimum expansion rate to be indicated was 0.00125% by weight of cement, which is considerably less than the quantity conventionally used. However, there exists a problem in that when a superplasticizer and aluminum powder are used in combination it has been confirmed that the speed of expansion is considerably increased, and in consideration of the fact that a fair amount of time elapses between mixing and grouting in actual work, it is thought necessary hereafter for examinations to be made of the quantity of aluminum powder to be used, and delayed gas generation of aluminum powder to be contemplated.

Binder (Cement, Fly Ash)
The problem of compatibility between superplasticizer and quality of cement has been one that has been pointed out from before, and within the scope of these experiments, even when using ordinary portland cement produced at the same plant, if the periods of shipment were to differ, and further, when the manufacturing plants differed, prominent differences were produced in fluidity and strength, especially, fluidity. Although the reason for this has not yet been established, the effect of a superplasticizer has a relation with Ca^{++} at the surface of cement particles, and it is thought the properties will vary according to the slightest differences in conditions during manufacture of cement. It has been confirmed in general, however, that by adjusting the dosage of water-reducing admixture in accordance with the quality of the cement, by using about 20% fly ash which by replacing cement reduces the influence of

difference in cement quality, and by adding extra-fine powder of siliceous material in case of cement showing overly prominent segregation, it is possible to reduce the influence of difference in cement quality on fluidity. Further, to replace a part of the cement by fly ash, as indicated in Figs. 8, 9 and 10, has an extremely good effect from the standpoint of increasing long-term strength, and especially, in case of massive concrete as in offshore structures where heat of hydration will be a problem, the combined use of fly ash and cement is desirable. However, for cases requiring short-term strength, there is a drawback with respect to strength gain when fly ash is used, and, of course, it should not be employed in such a case.

Influence of Storage Time of Mixed Grout

With concrete using a super-plasticizer, the impairment of consistency of the concrete resulting from storage after mixing, such as slump loss, is a problem. Accordingly, since in the case of grout mortar also a certain degree of time is required from mixing to the grouting operation, examinations were made in this regard.

Fig. 11 indicates an example of the results of experiments, and contrary to presumptions, the fluidity did not decrease at all with elapse of time after mixing so far as seen by P-funnel flow time, and strength of mortar increased albeit slightly. However, it was seen that there was an abrupt reduction in the expansion rate. As stated previously, there is a necessity for somewhat more study to be made regarding the expansion rate.

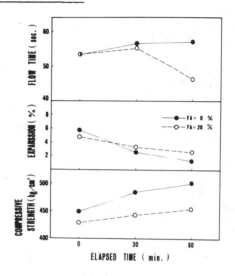

Fig. 11. Effect of time elapsed after mixing on properties of grout mortar.

PHYSICAL PROPERTIES OF HIGH-STRENGTH PREPACKED CONCRETE

Mechanical Properties of High-Strength Prepacked Concrete

Compressive Strength The compressive strengths of prepacked concretes made by injecting mortars using the superplasticizers indicated in Fig. 7 are shown in Fig. 12. According to the latter figure, a correlation can be seen between compressive strength of prepacked concrete and compressive strength of grout in the case of high strength also, and when the strength

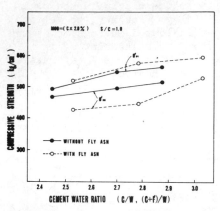

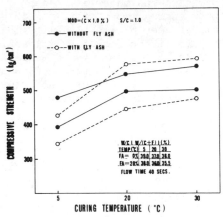

Fig. 12. Relation between compressive strength of pre-packed concrete and cement-water ratio.

Fig. 13. Effect of curing temperature on compressive strength of prepacked concrete.

of the mortar is high, the strength of prepacked concrete made using this mortar is also high, and the value at 91-day age is close to 600 kg/cm^2 regardless of whether or not fly ash is used. In Fig. 13, the effects when temperature as mixed and curing temperature have been varied are shown, and in the case of prepacked concrete the state of strength gain is poor at low temperature similarly to the case of grout mortar, while good results are obtained in the range of high temperature. This is in sharp contrast with the fact that fluidity is better for both conventional mortar and prepacked concrete mixed and cured at low temperature, and that the strength gain properties with respect to long-term age are good. This is thought to be due to the fact that the action of a superplasti-cizer of dispersing cement particles and preventing formation of flocs causes this dispersion effect to be lowered at low temper-ature as dispersion into primary particles is ef-fected applying electric charges to cement particles. In fact, the results given in Fig. 13 show the dosage of superplasticizer to be constant, while it is known that reduction in fluidity can be alleviated by in-

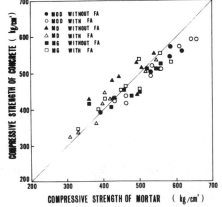

Fig. 14. Relation between com-pressive strengths of mortar and prepacked concrete.

creasing this dosage.

Finally, on determining the relationship between compressive strength of grout mortar and compressive strength of prepacked concrete pooling, for example, testing ages, water-cement ratios, etc., Fig. 14 was obtained. According to this figure, it may be said that there is a relationship of roughly 1:1 with compressive strength of grout mortar up to compressive strength of prepacked concrete of 500 kg/cm^2. Above this level the compressive strength of concrete is not proportional to strength gain of grout mortar, and there is some tendency for a ceiling to have been hit.

Tensile Strength, Flexural Strength, Modulus of Elasticity

Tensile and flexural strengths of prepacked concrete specimens made filling coarse aggregate in vertical forms and grouting mortar from the bottom of the forms were measured in a condition of the bottom surfaces of aggregate particles being subjected to tensile stresses. In this case, tensile stresses act at the interfaces between bottom surfaces of aggregate particles and mortar, the weakest part of prepacked concrete, and test results show the lowest values. The results of tests in the case of high-strength prepacked concrete were 37 to 42 kg/cm^2 in flexural strength and 30 to 34 kg/cm^2 in

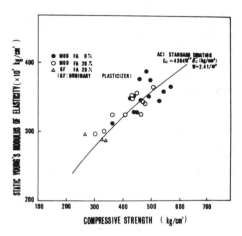

Fig. 15. Relation between static Young's modulus of elasticity and compressive strength of prepacked concrete.

tensile strength at 28-day age and the absolute values are not increased as much in degree as compressive strength with the ratio to compressive strength about 1/12 in case of flexural strength and about 1/15 in case of tensile strength, these ratios being smaller than in case of ordinary prepacked concrete.

Fig. 15 indicates relations between compressive strength and static modulus of elasticity of prepacked concrete. This figure is plotted for all concretes made varying various conditions, and as shown in the figure, there is a linear relationship between compressive strength and static modulus of elasticity in the case of high-strength prepacked concrete also, and it was indicated that the relationship is one which is appreciably close to that of the standard formula of ACI.

Bond Strength to Steel
When prepacked concrete is applied to

offshore structures there
will be a necessity for good
bond with steel to be possessed without exception.
Firstly, on testing bond
strengths between deformed
bars, round bars, flat bars
and high-strength prepacked
concrete following the method
prescribed in ASTM C 234, it
was found that high-strength
prepacked concrete indicated
25 to 30% higher values than
conventional prepacked concrete for both horizontal and
vertical bars whether comparing by pull-out quantity
and bond stress of steel, or
bond strength at time of
pull-out. In case of
horizontal bars, the ratios
of bond strength of steel
placed in the upper course

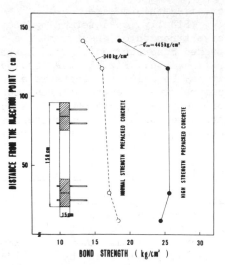

Fig. 16. Influence of distance
from injection point on bond
strength of plate bar.

to the bond strength of steel placed in the lower course were
more or less the same for high-strength and ordinary prepacked
concretes. However, as shown in Fig. 16, when variations in
bond strength of flat bars according to height grouted were
investigated manufacturing large-sized specimens, whereas in
the case of conventional prepacked concrete the bond strength
was continuously lowered with increasing height grouted, in
the case of high-strength prepacked concrete bond strength was
lowered only for the highest reinforcing bar course. This
signifies that foaming of aluminum powder does not act as expansive pressure at about 20 cm at the top layer, and it is
probably for this reason that a difference is allowed between
upper and lower courses even in the ASTM method. Since in the
case of prepacked concrete the top 30 to 50 cm is generally
placed as an allowance, it is thought this bond strength reduction at the top layer actually will not be a problem.

Physical Properties of High-Strength Prepacked Concrete

Drying Shrinkage and Creep Drying shrinkage and creep were
measured using specimens having cross sections of 15 x 15 cm.
The age at which these tests were started was 28 days from the
consideration that strength should have been adequately gained
prior to testing. The conditions for drying were 20°C, 60% RH.
    Regarding drying shrinkage, when high-strength prepacked
concrete and ordinary prepacked concrete are compared, it appears that the former shows values 15 to 20% lower. As for
creep tests, since the loading stress ratio was kept constant
at 0.2, stresses of 85 to 89 kg/cm^2 were transferred to high-

strength prepacked concrete, and 64 kg/cm^2 to ordinary prepacked concrete, but when indicating creep strain by unit creep
strain, practically no difference was recognized between the
two. In case of concrete placed by normal methods, it has been
reported that unit creep strain of high-strength concrete is
reduced to approximately 50% of that of ordinary concrete [8],
and that a large difference could not be seen in case of prepacked concrete is thought to be due to coarse aggregate particles having contact points with each other and the interlocking
effect reduces creep.

Permeability Holes of 13-mm diameter were made at the centers
of specimens of 30-cm height and permeability was tested under
water pressure of 10 kg/cm^2. As a result, when compared by
diffusion coefficient, values of 1.0 to 2.1 x 10^{-4} cm^2/sec are
indicated for high-strength prepacked concrete and about 2.4
x 10^{-4} cm^2/sec for ordinary prepacked concrete, which were
somewhat higher than the permeability diffusion coefficient 5
to 10 x 10^{-4} cm^2/sec indicated by concrete specimens made by
normal methods. However, values of the above degree will be of
no problem for concrete for offshore structures.

Durability Against Freezing and Thawing High-strength prepacked concrete and ordinary prepacked concrete specimens were
tested by the freezing-and-thawing-in-water method according
to ASTM and as a result both indicated values of about the same
degree, but it was seen that for high-strength prepacked concrete with small expansion due to aluminum powder there were
cases of inferior durability. Consequently, it will be necessary for the expansion rate to be increased even at the sacri-
fice of some amount of strength when severe meteorological
actions are anticipated.
      Besides the above, durability tests were carried out for
the cases of using marine sand, of using sea water as mixing
water, and of immersion in sea water. It was indicated that
it is necessary to increase water-cement ratio by 0.02 to 0.04
to satisfy the requirements of fluidity in cases of using
marine sand and sea water, while the stage that data can be
obtained has not yet been reached with respect to durability
against sea water.

GROUTING PROPERTIES AND STRENGTH DISTRIBUTION PROPERTIES USING
LARGE-SIZED FORMS

Model specimens were manufactured with large-sized forms of
width of 5 m, depth of 2 m and height of 3 m (30 m^3) having
front panels of transparent acrylic plastic, and examinations
were made of grouting properties of conventional grout mortar
and high-strength mortar, and their strength distribution
properties (see Photo. 1).

Photo. 1.   Grouting experiments using large-sized forms.

Experimentation Method
The coarse aggregate was 40- to 80-mm crushed stone, a kind
used in general.
      Grout pipe was of inside diameter of 32 mm encased in a
perforated outer pipe (punched pipe) for a double-pipe system,
and the inner pipe was drawn up as mortar was injected. Two
grout pipes were set at a spacing of 3 m.
      · The mortar mixer was an oil-hydraulic high-performance
type with approximately 2.5 m^3 of mortar manufactured per hour,
and pumping was done with two Monopumps.
      The rate of mortar rise was approximately 50 cm/hr which
was about average.
      The items of examination were quality control of injected
mortar, gradient of mortar surface (flow gradient), grouting
control of injection pressure, etc., internal temperature,
internal stresses, lateral pressure of mortar and core strength.

Grouting Properties
The consistency was around 17 sec for conventional mortar and
around 90 sec for high-strength mortar, and the flow gradient
of mortar surface was roughly 1:2.5 for the former and roughly
1:4 for the latter. In effect, as indicated in the chapter on
flow analysis of grout mortar, in the case of high-strength
mortar it was confirmed that the grouting property of mortar
into voids of coarse aggregate is good even though the flow
value according to P-funnel is high.

Strength Distribution Properties
Core strength tests under this study are presently still ongo-

ing. According to results of preliminary experiments, strengths in case of ordinary prepacked concrete were around 200 kg/cm^2 and those in case of high-strength prepacked concrete around 360 kg/cm^2.

In case of high-strength prepacked concrete, since the flow of mortar into voids of coarse aggregate is good, the average value of compressive strengths of cores was approximately 1.8 times that for ordinary prepacked concrete, and scatter due to distance from grout pipe and height was small.

A portion of results of grouting tests of large-sized specimens assuming application of high-strength prepacked concrete to large-scale offshore structures has been indicated above. Although a comprehensive examination is still presently under way, it may be said that the characteristics of high-strength mortar were indicated in the case of injection into large-sized forms also, and since features such as lessening of flow gradient and evening out of core strengths were obtained, it is considered that high-strength prepacked concrete can be amply applied to large-scale offshore structures.

APPLICATION OF HIGH-STRENGTH PREPACKED CONCRETE TO OFFSHORE STRUCTURES

It has been described up to the preceding chapter that the characters of high-strength prepacked concrete are compressive strength of more than about 400 kg/cm^2, good flow properties, and practically zero bleeding. Because such superior qualities are possessed, high-strength prepacked concrete can be applied in many ways to construction of offshore structures, examples of which are indicated below.

Application to Mass Concrete

Foundations of long bridges, offshore airports, and oil rig platforms will be concrete structures of large scale, and a prepacked concrete construction method of good grout fluidity and by which high strength is obtained can be utilized to a considerable extent.

For example, adoption of the prepacked concrete method for Honshu-Shikoku bridges has been decided on for reasons such as marine phenomena conditions. With large-sized structures, when high-strength prepacked concrete is used, fewer grout pipes can be used since groutability of mortar is good, and moreover, since injection can be done to the minutest corners there will be the merit that reliability will be improved.

Application to Prestressed Concrete Structures

Since compressive strengths in excess of about 400 kg/cm^2 can be attained even with underwater prepacked concrete, it will be possible for applications to be made to prestressed concrete structures.

For example, most such structures are prefabricated on

land and are submerged underwater, but since prepacked concrete can be used at the joints between these members, it may be said that construction of marine structures has been made easier.

The combined use of prefabricated members and high-strength prepacked concrete is conceivable for construction of sea berths, oil rig platforms, etc. also.

Application of Grout

In construction of oil rig platforms in the North Sea, after submerging of concrete structures to the seabottom, it is necessary for gaps with the seabottom to be grouted, along with which ducts for prestressing steel rods must also be grouted. In such case, since the depth of water will be more than about 150 m, grout with no bleeding will be required.

High-strength mortar shows no bleeding, fluidity is good, and high strength can be obtained, so that it may be considered as being suitable as a grout material.

Examples of applications of high-strength prepacked concrete to offshore structures have been indicated in the above, and it is thought that if the chracteristics were to be ingeniously utilized, this type of concrete can be employed for many uses and will amply demonstrate its great potential.

CONCLUSIONS

Experiments were conducted on fluidities, physical properties and grouting properties using large-sized specimens with respect to high-strength grout mortar and high-strength prepacked concrete manufactured applying high-performance water-reducing admixtures, or superplasticizers, as admixtures for prepacked concrete, and examinations were made of possible applications to offshore structures.

The following may be said within the scope of the experiments:

(1) It is more reasonable to analyze the flow properties of grout mortar for prepacked concrete as slip velocity fluidized flow influenced by thixotropy, strain hysteresis and hydration of cement.

(2) Since dispersion of cement particles is good in high-strength grout mortar, unlike conventional grout mortar the relation between pressure gradient and flow velocity is a roughly straight line passing the origin. In effect, the mortar may be considered as being close to a Newtonian fluid.

(3) About 60 sec as measured by P-funnel is suitable as the consistency of high-strength grout mortar, which is much higher than the conventional range of 16 to 20 sec.

(4) However, groutability into coarse aggregate voids is good and the flow gradient is 1.5 to 2 times smaller than ordinary grout mortar even in experiments on large-sized models.

(5) The bleeding rate of high-strength grout mortar is zero, but expansion is necessary in use for prepacked concrete.

(6) Compressive strength of high-strength prepacked concrete was about 500 kg/cm^2 with 15- x 30-cm cylinder specimens,
but about 400 kg/cm^2 with large-sized specimens.

(7) Given a suitable rate of expansion of mortar the
physical properties of high-strength prepacked concrete will
naturally be improved in comparison with conventional prepacked
concrete.

(8) It is believed that the characteristics of high-
strength grout mortar and high-strength prepacked concrete can
meet needs in relation to construction of offshore structures
which are bound to increase in the future, and will lead to
broader scopes of design and construction of offshore structures.

ACKNOWLEDGEMENTS

The authors wish to express their sincerest gratitude to all
those who cooperated in the study.

REFERENCES

[1] Nagataki, S. and Moon, H., Studies on the Flowability
of Grout Mortar for Prepacked Concrete, Review of 28th General
Meeting, The Cement Association of Japan, May 1974.

[2] Nagataki, S. and Yonekura, A., The Study on the Flowability of Fresh Mortar Analyzed by Coaxial-Cylinder Viscometer
Tests, Review of 29th General Meeting, The Cement Association
of Japan, May 1975.

[3] Nagataki, S., Estudio Sobre la alta Resistencia del
Prepacked Concrete, 4° Simposio Internacional Sobre Tecnologia
del Concreto, March 1979.

[4] Nagataki, S. and Moon, H., Basic Study on the High
Strength Prepacked Concrete, Review of 27th General Meeting,
The Cement Association of Japan, May 1973.

[5] Ish-Shalom, M. and Greenberg, S. E., The Rheology
of Fresh Portland Cement Paste, Proc. 4th International Symposium on the Chemistry of Cement.

[6] Hattori, K., Properties of Admixtures for High
Strength Concrete and Their Water Reducing Mechanism (in
Japanese), Concrete Journal, Vol. 14, No. 3, March 1976.

[7] Murata, J., Fundamental Studies on the Rheology of
Fresh Concrete (in Japanese), Concrete Journal, Vol. 15, No. 1,
Jan. 1977.

[8] Nagataki, S. and Yonekura, A., Studies of the Volume
Changes of High Strength Concrete with Superplasticizer, Jour.
of Japan Prestressed Concrete Eng. Assoc., Vol. 20, Extra
Number, May 1978.

PART 4 OBSERVATION, TESTING AND PROTECTION
OF OFFSHORE STRUCTURES

MODEL TESTS WITH OCEAN STRUCTURES

Kai Kure

Shipresearch Laboratory, Lyngby, Denmark

ABSTRACT

The paper considers a range of ocean structures amenable for
study in model basins. Service performance quality of a new
design can be studied in the laboratory as soon as the first
plans and drawings of a new concept has been made. In case
of operational problems, or even disasters, laboratory testing with scale models proves invaluable. The paper discusses a range of problems which can be studied, and the ocean
environments to be modelled in the laboratory.

The building in the laboratory of such a Lilliputian ocean
world is, however, not straightforward. A range of shortcomings have to be lived with. Acceptance of these is no
longer the best available solution, since computer controlled servos were introduced to handle residuary processes.
An overview is given and particular cases are dealt with.

Hybrid model test facilities combine classical physical
model test laboratories with computer controlled residuary
force servos.

INTRODUCTION

Mass produced vehicles like motor cars are studied as proto-
types before production starts. This is not possible for
ships and ocean platforms and other ocean structures even
if they are similar and built in relatively long series.

Many aspects related to the design can be treated on the
drawing board alone or in computers. Many details of the
structure, platform, ship, and especially the equipment,
have been used in similar environments and have been classified as applicable for marine use. Many other aspects of
the structures such as loading, strength, and capsize safety

are subject to norms and standards for construction, which are naturally on the conservative side. Large safety factors are not an indication of high safety, but of very vague ideas of the lifetime operational loads.

Scale models are in most cases built of the new design when it has been completed, or at an earlier stage for marketing purposes, or to give a three dimensional model to allow arrangement studies much better than two dimensional drawings permit.

More benefit can be obtained from scale models, in case they are used for live studies in laboratory environments made for special purposes, or made to model average operational or lifetime extreme cases.

Lilliputian worlds with ocean operations are comparable to real worlds, in case the governing model laws are complied with. Geometric similarity of models must be accompanied by dynamic similarity of the forces acting, in order to yield relevant results from the model studies.

Visual recording of the behaviour in the laboratory is straightforward on film or video tape from above or below water. This is a perfect supplement for marketing purposes to the fine detailed scale models. But instrumentation, measurement, data transfer, data analysis, and computers are inavoidable to obtain the full benefit from laboratory model testing or equivalent model testing in suitable natural environments in lakes or sheltered ocean areas.

Model testing has a science of its own. The related means of test performance have been considered in the following.

OCEAN STRUCTURES IN THE MODEL BASIN

In this context 'ocean structures' mean any fixed or floating platform or structure used in an ocean environment.

This wide sense of the term is restricted by exclusion of all vessels for transport, fishing, naval, or pleasure purposes. This leaves ocean structures used by the offshore industry and by the corresponding deep ocean operations, such as ocean thermal energy platforms and deep sea mining.

Fig. 1. depicts the kinds of structures dealt with. The figure was used in "Kofoed Jacobsen, B. (1979)" in a less wide coverage to illustrate the difference between offshore operations on the continental shelf and deep sea nodule mining. Table 1. lists a range of the ocean structures and operations considered. Additional types can be added as amenable for study in model basins.

Table 1.   Subjects

Buoys
Single point mooring buoys
Tanker approach
Tanker attach
Tanker loading
Tanker detach
Offshore barges, tug boats
Transport of jackets
Launching of jackets
Supply boats at fixed platforms
Transport of jack ups
Pipelay vessels and operations

Tension leg platforms
Semisubmersibles
Launch and Capture of diving bells
Submersibles
Drill ships

OTEC platforms
Deep sea mining vessels

Testing in the model basin of ocean structures and operations
permits a great many problems to be solved or studied. They
may be straight measurements of behaviour or design variables, or they may be three dimensional live studies for
concept development, or any intermediate stage. They may
finally be used for reconstruction of disasters or operational pitfalls for evaluation and study for technical and
legal application.

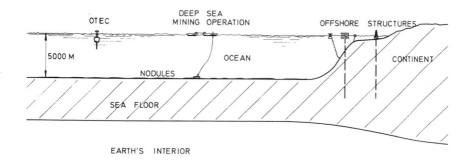

Fig. 1.   Various Ocean Operations
           and Structures

TYPES OF PROBLEMS

Model tests with ocean structures are prepared and performed to study certain aspects of the structure. The set up,
the instrumentation, the data sampling, and the analysis
made on-line during the testing and afterwards are all specifically selected to yield precisely to answers asked for.
The types of problems considered vary from one test series
to the other. In some cases it is a matter of evaluating
the overall habitability of a new concept as a basis for
decisions on further development, or acceptance. This might
be the case for a new floating offshore hotel vessel, where
habitability is the most important aspect besides safety
and operational economy.

In other cases a test series is performed to study loads on,
say, a telescopic gangway from one platform to another.

Table 2.   Problems
Overall motions, accelerations
Local motions, accelerations
Positioning forces
Capsize safety, intact condition
Collision forces
Capsize safety, damaged condition
Structural loads, primary strength
Structural loads, secondary strength
Loads on structural details
Loads on equipment
Loads for elastic response
Interaction between units
Launching process

The question asked to the model testers are often related
to computer analyses of the phenomena under study. Some
problems, like hydrostatic behaviour related to still water
and body geometry only, can be solved by computers to any
degree of accuracy wanted. Other more complex phenomena,
say wave loads on structural members or drifting forces for
design of positioning systems, need model testing in conjunction with the computer calculation because of the semi-
empirical or idealized conditions for which the calculations can be performed.

In order to ask the right questions to the model testers, it
is necessary to clarify the nature of the problem from Table
2. Is it a matter of evaluating a design philosophy for a
new concept, or is it a matter of obtaining numerical values for the general motion - or structural - response?
The latter would make it possible to derive design loads

from environmental data for the operational area.

Important testing refers to the design extreme value itself,
either for motions or structural loads. That gives rise to
a different test specification than for the general response
determination. In terms of modern design criteria, based on
risk assession and use of partial safety coefficients, Faulkner, D. (1978), Kure, K. (1979), it is necessary to evaluate
the accuracy of the load determination method. Test specifications can be selected to answer this question.

Many norms and regulations prescribe the design environment,
and the testing may be made to conclude, if compliance with
the norms is achieved. Regulations often accept alternative
and well documented design load determination. This will
request yet another test preparation and performance.

Sometimes, however, detailed clarification of intentions is
straightforward. The purpose might be to obtain a video
tape of e.g. the launch and re-capture of a diving bell into
a vessel or platform. The tests are then specified simply
by loading condition of the vessel, the bell, and the environments. The video tape, or the film, is then simply taken
from above or below water, when the platforms and other
units are in operation.

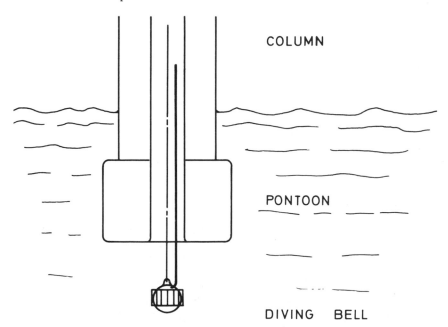

Fig. 2.   Launch of Diving Bell from
           Floating Structure

Ocean Environments

Wind, waves, and current characterize the ocean environments, which determine the behaviour of the ocean structure under study in the laboratory. Other phenomena are sometimes crucial, such as ice floes or continuous winter sea ice. Special cases are icebergs, either antarctic table bergs or arctic glacier bergs. Icing due to spray water and low temperatures, water temperature effects on steel strength, salinity and corrosion, biological fouling, earthquake and earthquake generated ocean surface waves are factors rarely dealt with in model basins up till now.

Environments considered in model testing of ocean structures are combinations of wind, waves, and currents and their variation over the site, e.g. velocity profiles of wind and current over and below the water surface.

Representative values for waves and the corresponding generating wind have been listed in Table 3.

Table 3.   Ocean Environment Data

Representative Values

Seaway		Generating wind		
Sea State	Frequency of occurrence pct.	Speed m/sec.	Min. Duration hours	Min. Fetch km
5	10.	10	10	200
6	1.	15	20	400
7	0.1	20	30	1000
8	0.01	25	50	2000
9	0.001	30	100	4000

Ocean waves are generated by the ocean winds over the area as listed in the table, or they are generated by ocean winds over distant areas and are present in the form of swell in the local area.

Each sea state occurs with a representative frequency as listed. The sea state can be described by a mathematical spectral analysis into wave length components, like white light through a prism. Combination of all components produces again exactly the original wave pattern as for the reversed white light phenomenon. The individual peaks of a sea state appears at the location considered with a frequency of occurrence described by numerical values, Ochi, M. (1978). They are rather small for the high peaks. The extreme peaks can occur only when the peaks of all spectral components occur on top of each other at the same instant, at the location considered.

This happens in nature by chance now and then, e.g. once in a hundred years or less.

Table 3. lists corresponding quantities, each by one single value. They are averages, representative values. Natural extreme values are not fixed numbers, but must be seen in probability form in the following way.

Consider at a given location 100 possible "sister storms". Each storm of the same strength will have its own set of data corresponding to the value of Table 3. They are all different but can be represented by selected statistics. The same holds true for the extreme values, either they are wave heights or wind gusts or structural responses caused by the environment.

LABORATORY SCALE MODELS

Models of ships and ocean platforms are made by reducing all dimensions in a chosen ratio. An offshore platform model can be made with many fine details and even have operating model winches and/or reciprocating machinery, motion compensator, etc.

To test such a model as prototype for a full-scale version, either to be built, in operation, or maybe lost in a disaster, it is necessary to construct model environments in the same scale. Waves of reduced height and length, current and wind, and any other environmental factur, must be simulated to study their individual and combined effects.

This is, however, not as straightforward as it may sound. The conditions are discussed in the following paragraphs of the chapter, and the solutions in the subsequent chapters. Waves, inertia forces and gravity forces are first dealt with, wind and current forces later. Other forces become important when models get very small, i.e. when waves are measured in centimeters instead of meters. Then surface tension forces take over. This is normally not applicable and is not discussed in the text.

Waves and Gravity Forces
Various geometric ratios govern any model set-up which represent a real world structure. Table 4. lists the most important ones.

The last ratio in Table 4. is due to the fact that water is used for both full-scale and model tests at the same specific weight, since the laboratory is located on the planet Earth. For a laboratory on the Moon, it would be different, and also for another fluid used on Earth. In order to balance

Table 4.   Basic Ratios

	Symbol:	Example:
Linear scale	α	1:40
Areas	α^2	1:1600
Volumes	α^3	1:64000
Displaced volumes of water	α^3	1:64000
Weight acc. to Archimedes	α^3	1:64000
I.e. gravity forces	α^3	1:64000

the gravity forces against inertia forces due to motion accelerations, these forces must scale precisely as the gravity forces. This means, since the acceleration due to gravity is the same for the real world offshore and the Lilliputian world in the laboratory, that any acceleration must
be the same in the two worlds.

Considering a model test of Galilei's classical experiment
from the tilted tower in Pisa in medieval times, it is possible to see that the ratio of model time to real time is the
square-root of the linear scale. This result is the model
law, which ensures exactly right equivalence of inertia forces to gravity forces.

Table 5.   Laboratory Environment Data

		1:40 from Table 3.	
Seaway		Generating wind	
Sea State	Frequency of occurrence pct.	Min. Duration hours	Min. Fetch km
5	10	1.5	5
6	1	3	10
7	0.1	5	25
8	0.01	8	50
9	0.001	16	100

In the Lilliputian world, having the same acceleration due
to gravity as the real world, the extreme wave once in a
hundred years would appear by similar chance in the laboratory once in a sixteen years. This rare event, and the figures from Table 4., indicate the need for particular techniques to be applied in the laboratory. One of them can be
generation of extreme waves at location and time needed for
the test, made intentionally and dispensing from natural pro-

bability. This can be obtained by use of a digitally controlled wave maker in the model basin. Precise knowledge of
the progression of the individual wave length components
from the spectral analysis of the seaway is necessary in order to prepare the control data. The laboratory duration is
about 5 minutes per test, Aage, C. (1972).

Another technique is to generate an extreme sea state of random waves of prescribed spectral composition and run it for
a sufficiently long period of time to cover a satisfactory
number of wave peak occurrences. The laboratory duration of
a six hour storm would be about one hour's continuous testing time.

Fig. 3.   Offshore Operations
           in Lilliputian World

Wind and Current Forces

Flow around fixed bodies in natural, i.e. viscous fluids like
air and water, is governed by the Reynolds' model law. This
law prescribes how time must vary from real life to Lilliputian laboratory life in order to maintain the correct ratio of
viscous forces to inertia forces. In the preceding paragraphs it was discussed how the correct ratio of inertia forces to gravity forces was maintained in the laboratory by reducing duration in real time by the square-root of the linear
scale.

The maintenance of viscous – to inertia – forces requires increase of model velocities, measured in full-scale-meters-per-second, by a factor equal to linear scale ratio. The two requests cannot be complied with simultaneously.

Under the fulfilled condition, the force on the fixed body would be measured with identical c_t in the formula

$$F = c_t \cdot \tfrac{1}{2} \rho V^2 S$$

on both model and full-scale.

> F is force,
> ρ is fluid density,
> V is velocity, and
> S is representative area.

If the velocity differs from the above requirement, the coefficient would not be the same for model and full-scale.

However, applying the required velocity in the laboratory would generate forces which would be high by a factor of the cube of the linear ratio. This is 64000 times too high in the example mentioned for the same fluid, or about 80 times using air for water in the model.

It is necessary to adopt another technique than merely blowing a wind or setting up a current in the laboratory to simulate real world because of the impossible conditions required by Reynolds' model law.

Using the wind tunnel with a completely restrained model and a high velocity, the resulting forces can be measured accurately without interference on another test condition. Provided Reynolds' law is complied with, the right answer can be obtained even when air is used instead of water in current force measurements.

The measured quantities are transferred to the wave basin test set-up in their correctly reduced magnitude by one of the wind and current servos described in the next chapter. See also Fig. 3.

Similar shortcomings of laboratory scale models due to other causes and conditions are handled similarly, as dealt with in subsequent chapters. The solutions are computer controlled force servos operating in real – i.e. model – time. They complement the physical models in laboratories on the planet Earth, where the same acceleration due to gravity exists as in the planet Earth's full-scale life.

The complete test set-up is therefore a hybrid version with both physical models and computer controlled force servos.

This sophisticated technique is proven very accurate and reliable by use of modern control theory and means, in elegant and easily operative test set-ups.

THE HYBRID MODEL TEST FACILITY

The various model laws and physical conditions of laboratory testing of scale models of ocean structures require the adoption of a hybrid form of test facility containing both pure physical facilities and computer controlled servos, as explained in the preceding chapter. The pure physical facilities are the wave basin, the wind tunnel, and the models. The computerized parts involve physical force servos controlled by the computers, which are using the appropriate software for the residual process simulation. Finally, extensive instrumentation and data analysis equipment is necessary together with pure registration means such as video tape recorders or film cameras.

The Basin

The basic part of the model test laboratory for ocean structures is the wave basin. Several sizes and arrangements are used and many different kinds of the basic equipment is applied. Fig. 3. shows a wave basin for ocean structure testing. The water contents is normally 4 to 6 million gallons of water. Such a basin is suited for model tests in a scale of about 1:40. The model displacements are then big enough to carry the required instrumentation and equipment.

A wave probe is used for checking the generated waves continuously and sometimes feed a control signal back to the generator. A range of other instrumentation is used for measurements and analysis of motions, forces, and other responses. Recordings are made on magnetic tape and analysis by means of on-line computers.

The Wind Tunnels

Environmental forces caused by wind and current on the above water part and on the below water part respectively are best measured in a wind tunnel. The reason is explained earlier in the text to be the Reynolds' model law, which answers the right ratio of viscous to inertia forces.

The natural wind, and sometimes also the current, vary vertically from one layer to the next. In addition to the average speed variation, the wind is characterised by its turbulence contents which also varies with height over the sea surface.

Wind tunnel facilities offer possibilities to include such characteristics in the test environment. There are two main types, the circulation tunnel where the same volume of

air passes the measuring section of the tunnel, and the
straight flow tunnel normally with a long entrance section,
specifically made for generation of the above mentioned natural wind characteristics. Measurement sections at the
tunnel vary from about 1 m by 1 m and up to very large sizes
in aeronautical laboratories.

The test model size must be made to fit the tunnel size.
The tunnel wind speed is of the order of magnitude a 100 m
per second in an average tunnel. An electronic balance is
normally fitted in the tunnel to measure the forces and moments acting on the model structure. Instrumentation for
flow velocity is standard equipment. A typical wind tunnel
test programme and results are presented by Bjerregaard, E.
T.D. (1978).

Fig. 4.   Semisubmersibel Platform in Wind tunnel

The Models
Models of the ocean structures are made of various materials and are often composite construction with some parts of
wood or fibreglass and other parts of metal sheets and profiles.

The type of problem to be studied determines to some extent
whether the model can be made rigid, whether it must be segmented with rigid parts, or whether it must be made flex-

ible. Models for overall motions of the platform and wave
motions up and down the structure can be made rigid. They
must be loaded, and the weight dispositioned until the total weight, including instrumentation, and its distribution
corresponds with the full-scale values of weight and weight
moments of inertia referred to the three main axes, vertical, longitudinal, and lateral.

For measurements of sectional forces in the model structures, segmented models can be used having force gauges between the individual segments. In such models, where the
segments are rigid, the weight and its distribution, including that of the instrumentation onboard, must correspond
to full-scale platform, segment by segment. Special care
must be taken to the stiffness of each force gauge, not
simply to be suitable for the range of forces to be measured but also to prevent elastic vibrations to interfere with
the measurements.

The most versatile, but most expensive type of model, is the
flexible type. In this model type the elastic properties
of the full-scale structure have been reduced according to
model laws not discussed in the chapter on modelling, but
of similar nature as the other laws. Composite materials,
often involving PVC or acrylic sheets and profiles, must be
used to comply with flexibility requirements. Weight distribution and total weight must be complied with in much
finer details than for the overall figures alone for completely rigid or for partly rigid segmental models. Special models are normally needed for the wind tunnel tests.
They must be modelled to a much finer degree of detail on
the above water parts than normally necessary for basin
testing. Some details contribute erroneously to the test
results and must be omitted or replaced by equivalent details to obtain the right results. The wind tunnel models
are normally smaller than the wave basin models and are always rigid construction as long as overall results normally
are the only ones needed.

The Residuary Process Servos

In laboratory tests of ocean platforms and operations, it
is not possible to perform modelling in such a way that all
forces are active in their right proportion simultaneously
by straightforward modelling. The previous chapters explained the various reasons.

There will be small forces due to residuary processes which
cannot, for one reason or another, be included in the test
rig-up. They can be classified as follows:

Table 6.   Residuary Processes

1) excluded environmental forces
2) model laws, not complied with
3) complicated mechanical systems
4) facility restrictions

Residuary process servos are considered in a wide sense covering both passive and active systems. A passive system is
the classical tow rope force applied to propulsion tests in
the model basin. The application refers to category 2) in
Table 6. and is due to differences in propulsion resistance
because of erroneous frictional resistance when the Reynolds'
law is not complied with.

The same passive technique may be used to simulate excluded
forces due to wind and/or current of category 1). This is
in most cases too primitive, but is nevertheless used for
many tests.

Tests of launch and re-capture of diving bells, Fig. 2.,
need compensation for air compressibility by additions to
the air volumes in the system.

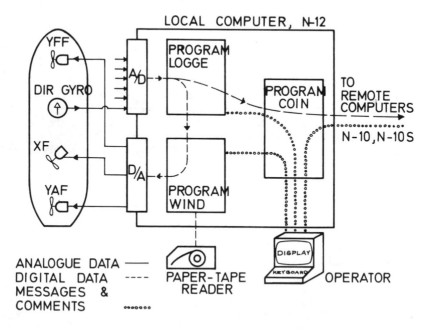

Fig. 5.   Wind and Current Servo System

A modern type residual process servo is the wind and current simulation equipment presented in Chislett, M.S. (1977) and in Kofoed Jacobsen (1979) and shown diagrammatically in Fig. 5. The wind and current forces measured in the wind tunnel depend on the position and heading of the platform or vessel considered, relative to the wind or current and to other structures nearby, which may cause lee effects.

A computer controlled closed loop servo system applies the forces necessary on the models by means of fan thrusters and feedback sensors. Input signal is generated by heading and location sensors for the wind effects and by additional drift velocity sensors for the current effects.

A microprocessor computes the instantaneous values of the forces to be applied by means of special software programmes based on the mathematics of the phenomena, and the data measured in the wind tunnel. The feedback sensor provides the response for comparison and on-line adjustment. Fig. 3. shows the fan thrusters of the servo system mounted on an oil tanker model.

MINING VESSEL MODEL   ORE SHUTTLE MODEL

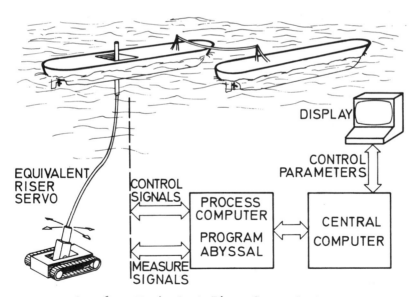

Fig. 6.   Equivalent Riser Servo System

A similar system, referable to category 4) in Table 4., is shown diagrammatically in Fig. 6. Model testing of deep ocean operations from the sea surface cannot possibly model the complete depth of water, Kofoed Jacobsen, B. (1979). For a nodule mining operation, it is hence necessary to adopt a residual force servo to apply the sectional forces at the lower end of the model marine riser.

A software programme called 'abyssal', with reference to deep ocean abyssal plains, computes on-line the instantaneous value of cross-sectional forces in the marine riser due to the excluded lower part of the riser. The overall motions and loads on the surface units are then always having the right values.

A similar system is applicable in simpler form for OTEC platform testing. They are stationary and not moving like the nodule mining units. The same equipment can, though, be applied.

A diagram showing a system from category 2) and Table 4. is shown in Fig. 7. It refers to the servo system simulating the complicated mechanical system of a motion compensator between a tanker and the loading terminal to which it is moored offshore. From sensors at both ends of the physically modelled mooring hawser, signals are sent to the computer which operates on data of the full-scale motion compensator characteristics, to produce the right compensator piston force in model scale. Apart from simulating the force, the system is valuable by giving easy access to changes in compensator characteristics for optimization purposes in the compensator development.

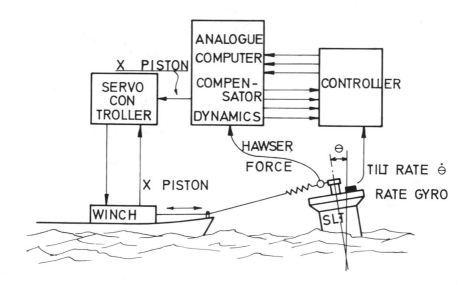

Fig. 7.   Motion Compensator Servo

The servo system is described together with an application case by Smitt (1978).

CONCLUSION

Scale models of ocean structures can be used with great success to study the future behaviour at sea. The studies can be made either for design purposes, for preparation of operation manuals, or for studying the details of a disaster. They are also very applicable for preparation of norms and standards for a specific type of vessels or structures.

To this end every step, measurement and analysis must be considered in the light of the science concerned with the particular form of laws of nature which govern the comparability of real and Lilliputian worlds. New technologies have widened the scope of model testing of ocean structures.

REFERENCES

Aage, C., Kaplan, P., Kure, K. (1972). ITTC Transactions, Vol. 4. Background Papers.

Bjerregaard, E.T.D., Velschou, S., Clinton, J. (1978). Wind overturning Moments on a Semisubmersible. OTC Paper No 3063. Houston, Texas, 1978.

Chislett, M.S. (1977). OTC Paper No 2740. Houston, Texas, 1977.

Faulkner, D. (1978). Towards a Unified Approach to Ship Structural Safety. Proceedings RINA (1978).

Kofoed Jacobsen, B. (1979). Deep Sea Mining Model Tests. OTC Paper No 3453. Houston, Texas, 1979.

Kure, K. (1979). Capsize Safety. SNAME STAR Symposium. Houston, Texas, April 1979.

Ochi, M. (1978). Wave Statistics for the Design of Ships and Ocean Structures. Transactions SNAME, 1978.

Smitt, L. Wagner, Naess, Th. (1978). Model Tests of an Active Pneumatic Bow Hawser load Compensator. EUROPEC Paper No 66. London, England, 1978.

EXEMPLES D'EXTENSOMETRIE DANS LES ESSAIS DE STRUCTURES MARINES EN BETON

J. TRINH   A. FERRARO MAIA
C.E.B.T.P.   C.O.P.P.E.
FRANCE   BRESIL

Dans les études expérimentales de structures en béton en milieu marin, menées en France, par le Centre Expérimental de Recherches et d'Etudes du Bâtiment et des Travaux Publics C.E.B.T.P., et le Centre National pour l'Exploitation des Océans C.N.E.X.O. [KAVYRCHINE, PEYRONNET, TRINH (1979)] , il a fallu rechercher des méthodes d'extensométrie adaptées à ces conditions d'expérimentation. La caractéristique demandée est la fiabilité dans le temps, dans un milieu humide voire fortement agressif. On connait des dispositifs qui répondent plus ou moins bien à ces exigences, certains ont déjà fait leurs preuves dans des situations quelque peu analogues en génie civil. Nous nous proposons de présenter ici les résultats d'une application de deux systèmes qui nous ont paru être prometteurs : le capteur sonore ou Coyne, et la jauge dite type Carlson. Ceux-ci sont déjà d'un usage assez courant dans les laboratoires et les réalisations industrielles, aussi nous ne ferons ici qu'un bref rappel des principes et des caractéristiques essentielles.

METHODES D'EXTENSOMETRIE EXAMINEES

a) Le capteur à corde vibrante est constitué d'un fil fin en acier (corde à piano), tendu entre les extrémités de la base de mesure. La corde est mise en vibration, et c'est par les variations de sa fréquence (son fondamental) qu'entrainent des variations élastiques de sa tension, que l'on déduit celles faibles de longueur entre les points de fixation. L'appareil ici examiné est le témoin sonore Télémac C 110 destiné usuellement à des mesures dans le béton. La corde, elle-même, est placée à l'intérieur d'un tube vide en acier étamé. Elle est attachée rigidement aux deux flasques d'extrémité. Les électro-aimants - d'excitateur et de récepteur - sont dans un petit bloc latéral à mi-longueur (fig.1). L'étanchéité a été améliorée sur les capteurs employés, cachetage renforcé avec de la résine aux abouts du tube et à la connexion du câble avec les électro-

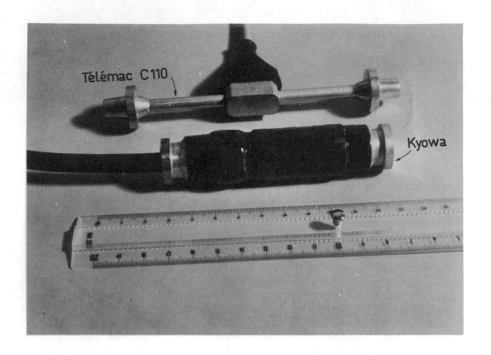

Fig. 1

aimants.

La lecture de la fréquence F, au moyen d'un fréquencemètre, est faite en régime permanent de vibration obtenu grâce à un conditionneur. La déformation relative ε_i, est donnée par la relation :

$$\varepsilon_i = K_1.K_2 \mid F_i^2 - F_o^2 \mid \tag{1}$$

Dans laquelle, K_1 est un coefficient fonction des caractéristiques de constructions du capteur (longueur de la base, coefficient de température,...) ;
K_2, le coefficient de jauge du capteur ;
Fo. et Fi, sont respectivement les fréquences relevées à l'état de référence et à l'étape de mesure. Ces capteurs, réglés en traction, permettent en pratique d'atteindre un allongement maximal de 1,5 °/oo environ.

Théoriquement le capteur sonore est insensible aux variations thermiques, il y a néanmoins en pratique une influence faible. Celle-ci sera négligée ci-après.

b) La jauge type Carlson, est un extensomètre à résistance électrique. La déformation se déduit de mesure de variation de résistance électrique d'un fil conducteur entrainé dans la déformation, celle-ci est d'origine d'actions mécaniques ou encore de changement de température.

Le capteur utilisé est la jauge Kyowa (fig. 1). Il est composé d'un cylindre métallique déformable (partie en soufflet), muni de deux barres rigides solidaires chacune à un bouchon d'extrémité. Entre les barres de support, sont tendus sur des plots isolants deux enroulements de fils, comme l'indique le schéma a) de la figure 2. La jauge est noyée dans le béton, qui lui transmet aux extrémités - et par conséquent aux fils conducteurs-les déformations. L'intérieur du cylindre est rempli d'huile de protection.

L'appareil de mesure consiste essentiellement en un pont de Wheastone, dont un ou deux des quatre bras sont constitués par les résistances variables de la jauge. Selon le montage (fig. 2a et 2b), on obtient à partir de variations du potentiel **e** , soit la déformation totale ε_{ti} (mécanique et thermique), soit la température seule. La température à chaque moment, est donnée par la relation :

$$T_{°c} = [(1+8e_2)R_c - R_o].\beta \tag{2}$$

et la déformation ε_{ti} , par :

$$\varepsilon_{ti} = 8f.\Delta e_1 + b.\Delta T \tag{3}$$

Ro désigne la résistance totale des deux enroulements à 0°C ;
β , la constante de température caractérisant la variation de résistance avec la température ;
f , la constante de déformation indiquant la variation du rapport $\frac{R_1}{R_2}$ avec la déformation ;
b , la constante de correction pour la température.

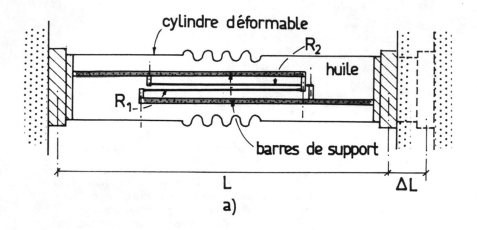

a)

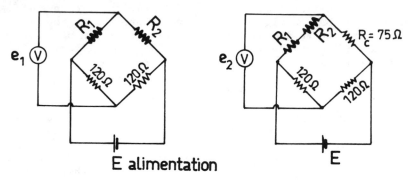

b) mesure de déformation

$$\varepsilon = \frac{\Delta L}{L}$$

c) mesure de température T

FIG. 2 - Extensomètre du type Carlson

En connaissant la dilatation thermique k du béton
($\approx 10^{-5}$/°C), les déformations qui résultent du chargement
sont :

$$\varepsilon_i = \varepsilon_{ti} - k.\Delta T \qquad (4)$$

La plage garantie de mesure de la jauge Kyowa s'étend entre
0,5 °/₀₀ en allongement, jusqu'au 1 °/₀₀ en raccourcissement. En
pratique elle est plus étendue, jusqu'à 1 °/₀₀ environ en allongement. Il existe maintenant d'autres extensomètres du type
Carlson ayant un domaine d'utilisation bien plus étendu.

APPLICATION A UNE EXPERIMENTATION - RESULTATS

a) Ces deux méthodes sont appliquées, entre autres, dans une
étude en zone des marées de poutrelles en béton armé soumises à
des charges répétées, recherche décrite dans la référence pré-
citée. Des capteurs Télémac et Kyowa, sont posés dans les poutre
les indexées A1 et B1, sollicitées à des flexions relatives basses (0,1 Mu ≤ M ≤ 0,37 Mu, Mu est le moment ultime par insuffi-
ance d'acier tendu) pour que les effets de fatigue soient peu
probables. Ils sont placés, avant le bétonnage, au niveau des
armatures principales et attachées à celles-ci. Les allongements
calculés à ce niveau, varient sous les cycles de chargement entre
0,25 à 0,9 °/₀₀ environ. Les conditions d'épreuve y sont donc
assez sévères : charges cycliques, conditions ambiantes de la
zone de marnage, béton d'enrobage fissuré ...
   La photographie de la figure 3 montre le dispositif expérimental, ainsi que celui de mesures. Les lectures de déformations sont faites, au stade de référence, puis après des nombres
donnés Ni de répétitions de charge. La charge est maintenue
constante à des intensités désirées durant la phase de mesure.
b) Nous indiquons ci-après les observations relevées au cours
des 3 premiers mois d'essai, pour environ 950 000 cycles de
chargement.
   Les figures 4 et 5, présentent, respectivement pour les
poutrelles A1 et B1, les allongements relatifs ε mesurés sous
la charge maximale (courbes indicées M) et la minimale (indice
m), en fonction du nombre de cycles réalisés. Les diagrammes
présentent sensiblement la même allure de variation dans chaque
cas. Si les valeurs fournies pour les deux dispositifs diffèrent
quantitativement - faiblement dans A1, et de manière plus prononcée dans B1 - cela s'explique aisément par leur position
relativement à la fissuration apparue, comme l'indiquent les
schémas joints. La dispersion, moins importante dans A1, peut
aussi provenir d'une armature plus distribuée qu'elle ne l'est
dans B1. L'allongement calculé par la théorie classique du béton
armé (béton tendu négligé,...), s'élève à 0,9 °/₀₀ environ, donc
toujours plus élevé.
c) Nous avons tenté, par un calcul plus fin, de considérer, d'une
part le béton tendu et la non-linéarité du béton en compression,
et simuler d'autre part les effets de la redistribution des
efforts internes par suite du fluage, ici accéléré par le charge-

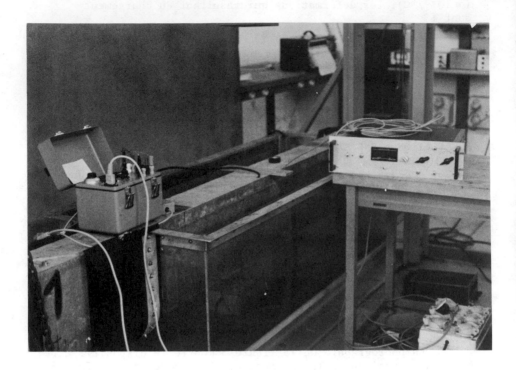

Fig. 3

ment cyclique [BAUS, BRENNEISEN (1975)]. En effet, les résultats précédents montrent que les déformations croissent graduellement avec les cycles de chargement. Et comme le niveau de contrainte et sa variation, restent limités, ainsi que le nombre de cycles effectués jusqu'ici, il est fort improbable que cela résulte à la fatigue.

Le calcul effectué, afin de considérer la déformation moyenne de la membrure tendue et le fluage, a adopté les hypothèses suivantes.

. Les schémas de comportement du béton représentés sur la figure 6 [FERRARO MAIA (1979)].
. Le coefficient de fluage du Code Modèle[CEB-FIP (1978)] :

$$\varphi(t,t_0) = \beta_a(t_0) + \varphi_d \cdot \beta_d(t-t_0) + \varphi_{f_1} \cdot \varphi_{f_2} [\beta_f(t) - \beta_f(t_0)] \qquad (5)$$

avec $\beta_a(t_0) \simeq 0$, car les essais débutèrent à environ 4 mois et 1/2 d'âge du béton ;

φ_d = 0,4 ;

φ_{f_1} = 0,8 (ambiance de la zone de marnage) ;
φ_{f_2} = 1,12, correspondant à une épaisseur fictive h_0 = 1500 mm.

. Pour traduire l'équivalence entre le chargement dynamique à 0,1 hz (soit 8640 cycles/jour),et un chargement soutenu à l'effort maximal, la relation empirique suivante a été retenue :

$$t_{jours} = t_1 \cdot exp_{10} \left(\sqrt{\frac{N}{8640 \cdot t_1}} \right) \qquad (6)$$

en prenant t_1 = 10 jours.

Les résultats de calcul sont portés sur les figures 4 et 5, pour permettre la comparaison. Ils semblent, dans ces cas-ci, suivre assez bien le phénomène. Ainsi, la déformation de fluage sous charge soutenue pendant t = 1000 jours par exemple, est obtenue au bout de 40 jours dans ces conditions de chargement cyclique (ou vers 350 000 cycles).

Nous insistons sur la nécessité de plus large vérification pour apporter la confirmation de la validité de cette méthode, qui n'a été vérifiée qu'avec ces exemples-ci à titre d'orientation.

CONCLUSION

Les deux méthodes extensométriques visées, dont le comportement a été examiné en laboratoire dans des conditions néanmoins relativement sévères, apparaissent donc assez prometteuses pour une éventuelle utilisation dans les structures en mer. Au travers de ce court exposé, nous avons cherché à apporter notre modeste contribution à une question très actuelle d'instrumentation des structures off-shore.

REMERCIEMENTS

Nous tenons à exprimer ici nos remerciements à toutes les personnes du C.E.B.T.P. et du C.N.E.X.O., qui ont participé ou contribué à la réalisation de l'étude, en particulier MM. GOSSELIN

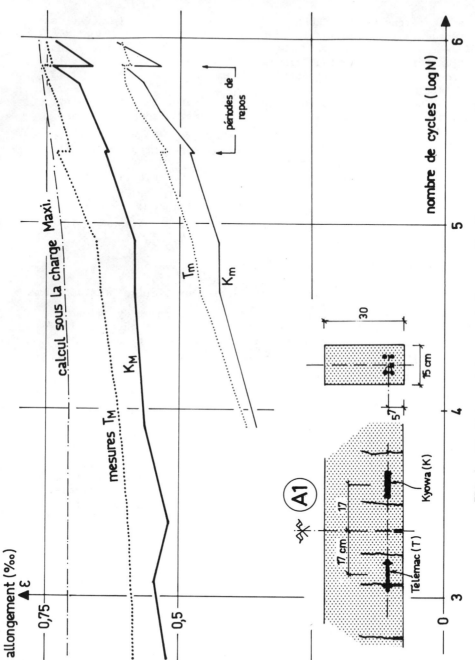

FIG. 4 - Résultats expérimentaux de la poutrelle A1

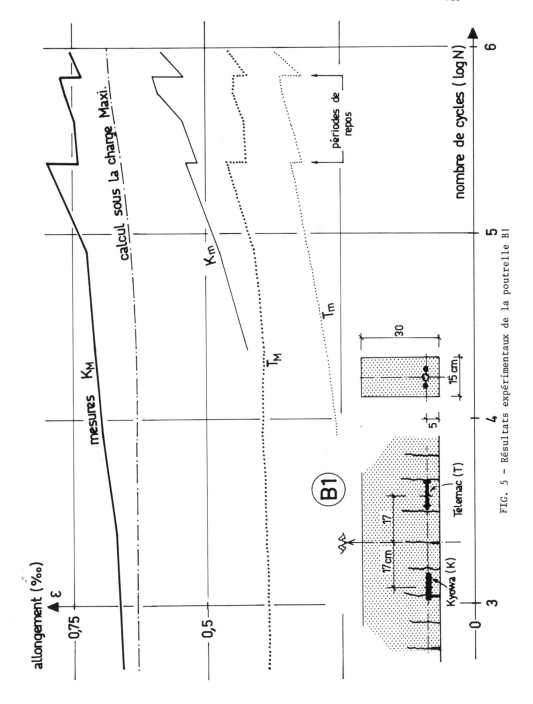

FIG. 5 – Résultats expérimentaux de la poutrelle B1

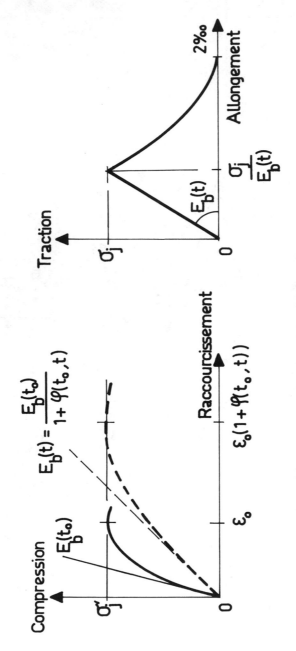

Comportement uniaxial du béton armé
(t_o âge du béton au début du chargement)

FIG. 6 –

et CHOQUEUSE, pour leur aide précieuse dans les mesures.

REFERENCES

-BAUS R., BRENNEISEN A. (1975) : Fatigue des Constructions en
béton. Colloque comportement en service des ouvrages en béton,
Rapport final, Liège, pp. 57-103.
-CODE MODELE C.E.B. - F.I.P. (1978) Bulletin d'Information
124/125-F, Paris.
-FERRARO MAIA A., (1979) : Analyse non-linéaire des portiques
plans en béton armé ou précontraint compte-tenu du comportement
rhéologique du béton. Thèse de Docteur-Ingénieur, Université de
Paris VI.
-KAVYRCHINE M., PEYRONNET J.P., TRINH J. (1979) : Etudes expérimentales du comportement en milieu marin des structures en béton.
Communication proposée au Colloque International sur les structures en Mer, Rio de Janeiro.

A NEW APPARATUS FOR THE SIMULATION OF SINUSOIDAL MOTIONS USED
FOR THE CALIBRATION OF ACCELEROMETERS MOUNTED IN WAVERIDER
BUOYS, OR OTHER EQUIPMENT.

Vadasz F., Amnon

INTEVEP - Venezuela

INTRODUCTION

During the last few years the world has witnessed an increase
in energy consumption. As the demand for oil increases, it becomes necessary to explore and drill for oil in the open seas.

One of the main concerns in the design and construction of offshore structures is the behavior of the waves in the area under
study. The dynamic efects of the waves as well as the difficulties that can be expected in the installation and maintenance of the offshore structures must be predicted by properly
measuring the wave amplitudes and periods.

There are several different wave height measuring devices already available in the market. Some instruments such as wave
staffs, pressure transducers, radars, infrared and sonic systems,
upward looking sonars, sonic surface viewers, etc., are used for
shallow waters where the bottom contours can have an influence
on the wave shape, height and velocity; and others that can be
installed on ships, buoys, aircrafts or satellites are used for
deep waters, for instance, accelerometer devices, stereophoto-
graphy and lasers.

One of the most widely used wave measuring devices are the Wave
rider buoys. The wave amplitude signals are obtained by the
double integration of a signal generated by an accelerometer
fixed inside Waverider buoys. These buoys may also contain a
cassette recorder where the amplitude signals can be stored on
a tape (which would be replaced periodically by a ship) at varying intervals of, for instance, one second for about twenty
minutes each four hours. The accelerometer signals may also
be recorded on a strip chart recorder, by telemetry, which may
be located on a ship, a platform or at shore, as long as the
Waverider buoy is within fifty kilometers from the recorder,(see
Figure 1) or the amplitude information can be reduced with a

microprocessor within the buoy and then it can be transmitted
over long distances via the synchronous meteorological satellites.
Waves with periods longer than two seconds can be recorded.
Therefore, the data obtained from the Waverider buoy will provide
information about the amplitude and frequency of the waves.

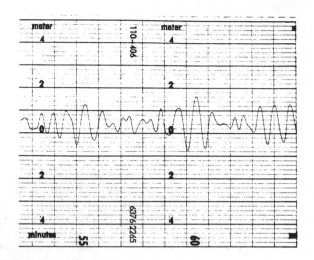

Figure 1. A Typical stripchart recording of
wave amplitudes detected by a Waverider Buoy

Just as with any other instruments, the accelerometer of a Waverider buoy must be checked for proper operation, therefore it
needs to be calibrated periodically. There are several methods
for calibrating the accelerometers of the Waverider buoys as
will be discussed later. In this paper the calibration methods
are analysed, and a new apparatus which permits the simulation
of sinusoidal waves of any desired amplitude and frequency is
described.

ACCELEROMETER CALIBRATION

To measure the amplitude of a wave, the accelerometer signal
given by the accelerometer of a Waverider buoy, is integrated
twice thus obtaining the desired displacement signal.

In order to insure that the signals given by the accelerometer
are correct, it is imperative to calibrate the accelerometer
periodically. Since the accelerometer is installed inside the
Waverider buoy, it is necessary to calibrate the whole buoy
system.

In the calibration of a Waverider buoy's accelerometer one must
comply with the following manufacturers restrictions: a) the

horizontal acceleration induced to the buoy must stay well below 0.5 g; also, b) the buoy may not be spun more than six turns
in two minutes, otherwise the accelerometer suspension will en-
tangle.

There are several methods that can be used to calibrate acceler
ometers, however, the one used for input signals with long periods (in this case 3 seconds or longer) preferably require pe
riodic motion. The manufacturers of the Waverider buoys suggest to use a vertical sinusoidal or simple harmonic motion;
however, if a non-sinusoidal periodic motion is used to calibrate the Waverider buoy, then the excitation can be expanded
as a Fourier series of sinusoidal components. In this case,
each of its components is subject to the nominal amplitude and
phase transfer characteristics of the accelerometer, but in
order to figure out what the output should be, it is necessary
to determine a sufficient number of harmonic components and
then construct the output waveform. Obviously to avoid compli
cations and possible inaccuracies, the simplest solution is to
use a sinusoidal input for calibration purposes. The analysis
of results from input movements which contain higher harmonic
frequencies (for instance, triangular) is difficult due to the
phase shift in the Waverider buoy's response.

Due to the low frequency of the periodic motion required for the
calibration of the accelerometers the sinusoidal motion is generated mechanically rather than electronically. The following
are the known methods used for sinusoidal motion simulation:

1.- Rubber Mooring Shock Cord Method.
     This method consists simply in hanging the buoy from a
crane or other structure using a rubber mooring shock cord (diameter = 3.6 cm, stiffness = 60 New/m) as is shown in Figure 2.
Using a rope the buoy is pulled down until it barely touches
the ground; then the rope is released thus the buoy will start
moving. The rubber cord has a spring like characteristic with
some damping, therefore the Waverider buoy will exhibit a damped
sinusoidal motion.

     This method of calibration is fairly simple and inexpensive;
however, there are several disadvantages which are explained as
follows:
a) Due to the rubber cord's own damping characteristics, the
motion induced to the Waverider buoy is also damped (damped
sinusoidal).
b) The amplitudes that can be induced to the Waverider buoy
are limited to the length of the rubber cord. If the rubber
cord is stretched more than its linear elastic limit (tear =500
New/cm^2), then the motion induced on the Waverider buoy is non-
sinusoidal.
c) In order to increase the frequency of motion induced to the

Waverider buoy, it is necessary to shorten the length of the
rubber cord, thus introducing the problem mentioned in (b) a-
bove.
d) Some sort of a crane or tall fixture (the length of the rub
ber mooring cord used in this method usually ranges from 10 to
15 meters) is needed in order to hook the upper end of the rubber mooring cord.
e) This type of setup introduces inaccuracies in the measurent
of the amplitudes.

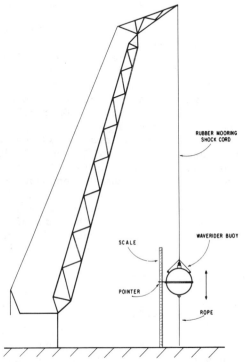

Figure 2.   Rubber mooring shock cord method.

2.- Springs Method.
    In this method the Waverider buoy is connected to the coun-
terbalance weight by a non-stretchable steel wire rope, as is
shown in Figure 3.   This steel wire ripe is forced to pass on
two pulleys (or a large diameter wheel) fixed to the ceiling.
The bottom of the Waverider buoy and of the counterbalance
weight is connected to the ground by means of springs with the
same spring constant.   The counterbalance weight has a pointer
which indicates on a scale the amplitude of the motion.   The
starting motion is given to the system manually.   The frequency
of the damped sinusoidal motion induced to the buoy can easily
be changed by adding springs or using springs of different
spring constant.

Eventhough this method is fairly simple and is an improvement relative to the rubber mooring shock cord method, it also presents some disadvantages, these are:

a) Due to the springs own damping characteristics, the motion induced to the Waverider buoy is also damped (damped sinusoidal).
b) The amplitude of the motion that can be induced to the Wave rider buoy is very limited in relation to the size of the rig due to the limitation in the springs lengths. If large amplitudes are desired, then the springs will over-stretch thus surpassing their linear elastic limit, therefore the motion induced to the buoy would be non-sinusoidal and unacceptable.

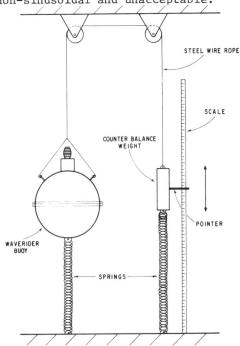

Figure 3.   Springs Method.

3.- Pendulum Method.
     This method is basically a combination of the horizontal swinging of a pendulum and a purely vertical oscillation on a vertical test stand, as is shown in Figure 4. The amplitude of the sinusoidal motion induced to the Waverider buoy is controlled by the amplitude of motion imparted to the swinging pendulum. The frequency of oscillation can be increased or decreased by shortening or lengthening the distance between the pendulum weights and the oscillation pivot, or by simply reducing or increasing the weight of the pendulum. The method is fairly accurate provided the weight used for the pendulum is heavy e- nough, however, there are also the following disadvantages:

a)   The motion produced by a swinging pendulum exhibits aproximate sinusoidal motion only for small oscillation amplitudes of the pendulum. Therefore, the amplitudes induced to the Waverider buoy are also small.

b)   In order to change the frequency of oscillation the weight of the pendulum, or its length, or both must be varied.
If the weight of the pendulum is too light, then the motion induced to the Waverider buoy is not sinusoidal, and if its length is too short then the amplitude of motion induced to the buoy is too small as was pointed out in (a) above.

c)   If larger amplitudes of sinusoidal motion are desired, then it would be necessary to build an unrealistically large apparatus, thus cost, physical space, and other problems would arise.

d)   The vertical oscillation induced to the Waverider buoy are in reality damped sinusoidal, since the pendulum's amplitude is reduced at each stroke; thus it is necessary for a person to continually give the pendulum a push in order to maintain an approximately constant pendulum amplitude.

This method can also be combined with the springs method by connecting with springs the Waverider buoy and/or the counterbalance weight to the ground.

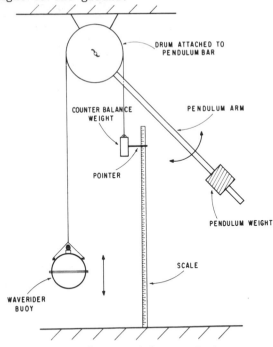

Figure 4.   Pendulum Method.

4.- Vertical Rotating Arm Method.

This method consists in placing the buoy on a vertical rotating arm. The arm rotates about a fixed point, therefore the

buoy describes a circular path. Since the accelerometer inside
the buoy only reacts to vertical displacements, then the motion
that the accelerometer actually sees is sinusoidal or simple
harmonic.

Figure 5 shows the test apparatus. There the rotating arm
may be set in motion by an electric motor of variable angular
velocity. The high RPM of the electric motor is reduced to 2
to 25 RPM by a system of timing belts which connect the motor
to the rotating arm. The Waverider buoy is kept in its upright
position by a combination of gears and chains. There is a coun
terbalance weight or another Waverider buoy at the arm end opposite to where the Waverider buoy is fixed. The amplitude of
the sinusoidal motion induced to the buoy can be of either 1,2,
or 3 meters. This method is accurate, since the amplitude of
motion can be exactly measured, and the frequency of rotation
can be precisely controlled, however, this method also presents
the following disadvantages:
a)   There is no known test apparatus built for testing 6900 series Waverider buoys. The only ones built are for testing
strictly the 6000 series Waverider buoys which are of smaller
size and weight.

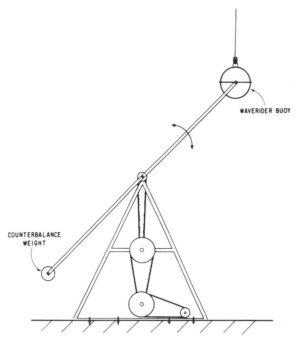

Figure 5. Vertical rotating arm method.

b)   Changing the amplitude takes about one day as it is necessary to reposition the buoy mounting and also reposition the

c) The amplitude settings are limited to either 1, 2 or 3 meters.

d) There is a limitation on the maximum angular velocity that can be induced to the Waverider buoy, since it is required for the horizontal acceleration to stay well below 0.5 g.

e) The actual physical space taken up by the apparatus is large. For larger amplitudes, an even larger apparatus would be required.

f) The apparatus needs to be well anchored, since an improper balance between Waverider buoy and the counterbalance weight could cause serious dynamic problems at large angular velocities.

NEED FOR A NEW SINUSOIDAL MOTION SIMULATOR (Patent Pending)

The description of the various known methods, to induce to the Waverider buoy a sinusoidal or simple harmonic motion, show that there is plenty of room for improvement.

One of the survey studies that must be performed at the Orinoco River Delta Offshore project and in the near future for the whole Venezuelan coast concerns wave behavior, so several 6900 Datawell Waverider buoys (see characteristics in Table I) were purchased for this purpose.

T A B L E   I
6900 SERIES DATAWELL WAVERIDER BUOY SPECIFICATIONS

Hull diameter	0.9 m
Height including mooring eye and antenna spring	1.30 m
Weight	160 Kg
Static buoyancy	2350 N
Dynamic buoyancy	1760 N
Drag Area $C_D A$	0.4 m^2
Horizontal drag (V = 1.1 m/sec)	240 N
Line force (V = 1.1 m/sec)	340 N

In order to calibrate the accelerometer of the Waverider buoys it was decided to buy or design an apparatus that can simulate sinusoidal motions of selected variable amplitudes (say 1 mt to 3.5 mts) and variable periods (say 3 secs. to 40 secs.).

The search for such an apparatus turned out to be fruitless. The one that would have been fairly acceptable was the Vertical Rotating Arm Method, however, due to the disadvantages already discussed previously this method was discarted.

In the search for a new sinusoidal motion simulator, the following factors were taken into consideration:

a) The apparatus must accomodate 6900 Datawell Waverider buoys.

b) The amplitude of the sinusoidal motion induced to the buoy must range from 1 mt. to 3.5 mts.

c) The period of the sinusoidal motion induced to the buoy must be variable from 3 secs. to 40 secs.

d) The apparatus should have features which permit an operator to change the amplitude and period settings in a reasonably short length of time.

e) There should be no horizontal component of acceleration acting on the buoy.

f) The sinusoidal motion induced to the buoy must be free of external effects shuch as damping.

g) The apparatus should preferably be compact.

h) The apparatus should preferably be simple to transport from one place to another.

Several conceptual designs were developed keeping the above factors in mind. The one discussed below satisfies all these requirements.

The basic idea is to induce to the Waverider buoy only a linear vertical sinusoidal motion, thus eliminating all horizontal acceleration components, and reducing the physical space required by the apparatus.

One way to produce a sinusoidal motion is using a Scotch-Yoke type mechanism. Of course, there are other feasible alternatives (electronical and/or mechanical), but this one is the simplest. Basically the whole arrangement is shown in Figure 6. There a large disk (used to obtain a flywheel effect), with a roller fixed on it, is rotated by means of a variable speed electric motor. The roller is at the same time inside a guide which has a rack R_a (which is forced to move linearly) fixed on it. The rack is engaged to a gear E. This gear has a chain gear P_m fixed to it through a bar B which does not permit relative motion between them. Gear P_m in turn transmits the motion to a chain C_h. This chain forms a closed loop with the Waverider buoy and the counterbalance weight.

When the disk D is set in motion, its rotation is transformed into linear sinusoidal motion as the roller R moves inside the guide G. This sinusoidal motion is transmitted to gear E through the rack R_a. Gear E now exibits oscillating sinusoidal motion. The sinusoidal motion is amplified from gear E to chain gear P_m, by a factor equivalent to the ratio of the radius of the chain gear P_m over the radius of the gear E. (i.e., amplification factor $\equiv$ Radius P_m/Radius E.) Finally the oscillating sinusoidal motion is transformed again into linear sinusoidal motion as the chain gear P_m transmits the motion to the chain C_h ; since the Waverider buoy and the counterbalance weight form a closed loop with the chain, they will also exhibit the linear sinusoidal motion.

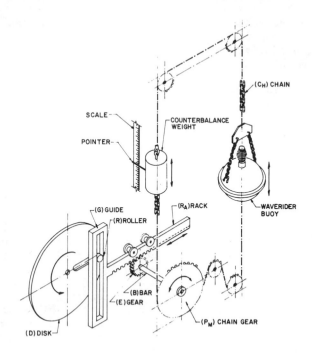

Figure 6. New calibration apparatus (patent pending).

The amplitude of the sinusoidal motion induced to the Waverider buoy can be varied by simply changing the distance of the roller R to the center of rotation of the disk D (for greater distances a larger amplitude is obtained). The period of the sinusoidal motion can easily be selected by means of an electronic control ler which controls the angular velocity of a direct current electric motor.

It is important to mention at this point that the counterbalance weight may be replaced by another Waverider buoy, therefore, both of them may be calibrated simultaneously.

Figure 7 shows a photograph of the full size prototype apparatus which is actually been used in Guiria, Venezuela as standard equipment.

Figure 8 shows part of the electric motor, the gear reducer and the disk. Notice the slot in the disk and the roller; as was explained previously, the amplitude of the sinusoidal motion induced to the Waverider buoy is controlled by the position of this roller.

The existing prototype can accomodate 6900 Datawell Waverider
buoys (0.9 meter diameter), 6000 Datawell Waverider buoys (0.7
meter diameter), or any other type Waverider buoy or equipment
as long as its diameter is less than 0.92 meter, and its weight
is less than 225 kilograms. The only modification that must be
performed to the apparatus is to make the counterbalance weight
equal to the Waverider's or other equipment's weight.

Figure 7. A general view of the prototype apparatus.

The existing prototype permits amplitudes which can be easily
varied from 0.8 meter to 3.8 meters, and the period of the sinu
soidal motion induced to the Waverider buoy can be varied from
2.5 seconds to 40 seconds or more. This is a desirable feature
since, even though for calibration of the Waverider buoy's accel
erometer a period of less than 30 seconds is usually used, there
can be other equipment or instruments which need to have a
sinusoidal motion input with periods greater than 30 seconds
(the prototype permits periods of up to 60 secs.).

Since the motion induced to the Waverider buoy is a vertical
linear sinusoidal motion, there is no horizontal component of
acceleration acting on the buoy. There is also a guide which
insures that the buoy will not spin while being tested.

Figure 8.   View of the rotating disk and roller.

The motion induced to the Waverider buoy is perfectly sinusoidal,
as is witnessed by the strip chart recordings shown in Figure 9.

The Waverider buoy moves vertically, as well as the counterbalance weight (or other Waverider buoy) therefore this prototype
design is as compact as it can be for the large amplitude feature; of course, the design also permits the operator to easily
perform maintenance or amplitude adjustment.

The apparatus does not have to be anchored since the horizontal
components of motion acting on the structure are insignificant.
This feature is obviously advantageous if the apparatus has to
be taken to different testing sites.

After having carefully studied the known methods of simulating
sinusoidal motion, it was concluded that a very important feature that the new apparatus must have is to permit the operator
to change the amplitude, of the sinusoidal motion, in a reasonably short lenght of time. As was explained previously it is
only necessary to change the position of the roller (see Figures

6 and 8) to change the amplitude of the motion. The roller is
held in its position in the slot by a nut; therefore, it is only
necessary to loosen the nut, select the new position of the
roller, and tighten the nut. This whole operation can be performed in less than ten minutes.

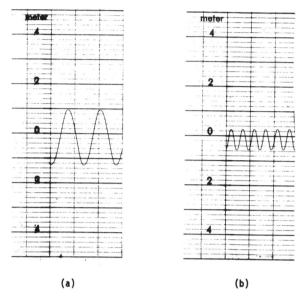

(a)   (b)

Figure 9. Sample stripchart recordings: (a) Amplitude 2.2 meters
                                        (b) Amplitude 0.8 meters.

Table II presents the ranges of the sinusoidal motion amplitude
and period for all the methods for simulation of sinusoidal
motion discussed in this paper.

T A B L E   I I
SIMULATED SINUSOIDAL WAVE MOTION
AMPLITUDE AND PERIOD

METHOD	AMPLITUDE (Peak to Peak in meters)	PERIOD (In seconds)
RUBBER MOORING		
CORD	< 1.90	Aprox. 4.5
SPRINGS	$\leq$ 0.80	Depends on spring constant
PENDULUM	< 0.80	Aprox. 4.5
ROTATING ARM	1,2 or 3	2.5 to 30
NEW DESIGN		
(PROTOTYPE)	0.80 to 3.80	2.5 to 40 or more.

CONCLUSIONS

A new apparatus used to simulate sinusoidal motion was described. A prototype using the new concepts presented in this paper was built and tested. Stripchart recordings show that the motion induced to the Waverider buoys is sinusoidal, and free of higher harmonic components.

The new apparatus also has the following advantages:

1. There are no horizontal components of acceleration acting on the buoy.
2. Different size Waverider buoys and other equipment may be tested on the apparatus.
3. The amplitude of the sinusoidal wave motion induced to the Waverider buoy can be easily varied from 0.8 meter to 3.8 meters.
4. The period of the sinusoidal wave motion induced to the Waverider buoy can be easily varied from 2.5 to 40 seconds or more.
5. The apparatus is compact relative to the size of the maximum wave amplitude permitted.
6. Since the horizontal forces acting on the frame are negligible, the apparatus does not have to be anchored; i.e., it can be moved to different testing sites easily.
7. The change of amplitude and frequency of oscillation settings can be done in a very short length of time.
8. Replacing the counterbalance weight by another Waverider buoy, it is possible to calibrate both of the buoys simultaneously.

This apparatus provides a faithfull data record of the amplitude and frequency of the ocean waves.

REFERENCES

BLAIR, P.M. (1974) "Buoy for Recording Ocean Wave Height and Period", International Symposium on Ocean Wave Measurement and Analysis, Vol. I, p.p. 254-271.

BOWLER, E.H. (1974) "A description of Three Wave Measuring Instruments", International Symposium on Ocean Wave Measurement and Analysis, Vol. I, p.p. 562-584.

BRISCOF M.F., and GOUDRIAAN E. (1972) "Research Use of the Waverider Buoy in Deep", Underwater Journal, August, p.p.142-148.

MIDDLETON F.H., LEBLANC L.R., and CZARNECKI M.F. (1976) "Spectral Tuning and Calibration of a Wave Follower Buoy", Proceedings of the Offshore Technology Conference, Paper No. OTC 2597.

RIBE R.L., and RUSSIN E.M., (1974) "Ocean Wave Measuring Instrumentation", International Symposium on Ocean Wave Measurement and Analysis, Vol. I, pp. 396-416.

VERHAGEN C.M., GERRITZEN P.L., and VAN BREUGET J.G.A. (1976) OPERATION AND SERVICE MANUAL FOR WAVERIDER, Datawell by, Laboratorium voor Instrumentatie, Haarlem, Netherlands.

STRUCTURAL INTEGRITY MONITORING FOR OFFSHORE

G.Bombassei, M.Mazzon

Tecnomare S.p.A., Venice, Italy

ABSTRACT

Due to the fatigue stresses and random damages an oil
platform needs an accurate control and in-service inspection
in order to ensure an adequate safety level during operation
The integrity monitoring of the offshore structures is a pro
blem of growing importance due to the installation of offsho
re platforms in deeper waters with severer environments.
The costs of the diver inspections are strictly related to
these factors. Moreover the survey is weather-dependent and
cannot cover efficiently the deeper areas of the structures.
In order to optimize the structural maintenance, the instrumental monitoring of the offshore platforms has become a very useful tool. It permits to have continuously under control
the behaviour of a whole platform independently of the environmental conditions.
The instrumentation system may be both stress and vibration
oriented. Its purpose is twofold: failure prediction and detection. In this way it allows the best decisions on repairing and inspection intervention be taken.
Two instrumental methodologies have been developed using com
puter procedures both to process the experimental data and to
evaluate the actual strength and the remaining fatigue life
of the structure.
The first method is based on a permanent monitoring system
which measures the actual fatigue cycles in some selected
braces of the structure and outputs periodical reports on the
expected fatigue life of each structural member.
The second one is based on a mobile vibration monitoring instrumentation. It has been developed in order to check the

state of an offshore platform by means of the time variations
of its actual frequency vibration spectra.
Following the present trend of the offshore monitoring, a com
plex system for a large platform in the North Sea will be out
lined.
The paper describes the fundamentals of the methods and outli
nes their future development in accordance with the prelimina
ry results of a more general diagnostic research project.

INTRODUCTION

Research and exploitation of marine resources is developing in ever more hostile environments and harder conditions.
The safety problem of offshore structures, systems and operat
ions is assuming a growing extension and importance.
The question is manifold and will become one of the kernels
of marine technology development in the years to come.
This trend is also shown by the course of the Organizations
operating in the field.

An important aspect of the problem is the acquisition of the
ability to control the structure integrity of offshore platforms during their operating lifetime.
The term diagnostic refers to the systems, methods and procedures necessary to achieve this purpose.
Application of diagnostics can be divided into three themes,
as follows:
- Continuous structural monitoring in order to determine the
  ageing processes and possible failures;
- Periodical checks of the structures from the beginning of
  their life in order to detect eventual damages;
- Occasional controls in order to verify the structural integrity of old structures.

In this way the following general purposes can be achieved:
- A continuous control of the offshore structures throughout
  their life;
- Reduction of the total cost (investment and exercise) to a
  minimum by means of a proper survey programme, maintenance
  diagnostics and repairs to be established at the design sta
  ge;
- Rationalization of design methods for big offshore structures taking into account safety, exercise, diagnostics and
  maintenance;
- Reduction to a minimum of the number of the inspections due to
  the possibility of their programming on the basis of previous

ly collected data;
- Possibility of orienting future inspection toward the most
  critical joints according to the data gathered.

Two kinds of control systems cover the application of the
three themes mentioned above. Moreover a further development
may improve these techniques especially in their application
to unconventional and deep-sea offshore structures.

The first of these systems serves to carry out the continuous
monitoring of a structure, setting out to calculate in real
time the total fatigue and to foresee possible failures.
The other systems will carry out periodical or immediate
checks on structures either in good or in poor conditions in
order to determine their integrity.

MOBILE STRUCTURAL MONITORING SYSTEM

The periodic and immediate control of the offshore plat
form during exercise is necessary in order to verify changes
in the status of the structure through the time and to ascertain the relevance of the eventual damage for structural safety.

These controls consist of verifying the integrity of the main
beams, the welding of the principal joints, marine corrosion
and sea bottom scouring around the platform bases. Moreover,
any damage capable of causing a variation of structural
strength can be pointed out.
The structural monitoring system controls the dynamic response of the whole platform to the external loads and then performs the structural check.
The system completes the vibrational data collected and record
ed in field and compares them with the data obtained by means
of a computer program procedure.

By means of a computerized procedure the strength of the designed platform is calculated. With the subsequent periodic
surveys of the dynamic characteristics an accurate evaluation
of the strength variation can be made.

METHODOLOGY

The first step in the whole monitoring procedure is
the generation of the mathematical model of the platform under examination by the finite element technique.
This phase is based on the design drawings, documents and

other available information about the actual structure.
Once the best mathematical model is available, a sensibility
dynamic analysis is carried out in order to relate the extension of the possible structural damages (corrosion of the
beams, sea bottom scouring, breakages) with the correspondent
changes in the dynamic response of the platform to the external loads.

The second step of the diagnostic procedure consists in collecting and recording the deck acceleration values and the
sea surface elevation.
This phase is carried out in field recording some data samples
of a time duration of about 20 minutes each.
Fig.1 shows the accelerometer unit with its signal amplifier
during a monitoring campaign.

The data collected in field are then processed onshore in order to transform them to a format comparable with the theoretical results obtained with the sensibility dynamic analysis.
The first transformation of the signals is made immediately after
their amplification by the pulse Code Modulator. In this way
the signals are directly recorded in digital format.

In the following step the data recorded on tape are made consistent with the type of computer available.
The Fourier transform is then applied to the signal time histo
ries in order to obtain a set of the most significant structu
ral transfer functions between sea forces and relative platform accelerations.
By doing that, the following parameters play the leading role:
- The signal sampling frequency must be chosen in order to mi
  nimize the aliasing errors within the useful frequency range. The technique consists in filtering the signal at a fre
  quency slightly higher than the maximum one of interest and
  consequently in determining the sampling frequency.
- The number of the samples to be processed, i.e. of the signal duration, must be sufficient to obtain an adequate separation between peaks near each other.

The final results of the whole data processing procedure are
frequency dependent functions whose characteristics can be re
lated only with the inertia and stiffness properties of the
platform where the signals have been collected.

Comparing the set of transfer functions obtained from the collected data with the theoretical one it is possible to detect
the existence of structural damage and its importance.

Fig. 1   Portable accelerometer unit and its signal
amplifier during a campaign in the Red Sea

Fig. 2   The arrows indicate the strain gauged sections
of a platform jacket during construction

Once the dynamic mathematical model is in good accordance
with the actual situation of the platform it may also be used
to calculate the structure responses in terms of displacements,
forces in bar elements and stresses to the several design load
conditions complying with the followed Code. In particular an
accurate evaluation of the remaining fatigue life for the most
important structural joints can be carried out.

MONITORING SYSTEM COMPONENTS

The Structural Monitoring System collects records and
processes acceleration values. Its components are:
- the mobile part, constituted of 5 accelerometers, 1 wave me
  ter and a PCM encoded recording unit;
- the onshore part consists of the electronic calculation facilities in order to process the data previously collected
  and to carry out the structural check procedure.

The offshore unit is subdivided into three subunits containing
the accelerometers and the signal amplifiers. Each accelerome
ter has a sensibility axis either horizontal or vertical.
Due to the low intensity of the acceleration, each measuring
subunit does not need any connection to the structure in order to be installed on the platform deck.
The wave meter may be either installed on a platform leg (wave
staff type) or placed on the deck (if other types of instrument are used).
The PCM encoded recorder and the current supply unit are placed in a sheltered zone of the platform.

The most significant elements of the onshore part of the
system are the computer CDC 6600 and its interface with the
PCM encoded recorder.
The software is composed of several programs in order to trans
form the time-sequences of the data into frequency spectra and
carry out the whole structural verification procedure until
the final check.

RESULTS

Occasional monitoring has been applied so far to check
the structural integrity of six offshore platforms located in
the Adriatic and the Red Sea.
In most cases no relevant strength loss or fatigue life short
ening has been found except in two cases where some serious
damage has come to light.

As a result of the occasional diagnostic procedure the follow
ing data have been obtained:
- Detailed situation of the actual platform structures in relation to operative and storm conditions;
- Evaluation of their remaining fatigue life;
- Some modifications (like the replacement or the addition of
  structural members) in order to improve the strength of the
  damaged platforms.

CONTINUOUS MONITORING SYSTEM

Using a continuous monitoring of fixed structures it is
possible to combine design techniques with data measuring instruments, diagnostic methods and technical practice for inspection and/or repairs.

This paragraph describes the integrated design, instrumental
check methodology for offshore structures consisting of a pro
cedure of multidirectional fatigue analysis and data-collect-
ing, and an analysis system.
This system is installed on a platform in a water depth of 70
meters in the Adriatic Sea and is also being set up for a
steel gravity platform to be installed in a water depth of
100 meters in the North Sea.

The continuous monitoring system may be vibration and/or stress
oriented depending on the instruments and the software procedures.
The stress-oriented instrumentation consists of strain-gauges
applied to particular sections of some main members previously chosen in order to comply with the whole diagnostic procedure.
Fig.2 shows two of these sections on a jacket during construc
tion.

The vibration oriented instrumentation is composed of a set of
accelerometers located on the platforms both above and below
the sea level.
The structural information, given by the variation of the cha
racteristics of the acceleration measured during the platform's
life, is quite similar to that obtained from occasional monitoring.
This system permits the user to detect both the global decay
of the stiffness and the immediate and relevant damage to
the platform.
However continuous monitoring simplifies the data processing

due to the possibility of getting available acceleration values ever below the sea level.
The stress-oriented system provides, as a direct output, perio
dical reports on the up-to-date fatigue cycles that the structure has supported.
As a result of the following procedure the remaining fatigue
and failure probability of every member is calculated.
A good knowledge of the platform conditions may be obtained
by the use of both the above mentioned systems.

The design of this system is part of an integrated technique
which considers the instrumental results as a tool to improve
the control of the operating structure.
The stress data are used in order to up-date periodically the
fatigue verifications.

The fatigue calculation is carried out to verify the existence
of an acceptable degree of safety during the operative life
foreseen for the structure, as compared with the fatigue limit.
The fatigue limit is such a state of accumulated damage that
the application of a further load cycle would cause the collap
se of one of the elements of the platform.

The parameters which characterize the evaluation of the fatigue damage are:
- variations in the stress state $\Delta\sigma$
- stress concentration coefficients   K
- number of cycles for each class of $\Delta\sigma$

The evaluation of the fatigue damage influences, therefore,
the geometric design of those structural zones in which more
$\Delta\sigma$ and relative concentration coefficients are found to be pre
sent; for example critical zones are mainly the welded joints
of the tubular members forming the principal structure of a
platform.

The fatigue calculation is performed in accordance with the
procedure outlined here-below:

a) Based on statistical data for the distribution of wave
   height and significant characteristic periods in the particular area concerned a computer program supplies information regarding the distribution of waves in classes depend
   ing on:
   - wave direction θ_i (i = 1, 2 .... a)
   - wave height Hj (j = 1 , 2 .... b) and associated period T_1
     (1 = 1, 2 .... c)

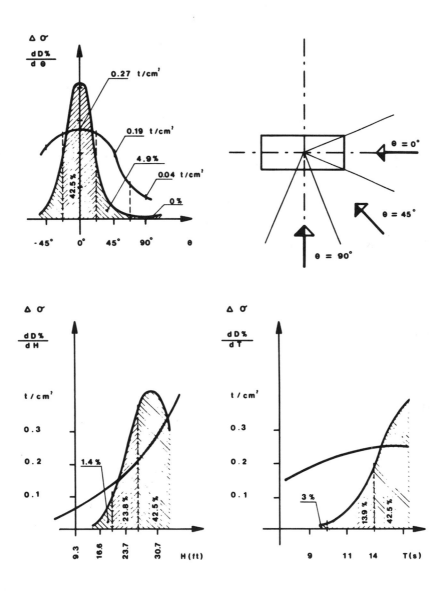

Fig. 3   VARIATION OF THE STRESS STATE AND OF THE PERCENTAGE
OF FATIGUE DAMAGE IN A STRUCTURAL JOINT AS FUNCTION
OF THE SEA STATE PARAMETERS

- number of waves per height N_1 (h = 1, 2 .... d), direction and period.

b) Calculation of the hydrodynamic forces applied to the struc ture and generation of the load conditions to be analyzed.

c) Calculation of the stress values at the end of each tubular member for each loading condition.

d) Determination of the fatigue life of every joint of the structure calculating the permissible number of cycles NC with reference to the S-NC diagram for each stress level $\Delta\sigma$ and subsequently the cumulative damage D according to the Palmgren-Miner law.

F i g . 3   r e v e a l s   the trend of the $\Delta\sigma$ and the percentage of damage D, in a platform joint, as function of the parameters which characterize the probable sea state.
The diagrams show how the cumulative damage in the joint is influenced considerably by variations in each of the parameters θ, H, T.

INSTRUMENTATION SYSTEM COMPONENTS

The platform reliability increases considerably with the installation of a data monitoring system to check the actual loading conditions during operation.
There are several uncertain factors in the hypothetical environmental data, in the mathematical model used and in the actual behaviour of the materials.

For this reason international regulations tend to require pe riodical, programmed inspections, while some engineering bodies have studied and planned a continuous monitoring service for structural checks throughout operational life.
Usually the aim of these systems is the discovery of failures which have already occurred by means of an analysis of the dynamic response of the structure.

The system described in the following and installed on a platform in the Adriatic Sea checks the fatigue life by measuring the actual stress cycle numbers which have taken place during the life of the structure.
For both economical and technical reasons the number of strain gauges and accelerometers has been minimized by the use of a correlation table previously calculated during the desing phase. This table makes it possible to find the stress level of the whole structure and to make an up-to-date analysis of

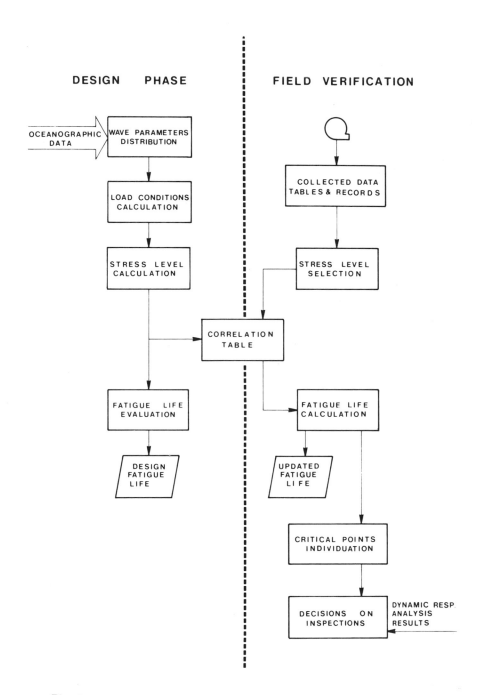

Fig. 4 FATIGUE LIFE CALCULATION AND VERIFICATION PROCEDURE

the fatigue life.

Ths system also allows the detection of important failures which have occurred (broken members,subsidence of foundations, etc.) and the programming of inspections based on a periodical ly up-dated table of the key joints.

The system consists of two separate parts, one installed on the platform and the other onshore, connected via radio.
On the platform is installed the equipment for data collection (sensors, signal conditioners) and the apparatus for their transmission ashore to a mini-computer, with peripheral units, including a magnetic tape unit, a printer, and a clock unit to govern the recording periods. The sensors installed on the structure are:
- 16 strain gauges
- 2 accelerometers to ascertain the horizontal acceleration of the deck
- 1 wave-staff for measuring wave heights up to 15 meters
- 1 anemometer
- 1 multiplexing unit.

The mini-computer at the shore base carries out a preliminary analysis of the data gathered, using the down-time between the recording periods, in order to obtain the statistical parameters of waves and stresses and to subdivide them into several classes of periods, directions and number of repetitions.

The final analysis is carried out by a large computer in order to:
- up-date the mathematical model of the structure studying the correlations between the acceleration frequency spectra and environmental data;
- evaluate the accumulated damage on all the structural member by means of the correlation table. Fig.4 shows the flow-chart of the whole procedure.

At the end of the analysis, the new fatigue-life forecast and the optimised scheduling of the diver inspections are obtained. The trend of the previously described methodology is to reach an ever increasing integration between the stress and the acceleration data collected on the platform.

A continuous monitoring system, where a good integration has been realized, is now under construction.
It will be installed on a large steel gravity platform located in the North Sea

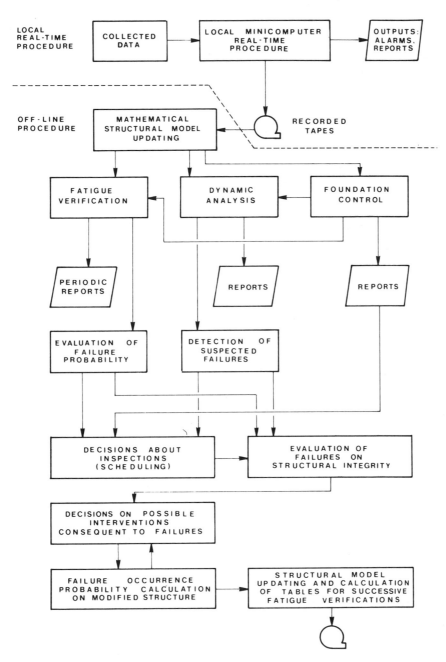

Fig. 5   MONITORING SYSTEM FOR A NORTH-SEA PLATFORM
          - GENERAL DATA PROCESSING PROCEDURE-

The system has been designed in order to operate through
out the whole operative life of the platform and consists of:
- accelerometer stations located on the three platform bases,
  on the deck and at an intermediate level below the sea surface;
- strain-gauges on the main platform members;
- foundation settlement sensors;
- oceanographic sensors;
- mini-computer located on the platform which collects the data from the several instruments (about 120 channels) and per
  forms the preliminary analysis and records some results on
  magnetic tapes so that they may be periodically processed by
  a large onshore computer.

As a result of this further analysis, the stiffness variations
are controlled by evaluating a set of transfer functions between the hydrodynamic loads and the structural response.
In this way it is possible to up-date the mathematical model
of the platform keeping continuously under control the safety
degree of the structure.
Fig. 5 illustrates the procedure of the data processing described above.

CONCLUSIONS

The presented methodology of structural diagnosis for
offshore platform is based on the possibility of reducing the
extension of underwater inspections by means of an adequate
analysis of the experimental data collected with several kinds
of sensors placed in various parts of the platform.

In order to reach the appointed goal wide computer facilities
and experience are required.
With the sharpening of the methodology and the growing of the
in-field collected data, the diagnostic procedures above described are becoming more and more important and reliable in
recent years.

The wideness of their application to existing platforms is now
more limited by the costs than by theoretical difficulties.
However,the exploitation of oil fields in ever increasing marine depths and hostile environments is generating growing
problems for the direct inspection of the submerged part of
the structures.

Being the diagnostic methodology here presented largely independent of these parameters it will be certainly improved in the
future in order to become completely autonomous and capable
to progressively substitute present direct inspection techi-
ques.

THE PRACTICAL VIBRATION ANALYSIS OF STRUCTURES WITH
PARTICULAR REFERENCE TO OFFSHORE STRUCTURES

Brian R Ellis*
Alan P Jeary*
Renato da Fonseca Vasconcellos**

*Building Research Station, Garston, UK
**Engequil Engenharia e tecnologia Ltd, Rio de Janeiro, Brasil

INTRODUCTION

Offshore structures are likely to be subjected to considerable
dynamic forces from wind and wave action, and it is generally
considered important that the dynamic response of any projected
structure be checked for serviceability as well as for ultimate
failure.

For the designer the problems of checking the dynamic response
of a structure are considerable. It is difficult to predict
the behaviour of large structures on land, but in the sea,
effects such as soil-structure and water-structure interaction
may be significant yet their precise influence on the dynamic
behaviour of a structure is not well understood.

The purpose of this paper is to assess whether the behaviour of
a projected structure can be predicted accurately, and to
examine methods of testing existing structures to obtain their
overall dynamic properties. An example of the results which
were obtained for a small offshore structure is given.

The effects of soil-structure interaction are discussed in the
Appendix.

THEORETICAL PREDICTION

In order to assess the accuracy which can be expected in predicting the dynamic behaviour of offshore structures, it is
necessary to compare the design predictions with the actual
behaviour of the structure. However, because data on the
behaviour of offshore structures are rarely published it is

impossible to gain a reasonable estimation just for offshore
structures. An estimation of the accuracy of predicting the
behaviour of structures on land can be made, and because
similar methods of prediction are used for offshore structures,
it seems reasonable to suggest that similar accuracies may
result.

The designer must initially predict the natural frequencies of
the fundamental normal modes, and although it is commonly
believed that a complex finite element model will provide
reasonable answers it is seldom appreciated that results with
errors of ± 50% may be expected. To give the reader an idea of
the accuracy to be expected, the measured and predicted frequencies of 17 tall buildings are correlated (Tables 1 and 2).
The simple predictor which assumes the fundamental frequency to
be inversely proportional to the number of stories has a better
correlation coefficient (0.911) with the measured frequencies,
than do the computer predictions (0.835). Errors greater than
± 50% are not uncommon for either method. Therefore, even if
it were possible to provide accurate spectra for load versus
frequency for any specific load state, the estimation of forces
on the structure (and the resulting calculated response, and
stresses) would be in error.

The prediction of damping values is even more difficult, because
so little is known about the mechanisms of damping. Therefore
designers are advised to consider measured damping values from
similar structures rather than to attempt to calculate them
theoretically.

Even when the natural frequencies and damping ratios are known,
it is questionable whether the available predictors will
provide reasonable estimates of structural response. Consider
the results obtained from tests on a 190 m tall building in
London (Ref 1). In this instance, it was shown for several
different methods of prediction, using the measured natural
frequencies and damping ratios, that 'the predictors are each
slightly more than an order of magnitude too large'. There is
no reason to suppose that predictors used for offshore structures will be any better.

It must be concluded that present theoretical methods for
predicting the dynamic response of structures are inadequate,
and it is necessary to monitor the actual behaviour of structures in order to

1. Obtain information on the integrity of the structure

2. Provide data on which to base future theoretical
   predictors.

TABLE 1   MEASURED AND PREDICTED NATURAL FREQUENCIES OF 10 BUILDINGS DURING THE SAN FERNANDO EARTHQUAKE – February 9, 1971

Building Name	No of storeys	Dimensions (m)			Mode Direction	Measured frequency (Hz)			Freq $F = \frac{10}{N}$	Freq $\frac{\sqrt{b}}{0.091\,H}$	Frequency or range of freqs by other models	Types of modelling used in 1	Reporters and ref No
		Ht	length	width		Pre–	During earthquake	Post–					
Sheraton Universal Hotel	19	56	56	17.5	N	0.82	0.43	0.72	0.53	1.47	0.46	Girder, column & shear wall model	J Blume and Associates 4
					W	0.79	0.45	0.67		0.82	0.45		
Bank of California	12	48.5	49	18.5	N 11 E		0.45	0.59	0.83	1.59	0.55 – 1.17	Various frame & shear wall models	J Blume and Associates 4
					N 79 W		0.33	0.62		0.97	0.40 – 0.77		
Holiday Inn Orion Ave	7	20	49	19	N	2.08	0.62	1.47	1.43	2.39	1.07 – 1.85	Column, beam, slab model	J Blume and Associates 4
					W	1.89	0.81	1.39		3.82	1.16 – 1.56		
Holiday Inn Marengo	7	20	49	19	N 38 W	1.89	1.00	1.56	1.43	2.39	1.16 – 1.56	Column, beam, slab model	J Blume and Associates 4
					S 52 W	2.04	0.83	1.58		3.82	1.07 – 1.85		
Bunker Hill Tower	32	103	38	27.5	N 53 W		0.30	0.39	0.31	0.66	0.28	Bare frame model	J Blume & Associates 4
					N 37 E		0.29	0.38		0.56	0.25		
KB Building (Venturia Gloria)	15	64.5	50.5	25	S 09 W		0.31	0.42	0.67	0.85	0.29	Lumped mass, column & shear wall model	Conrad Associates 4
					S 81 E		0.36	0.44		1.21	0.30		

TABLE 1 Contd.

| Building Name | No of storeys | Dimensions (m) | | | Mode Direction | Measured frequency (Hz) | | | Freq $F = \frac{10}{N}$ | Freq $\frac{\sqrt{b}}{0.091\ H}$ | Frequency or range of freqs by other models [1] | Types of modelling used in [1] | Reporters and ref No |
		Ht	length	width		Pre-	During earthquake	Post-					
Muir Medical Centre	11	38	43.5	27	N	1.11	0.71	0.98	0.91	1.90	0.67	Lumped mass, column & shear wall model	Conrad Associates 4
					E	0.97	0.62	0.88		1.50	0.62		
Kajima International Centre	15	58	30	20	N 36 E	0.76	0.34	0.48	0.67	1.04	0.30	Lumped mass, distributed stiffness model	Conrad Associates 4
					N 54 W	0.53	0.36	0.47		0.85	0.31		
Certified Life Building	14	49	38	18.5	N 78 W	1.14	0.83	1.04	0.71	0.96	1.47	Lumped mass, distributed stiffness model	Conrad Associates 4
					S 12 W	1.23	0.91	1.11		1.38	1.28		
Union Bank Square	39	151.5	60	30	N 52 W	0.35		0.24	0.26	0.40	0.20[1] 0.24[2]	1. Flexible Joint Model. 2. Rigid Joint Model.	Conrad Associates 4
					S 38 W	0.25		0.27		0.56	0.18[1] 0.21[2]		

TABLE 2   MEASURED AND PREDICTED NATURAL FREQUENCIES OF 7 TALL BUILDINGS

Building Name	No of storeys	Dimensions (m)			Mode Direction	Measured frequency (Hz)	Predicted frequency $F = \dfrac{10}{N}$	Predicted frequency $\dfrac{\sqrt{b}}{0.091\,H}$	Frequency or range of freqs by other models 1		Types of modelling used in 1	Reporters and ref No
		Ht	Length	Width								
Health and Welfare Building, Ottawa Canada	19	71.5	42.5	27		0.78	0.53	0.8	0.72	2.03	Frame action model, frame & core action	Crawford and Ward 5
						1.01		1.00	0.71	2.13		
Canadian Imperial Bank of Commerce	44	184	42.5	30.5	Perpendicular to long axis	0.22	0.22	0.33	0.31		Shear type structure with fixed columns	Ward and Crawford 6
					Perp. short axis	0.22		0.39	0.26			
CIL House	34	131	51	34	Perp. long axis	0.22	0.29	0.49	0.39		Shear type structure with fixed columns	Ward and Crawford 6
					Perp. short axis	0.25		0.60	0.33			
Post office Building	10	45	81	22.5	Perp. long axis	1.45	1.0	1.16	1.33		Shear type structure with fixed columns	Ward and Crawford 6
					Perp. short axis	1.69		2.20	1.11			

TABLE 2   Contd

Building Name	No of storeys	Dimensions (m)			Mode Direction	Measured frequency (Hz)	Predicted frequency $F = \frac{10}{N}$	Predicted frequency $\frac{\sqrt{b}}{0.091\,H}$	Frequency or range of freqs by other models 1	Types of modelling used in 1	Reporters and ref No
		Ht	Length	Width							
Canadian Dept of Agriculture Admin Building Ottawa	11	40	94	22.5	Short axis	0.89	0.91	1.30	0.51 – 1.73	Various frame & shear wall models	Ward 7
					Long axis	0.93		2.66	0.63 – 1.09		
	37	99.8	23	23	NS	0.66	0.27	0.53	0.64	Lumped mass cantilever beam	Taoka, Furumoto Chiu 9
					EW	0.71		0.53	0.68		
	27	73.4	62	18	Trav.	0.74	0.37	0.64	0.74	Equivalent frame model	Taoka, Furumoto Chiu 9
					Long.	0.89		1.17	0.95		

RESEARCH ON THE BEHAVIOUR OF ACTUAL OFFSHORE STRUCTURES

In order to improve the state of knowledge about deep water
structures, a considerable research effort is necessary. Some
theoretical research has taken place in this field (Ref 11, 12,
13, 14, 15) although this has tended to concentrate on the
behaviour of gravity structures. At the present it is doubtful
whether this theoretical work will produce any immediate
improvements in engineering practice.

The cost of practical research projects can be prohibitively
high, however, a relatively inexpensive way of studying individual structures, would be to use a system similar to that
adopted at the Building Research Establishment (BRE) in the
study of tall buildings. In this way a comparison of design
expectations and actual behaviour could lead to an improvement,
or rationalisation of design. This would involve the testing
of existing offshore structures and it is suggested that the
most efficient way to achieve this is:

1. Perform forced vibration tests to determine the structures
   dynamic characteristics.

2. Instrument existing platforms and record sufficient data
   (on ambient response) to enable spectral analysis techniques to be used to determine the structures response to
   various sea states.

3. Combine 1 and 2 to derive the modal forces exerted on the
   structure by the various sea states.

The forced vibration tests will allow a measurement of the
actual dynamic structural parameters and the 'calibration' of
each structure. It is not certain what force will be necessary
in these tests, as no testing enabling calibration of fundamental mode activity of offshore structures is known to the
authors. However, a system has been developed which allows the
addition of extra synchronised vibration generators. Theoretically more generators can be added until the force is large
enough. The BRE system is based on this principal, and at
present, can produce a force of 3080 Newtons (peak-peak) at
0.6 Hz. For work on very large buildings smaller forces have
proved adequate for even lower frequencies (Ref 1). However,
smaller vibration generators are not likely to be adequate for
large offshore structures.

In order to record the response of the structure to ambient
(wave) loading, high quality instruments are essential (if the
results obtained are to be useful). Existing technology, using
servo-type accelerometers is adequate for this purpose. This

allows displacement resolution to be better than the wave-length of visible light.

The spectral analysis (using ensemble averaging techniques) is feasible, as mini computers designed specifically to deal with vibration data are now available. The computer system must be backed by a disc system in order to store large quantities of spectral information.

The methodology is discussed in the following section.

DYNAMIC TESTS

There are several methods of measuring the dynamic character-istics of structures, but they fall conveniently into two main categories. The first is directly measuring the structural response caused by artificially induced vibrations (forced vibrations), and the second is to record the response caused by ambient vibrations (waves) and use random data analysis techniques to analyse the recorded response. These two methods are discussed below.

The response can be monitored using accelerometers, velocity transducers, or displacement transducers, but whatever type of transducer is used it is of major importance that the system be correctly calibrated and constantly checked to avoid errors. Accelerometers which work down to DC level can be calibrated using earths gravity, but the calibration of velocity and displacement transducers is not so simple. If the signal from the transducer is to be recorded it is usually advantageous to use some signal conditioning equipment to optimise the signal to noise ratio.

a) Forced vibration tests
The basic idea is to fix a mechanical vibration generator to the deck of the structure and introduce known forces at known frequencies to the system. For this type of experiment it is necessary to have a vibration generator in which the frequency control is both accurate (to at least 0.01 Hz) and stable. The unidirection sinusoidal force, which is normally produced by two contra rotating masses, can be varied by changing the eccentric mass.

The objective of the tests is, usually, to describe the lowest frequency normal modes of the structure, and this involves obtaining the following information for each mode.

1. Resonant frequency

2. Damping ratio

3. Direction

4. Mode shape

5. Stiffness

It should be remembered that the first two items will vary with
the amplitude of motion.

The resonant frequencies can be identified by incrementing the
frequency of the excitation force, and noting which frequencies
produce peak responses. At each resonance the modal direction
can be found by noting the direction in which a peak response
occurs, the mode shape can be obtained by measuring the
response at various positions up the structure, and the damping
ratio can be obtained by suddenly stopping the excitation and
monitoring the ensuing decay. The variations with amplitude of
motion can be observed by increasing the eccentric mass of the
vibrators and repeating the measurements.

As a result of these tests the following information can be
obtained.

1. The peak acceleration response, $\hat{\mathbf{x}}_r(Z_1)$, in the rth
    mode at a height Z_1 up the structure.

2. The modal damping ζ_r.

3. The resonant frequency, f_r.

4. The peak force, $\hat{F}_r$, generated by the vibrator at that
    frequency and applied at a height Z_2 up the structure.

5. The mode shape, $\phi_r (Z)$.

The modal stiffness, K_r, can then be determined from the
following equation.

$$K_r \; = \; \frac{\hat{F}_r \, \phi_r (Z_1) \, \phi_r (Z_2) \, 4\pi^2 \, f_r^2}{2\hat{x}_r (Z_1) \, \zeta_r} \qquad (1)$$

An additional assessment of the modal stiffness can be obtained
by first computing the modal mass, M_r, from the design mass per
unit height, $m(Z)$, knowing the mode shape ϕ_r and the height of
the structure H.

$$M_r \; = \; \int_0^H m(Z) \, \phi_r^2 (Z) \, dZ \qquad (2)$$

$$\text{Then} \quad K_r \; = \; 4\pi^2 \, f_r^2 \, M_r \qquad (3)$$

The modal stiffness as it is described above will vary with the amplitude of motion. It is really a convenient simplification for each mode, of the more complex transfer function of the structure.

The one major fault with forced vibration tests for offshore structures, is that the generated response is often smaller than the ambient response and this can impose severe limitations on the testing.

The largest vibration generator at the BRE is one of the most powerful and probably the most accurate in the world. However it can only produce 3080 Newtons (peak-peak) at 0.60 Hz, and although there are a few larger vibration generators throughout the world, it is doubtful whether they could be easily employed for this type of work. (0.60 Hz is a typical value of a fundamental frequency of a large offshore structure).

b) Ambient vibration testing
It is possible to make use of naturally occurring forces in order to identify a structure's dynamic characteristics. The basic technique involves recording the motion of the structure caused by naturally occurring forces, and then analysing the recording using a computer. The analysis may be made either by real time curve fitting or by spectral analysis. The reason for attempting real time curve fitting is that very short data records can be employed, although as yet, no accuracies have been assigned to results obtained in this way. The more usual method involves the use of spectral analysis techniques.

Before performing any statistical analysis on random data, it is a wise precaution to check whether the data being used form a stationary sample. This means that all statistical properties remain invariant with time, and spectral analysis techniques can then be used to give results in terms of mean levels, resonant frequencies, and damping values. Should the samples used not be stationary then it is possible to obtain misleading results. In the case of wind or wave excited structures it is very difficult to obtain continuous records which remain stationary for a sufficient time. Therefore in order to use standard spectral techniques, the data need to be preselected to form stationary samples, and one method of doing this is known as ensemble averaging.

Ensemble averaging involves the labelling and storing of data, and subsequent retrieval of like sections from the store. In the case of an offshore structure the necessary labels are mean sea level, wave height, wave direction, current velocity, current direction, wind direction and wind speed. The spectra from short periods are stored on disk files with a series of labels attached to each section. Subsequently intervals for each label are selected and a search is made for spectra which have all labels within similar bands. These spectra are then added and averaged in the normal way. This technique forces the data to form stationary samples (with the one proviso that sections with large trends are excluded) and normal statistical inferences can be made. It is evident that this increases the data requirement by a very large amount.

There are two types of error associated with the estimation of spectral ordinates and these are termed variance and bias errors.

Variance errors occur because analyses do not use infinite record lengths and infinitely short sampling times. Any real quantities (eg less than infinite) for record length and sampling frequency, introduce variance error. If the record length is termed T and the sampling frequency B then the variance error is $(BT)^{-\frac{1}{2}}$. Practically a BT product of 100 is often found to be achievable and this results in a variance error of 10% (0.1).

Bias error is caused when there is a rapid change of amplitude with respect to frequency in a spectral density function, this is normally caused by the presence of a resonance peak in a spectrum. Bias errors are caused by having too few points of resolution in a spectrum in the region of a resonance. Each point gives an average for the region in which it is situated and if the amplitude changes rapidly in this region then the average value is not representative.

These two types of error constrain the lengths of data that must be used. To give an example of how to calculate these errors assume that BT = 100. ie that a variance error of 10% is acceptable.

Next, assume that $B = B_r/4$

where B_r is the half-power bandwidth of a response in mode r.

This implies that the bias error will be about 4%.

Now $T = \dfrac{100}{B} = \dfrac{400}{B_r}$

and $B_r = f_r \,/\, Q_r$

where f_r is the natural frequency of the mode r

and Q_r is the 'quality factor' of the mode r

where $Q_r = \dfrac{1}{2\zeta_r}$

and ζ_r is the ratio of actual damping to critical damping in mode r.

Thus $\quad T = \dfrac{400 Q_r}{f_r} = \dfrac{200}{\zeta_r f_r}$

The length of the record to give a total error (ϵ) of

$$\epsilon = \sqrt{(\text{variance error})^2 + (\text{bias error})^2}$$

$$= \sqrt{10^2 + 4^2} \qquad = 11\%$$

is $\quad T = \dfrac{200}{\zeta_r f_r}$

Typically for a large offshore structure the value may be

$$\zeta = 0.01 \quad \text{and} \quad f = 0.6 \text{ Hz}$$

This implies that $T = \dfrac{200}{0.01 \times 0.6}$ secs $= 33333$ secs

$$\simeq 9.3 \text{ hrs of stationary data}$$

$$\text{to give } \epsilon \simeq 11\%$$

To give an example of the record lengths necessary for a rigorous analysis, consider a building which the BRE have been observing recently. The building is the Sheffield University Arts Tower (Ref 2), and the lowest natural frequency is 0.68 Hz with the corresponding damping ratio = 0.86% critical.

Now $T_p = \dfrac{200}{0.0086 \times 0.68} = 34199$ secs

$$\simeq 9.5 \text{ hours for } \epsilon = 11\%$$

The range of directions recorded was $255° - 350°$ and the range of wind speeds was $8.5 - 13.3 \text{ m/s}$.

If the resolution of wind speed is 0.1 m/s and of wind direction 5°, then the minimum record length required to compute spectra for all the options is

$$T = Tp \ \frac{4.8}{0.1} \ \frac{95}{5} = 8664 \ \text{hours.}$$

However if a BT product of 50 is acceptable (Variance error = 14%), wind speeds are resolved to 0.5 m/s, and directions 10°, then the record length necessary is at least

$$T = \frac{Tp}{2} \ \frac{4.8}{0.5} \ \frac{95}{10} = 433 \ \text{hours.}$$

In practice, the wind blows more often from some directions, and in this case a BT product of 50 can be obtained for certain combinations of wind speed and direction in much less than the time noted above. In the case of the Sheffield Arts Tower 200 hrs has been sufficient.

If it is possible to perform both forced vibration and ambient vibration tests, it is possible firstly to calibrate the structure by forced vibration tests and then use the structure as a transducer to measure the modal forces applied by any load state (Ref 16).

A STUDY OF THE BEHAVIOUR OF THE NEW CHRISTCHURCH BAY TOWER (Ref 3)

It has previously been stated that published reports on the measured behaviour of offshore structures are scarce, however the BRE are involved in monitoring the behaviour of a small gravity offshore structure, and this provides an example of the type of results which can be expected from vibration tests. Because the structure (the new Christchurch Bay Tower) was only 20 m tall, with a mass of 830 tonnes (Fig 1) it was not necessary to use the large vibration generators, and a small generator provided an adequate range of forces to investigate the fundamental modes.

The testing programme was similar to that previously described. The forced vibration tests established the orthogonal translation mode directions (Fig 2), the resonant frequencies (Fig 3), the mode shapes and the damping ratios (Table 3). A 12 hour continuous recording of the tower's response to wave loading was taken, and the data were taken to the BRE for analysis. The data were found to form a non-stationary sample, and were analysed merely with a view to noting the reason for non-stationarity. Fig 4 shows a power spectral density (PSD) for

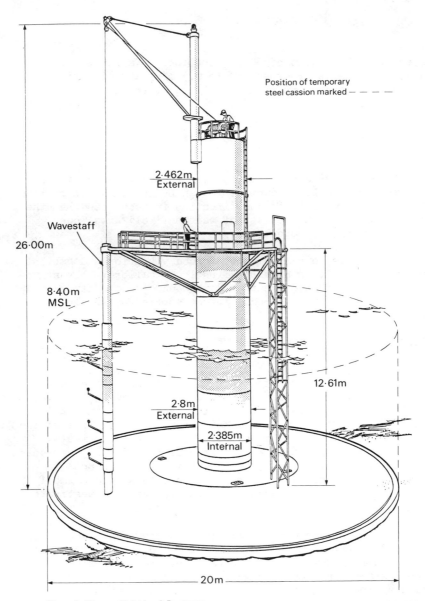

Figure 1 The new Christchurch Bay tower

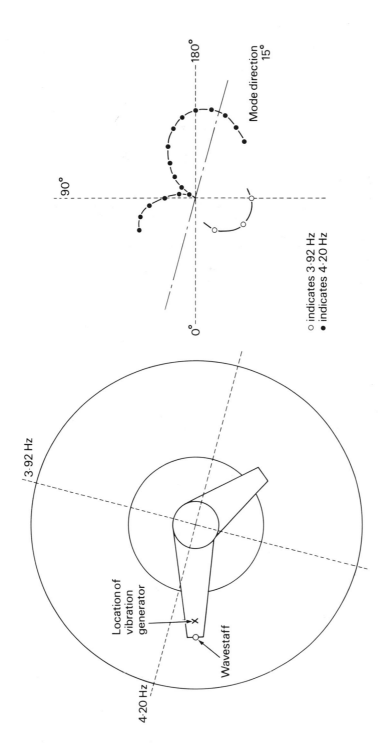

Figure 2 Mode direction shown on plan view of structure and results of mode direction test

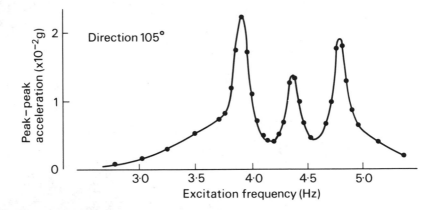

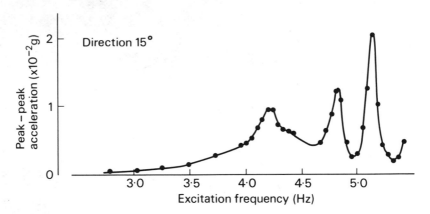

Acceleration monitored at deck level
Applied force = $41{\cdot}78f^2$ (peak−peak) Newtons
f = frequency (Hz)

Figure 3 Frequency sweeps with wavestaff in position

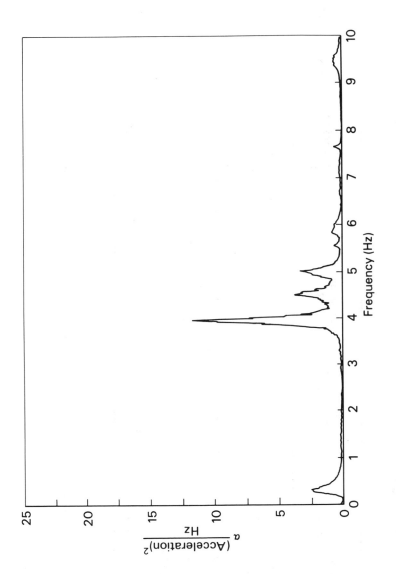

Figure 4 Power Spectral Density for the 105° direction

TABLE 3   RESULTS OF THE FORCED VIBRATION TESTS ON THE COMPLETE TOWER AT CHRISTCHURCH BAY

Mode Direction	Resonant frequency (Forced vibration test) Hz	Damping % critical	Peak-peak Amplitude of motion at deck	Peak-peak Force at deck
105	3.92	1.29	$3.62 \ (\times 10^{-4} \ m)$	642 N
105	4.36	–	$1.77 \ (\times 10^{-4} \ m)$	794 N
15	4.20	1.32	$1.36 \ (\times 10^{-4} \ m)$	737 N
15	5.12	1.47	$1.95 \ (\times 10^{-4} \ m)$	1095 N
Torsion	4.77	1.31	$2.87 \ (\times 10^{-5} \ rads)*$	5351 Nm*
	4.81	–	$1.11 \ (\times 10^{-5} \ rads)*$	3141 Nm*

} Same mode

* Calculated assuming the centre of the main tower to be the torsion centre

the 105° direction in the range 0-10 Hz. Fig 5 shows the response taken from two consecutive 2.84 hr periods (equivalent to BT = 100), for the 15° direction, in the region of major response (3.75 - 6.25 Hz), and indicates that not only amplitudes of response, but also frequencies of response appeared different in the two cases.

At present, data are being collected to enable ensemble averaging to be used to produce accurate response spectra and sea spectra for various sea states. It is only by using these methods, that any real advance in understanding the holistic behaviour of offshore structures will be made.

CONCLUSIONS

It has been shown that the theoretical methods of analysing structures are inadequate, and it has been suggested that actual tests on structures are necessary. Two methods of testing of structures are presented, and the respective advantages and disadvantages have been shown.

The main conclusions to be drawn are:

1) Theoretical analyses will not provide a reasonable prediction of the actual structural behaviour,

2) To check the integrity of a structure, dynamic testing is necessary, and this can be either

   a) Forced vibration tests

   or b) Ambient vibration tests

3) Data from actual structures need to be gathered before there is any possibility of improving present theoretical methods of prediction.

ACKNOWLEDGEMENTS

The work reported in this paper forms part of the research programme of the Building Research Establishment. The construction and operation of the Christchurch Bay Tower forms part of the programme of work of the Offshore Energy Technology Board which is funded by the Department of Energy.

The authors would like to express their appreciation of the helpful comments and advice by Mr V C M deSouza of Proconsulte construçoes Ltda, RJ.

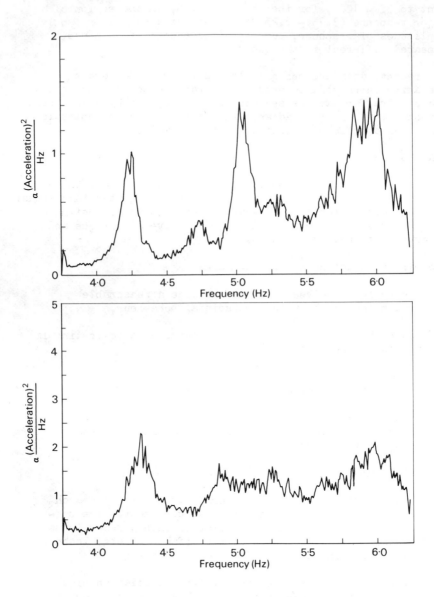

Figure 5   Power Spectral Densities for consecutive periods of data (15° direction)

REFERENCES

1) Jeary A P
   Ellis B R
   A study of the measured and predicted response of a 46 storey building. To be published in the proceedings of the international conference on 'Environmental forces on engineering structures', July 79, London.

2) Jeary A P
   The dynamic behaviour of the Arts Tower, University of Sheffield, and its implications to wind loading and occupant reaction. BRE Current Paper CP 48/78.

3) Ellis B R
   Jeary A P
   An initial study of the behaviour of the new Christchurch Bay tower. To be published in the proceedings of the Behaviour of Offshore Structures Conference, London 79.

4) US Department of Commerce - San Fernando, California, Earthquake of February 9, 1971, published in Washington 1973.

5) Crawford R
   Ward H S
   Determination of the natural periods of buildings. Bulletin of Seismological Society of America. Vol 84 No 6, 1964.

6) Ward H S
   Crawford R
   Wind induced vibrations and building modes. Bulletin of Seismological Society of America. Vol 56 No 4, August 1966.

7) Ward H S
   Dynamic characteristics of a multistorey concrete building. Proc Institute of Civil Engineers, Vol 43, 1969.

8) Pirner M
   The verification of dynamic response of tall buildings under wind loading. 10th Regional Conference on Tall Buildings, Bratislava, Czechoslovakia. April 1973.

9) Taoka G T
   Furumoto A S
   Chiu A
   Dynamic properties of tall shear wall buildings. ASCE Jnl of Structural Division, ST2 Feb 1974.

10) Foutch D A
   The vibrational characteristics of a 12 storey steel frame building. Earthquake engineering and structural dynamics, Vol 6, 1978.

4.84

11) Taylor R E   Structural dynamics of off-shore
                      platforms – paper 10. Proc. Conf.
                      Offshore Structures, 1974.

12) Warburton G B   Dynamic interaction for idealised off-
    Hutton S G   shore structures. Earthquake Engineer-
                      ing and Structural Dynamics 6(5), 557–
                      567, 1978.

13) Dungar R   The dynamic response of gravity plat-
    Eldred P J C   forms. Earthquake Engineering and
                      Structural Dynamics 6(2), 123–138, 1978.

14) Taylor R E   A two degree of freedom model for the
                      dynamics of offshore structures.
                      Earthquake Engineering and Structural
                      Dynamics 6(3), 331–346, 1978.

15) Taylor R E   The dynamics of offshore gravity plat-
    Duncan P E   forms – some insights afforded by a two
                      degree of freedom model. Earthquake
                      Engineering and Structural Dynamics
                      6(4), 455–472, 1978.

16) Jeary A P   Some observations on the dynamic sway
    Sparks P R   characteristics of concrete structures.
                      ACI Symposium on vibrations in concrete
                      structures, New Orleans, Oct 1977.

17) Ellis B R   A study of dynamic soil–structure
                      interaction. Proc. Inst. of Civil
                      Engineers. Paper No 8233, 1979.

APPENDIX. A STUDY OF DYNAMIC SOIL–STRUCTURE INTERACTION
(Ref 17)

The interaction between a structure and the surrounding soil
is a complex system which has been the subject of a large
amount of research work during the past 25 years. Unfortunately experimental data on dynamic soil–structure interaction
are limited, and consequently the theoretical work suffers
through the difficulty of comparing theory with practice. The
main reason why experimental data are not available, is that
although measurements can be made on complete soil–structure
systems, it is not a simple matter to evaluate the effects of
soil–structure interaction. Because of the increasing
requirement for experimental data, a project has been initiated
at the BRE to investigate the effects of soil–structure
interaction on the dynamic behaviour of structures. The idea
behind the experimental side of the project was to test one
structure, first on a rigid foundation, and then on various
different types of soils. Any change in the system behaviour

can then be attributed to the soil conditions. With the inevitable restrictions imposed by cost, it was necessary to conduct the experiments on a relatively small structure.

The structure consisted of a 2.6m dia concrete base, a 3.2 high 0.6m dia steel tower, supporting a steel platform, the complete structure had a total mass of 3800 kg.

For this paper the results of two experiments which serve to illustrate the difference in dynamic behaviour between the structure on a rigid base (the concrete laboratory floor), and the same structure on a flexible base are presented. The North field at the Building Research Station provided the flexible foundation, however the top soil and grass which covered the boulder clay were not removed as the intention was to provide a qualitative illustration of the effects of soil-structure interaction.

The model was tested in a similar fashion to that described previously under the heading, Forced vibration tests, and the effects of foundation conditions are shown with respect to resonant frequencies (Fig 6), damping ratios (Fig 7) and mode shapes (Fig 8).

These experiments demonstrated that:

1) With a change from a rigid to a more flexible foundation, the resonant frequencies of the fundamental normal modes decreased, the associated damping ratios increased and a characteristic change in mode shape occurs.

2) The variation in resonant frequencies and damping with amplitude of motion is significant.

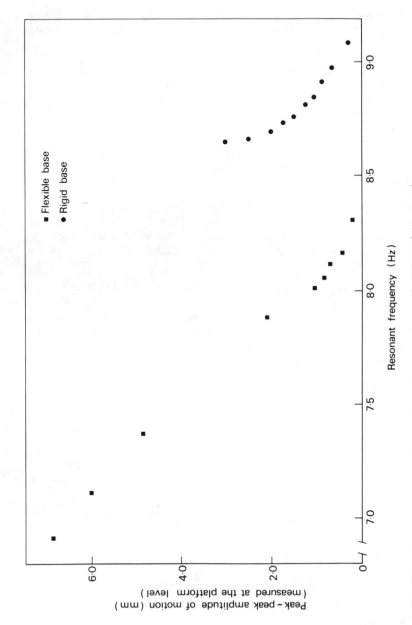

Figure 6 Relationship between the amplitude of motion and the resonant frequency for the lowest frequency mode

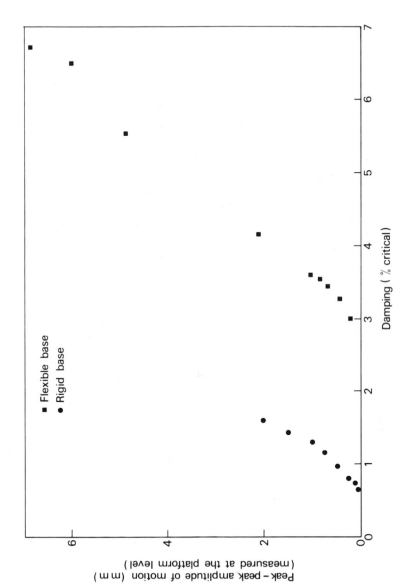

Figure 7 Relationship between amplitude of motion and damping for the lowest frequency mode

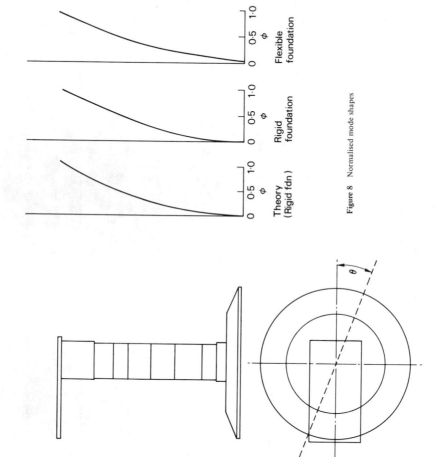

Figure 8 Normalised mode shapes

A NEW AUTOMATIC INDICATOR BY MEANS OF LASER TURBIDIMETER FOR
DETECTING THE ENVIRONMENTAL POLLUTION DURING SEA OPERATION
Hirotsugu Kimishima, Kunio Gokudan, Enji Sato

Tokai University,   "   Op. Tech. Co. Ltd.

1. INTRODUCTION

It has been often encountered in densely industrialized countries like Japan that sea water pollution has been caused by
sea works such as dredging, reclamation and excavation of sea
bottoms, which has made difficult to continue the works from
standpoint of environmental regulation.
The present Japanese regulation specifies the method by using
a quantitative analysis according to J.I.S. or Japan Industrial Standard. That is amount of suspended solids or so-
called S.S. is measured by a specified method using filter,
oven and weighing balance.
It is practically impossible, however, to conduct the quantitative analysis during field operation, thus several optical
methods have been devised in place of the analysis and used
in fields. But there are still several substantial problems
concerning reliability of the result even by those optical
methods, for example sampling method of sea water non-
uniformity of turbidity due to settling of ingredients, repro-
ducibility of small amount of sampled water in addition to
difficult optical phenomena.   [Hishida,K.(1972)]
In order to respond wide demands in this country, the authors
assembled a new automatic indicator by means of laser emitter,
conducted a long series of experiment for calibration and
found to be practically applicable for sea works, although
there are still some problems left regarding scientific
matters such as effects of sizes, shapes and colors of minute
suspended particles in turbid water.
This paper describes an apparatus, experimental results and
discussion.

2. METHOD OF EXPERIMENT

2.1 Principle
It is well known that penetrated light through a turbid medium

attenuates exponentially according to Lambert Beer's law, as shown in the following equation:

$$\log I = \log I_0 - k \cdot c \cdot l \qquad (2.1)$$

where, I and I_0 are both intensities of penetrated and source of lights, k and c are absorption constant and concentration of turbid water respectively, and l is a length of light path. The result in this case is considerably affected by color of particles in media and also by stain of window glass for projection of lights. [Sugano,A.(1975),Sato,T.(1962)] Since there are some investigations showing that ratio of scattering to penetrated light is proportional to concentration of turbid water and also the ratio is less affected by the above mentioned factors than the intensity of penetrated light alone, the authors decided to take ratio of both lights to minimize the above defects. [Sugano,A.(1972), Sato,T. (1963), Hishida, K.(1968)] Thus the following equation is deduced to determine optical turbidity:

$$\log D = k' + m (I_s / I_t) \qquad (2.2)$$

where, D is turbidity determined by an optical method, k' and m are constants determined by calibration on several media containing various particles, I_s and I_t are intensities of scattering and penetrated lights respectively. The optical turbidity is related with concentration by a series of experiments and the following linear equation is determined:

$$\log D = a + b \cdot p \qquad (2.3)$$

where, a,b are constants depending on species of particles and p is concentration by weight. Consequently measurement of intensities on both scattering and penetrated lights is connected with concentration by a simple linear equation. If logarithm of optical turbidity and concentration are taken on the coordinate and abscissa respectively, equation(2.3) should show straight lines. If amount of S.S. is wanted instead of concentration by weight, just a simple algebraic computation makes it possible to convert it.

2.2 Apparatus

The apparatus is composed of a laser emitter as a light source, container of sample turbid water and an indicator.

Light source He-Ne gas laser emitter, having a red mono-color beam, out-put 2mW, wave length 0.63μm is used, which assures comparatively better accuracy than ordinary light by intensive penetrative power and averages non-uniform turbidity through light path of fifteen centimeter.

Container Since the measurement should be conducted continuously during dredging operation, dirty test water is

preferably circulated by a pump to simulate field condition
besides constant bottom agitation of the container.

Light receiver   Several photo-diode elements are arranged at
angles of 0,10,20,30 and 40 degrees respectively from the
laser beam to know diffusion of scattering and are located at
equal distance from the light window. A small lens is set on
the laser beam to avoid pin-pointed projection of the beam
and to enlarge it into diameter of ten milimeter luminous flux.

Indicator   It is provided with amplifier,computer, either
analog or digital indicator,an oscillogragh recorder and a
warning buzzer or a lamp if necessary. Figure 1 is a
schematic drawing of the apparatus and Figure 2 is a photograph showing a whole set of each component.

2.3 Measurement
Intensities of penetrated and scattered lights are received by
photo-diode elements, converted into electric voltage,ampli-
fied, measured, computed and indicated.

2.4 Preparation of test water
Turbid test water was made by adding various ingredients into
pure or sea water as shown in Table 1, in which colors were
determined by a method specified in J.I.S. Z-8721,specific
surfaces and particle sizes were measured by the authors.
[G.T.S.G.(1967), Kubo,T.(1969)]
Considerable discrepancy of particle diameters was noticed
between specification in catalogs and measurement, which might
be due to the fact that flocculents conglomerated by minute
particles could not be dispersed by an ordinary agitator,

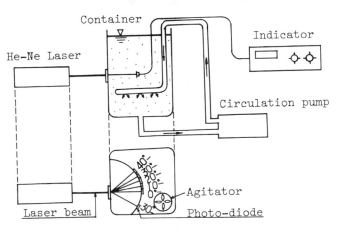

Figure 1 Schematic drawing of the apparatus

① Light source He-Ne Laser 2 mW, 0.63 μm Red mono-color	② Container with agitator Light path 15 cm Photo-diodes	③ Circulation pump
④ Indicator Amplifier Computer Adjusting dials	⑤ Oscillograph recorder	⑥ Allowable range setter Warning lamp or buzzer

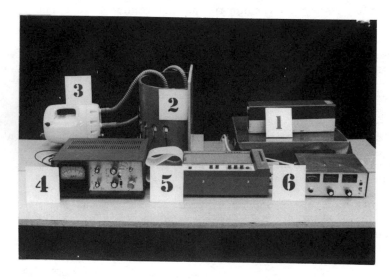

Figure 2 Photograph showing a whole set

and minute particles tended to be missing. [Takeuchi,Y.(1974)]
Original condensed water is poured into the container intermittently.   At each stage, changing turbidity of test water
is optically measured, sampled to check both concentration
and the S.S. by J.I.S. method.   Photographs are also taken
above the container to see diffusion of scattering light.

3 RESULTS AND DISCUSSION

3.1 Penetrated light
Figure 3 shows relation between intensities of penetrated
light and concentration   for some ingredients.   It is
noted that logarithmic intensities of penetrated light vary to
a large extent by materials.   Large differences of light
intensities are also noticed depending upon sizes of particles
even with the same kind of ingredients.

Table 1 Ingredients for test water

No	Ingredients	particle size(μm)		Color	S.P.G.	Specific
		measured	catalog			surface
1	Carborundum	3.3	3.0	Black	3.18	143.0 cm²
2	Kaolin	4.6		white	2.58	127.0
3	Sea-bottom sediment(C)	6.6		Black	2.59	87.8
4	Sea-bottom sediment(M)	7.8		Black	2.52	76.3
5	Carborundum	9.6	16.0	Black	3.12	50.0
6	Alumina abrasives	10.3	3.0	White	3.95	36.9
7	Alumina abrasives	15.7	0.3	White	3.94	24.2
8	Alumina abrasives	26.0	15.0	White	3.96	14.6
9	Carborundum	35.0	37.0	Black	3.20	11.3

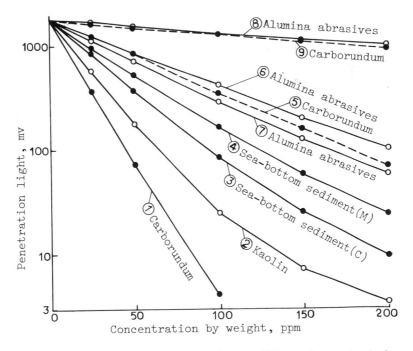

Figure 3 Relation between intensities of penetrated
light and concentration by weight

For example,when penetrated lights at 100 ppm are taken, intensity of particle size 35 μm of carborundum is 300 times as large as that of 3.3 μm, and that of 26 μm alumina abrasives is 5 times as large as that of 15.7 μm of alumina.
But as to effect of colors, intensities of penetrated lights are more or less the same and for example intensity of particle of 10.6 μm white alumina abrasives is 1.2 times as large as that of 9.6 μm black carborundum.   Those of sea bottom sediments are almost same because of the nearly same color and size. Thus it is noticed that intensity of penetrated light through turbid water is more affected by size of particles than color, and also most of curves in the drawing seem to be linear so far as concentrations by weight are within 100 ppm, and beyond 100 ppm , they start showing non-linearity, which is probably due to effect of multi-scattering.
In other words, if intensities of penetrated light alone are used to estimate turbidity,the size and grading of ingredients and also extent of concentration play relatively important roles for the result.

3.2 Scattering light
Figure 4 shows relation between intensities of scattering light and concentration by weight at an angle of 20 degrees from the optical axis.

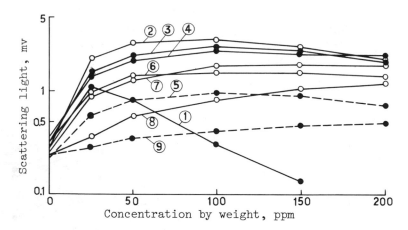

Figure 4 Relation between scattering and concentration

It is noticed that intensities of scattering light are only several hundredth of that of the penetrated light and they increase up to the concentration of approximately 50 ppm and then start decreasing from that of 100 ppm making convex shape except two curves, which are cases for large sizes of particles and showing monotonic increase in proportion to

concentration. An exceptionally steep decrease of scattering
light is also noticed as indicated by ①, which seems to
suggest particle color is associated with the intensity.
It is generally recognized that intensity of scattering light
is in proportion to total surface area of particles included
in an unit volume.   [M.M.Assn. (1974)]
For example, intensity of penetrated light of kaolin and sea
bottom sediments are small in comparison with other ingredients but on the contrary, those of scattering light are
rather large because of large specific surfaces of the ingredients.
Since the scattering phenomena are too complicated for the
civil engineers to manage by ordinary engineering level of
knowledges, the authors thought to be better to study the
phenomena as a whole instead of studying each factor separately such as size, specific surface and color etcs.

3.3 Ratio of scattering to penetration
Since the authors found that it was not advisable for estimation of turbidity to adopt either penetration or scattering
light alone through preliminary investigation, they decided
to take the ratio of scattering to penetration lights.
Simple ratio of the two intensities of lights did not show
in most cases linearity between logarithmic turbidity and concentration by weight, thus two constants were introduced to
adjust the origine and non-linearity as shown in the following
equation.
$$\log D = [k' + m (I_s / I_t)] \qquad (3.1)$$
Where D is optical turbidity, k' and m are constants determined by calibration, I_s and I_t are intensities of scattering
light at angle 10 degrees from the optical axis and penetrated
light respectively.
Since the ratio (I_s / I_t) gives extremely minute value, a
multiplier m is needed to express the optical turbidity.
The multiplier m is determined by the following way:
Intersection of coordinate with asymptotic extension of linear
part of the curves of scattering lights is taken I_{to}. Then
m is obtained from the next equation, $m = I_{to} / I_{so}$
The more the m, the better the linearity in low concentration.
The logarithm of the optical turbidity log D does not indicate
1 on the coordinate even when the concentration by weight is
0 ppm on the abscissa. Thus k' is introduced to coincide
the logarithm of optical turbidity at 0 ppm with log 1 on the
coordinate.
As a further refinement to ensure linearity, effect of multi-
scattering existing in the intensity of penetrated light is
eliminated by subtracting intensity of scattering light at
angle 10 degrees from that of the penetrated light.

Intensity of scattering light of the numerator I_s is measured
at angle of 20 degrees from the optical axis. Figure 5
illustrates relation between logarithm of optical turbidity

and concentration, and table 2 shows equation to connect
optical turbidity with concentration.   Correlation coefficients are very high as shown in the table.

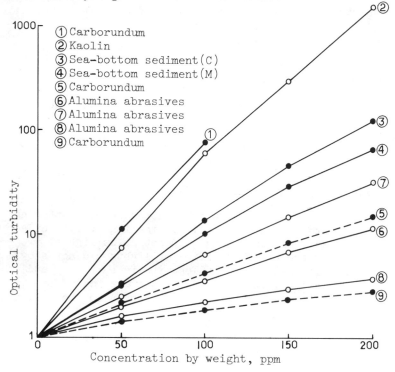

Figure 5 Relation between optical turbidity and
concentration by weight

So-called optical sensitivity, in which the ratio of optical
turbidity to concentration is taken on the coordinate is
plotted against average diameters of ingredients on the abscissa as shown in Figure 6.   It is noticed that ingredients
of smaller sizes have larger sensitivity irrespective of
particle colors.
Generally speaking, it is satisfactory to know relationship
between optical turbidity and concentration, but further calibration is needed in countries like Japan to relate the latter
with amount of S.S. or suspended solids because environmental
regulation is specified by S.S. under the present J.I.S. or
Japan Industrial Standard.
Conversion to S.S. from concentration is easily made by a
linear equation as shown in Table 3, and consequently S.S. or
amount of suspended solids is connected with the optical
turbidity.   The ratio of S.S. to concentration lies between
0.73 and 0.95 as shown by coefficients of equations in the
Table 3.

Table 2 Correlation between optical
turbidity and concentration

No.	Ingredient	Correlation coefficient	Regression * equation
1	Carborundum	0.997	D = 1.31 exp (0.041 p)
2	Kaolin	0.994	D = 1.09 exp (0.037 p)
3	Sea-bottom sediment(C)	0.994	D = 0.93 exp (0.025 p)
4	Sea-bottom sediment(M)	0.995	D = 1.13 exp (0.021 p)
5	Carborundum	0.998	D = 1.07 exp (0.013 p)
6	Alumina abrasives	0.997	D = 1.05 exp (0.012 p)
7	Alumina abrasives	0.998	D = 1.07 exp (0.017 p)
8	Alumina abrasives	0.986	D = 1.13 exp (0.006 p)
9	Carborundum	0.990	D = 1.12 exp (0.0047p)

* D: Optical turbidity, p: concentration (ppm)

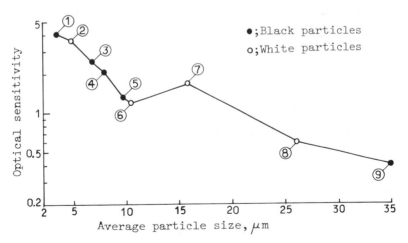

Figure 6 Relation between optical sensitivity
and average particle size

The wide variance of coefficients seems to come from particle
shapes and sizes.   When particles are angular and sharply
edged, they tend to plug up a filter by arching.

Table 3 Correlation between suspended
solid (S.S.) and concentration

No.	Ingredient	Correlation coefficient	Regression Equation *
1	Carborundum	0.999	S.S. = -0.42 + 0.95 p
2	Kaolin	0.999	S.S. = 5.20 + 0.90 p
3	Sea-bottom sediment(C)	0.987	S.S. = 6.72 + 0.73 p
4	Sea-bottom sediment(M)	0.997	S.S. = 0.22 + 0.80 p
5	Carborundum	0.999	S.S. = -0.42 + 0.95 p
6	Alumina abrasives	0.999	S.S. = 2.88 + 0.86 p
7	Alumina abrasives	0.999	S.S. = 3.93 + 0.94 p
8	Alumina abrasives	0.997	S.S. = -6.02 + 0.83 p
9	Carborundum	0.999	S.S. = -7.43 + 0.86 p

* p: Concentration (ppm)

Besides if sea water is used it has something different effect
from pure water, which is probably due to ionization.
The following Table 4 shows an example of calibration relating
optical turbidity with S.S. through concentration by weight.

Table 4 Estimated S.S. by this apparatus

S.S. (J.I.S.)	0	29	83	135	179
Optical turbidity	1	22	84	140	180

After adjusting the k' and m dials, computing circuits
contained in the apparatus give indication, record and warning
sign of S.S. in turbid test water from measurement of intensities of both scattering and penetrated lights.
According to computation, deviation of S.S. at 90 ppm is ± 5
ppm under 95 percent of confidence limit so far as S.S. of the
test water is within a range of 0 - 180 ppm.
Although satisfactory results are obtained in an experimental
room, it is necessary to conduct field tests under rough and
unstable field conditions in addition to unknown sea-bottom
sediments.   Field tests are going to be conducted in near
future.
There are some problems to be discussed here for preparation

of test water.   Particles over 2 mm or under 1μm are
missing in S.S. or suspended solids determined by the J.I.S.
method because it specifies usage of wire screen and filtering
paper.
As to particles of large sizes in S.S. there is not a large
discrepancy between concentration and amount of S.S. by J.I.S.
method because those of large sizes set quickly in field and
are not contained mostly in sea water. [Nishimura,H. (1974),
Takeuchi, Y. (1974)]   For example, if sedimentation times in
still water of two sizes of particles , 5μm and 50μm are
computed by Stokes theory, both times for drop of 30 cm are
280 and 3 minutes respectively.
But as to particles of small sizes, there is a large discrepancy between the two, because test water specified by S.S. of
J.I.S. method does not contain those of small particles under
1μm .   [J.I.S. (1966),   J.I.S. (1974)]
It is unreasonable and even difficult to prepare such test
water which does not include minute particles less than 1μm,
while natural sea water contains a lot of those particles.
Thus the authors decided to calibrate the apparatus by using
concentration by weight or absolute density instead of using
amount of S.S. .
This apparatus which can measure turbidities of 0 to 180 ppm
appears to be practically satisfactory, because total amount
of minute particles in sea water such as spilt water from
reclamation or that at check points of dredging operation
may not exceed the upper limit of 180 ppm.

4. CONCLUSION

An automatic indicator for detecting the environmental pollution during the sea operation such as dredging, reclamation
and excavation is assembled by using a laser emitter, photo-
diode and computing circuits.
A series of tests has been conducted in an experimental room
under various conditions.
Various kinds of sample water under continuous agitation,
having turbidity from 0 to 180 ppm in S.S. are measured by
an optical device to detect intensities of scattering and
penetrated lights.   Those intensities of lights are correlated with S.S. or amount of suspended solids through intermediary of the concentration by weight.
The following conclusion is drawn :

(1) The optical turbidimeter using the laser and computer is
    practically effective for detecting environmental pollu-
    tion so far as experiments in laboratory are concerned.
(2) Logarithm of optical turbidity is determined by ratio of
    intensity of scattering to penetrated lights under the
    the following linear equation:
$$\log D = [k' + m (I_s/ I_t)]$$

Here, D is the optical turbidity,k' and m are constants
determined by calibration on various ingredients contained
in test water, I_s and I_t are intensities of scattering and
penetrated lights

(3) Logarithm of optical turbidity is connected with concentration by a simple linear equation, thus the concentration
of the turbid water can be measured and indicated by the
optical measurement.

(4) It is necessary to correlate concentration once more with
S.S. or amount of suspended solids in countries like Japan
where environmental regulation is specified by S.S..
This conversion is made   by computing circuits contained
in the apparatus, because the latter is related with the
former by a simple linear equation.

(5) Either analog or digital indication, record and warning
sign of turbid water can be easily obtained at any time
during operation by adjusting dials to take into account
of local characteristics of turbidity such as colors,
particle sizes and microscopic ingredients contained in
individual sea water.

Acknowledgiment

This study was conducted for a part of request by Bottom-
Sediments Mangement Association and the authors are much
indebted to Dr. T. Yoshida, a chairman of its engineering
research committee, Mr. M. Fukushima and Mr. M. Taguchi, members of the committee for a great deal of assistance.
The authors would like to thank Dr. H. Yokota, Optical Engineering and Dr. T. Sasaki,Science Department of Tokai University for valuable advices.

References

M.M.Assn(1974) Turbidity, S.S. and Color. Guide Book for
          Measurement of Public Pollution,Tokyo,:441-447
G.T.S.G.(1967) Measurement for Gradings of Granular Materials.
          Granular Technology Study Group Report,Tokyo
Hishida,K.(1972) Oceanic Optics. Oceanography,Japan,4,9:7-10
Hishida,K. et al.(1968) Automatic Turbidimeter. Jr. of Japan
          Oceanography Society,Tokyo,24,6:307-309
J.I.S.(1966) Testing Method for Use of Factory Water. Japan
          Industrial Standard,Japan, K 0-101
J.I.S.(1974) Testing Method for Discharged Water from Factories
          Japan Industrial Standard, Japan, K 0-102
Kubo, T(1969) Granular Materials. Tokyo
Nishimura,H.(1974) Effect of Dredging and Reclamation on Pollu-
          tion of Coast. Earth and Foundation,Japan,22,9:
          3-10
Sato,T.(1963) Integrated Turbidimeter and its Data.Water
          Disposal Technique,Tokyo,4,4.5.6.

Sato,T.(1962) Measurement of Turbidity bythe Integrated Turbi-
           dimeter. Water Disposal Technique,Tokyo $\underline{4}$: 37-42
Sugano,A.(1972) Measurement for Turbidity and Transparency.
           Industrial Water, Japan, $\underline{160}$: 9-16.
Sugano,A.(1975) Progress of Water Testing. Industrial Water,
           Tokyo,$\underline{200}$: 1-7
Takeuchi,Y.(1974) Dredging and Pollution. Reclamation and
           Dredging,Japan,59:7-22

FIRE DESIGN AND PROTECTION OF OFFSHORE STRUCTURES

Olav Furnes   Arne Sele

Det norske Veritas   Det norske Veritas

INTRODUCTION

It is initially convenient to classify fires associated with offshore installations in two groups:

1. Fires of global extent:
    Such fires are external to the structure and act upon a major portion of it. They will typically arise as the result of a large spill of hydrocarbons, such as may be associated with a blowout.

2. Fires of local extent:
    Such fires act upon a limited portion of the structure. They are normally contained within a limited number of compartments, and will most frequently arise as the result of the rupture of a transport or storage facility for hydrocarbons.

DnV operates a data base on offshore casualties going back to 1970. Table 1 which covers the period from 1/1 - 1970 to 1/1 - 1977, gives data regarding accidents where fire has been the primary effect.

It is seen that global fires causing a total structural loss are relatively infrequent and that no lives have been lost in connection with such fires in the period considered. The bulk of losses of structure and lives are clearly associated with local fires. Fires account for about 15% of accidents causing structural loss and 10% of fatalities when considering both fixed and floating structures. For fixed structures fires account for 25% of accidents causing structural loss and 60% of fatalities.

4.104

	STRUCTURAL LOSS					SUM
	TOTAL	SEVERE	DAMAGE	MINOR	NO	
NUMBER OF FIRES ON ALL TYPE OF UNITS	3	5	11	14	—	33
NUMBER OF FIRES ON FIXED STRUCTURES	2	5	6	8	—	21
NUMBER OF FATALITIES DUE TO FIRE ON ALL TYPES	—	7	2	3	—	12
NUMBER OF FATALITIES DUE TO FIRE ON FIXED STRUCTURES	—	7	2	3	—	12

Table 1   —   Offshore fires 1970-1977

Although limited, the above data indicate that localized fires contribute very significantly to losses especially in terms of fatalities on fixed structures. Emphasis should be put both on reducing fatalities and on ensuring that the consequences are not disproportionately large.

PROTECTIVE MEASURES AND DESIGN TARGETS

Although the consequence of a global fire is large the frequency of such events appear to be modest (table 1). It is at present not considered economically advantageous to provide structures which can sustain the full duration of such a fire. Human life must, however, always be protected by ensuring that the structure can sustain an exposure of adequate duration to ensure evacuation. The elements which require consideration are those parts of the primary structure which are externally exposed or will become so due to the failure of shielding secondary structure.

The frequency of local fires appears to be an order of magnitude larger. The main consideration in this case is, however, that the consequences are not disproportionately large. In order to achieve this the fire must be confined. It thus becomes necessary to consider both secondary structure and exposed primary structure.

Fjeld et. al. (1978) have analyzed crew risks on a large integrated platform. They conclude that the most significant passive protection is achieved by the provision of fire resistant (compartmentalising) walls. Amongst active measures they find sprinkler type systems moderately effective (90%). Shut down valves in the fire zone are not considered reliable. Mainly due to operational inabilities even in moderately rough weather, conventional fire fighting vessels are also considered of little value.

Based on the criteria that loss of lives should not occur
as a secondary consequence of an accidental fire, it is recommended that a safe haven is provided which can be safely
reached and in which the crew can find shelter until active
measures can be implemented to combat the fire. Thus the
following design criteria have been recommended:

Area of concern	Acceptable damage
One escape way	Only local damage the first 1 hour after initial event
Quarters	No damage the first 2 hours after initial event
Safe haven	No damage the first 6 hours after initial event
Main structural element	Only local damage the first 6 hours after initial event

Table 2 -   Design Criteria

ACTION OF GLOBAL TYPE FIRES

Flame surface temperatures of pool fires have been measured
for several hydrocarbons as shown in table 3.

REPORTED FLAME SURFACE TEMPERATURES OF POOL FIRES			
FUEL	TEMPERATURE (°K)	AUTHOR	METHOD
ETHANOL	1560	RASBASH ET AL	HOTTEL & BROUGHTON
BENZENE	1460	''	''
PETROL	1520	''	''
KEROSINE	1480	''	''
BENZENE	1450	KAHRS ET AL	SCANNING SPECTROMETRY
MIXED SOLVENT	1500	''	''

Table 3

It is seen that the data are all centered around 1 250°C
(2 300°F). An evaluation of the thermal insult can either
be based on this or on a semiempirical approach such as that
of Brown et al (1974):

$$q_s = q_{sm} (1-e^{-bD})$$

where: q_s = surface flux from a pool fire
q_{sm} = maximum surface flux for a large fire
b = size coefficient
D = fire diameter

For L.N.G. Fires q_{sm} = 37 000 kcal m^{-1} h^{-1}
and b = 0.018 m^{-1} has been found from experiments.

ACTION OF LOCAL TYPE FIRE

Kawagoe first formulated a heat balance equation for a compartamental fire and obtained a solution. This approach has been further developed by Ödeen, Magnusson and Thelandersson. The principal factor in these solutions is the opening factor:

$$\text{Opening factor} = \frac{A}{A_t} \sqrt{H}$$

where: A = Area of vertical ventilating openings
A_t = Area of the bounding surface of the compartment
H = Average height of ventilating openings

Also in this case it is necessary to calibrate in order to account for fuel type. Figure 1 shows typical predicted time-temperature curves for compartmental fires with fuel in the form of wood cribs. For the case of hydrocarbon pools, results are not available at present. It can, however, be expected that the results obtained for wood fueled fires will provide a reasonable assessment as long as the fire is ventilation controlled. As it can be seen from Fig. 2, most fuels appear to have approximately the same thermal yield per unit of oxygen.

Fuel bed controlled fires have been investigated (Magnusson 1971) for the case of wood cribs and furniture fuel. Such fires can be treated theoretically. In practice it will, however, be difficult to define the nature of the fuel bed adequately. It is of importance to note that the assumption of ventilation control will in all cases provide a conservative estimate. For the case of hydrocarbon fuels in particular it will until details of tests are available be necessary to assume ventilation control.

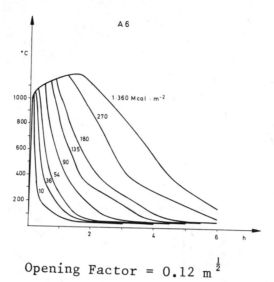

Opening Factor = 0.12 m $^{\frac{1}{2}}$

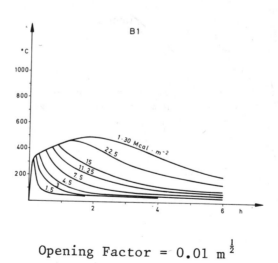

Opening Factor = 0.01 m $^{\frac{1}{2}}$

Fig. 1. From Magnusson and Thelandersson (1970)

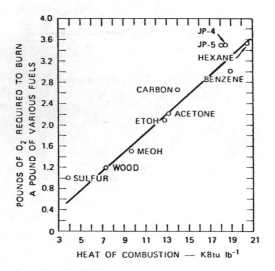

Fig. 2.

TRANSIENT TEMPERATURE DISTRIBUTION

The problem of obtaining closed form solutions for transient
temperature distributions including non-linearities has provided some restraint to theoretical methods of predicting
capacity of thermal exposure. The more recent development
of finite element programs and especially those employing
the superelement technique has made it possible to tackle
the most complex problems. Such programs have been developed by DnV and are included in the SESAM package. These
programs cater for the most complex three dimensional geometries, time variable heat source temperatures or fluxes and
time, location and temperature dependent thermal properties.
Designers and researchers are thus provided with a tool cate-
ring for all practically desireable levels of sophistication.

MATERIAL PROPERTIES OF THERMALLY EXPOSED STEEL

The thermal dilation of steel is about $12 \times 10^{-6} \, {}^{o}C^{-1}$ at $0^{o}C$
and increases slightly with increasing temperature. Above
$700^{o}C$ there is a slight contraction due to the austentite
transition whereupon the dilation continues at the same rate.

The thermal conductivity is high (approx. 40 kcal/m^{o}C) and
the thermal capacity approximately 70 kcal m^{-3} $^{o}C^{-1}$.

The tensile yield strength of steel reduces fairly uniformly
with increasing temperature.

The ultimate tensile strength tends to increase moderately
up to $300^{o}C$ for hot rolled steels and to decrease moderately
for cold worked steels.

Beyond approx. $300^{o}C$ there is a fairly uniform and rapid reduction in both cases. The strain at rupture increases with
increasing temperature.

The development of the modulus of elasticity with temperature
appears to vary significantly even for very similar steels.
The reduction in the modulus is, however, less than the reduction of the yield strength. Consequently the yield strain
will reduce with increasing temperature.

For fire exposed steel the primary creep is fairly insignificant, the dominant contribution being secondary creep. The
latter effect can be described by the following expression
(Lie (1972) and Harmathy et. al. (- -)):

$$\varepsilon_{ts} = Z \exp \left(\frac{\Delta H}{RT} \right)$$

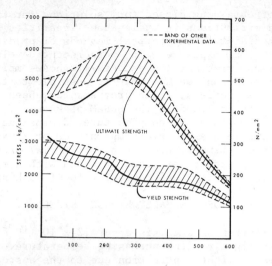

Strength of thermally
exposed steel

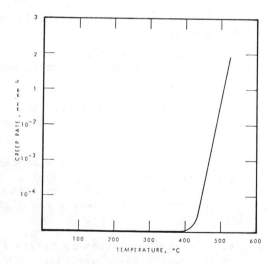

Creep of thermally
exposed steel

Fig. 3. from Lie (1972)

where: ε_{ts} = secondary creep rate
        Z^{ts} = Zener – Hollomon parameter (function of stress)
        ΔH = activation energy
        R = gas constant
        T = absolute temperature

This effect is illustrated in Fig. 3. At a certain critical temperature depending on type of steel and sustained stress, the creep rate increases very rapidly.

RESPONSE OF STEEL STRUCTURES

As steel members consist of small material thickness they will rapidly aquire the temperature of the surroundings if unprotected. In order to achieve any substantial capacity of resisting fire exposure some form of protection must be provided.

Due to the extreme rates of creep which are achieved above certain temperature levels both load capacity and deformations have to be considered when determining the member capacity for thermal exposure.

Robertson and Ryan and later Thor (1973) have proposed criteria for acceptable deformations in a fire situation. Robertson and Ryan's consideration is that there is no well defined yield stress of steel at elevated temperatures. The problem is of defining when a beam is no longer functional. They reasoned that a beam could suffer large deflections or could deflect at a high rate and yet be capable of supporting the imposed load. When, however, the deflection and the rate of deflection both were large it could be taken that the beam no longer could become stable.

Thor takes a more practical approach and suggests that when deflections become excessive supports will be lost and the structure will fail. He also shows that for practical cases such a deflection criteria will be associated with a high rate of deflection in any case. Thus the following criterion is proposed:

$$Y = \frac{L^2}{800h}$$

where: L = distance between points of zero moment
        h = beam depth
        Y = central deflection of beam

INSULATION

The traditional approach to obtaining a significant resistance to fire exposure from steel structures has been to provide thermal insulation. Traditionally plaster and concrete

4.112

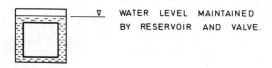

WATER LEVEL MAINTAINED
BY RESERVOIR AND VALVE.

Fig. 4.

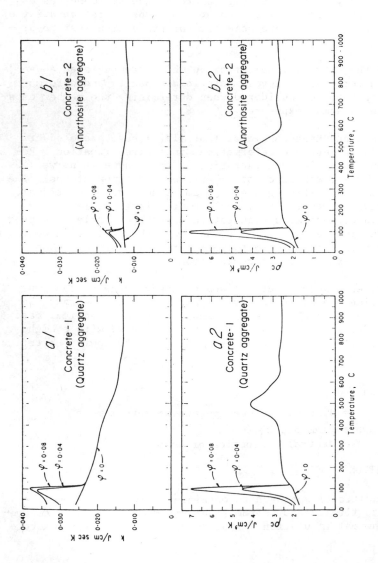

Fig. 5. Thermal properties of thermally exposed concrete.
From Harmathy (1965).

have been used. These are now largely being replaced by pro-
prietary coatings containing fibers or refractory materials.
Recently the development of intumescent coatings has also
regained momentum.

WATER COOLING

Although this method of fire protection was conceived in the
last century it has only found application in recent years.
So far, water cooling has in essence only been applied to non-
horizontal members. The problem of formation of steam pockets
at flow restrictions has, to date, prevented any significant
application to horizontal members.

It is tentatively suggested that these considerations may be
overcome by providing a non-structural external water retai-
ning skin and filling the cavity rather than the actual member as shown in principle in Fig. 4.

The upper void permits the recirculation of steam. Alternatively steam may be permitted to dissipate directly by per-
forating or omitting the top cover. In the case of large
members it is anticipated that the weight penalty will be
modest.

MATERIAL PROPERTIES OF THERMALLY EXPOSED CONCRETE

Due to the heterogenous nature of concrete its response to
thermal exposure is more complex. In addition to this, concrete structures contain varying amounts of steel reinforcement which adds further complicating aspects.

Harmathy (1965) has developed data for extreme values of concretes thermal capacity and conductivity. These properties
principally depend upon humidity and aggregate and are shown
in Fig. 5.

It is seen that when present, moisture contributes significantly both to capacity and conductivity in the initial phase.
The second peak in the heat capacity curve is mainly due to
the dehydration of calcium hydroxide.

The strength of thermally exposed concrete is principally dependant on aggregate and stress history and decreases with
increasing temperature as shown in Fig. 6 and 7. For loaded
specimens especially, there is a pronounced difference in
performance between silicious and non-silicious aggregate.

The modulus of elasticity also decreases with increasing
temperature.

Several similar relationships have been proposed to describe
thermal creep. One such form is:

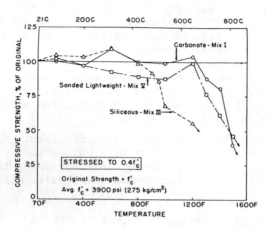

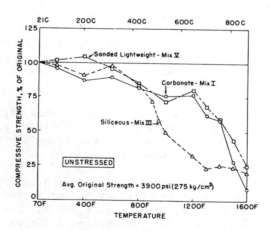

Fig. 6.   Compressive strength of thermally exposed
          concrete.   From Abrams (1968)

4.115

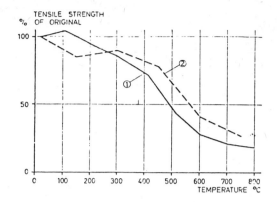

Fig. 7. Tensile strength of
thermally exposed
concrete.
From Thelandersson
(1972).

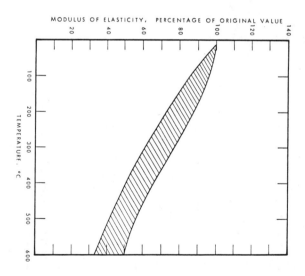

Fig. 8. Modulus of elasticity
for concrete.
From Lie (1972).

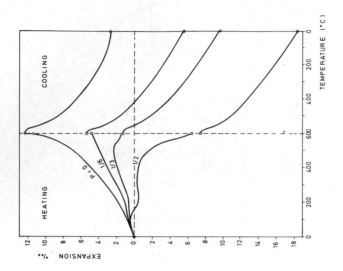

Fig. 10. Thermal dilation of concrete under stress. From Weigler and Fischer (1968).

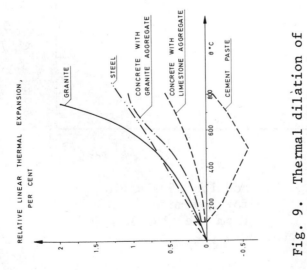

Fig. 9. Thermal dilation of unstressed specimens. From Petterson (1965).

$$\varepsilon_c = B \log (t + 1)$$

where: ε_c = strain in percent
B = constant
t = time in hours

From data given by Cruz, Maréchal and Gvozdev one can obtain the following expressions for creep at $400^{\circ}C$ under 45% of ultimate stress at $20^{\circ}C$:

For quartz aggregate concrete: $\varepsilon_c = 0.3 \log_{10} (t + 1)$
For calcareous aggregate concrete: $\varepsilon_c = 1.4 \log_{10} (t + 1)$

The above is based on too sparse data to have general application. It does, however, appear that calcareous aggregate concrete suffers creep strains which are substantially greater than for quartz aggregate concrete.

The thermal expansion of unrestrained and unstressed concrete depends primarily on the aggregate. When concrete is heated under constant stress the dilation is substantially reduced, and at high levels of stress contraction is observed. Only a small fraction of this stress induced deformation is due to creep and recoverable elastic deformation. The major effect is irreversible transient thermal strain.

Little is published on concretes strain at fracture. It has been found that concretes strain at the point of maximum stress increases with increasing temperature for specimens unstressed during heating. For stressed specimens it does, however, appear that the ultimate strain is not significantly affected by heating.

RESPONSE OF CONCRETE STRUCTURES

In spite of sparse and incomprehensive data, it is already at this stage possible to predict the response of concrete elements to fire exposure with reasonable accuracy. Concrete structures derive their high fire resistive capacity mainly from their relatively large cross sectional dimensions. Initially only the surface layers are significantly degraded by the action of fire. The core and reinforcement retain their initial properties for a prolonged period due to the thermal protection provided by the surface layer, providing this remains intact. Thus calculations on element strength are not grossly vulnerable to inaccurate assumptions regarding the thermal material properties.

Principally due to the transient strain of concrete, thermal restraint forces are significantly smaller than indicated by the unrestrained thermal expansion. It is worth noting that the thermal restraint forces will not at any time exceed the

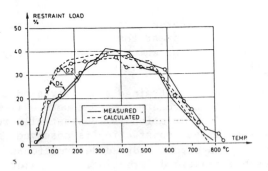

Measured and calculated restraint load (in per cent of
ultimate load at ambient conditions) as a function of
temperature for specimens being heated under fully restrained
expansion. Rate of heating: 5° C · min^{-1} (D2) and 1° C · min^{-1} (D4)

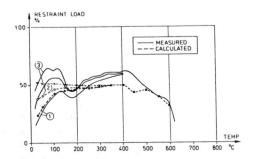

Measured (full lines) and calculated (dashed lines)
restraint load (per cent of ambient strength) as a function
of temperature for specimens heated under fully restrained
expansion. Rate of heating: 2° C · min^{-1}. Initial loading:
15 (1), 30 (2) and 45 % (3) of ultimate load at ambient
conditions.

Fig. 11.   From Anderberg and Thelandersson (1976).

crushing strength of thermally exposed concrete. Thus restrained thermal expansion cannot induce crushing alone or
in combination with an initially sustainable preload.

SPALLING OF REINFORCED CONCRETE

The bulk of traditional construction is subject to the requirement that it shall be capable of sustaining one to two
hours fire exposure. Spalling substantially occurs subsequent
to 10 to 30 minutes of exposure to the standard type fire
tests. The standard fire curves can in general terms be taken as an upper limit of the exposure suffered in a normal
building fire. For less onerous exposures, the tendency to
spall can be anticipated to reduce considerably. The overall significance of spalling is thus modest and furthermore
catered for in a general way by the traditional test performance based design.

Offshore structures subject to hydrocarbon fires will in most
cases almost instantaneously be subject to high temperatures
exceeding those of the standard fire curve. Consequently
very steep thermal gradients will be achieved in exposed concrete. Furthermore there is the requirement of substantially
larger periods of safe exposure and tight restrictions on
the weight and dimensions of structural members. Spalling
causing premature degradation of the reinforcement thus
possibly takes on quite different order of significance in
this context.

So far efforts specifically aimed at investigating spalling
of thermally exposed concrete are limited. Three effects
have been considered as contributing to this phenomenon:

1.   Thermally unsound aggregate particles:
      A number of investigators have registered that aggregate
      particles which exhibit physiochemical transitions ac-
      companied by substantial expansion cause spalling in the
      form of local popouts. It has been believed that the
      transition from α-quartz to β-quartz at 575°C also has
      this effect. The accompanying volumetric expansion is,
      however, only relatively moderate of the order of 2.5%.
      Available evidence suggests that this is at most a
      secondary effect.

      In the case of concrete exposed to hydrocarbon fire,
      the subsequent conversion from β-quartz to tridymite
      occuring at 810°C and causing a 14% volumetric expansion
      could be highly significant and deserves further inves-
      tigation.

2. Moisture spalling:
   Nekrasov has shown that moisture pressures in refractory concretes can be a principle cause of spalling. The permeability of this concrete was, however, artificially reduced by the addition of finely ground aggregates. It still remains to establish how substantial this effect is in relation to normal structural concrete. This obviously is of primary concern in offshore applications.

3. Spalling due to thermal dilation of surface layers:
   This general concept has traditionally been widely held to be a primary cause of spalling. In view of the recent findings regarding the magnitude of the transient strains in thermally exposed concrete, it appears that this effect must be discounted as a possible cause of spalling.

Moisture and thermally unsound aggregate can, however, not account for all phenomena observed in connection with spalling. It is particularly notable that reinforced concrete is far more prone to spall than plain concrete. In view of this a fourth effect merits investigation:

4. Spalling by bond failure:
   It has been observed that thermally induced compressive stresses in the surface layers of exposed concrete, cause tensile cracking in the cool central core. In this event the induced tensile force will be transferred to the reinforcement at the location of the crack, but not remotely from this location. Thus bond stresses will be set up in the reinforcement.

   Due to thermal exposure, the tensile strength of the concrete in the surface layer will deteriorate. As a consequence the bond strength will also deteriorate.

   The combined effect of bond strength deterioration and bond stresses induced at cracks, could cause failure by spalling as observed in the case of high bond stresses at splices (Tepfers (1973)).

CONCLUSION

Substantial progress has been made in the field of structural fire engineering in recent years. As a result of this, rational design requirements are beginning to replace the traditional empirical approach in several structural codes. Due to the large sizes of structural components, the traditional test based design methods are anyhow hardly feasable in the case of offshore structures. The evaluation of fire exposure performance will thus largely have to be based on analysis.

Offshore fires differ from onshore fires in that they involve
a hydrocarbon fuel which results in substantially higher temperatures at a very early point in the development of a fire.
Due to the restraints on personnel evacuation and the lack of
reliable active protection, it is necessary to provide for a
substantial passive protection in order to achieve adequate
crew safety.

For steel structures it thus has become desireable to concentrate on developing passive protection systems with a capacity for sustaining long and intensive fire exposures. Concrete
structures have a far greater capacity to sustain fire exposure. For the cross sectional sizes typical of offshore
structures, material deterioration of the outer layer will not
significantly reduce the load capacity of the gross section.
Spalling will tend to be the effect determining the element's
performance.

REFERENCES

Abrams, M.S. (1978) "Compressive Strengths of Concrete at
Temperatures to 1 600°F". Portland Cement Association, Ser.
1387-1.

Anderberg, Y. and Thelandersson, S. (1976) "Stress and Deformation Characteristics of Concrete at High Temperatures -
Part 2". Lund.

Brown, L.E., Wesson, H.R. and Welker, J.R. (May 1974)
"Predict LNG Fire Radiation". Hydrocarbon Processing.

Fjeld, S., Andersen, T., Myklatun, B. (1978) "Risk Analysis
of Offshore Production and Drilling platform". 10th Offshore
Technology Conference, Houston, OTC 3152

Harmathy, T.Z. (1965) "Effect of Moisture on the Fire Endurance of Building Elements". A.S.I.M. special technical publication No. 385.

Harmathy, T.Z. and Stanzak "Elevated - Temperature Tensile
and Creep Properties of Some Structural and Prestressing
Steels". A.S.T.M. Special Technical Publication 464.

Lie, T.T. (1972) "Fire and Buildings". Applied Science Pub-
lishers, London.

Magnusson, S.E. and Thelandersson, S. (1970) "Temperature -
Time Curves of Complete Process of Fire Development". Acta
Polytechnica Scandinavia, No. 65, Stockholm.

Magnusson, S.E. and Thelandersson, (1971) "Comments on Rate
of Gas Flow and Rate of Burning for Fires in Enclosures".
Lund Institute of Technology, Lund, Sweden.

Petterson, O. (1965) "Structural Fire Engineering Research
Today and Tomorrow". Acta Polytechnica Scandinavia, No. 33,
Stockholm.

Tepfers, R. (1973) "A Theory of Bond Applied to Overlapped
Tensile Reinforcement Splices for Deformed Bars". Chalmers
University of Technology, Division of Concrete Structures,
Publication 73:2, Gothenburg.

Thelandersson, S. (1972) "Effect of High Temperatures on Tensile Strength of Concrete". Nordisk Betong, No. 2.

Thor, J. (1973) "Deformation and Critical Loads of Steel
Beams under Fire Exposure Conditions". Nat. Swedish Inst.
for Building Research, Stockholm.

Weigler, H. and Fischer, R. (Feb. 1968) "Beton bei Tempera-
turen von $100^{\circ}C$ bis $750^{\circ}C$". Beton, No. 2.

Welker, J.R. and Sliepcevich, C.M. (1970) "Susceptibility of
Target Components to Defeat by Thermal Action". University
of Oklahoma Research Institute Report, No. OURI - 1578 - Fr.
Noumann, Oklahoma.

Appendix
The effect of the preceeding treatment is illustrated with
the following simple example:

Scenario:
A 6 x 6 x 3 m high room contains a 5 m^3 tank for hydrocarbon
fuel:
Density   : 0.8
Calorific value: 10 Mkal/kg
Oxygen demand : 11 m^3 air/kg

For wood we have:
Calorific value: 4.5 Mkal/kg
Oxygen demand : 5.0 m^3 air/kg

Apart from the fire hazard there is an explosion hazard. It
is thus desirable for the latter purpose to provide as large
a deflagration vent as practical. Two vent sizes are considered:

1) Height = 2   m   width = 6.0 m   opening factor = 0.12 $m^{\frac{1}{2}}$
2) Height = 1.5 m   width = 0.8 m   opening factor = 0.01 $m^{\frac{1}{2}}$

The horizontal structure forming the ceiling is required to
sustain an imposed design load of 10 kNm^{-2}. The portion of
the load sustained during a fire exposure is estimated at
5 kNm^{-2}.

Two different structures are investigated:

1)   200 mm concrete slabs. The slabs are encastré and two
      way spanning and have a 50 mm screed. The concrete is
      grade 30 and the reinforcement is 10 mm cold worked bars
      with a characteristic strength of 460 MPa at 250 mm
      centers with 25 mm cover.

2)   A steel structure clad with corrugated sheeting and with
      steel plate floors. The floors are supported on simply
      supported one way spanning HE 200 - A at 2 m centers.

Fire load: $5 \times 800 \times 10/144 = 275$ MCalm^{-2}.

Fig. A2 shows the calculated temperature distribution when the
concrete slab is subjected to the fire with the small vent.
After 4 hours the steel temperature will only have reached
350°C and only 20 mm of concrete will have been subjected to
temperatures exceeding 400°C. It is thus immediately seen
that the section has suffered no significant loss of load capacity at this advanced stage providing it has remained intact. From this point in time deflection will, however,
start to increase more rapidly as creep of the bottom reinforcement starts to take significant effect.

Due to the end fixity there will be induced a net axial force.
Cracking will occur after about 4 hours and will cause the
bars to yield. Cracking in the first direction can be anticipated to occur at random centres with a minimum spacing
of about 200 mm. Due to the bond stresses induced, it is
anticipated that cracking in the second direction will be
induced at bar centres = 250 mm. (Tepfers (1973)). This
will cause the bond stresses (σ) to distribute uniformly
along these bars.

Bar force = 0.036 MN

Due to bars with uniform
bond stress: $\sigma = \dfrac{4 \times 0.036}{\pi \times 0.1 \times 0.25} = 1.8$ MPa

Due to bars with no
uniform bond stress: $\kappa^2 = \dfrac{4 \times 270 \times 30}{10 \times 0.2 \times 10^6} = (0.127/mm)^2$

$\sigma = \dfrac{10^2 \times 0.127 \times 400}{4 \times 0.250} = 5.0$ MPa

The tensile strength of the concrete at the level of the
reinforcement is of the order of 3 MPa $<(5.0 + 1.8)$ MPa and
thus spalling must be anticipated. Subsequent to spalling
it must be anticipated that the slabs flexural load capacity
will deteriorate very rapidly due to the direct exposure of
the reinforcement.

The calculated temperature history of the same slab subject to the fire with the large vent is shown in Fig. A3. In this case cracking will occur after about two hours and as in the previous case this will result in spalling.

As seen from the plot of load capacity, the slab will not fail due to loss of strength in this case. This is due to the beneficial effect of continuity which is mainly due to that the support moment capacity is only marginally reduced. If the slab were simply supported and required to carry the full design load, it would fail due to insufficient load capacity after $1\frac{1}{2}$ hours.

The limiting condition in this case is thus spalling and also deflection which would start increasing very rapidly after about 2 hours. (In the case of a simply supported slab, spalling would also be anticipated to occur at a very much earlier time).

Uninsulated steel will virtually follow the temperature of the fire. In the case of the small vent it is immediately seen that the beams will not fail due to insufficient load capacity. Deflection will be the limiting criteria. Using mild steel, the beams can be anticipated to sustain one hours exposure to this fire before deflection becomes excessive. The deflection will, however, be sensitive to moderate increases in temperature.

In practice it will normally be necessary to provide insulation in order to limit the temperature rise on the unexposed surface. The beneficial effect of this will, however, be partially offset by the increased temperature within the compartment.

With the large vent structural failure will be almost immediate if the steel is uninsulated.

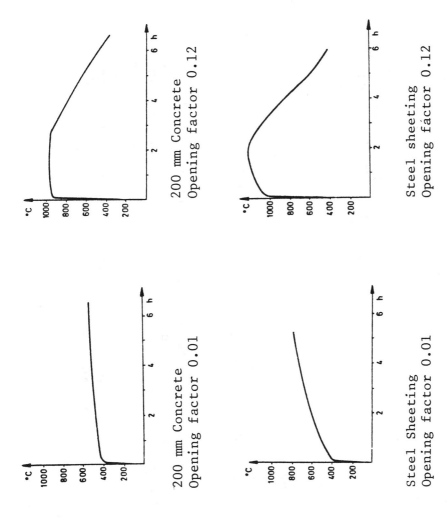

Fig. Al — Time-temperature curves for the fire.

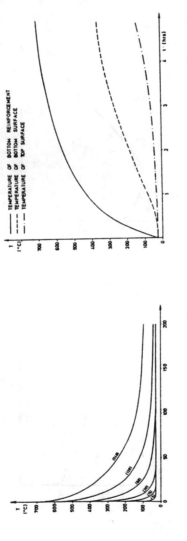

Time—temperature curves for
various locations in the
slab.

Temperature distribution
through cross section
for 5, 15, 30, 60, 120
240 mins. exposure.

Fig. A2 — Thermal distribution in slab subject to fire with
opening factor of 0.01 m^2.

Temperature distribution
through cross section
for 5, 10, 15, 30, 60,
120, 240 and 360 mins.
exposure.

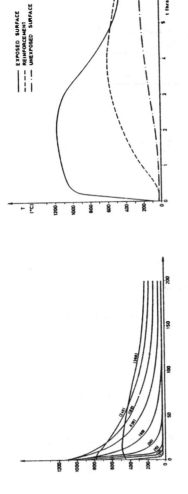

Time-temperature curves for
various locations in the
slab.

Fig. A3 – Thermal distribution in slab subject to fire with
opening factor of 0.12 m$^{\frac{1}{2}}$.

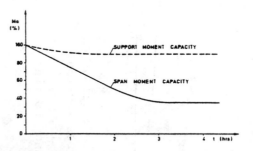

Fig. A4 - Development of moment capacity.

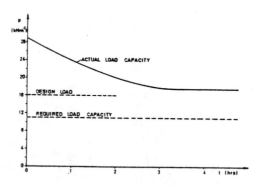

Fig. A5 - Development of load capacity.

ECRAN DE PROTECTION ANTI-COLLISION

A. Vitalis, R. Lacroix, B. Bonnemaire

Sea Tank Co

1. INTRODUCTION

Le système proposé ici est un écran de protection flottant et
autonome, capable de protéger tout obstacle, naturel ou arti-
ficiel, des dangers de collision. Sa taille, ainsi que sa géométrie, varient pour s'adapter à chaque type d'application,
dont quelques exemples sont énumérés ci-dessous :

- protection de sites côtiers, ou de structures offshore, situés en bordure de voies maritimes très
  fréquentées ;
- protection, contre les icebergs à la dérive, des
  structures offshore opérant en zone arctique ;
- protection de musoirs et de toute avancée artifi-
  cielle en mer ;
- délimitation des chenaux d'accès et des zones
  d'évitage, etc...

L'originalité du système réside dans les points mentionnés ci-
dessous :

- il peut, de par sa conception, s'adapter à de nombreux cas de protection ;
- il peut stopper un navire sans l'endommager ;
- l'écran de protection reste opérationnel après une
  collision ;
- il est enfin adaptable à toute profondeur d'eau du
  site.

2. DESCRIPTION GENERALE

2.1. Principe du système

Le principe du dispositif présenté est de développer, pendant
son action, une puissance d'amortissement suffisante pour an-
nuler l'énergie cinétique du corps flottant en mouvement, stop-
pant ainsi sa course à une distance raisonnable de la zone à
protéger.

Cette fonction est assurée grâce aux propriétés élastiques des aussières en nylon, qui peuvent supporter de grandes charges, tout en conservant un bon coefficient d'élasticité. Ainsi, en cas de collision, l'énergie développée par la déformation des lignes d'ancrage en nylon permet de stopper le navire.

2.2. Arrangement général
Les principaux constituants du système de protection (voir figures 1 et 2) sont :
- un écran flottant de forme polygonale, entourant partiellement ou entièrement le site à protéger. Chaque côté de l'écran comporte plusieurs câbles, tendus entre 2 flotteurs principaux situés à chaque extrémité, et maintenus au niveau de l'eau par quelques flotteurs intermédiaires ;
- des lignes d'ancrage, constituées de chaînes et de câbles nylon, connectées aux flotteurs principaux. L'ancrage proprement dit est effectué par ancres ou par pieux battus, suivant la nature du terrain et l'effort de retenue demandé. Ces lignes d'ancrage sont mises en tension, de manière à retenir le système polygonal en équilibre.

2.3. Action de l'écran
Quand un navire dérive sur le système de protection, il déforme l'écran polygonal, entraînant avec lui les flotteurs principaux, ce qui tend les lignes d'ancrage en nylon. Le navire est ainsi stoppé par l'énergie emmagasinée, puis repoussée jusqu'à ce que l'écran de protection retrouve un nouvel état d'équilibre. Le système retient ainsi le navire en difficulté, l'empêchant de récidiver, jusqu'à ce qu'il se soit dégagé de lui-même, ou aidé par un navire de secours.

2.4. Capacité du système
Les études entreprises sur le sujet, et brièvement exposées ci-après, ont permis de déterminer les dimensionnements respectifs des composants. Pour permettre une action efficace et une ré-utilisation immédiate de l'écran, un facteur de sécurité de 2, par rapport aux taux de travail maximal, a été pris en compte, qui s'applique :
- sur le dimensionnement de tous les constituants, spécialement les lignes d'ancrage nylon et les câbles de l'écran horizontal ;
- sur la réserve de flottabilité :
  . des flotteurs principaux, soumis aux réactions verticales de lignes d'ancrage en nylon ;
  . des flotteurs intermédiaires, sur lesquels le navire à la dérive peut exercer une action verticale et qui doivent donc toujours maintenir l'écran horizontal en surface ;

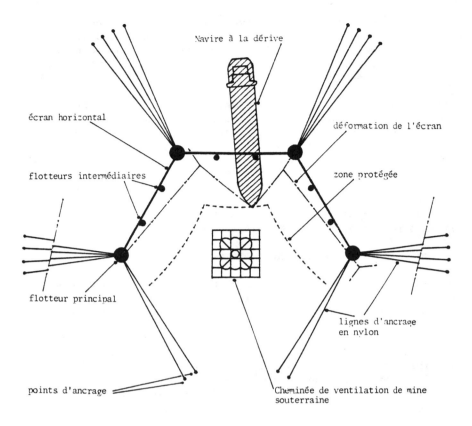

Navire à la dérive

écran horizontal

déformation de l'écran

flotteurs intermédiaires

zone protégée

flotteur principal

lignes d'ancrage
en nylon

points d'ancrage

Cheminée de ventilation de mine
souterraine

Figure 1 : ECRAN DE PROTECTION - VUE EN PLAN

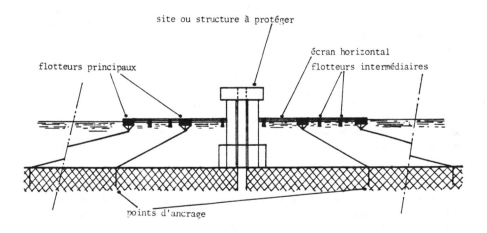

site ou structure à protéger

écran horizontal

flotteurs principaux

flotteurs intermédiaires

points d'ancrage

Figure 2 : ECRAN DE PROTECTION - ELEVATION

- sur la zone effective à protéger, c'est-à-dire que la déformation maximale de l'écran polygonal ne doit pas excéder la moitié de la distance initiale entre le système de protection et la structure à préserver.

Les études effectuées à ce jour ont porté principalement sur un écran de protection de gros gabarit, le but visé étant de stopper un navire de 400,000 DWT dérivant à 3 noeuds. Le dimensionnement d'un tel système peut paraître énorme a priori, et le coût assez élevé, mais comme le montrent les figures 1 et 2, il peut être justifié, par exemple, dans le cas de la protection impérative d'une structure offshore de ventilation de mine souterraine, située en bordure d'une voie maritime. Il est évident que pour des protections moins ambitieuses, les structures finales seront beaucoup plus légères, et de moindre coût.

3. ETUDE DU COMPORTEMENT DE L'ECRAN

Le comportement du système de protection soumis à un choc a été étudié sur ordinateur grâce à un programme de simulation qui détermine la déformation maximale de l'écran polygonal. Ce programme calcule dans un premier temps la loi de comportement des lignes d'ancrage en nylon, et applique ces résultats à une série de configurations de l'écran, chacune représentant un choc possible. On obtient ainsi les déformations maximales du système de protection pour des collisions venant de toute incidence, l'enveloppe de celles-ci délimitant la zone effectivement protégée.

Outre la représentation de l'écran de protection soumis à un choc, le programme donne, pour chaque cas considéré, les taux de travail de câbles en nylon et des côtés horizontaux, ainsi que l'énergie emmagasinée par chaque ligne d'ancrage. Cela a permis d'affiner le dimensionnement de chaque composant, pour arriver à la capacité requise, en respectant partout le coefficient de sécurité de 2.

3.1. Comportement d'un câble tressé en nylon
Le fabricant a donné les courbes d'élasticité de ce type de cordage tressé en nylon. Il faut préciser, et c'est ce qui justifie le fonctionnement du système de protection, que les taux d'allongement de ces aussières sont importants : ils atteignent 25 % sous la demi charge de rupture, et 33 % à la rupture.

Connaissant ces caractéristiques, il faut adapter la longueur et la taille du cordage à la profondeur d'eau du site, de manière à atteindre la capacité d'amortissement requise, tout en veillant à ce que la déformation de l'écran polygonal ne lui fasse pas perdre une partie de son efficacité.

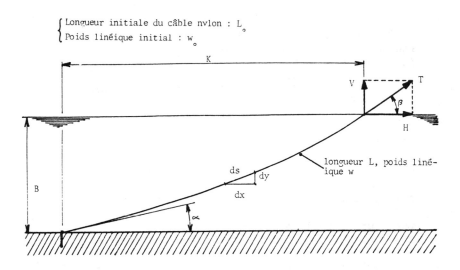

$\begin{cases} \text{Longueur initiale du câble nylon : } L_o \\ \text{Poids linéique initial : } w_o \end{cases}$

longueur L, poids linéique w

Figure 3 : PARAMETRES DES LIGNES D'ANCRAGE

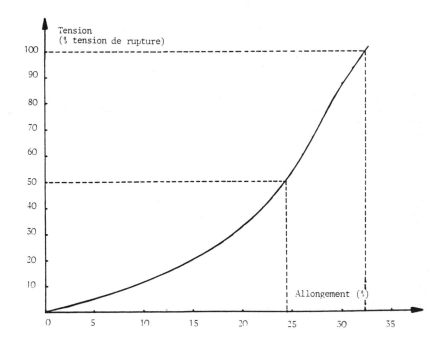

Figure 4 : COURBE TENSION - ALLONGEMENT D'UN CABLE VIKING BRAIDLINE NYLON

Les paramètres sont définis comme suit (voir figure 3) :

H : Effort horizontal exercé sur le câble.
T : Tension exercée dans le câble.
L_o : Longueur à vide du câble nylon.
L : Longueur sous charge du câble nylon.
w_o : Poids linéique déjaugé du câble nylon à vide.
w : Poids linéique déjaugé du câble nylon sous charge :

$$w = \frac{w_o \, L_o}{L}$$

B : Distance verticale entre les points haut et bas de la ligne d'ancrage.
K : Distance horizontale entre les points haut et bas de la ligne d'ancrage.
t : Allongement du câble nylon : $t = \dfrac{L - L_o}{L_o}$

s : Longueur de câble soulevé.
β : Angle du câble avec l'horizontale au point haut.

Les calculs ultérieurs nécessitent la connaissance de 2 lois :
- la loi K = K(H), qui lie le déplacement horizontal du flotteur à l'effort extérieur exercé, et qui permettra de calculer la déformation de l'écran,
- la loi E = E(H), qui lie l'énergie emmagasinée par le câble nylon à l'effort extérieur exercé, pendant son passage de l'état d'équilibre à une nouvelle position instantanée ; cette loi permettra de connaître, pour chaque configuration de choc, le travail développé par l'écran, ainsi que la contribution de chaque ligne d'ancrage.

3.11. <u>Loi K = K(H)</u> Cette loi résulte de l'écriture de l'équation de la chaînette, pour un câble pesant élastique de longueur L = L(H). Elle est déterminée à partir de la courbe T = T(t), donnée par le constructeur (voir figure 4), et qui peut être exprimée par une relation du type :

$$T(t) = T_o + a \, \text{Argsinh} \, m \, (t - t_o) \tag{1}$$

A titre d'exemple, cette loi est approximée, pour un câble Viking Braidline nylon de 21" de circonférence, par l'équation :

$$T(t) = 400 + 158.84 \, \text{Argsinh} \, \left[22.01 \, (t - 0.28)\right] \tag{1'}$$

L'équation de la déformée du câble s'écrit :

$$Y = \frac{H}{w} \cdot \cosh \left[\frac{wx}{H} + C_1\right] + C_2 \tag{2}$$

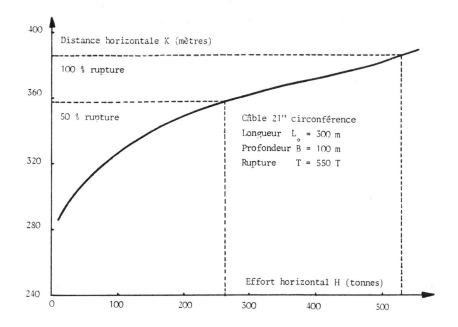

Figure 5 : LOI DEPLACEMENT - EFFORT HORIZONTAL D'UN CABLE VIKING BRAIDLINE NYLON

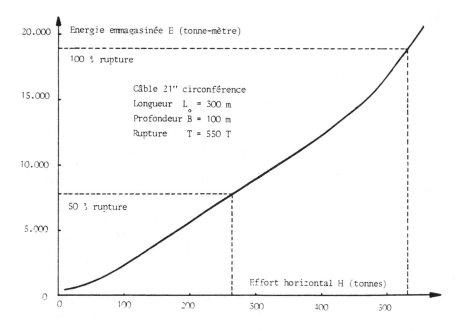

Figure 6 : LOI ENERGIE EMMAGASINEE - EFFORT HORIZONTAL D'UN CABLE VIKING BRAIDLINE NYLON

Les conditions aux bornes donnent les relations :

$$C_1 = \text{Argsinh} \frac{B}{\sqrt{L(H)^2 - B^2}} - \frac{wK}{2H} \qquad (3)$$

$$C_2 = -\frac{H}{w} \cosh C_1 \qquad (4)$$

On obtient ainsi la relation :

$$K = \frac{2H}{w} \cdot \text{Argsinh} \frac{w}{2H} \sqrt{L(H)^2 - B^2} \qquad (5)$$

qui permet d'établir la variation de K en fonction de H, à partir du moment où est connue la loi L = L(H).

La tension au point haut de l'ancrage vaut :

$$T(t) = \frac{H}{\cos \beta} \quad \text{avec :}$$

$$\cos \beta = \left(\frac{dx}{ds}\right)_{x=K} = \left[1 / \sqrt{1 + \left(\frac{dy}{dx}\right)^2}\right]_{x=K} \qquad (6)$$

d'après (2), on obtient :

$$\frac{1}{\cos \beta} = \frac{T(t)}{H} = \cosh \left[\frac{wk}{H} + C_1\right] \qquad (7)$$

Prenant les valeurs de C_1 et K dans les équations (3) et (5), on obtient :

$$T(t) - \frac{B L_o w_o}{2L} = \sqrt{\frac{H^2 L^2}{L^2 - B^2} + \frac{L_o^2 w_o^2}{4}} \qquad (8)$$

Cette relation permet, associée à l'équation (1), de calculer H en fonction de L, et donc d'établir la loi L = L(H). En réinjectant cette dernière dans l'équation (5), on détermine ainsi la loi K = K(H) (voir figure 5).

3.12. Loi E = E(H) L'énergie emmagasinée par le câble, lors du déplacement du flotteur soumis à un effort extérieur H, est calculée par intégration de la courbe H = H(K). La figure 6 montre la quantité d'énergie d'amortissement developpée par un échantillon de câble Viking nylon Braidline de 21" de circonférence.

3.13. Comportement d'une ligne d'ancrage Chaque ligne d'ancrage étant composée de plusieurs câbles nylon, il suffit de multiplier les résultats précédents pour connaître le déplacement et l'énergie emmagasinée par un mouillage dont le flotteur est soumis à un effort H.

Il faut noter que, dans le cas exposé ici, la capacité d'absorption d'énergie vient en grande partie de l'élasticité du matériau, la souplesse donnée par le travail de la ligne en chaînette intervenant pour peu. Il est cependant possible, notamment dans les cas d'une profondeur d'eau importante ou d'une capacité de retenue faible, d'imaginer le système de protection équipé de lignes d'ancrages plus classiques, leur élasticité provenant plus du travail en fil pesant que de l'allongement du matériau.

3.2. Comportement de l'écran horizontal

L'écran horizontal de protection est constitué, entre chaque flotteur principal retenant les lignes d'ancrage en nylon, de plusieurs câbles tendus ; on obtient ainsi une forme polygonale entourant la structure à protéger. Chaque côté de l'écran comporte un certain nombre de flotteurs intermédiaires, destinés à supporter les câbles, et à empêcher l'écran de s'échapper sous le navire.

3.21. Comportement d'un côté de l'écran

Les câbles horizontaux se comportent comme une succession de chaînettes symétriques, séparées par chaque flotteur (voir figure 7). Soit :

f : Effort horizontal exercé en chaque extrémité d'un câble d'un côté de l'écran.

N : Nombre de tronçons d'un côté, correspondant à (N-1) flotteurs intermédiaires.

n : Nombre de câbles tendus horizontaux

l_0 : Longueur de câble à vide entre chaque flotteur.

p_0 : Poids linéique du câble.

D : Distance horizontale entre 2 flotteurs principaux.

T : Tension en un point courant du câble.

La relation liant D à F = nf tient compte de l'effet de chaînette des câbles, ainsi que de l'élasticité du matériau.

a) Si nous négligeons dans un premier temps l'élasticité, l'équation de la déformée, pour un tronçon de longueur l_0, s'écrit:

$$Y = \frac{f}{p_0} \left[\cosh \left(\frac{p_0 x}{f} \right) - 1 \right] \qquad (9)$$

On en déduit la distance horizontale entre deux flotteurs :

$$d_1 = \frac{2f}{p_0} \text{ Argsinh } \frac{p_0 l_0}{2f} \qquad (10)$$

b) L'élasticité de la ligne est prise en compte de la manière suivante : le câble ayant une nouvelle longeur l et un poids linéique p, tels que :

$$p_0 l_0 = pl \qquad (11)$$

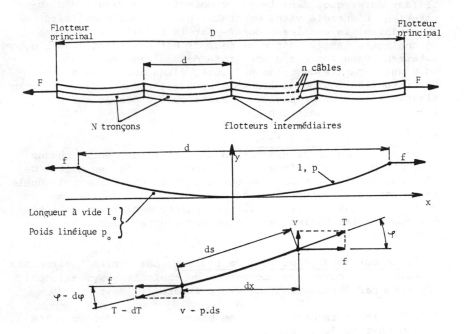

Figure 7 : PARAMETRES DE L'ECRAN HORIZONTAL

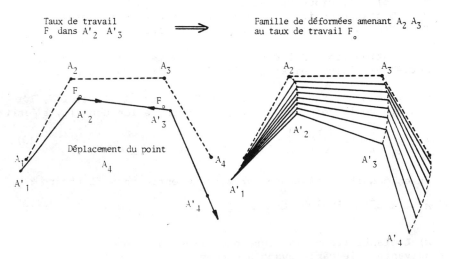

Taux de travail F_o dans A'_2 A'_3 $\Longrightarrow$ Famille de déformées amenant A_2 A_3 au taux de travail F_o

Déplacement du point A_4

Figure 8 : FAMILLE DE DEFORMEES DE L'ECRAN

Sa déformée s'écrit :

$$Y = \frac{f}{p} \left[\cosh \left(\frac{px}{f} \right) - 1 \right] \qquad (12)$$

si nous approximons sa nouvelle forme à une chaînette.
Compte tenu de la relation (11), et du fait que :

$$T = \frac{f}{\cos \varphi} = f \sqrt{1 + tg^2 \varphi} = f \sqrt{1 + \left(\frac{dy}{dx} \right)^2}$$

nous établissons l'équation :

$$T = f \cosh \frac{p_o \, l_o \, x}{fl} \qquad (13)$$

L'allongement élastique de l'élément ds s'écrit :

$$\frac{\Delta ds}{ds} = \frac{T}{ES} = \frac{f}{ES} \cosh \frac{p_o \, l_o \, x}{fl} \qquad (14)$$

E étant le module d'élasticité du câble et S sa section métallique.
Sachant que :
$dx = ds.\cos\varphi$ et $\Delta dx = \Delta ds \cos \varphi$, on arrange l'équation
(14), et on l'intègre, pour obtenir, tous calculs effectués :

$$\Delta x = \frac{fl}{ES} \qquad (15)$$

Cette relation montre que la prise en compte de l'élasticité
du câble se traduit, en projection horizontale, par un accroissement de distance dépendant de l'effort extérieur exercé, et
de la longeur du câble. Dans notre cas, on fait une bonne
approximation en écrivant que l'allongement de la ligne engen-
drera un accroissement de distance horizontale entre deux
flotteurs :

$$d_2 = \frac{fl_o}{ES} \qquad (16)$$

Au bout du compte, la distance horizontale, entre deux flotteurs principaux, pour un côté de l'écran composé de n câbles
et comprenant (N-1) flotteurs intermédiaires, sera :

$$D = N \, (d_1 + d_2)$$

soit :

$$D = \frac{2Nf}{p_o} \, \text{Argsinh} \, \frac{p_o \, l_o}{2f} + \frac{Nfl_o}{ES} \qquad (17)$$

pour un effort extérieur total valant :

$$F = nf \qquad (18)$$

Le comportement d'un côté de l'écran, c'est-à-dire la connaissance de la loi D = D (F), est entièrement défini à partir
des relations (17) et (18).

3.22. <u>Comportement de l'écran horizontal</u> Chaque flotteur
principal, comme le montre la figure 1, relie 3 composants, à
savoir :

       - 1 ou 2 côtés horizontaux, avec :
       - 1 ou 2 ancrages en nylon.

Le flotteur sera donc, pour chaque position instantanée, en
équilibre sous l'effet de 3 réactions, si l'on néglige les
efforts hydrodynamiques engendrés par son mouvement, qui
seront faibles en proportion.

Le principe du programme calculant la déformation de l'écran
a donc été de donner à un flotteur principal d'extrémité une
série de déplacements arbitraires, par rapport à sa position
d'origine, et de calculer dans chaque cas les nouvelles positions des autres flotteurs, ainsi que les efforts créés dans
tous les composants. On obtient par ce procédé une famille de
déformations de l'écran, amenant un côté donné à un taux de
travail F_o choisi (voir figure 8).

La simulation de choc dans ce cas là sera faite en superpo-
sant, à une configuration de la famille, le symétrique d'une
autre configuration, tel que les deux adjointes vérifient
(voir figure 9) :

$$A_2M + MA'3 = D (F_o) \qquad (19)$$

On obtient alors une configuration de choc, définie par le
point d'enfoncement de l'écran M, et par l'énergie d'amortissement reprise dans chaque ligne d'ancrage.

Pour obtenir toutes les configurations de choc, il suffit
d'explorer systématiquement la famille décrite précédemment,
puis de procéder de même pour les autres côtés de l'écran.

3.3. <u>Déformation maximale et capacité de l'écran</u>
Elle est obtenue en appliquant le procédé précédent aux fa-
milles de déformations amenant les côtés au taux de travail
maximal, valant la demi-charge de rupture.

L'enveloppe des points M d'enfoncement maximal de l'écran
détermine la zone intérieure effectivement protégée (voir
figure 10).

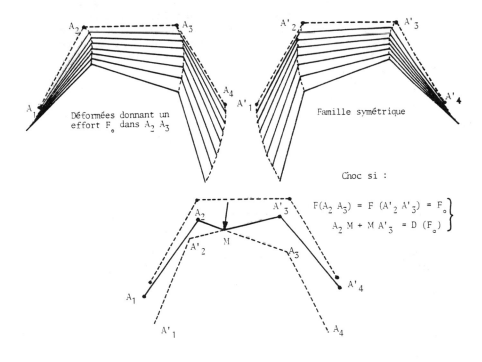

Figure 9 : CONFIGURATION DE CHOC

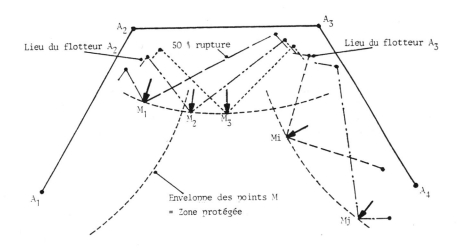

Figure 10 : DEFORMATION MAXIMALE DE L'ECRAN

L'énergie emmagasinée par les ancrages, pour chaque configuration de choc, est également connue dans le programme. Un
examen de ces résultats, pour l'exemple étudié, montre que
cette énergie effectivement dissipée par les ancrages lors
d'une collision varie très peu suivant l'endroit où se fait
le choc. Les valeurs significatives sont :

- 789.000 kilo Joules (kJ) pour un choc au centre
  de $A_2 A_3$;
- 814.000 kJ pour un choc sur $A_2 A_3$, près du flotteur A_2 ou A_3 ;
- 765.000 kJ pour un choc sur $A_3 A_4$ (ou $A_1 A_2$), près
  du flotteur A_3 ;
- 870.000 kJ pour un choc sur $A_3 A_4$ près du flotteur A_4.

On peut donc compter sur une énergie d'amortissement minimale
de 765.000 kJ.

Considérons maintenant un navire de 400 000 T de déplacement.
Il entraîne avec lui une "masse d'eau ajoutée" valant sensiblement 200.000 T. Sa vitesse de dérive étant supposée va-
loir 3 noeuds, soit 1,54 m/s, il possède une énergie cinétique :

$$\frac{1}{2} (M + m) V^2 = 715.000 \text{ kJ.}$$

On voit donc que l'écran étudié possède une capacité de retenue
propre à stopper ce navire.

Tous ces calculs impliquent que l'on fait l'hypothèse que le
navire glisse sans frottement sur l'écran, puisque la configuration finale du choc sur un côté a été supposée telle que :

$$F (M)_{A_2 M} = F (M)_{M A_3} = 50 \text{ \% de la charge de rupture.}$$

Cette restriction ne figure évidemment pas exactement la réalité, mais on sent bien que le dessin de l'écran, notamment la
connexion des câbles sur les flotteurs intermédiaires, devra
être réalisé de telle manière que le navire puisse glisser le
long d'un côté et stopper sa course sans risque de se bloquer
en un point précis.

4. ETUDE DES COMPOSANTS

Ayant maintenant connaissance de l'évolution géométrique de
l'écran au cours d'une collision, et de sa capacité de retenue,
il reste à étudier chaque composant, afin qu'il puisse permettre le travail escompté.

4.1. Flotteurs principaux

Les flotteurs principaux réalisent le lien entre les lignes
d'ancrage en nylon et l'écran horizontal ; en plus de leur
équipement propre à effectuer ces connexions, ils doivent :

- avoir une flottabilité suffisante pour reprendre le
  rappel vertical, exercé par les lignes d'ancrage
  soumises à la charge de rupture ;
- être protégés en cas de choc direct du navire sur le
  flotteur ;
- rester stables en toutes circonstances, et insub-
  mersibles en cas de brèche dans leur coque ;
- avoir une forme telle qu'ils puissent éviter un
  contact et un ragage des lignes en nylon sur le
  navire.

Toutes ces considérations ont amené à concevoir, en étude préliminaire, un flotteur en béton armé précontraint. Sa forme
générale est cylindrique, la partie inférieure comprenant des
bracons permettant d'avoir les points d'arrivée des lignes
d'ancrage à une distance appréciable sous l'eau (voir figure 11).
Pour permettre l'insubmersibilité, l'intérieur du flotteur
est rempli de mousse de polyuréthane expansée. Le devis de poids
laisse à la structure une flottabilité amplement suffisante
pour reprendre la réaction verticale.

4.11. Protection des flotteurs principaux

En cas de choc di-
rect du navire sur le flotteur, il est primordial que celui-ci
soit protégé, afin de pouvoir rester pleinement opérationnel
après la collision.

Une étude du choc prenant en compte la stabilité du flotteur,
ainsi que son inertie, a montré que la force d'impact pouvait
être entièrement absorbée par des défenses d'accostage cylindriques, préservant ainsi la structure. Les défenses envisagées
sont du type Kléber Colombes TC 200, et il suffit d'en disposer
plusieurs sur la face exposée pour protéger entièrement le
flotteur.

4.12. Stabilité du flotteur

Lorsque le flotteur est soumis,
directement ou par l'intermédiaire de l'écran, à un effort extérieur F exercé par le navire à la dérive, il subit simultanément la réaction verticale V des ancrages, liée à F, et
connue, d'après la loi de comportement des câbles nylon définie
précédemment. Il aura donc, sous un effort d'enfoncement V
donné, à rester stable sous l'effet du couple exercé par F, le
bras de levier de ce couple étant la différence de cote entre
le point d'attache des ancrages et le point d'application de
l'effort extérieur.

L'étude de la stabilité d'un flotteur principal est donc faite
en traçant, dans un premier temps, les courbes de moment de
redressement pour des flottaisons isocarènes, chaque cas cor-

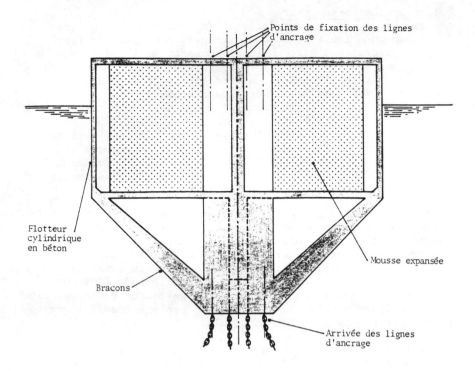

Figure 11 : SCHEMA D'UN FLOTTEUR PRINCIPAL

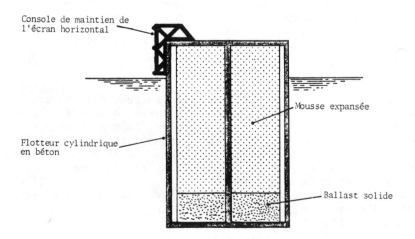

Figure 12 : SCHEMA D'UN FLOTTEUR INTERMEDIAIRE

respondant à une réaction verticale des ancrages donnée. Ensuite, on trouve la courbe finale de stabilité en joignant les points qui, pour chaque V, possèdent un moment de redressement équilibrant le couple inclinant dû à l'action de F (voir figure 13).

Les résultats pour le flotteur présenté montrent que celui-ci reste stable, prenant une inclinaison de 70° pour le taux de travail maximal des lignes d'ancrage, et de 76°, si celles-ci sont portées à leur charge de rupture.

4.2. Flotteurs intermédiaires
Leur but est de maintenir les câbles horizontaux au niveau de l'eau, sous l'action d'un effort vertical exercé par le corps à la dérive ; ils doivent donc :
- avoir une flottabilité suffisante pour empêcher l'écran de glisser sous le navire ;
- être protégés en cas de choc direct ;
- rester stable pour ne pas se retourner contre le navire.

La réponse à ces critères peut être donnée par des flotteurs cylindriques en béton armé, relativement élancés, et pourvus d'un ballast solide, le restant du volume intérieur étant rempli de mousse de polyuréthane expansée.

4.21. Protection en cas de choc
Le meilleur moyen de protéger le flotteur est de le soustraire à la collision, en le plaçant derrière l'écran horizontal. On peut donc imaginer qu'il supporte les câbles horizontaux par l'intermédiaire de consoles débordant son rayon, l'instabilité créée par ce couple inclinant, lors d'une action verticale sur l'écran, étant reprise par la contribution du ballast solide (voir figure 12).

Les études faites sur un exemple de flotteur intermédiaire ont montré qu'il restait stable sous l'action du navire, prenant une inclinaison maximale de 40°, ceci en considérant un espacement entre chaque flotteur de 80 m environ.

4.3. Lignes d'ancrage en nylon
L'action de ces lignes se limite au travail développé par les câbles nylon. Néanmoins, ceux-ci n'ayant une longévité garantie que si ils sont soustraits à tout frottement, il convient de les protéger, notamment :
- près de la jonction avec le flotteur, où le risque de contact avec l'objet à la dérive demeure ;
- au niveau du sol où le frottement et le soulèvement répétés des lignes conduiraient à une usure très rapide.

Dans ce but, la ligne d'ancrage ne doit comprendre que la partie en nylon strictement nécessaire à son bon fonctionnement,

4.146

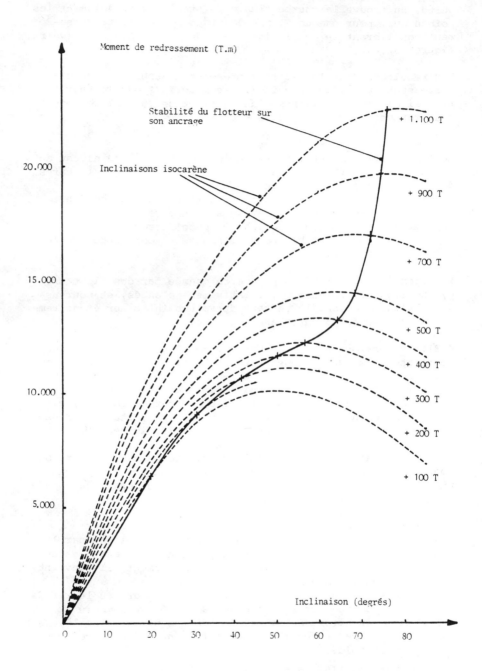

Figure 13 : STABILITE D'UN FLOTTEUR PRINCIPAL

chaque extrêmité étant faite de chaîne. De plus, la préten-
sion dans le système doit être telle que la partie nylon flotte
toujours entre deux eaux, évitant tout contact avec le sol.

La connexion des chaînes sur les bracons doit se faire par des
tirants traversant le flotteur, et mis en tension au niveau supérieur. Ce système aidera à la mise en place, et à l'inspection régulière des lignes.

L'ancrage sur le sol dépendra de la nature du terrain, mais se
fera de manière préférentielle au moyen de pieux battus, qui
assurent une précision de mise en place et une retenue plus
rigoureuse que des ancres classiques.

4.4. Ecran horizontal

Les câbles formant cet écran doivent être constitués de tronçons, connectés entre chaque flotteur intermédiaire, ceci dans
le but de permettre une maintenance plus aisée. La connexion
sur les flotteurs principaux doit être faite de telle manière
que le câble arrive toujours le plus tangentiellement possible,
ceci afin d'éviter tout blocage du navire entre l'écran et le
flotteur. De plus, elle doit permettre le tensionnement du système lors de la mise en place, ou des inspections.

L'écran étant conçu pour un certain niveau d'énergie à reprendre,
il peut soit arrêter un navire de fort tonnage dérivant lentement, ou une plus petite unité lancée à pleine vitesse. Le problème s'est donc posé de vérifier que la vitesse maximale d'attaque de l'écran était compatible avec celles courantes pour
des navires. Cette vitesse maximale existe du fait que, les flotteurs principaux ayant une certaine inertie dans leur mouvement,
le début du choc est presque entièrement repris par les câbles,
qui ne doivent pas dépasser leur demi-charge de rupture. Sachant
qu'un flotteur principal a un déplacement Δ et une masse ajoutée
Ma du même ordre, la vitesse maximale d'attaque, en négligeant
l'élasticité des câbles, est telle que :

$$V > \sqrt{\frac{F \cdot L_o}{\Delta + Ma}} \qquad\qquad (20)$$

F étant la tension dans le câble, et L_o la demi-longueur d'un
côté de l'écran.

L'étude montre donc qu'on atteint, au moment de l'impact, la
demi-charge de rupture dans les câbles, pour une vitesse d'attaque supérieure à 28 noeuds, ce qui couvre largement toute
vitesse de collision probable.

5. INSTALLATION ET MAINTENANCE

L'installation et la maintenance du système de protection sont
des points importants, qui nécessitent des procédures détaillées;

celles-ci n'ont pas été effectuées à ce jour. Il est néanmoins possible d'en faire ressortir les grandes lignes.

La construction des flotteurs principaux pourrait se faire sur barge, les structures étant érigées à l'envers. Ensuite, ces flotteurs étant mis à flot, une étude détaillée a permis de montrer qu'il était facile de les redresser, par ballastage d'un seul compartiment, exempt de mousse de polyuréthane à ce moment là. L'installation proprement dite pourrait alors comprendre les phases suivantes :
- mise en place des ancrages au sol, et des lignes d'ancrage , retenues par des pontons provisoires ;
- remorquage sur le site des flotteurs principaux, et connexion aux ancrages ;
- remorquage sur le site des flotteurs intermédiaires, et mise en place des tronçons d'écran horizontal, en s'aidant d'un treuil de tensionnement ;
- tensionnement final du système de protection, qui le rendra opérationnel.

La maintenance de l'écran de protection doit comprendre des inspections, régulières en temps normal, et systématiques après une utilisation du système. Ces visites peuvent amener à décider du remplacement de tout ou partie d'un composant. Leur fréquence doit être dictée par les recommandations des constructeurs et des bureaux de certification, ainsi que par toute expérience de l'évolution dans le temps de tel ou tel composant in situ. La maintenance du système sera grandement facilitée par le fait que, les lignes d'ancrage par flotteur étant multiples, aussi bien que les câbles horizontaux, leur remplacement partiel pourra intervenir sans détensionnement de tout l'écran de protection.

6. CONCLUSIONS

L'étude présentée ici permet de conclure à la viabilité générale du système. Il reste sûrement des réponses à donner à certains problèmes, mais on peut penser que, d'après les calculs mathématiques réalisés , ils ne suffiront pas à remettre en cause le concept lui-même. De plus, les études des composants n'en sont qu'au stade préliminaire, et leur forme n'est pas figée.

La conclusion logique de cette étude déboucherait sur des essais de comportement dynamique du système sur modèle réduit ainsi que, peut-être, sur des essais en grandeur réelle de comportement dans le temps pour étudier le vieillissement des composants.

Brevet Français N° 78.19.124 du 27.06.1978.